TRAP-NESTING
WASPS AND BEES:
LIFE HISTORIES, NESTS,
AND ASSOCIATES

KARL V. KROMBEIN

Chairman, Department of Entomology

Smithsonian Institution

SMITHSONIAN PRESS

Washington, D.C.

1967

SMITHSONIAN PUBLICATION 4670

LIBRARY OF CONGRESS CATALOG CARD NUMBER: 67-19732

PART OF THE COSTS OF PRINTING THIS PUBLICATION WAS BORNE
BY THE WASHINGTON BIOLOGISTS' FIELD CLUB TO SUPPORT
ITS PRIMARY OBJECTIVE OF RESEARCH ON THE FAUNA AND
FLORA OF PLUMMERS ISLAND, MARYLAND, AND VICINITY.

PORT CITY PRESS, INC.
BALTIMORE, MD., U. S. A.

PREFACE

For excellence in biological observations of insects, the studies recorded in the following pages are unsurpassed. "Trap-nesting Wasps and Bees: Life Histories, Nests, and Associates" is a model of scientific achievement which should be carefully examined and emulated by aspiring young students. Over a period of a dozen years the naturalist-entomologist Dr. Karl V. Krombein has pursued his investigations with persistence, perspicacity, and care. The purposes of his work are manifold, but high in priority has been his consuming desire to stimulate and encourage the ecological approach to the study of taxonomy.

The information presented in this report embraces the study of many thousands of individual wasps, bees, beetles, and mites obtained from more than 3,400 trap-nests, representing nestings of 75 different predaceous wasps, 43 nonparasitic bees, and 83 parasites and predators associated with them. No such extensive material, yielding so much important, new data, has ever been accumulated on the subject.

Dr. Krombein's technique of studying trap-nests is not new, but he has greatly expanded its use to make possible the acquisition of many new data. Had the investigator not been encumbered by the necessity of engaging in tedious, but necessary, routine detail even more highly significant results might have been obtained.

No effort was spared to examine and record the nature of the architecture of the nests, competition, correlation of cell size and sex, prey, and other features of the fascinating and complicated life histories of these insects. Thus, many lacunae in our knowledge of these animals have been filled. For example, Dr. Krombein has shown (1) that in 100 nests of 6 to 9 cells, each cell provisioned with an average of 23 spiders, more than 20,000 prey were used by the sphecid *Trypargilum t. tridentatum* and (2) that 20,000 caterpillars of a single species of olethreutid moth were used to provision 250 nests of a

Floridian vespid! The enormous pressure exerted on the populations of the two prey species has been clearly and convincingly demonstrated by these examples.

Among the many "firsts" disclosed in the following pages are the discovery that a certain megachilid bee constructed a brood chamber instead of a series of cells containing only one egg in each, the discovery that certain forms, previously considered discrete subspecies, are actually only color phases of one, and numerous facts concerning behavior and host associations of parasites and predators.

Abundant information is given on the trap-nesting technique and the methods of nest study. The author is explicit, leaving no doubt as to what should be done by those who wish to engage in similar investigations.

J. F. GATES CLARKE, *Senior Scientist*
Department of Entomology
Museum of Natural History
Smithsonian Institution

CONTENTS

This curious world which we inhabit is more wonderful than it is convenient; more beautiful than it is useful; it is more to be admired and enjoyed than used.

Thoreau, 1837

THE possibilities of utilizing the trap-nest technique while investigating the life history, behavior, and associates of solitary wood-nesting predaceous wasps and bees were brought to my attention by my esteemed friend Kenneth W. Cooper, now of the Dartmouth Medical School. His elaborate investigations of the bionomics of the vespid wasp *Ancistrocerus antilope* and its intricate relationships with the symbiotic mite *Kennethiella trisetosa*, and his ingenious and exquisitely designed set of experiments to investigate the orientation of larvae in the borings at the time of cocooning, have been an inspiration and challenge to all who have worked subsequently with this technique.

My study began in a modest way during the years 1953 and 1954 with a relative handful of some 70 nests. During the period 1955-1962 the number of traps set out in the field increased rapidly as the success of the technique was realized and as several collaborators were added. This activity reached a peak in 1961 with some 1,400 traps set out and a total of 986 nests received and processed. During 1963 and 1964 the project was sharply reduced with relatively few traps being set out (only in the Washington area and in Arizona) to ascertain some details not obtained in earlier nests.

Our numerous American solitary wood-nesting wasps and bees have not been the subject of previous intensive investigation except locally by the Peckhams in Wisconsin, by Medler and his associates in the same State, by Cooper in New York, and by the Raus in Missouri. A long-term study such as mine, conducted in several different faunal zones, could be expected to yield a great amount of information. Such was the case. During my study I had the opportunity to examine and record the nest

1

architecture and life-history data from approximately 3,400 nests from western New York, the metropolitan area of Washington, D. C.; coastal North Carolina, south-central Florida, and the desert floor of southeastern and south-central Arizona. In addition, K. W. Cooper sent me a few nests from Rochester, N. Y., Oak Ridge, Tenn., and Gainesville, Fla.

Many other ecological niches and several faunal zones still await similar investigation.

NOTEWORTHY FINDINGS OF THE STUDY

The several areas represented in this study have yielded important and largely unknown data on 75 different predaceous wasps and 43 nonparasitic bees. In addition, host relationships and life-history data were obtained for 83 parasites and predators associated with the host wasps and bees.

The information secured on nest architecture was quite detailed and thorough for almost all the nests. Regretfully, I cannot report the same for the life-history data on some of the wasps and bees and on the prey of some wasps. Two factors account for the lack of information: First, occupants of nests mailed to me by collaborators had usually entered the prepupal stage by the time the nests reached me, so that I could not secure data on the duration of the egg and larval feeding stages or on the prey stored by the wasps except where there had been egg mortality in one or more cells; second, in the more active years of the project the sheer number of nests obtained was so great that most of my available time had to be devoted to initial processing of the nests and the killing, pinning, and labeling of the emerging wasps, bees, and parasites.

A partial measure of the success of this project is afforded when one realizes that nesting and life-history data were published previously for only about a third of the wasps and bees, and their parasites and predators. Furthermore, a great deal of the previously published information consisted of scattered notes on fragments of the life history or prey preferences, which did not afford detailed knowledge on many facets of the bionomics of the species.

Some unexpected extra dividends accruing during the study were the new species and subspecies of wasps, bees, and parasites described from reared material. Among the wasps, it was necessary to describe no less than five new species from the Washington area alone; an additional new species was described from coastal North Carolina, and two new subspecies from southern

Florida. A new subspecies of the common eastern carpenter bee was described from southern Florida. Among the wasp and bee parasites two new species of chalcidoid wasps were described, one species from the Washington area and one from Arizona; an additional new species from Arizona remains to be described. An amazing number of new mites, mostly symbiotic species, was encountered. It was necessary for E. W. Baker to describe no fewer than 2 new genera and 13 new species from these nests; and 4 additional species still await description!

First instar larvae of the parasitic cuckoo wasps (Chrysididae) were preserved and also mature larvae of many other species of the solitary, free-living, and parasitic wasps and bees. Larvae of a number of species of Sphecidae, most of them not available from other sources, represented a substantial number of the species treated in H. E. Evans's recent monographic studies of the larvae of this family. The larvae from other families of wasps and bees still await taxonomic study.

From the standpoint of host-predator relationships, this study emphasized again the considerable pressure exerted on populations of other arthropods by the predaceous solitary wasps. Consider, for example, the pressure exerted on the snare-building spider population from predation by such a wide-ranging sphecid as *Trypargilum t. tridentatum*. It stored an average of 23 spiders per cell, an average of 6 to 9 cells per nest depending on the locality; and I studied only a few more than a hundred nests from the tremendous total nest production of this wasp throughout its range. As another example, the Floridian vespid *Euodynerus foraminatus apopkensis,* which stored an average of 10 caterpillars of an unidentified species of Olethreutidae per cell, made an average of 8 cells per completed nest. I had nearly 250 nests of this species.

Much of the information on nesting, prey preferences, and life history details will be useful eventually in helping to define the biological criteria which characterize the species and genera. One of the most fascinating developments in this area was the discovery that larvae of *Trypargilum* constructed such distinctive cocoons that the five North American species nesting in the traps could be identified from this feature alone, and this in spite of the finding by Evans that larvae of these same species were separable only with difficulty and on very trivial morphological criteria. Furthermore, comparison of the prey preferences of the three species of this genus in the Washington area showed that each had differences in this respect, one selecting entirely snare-building spiders, one about 90 percent snare-building and 10 percent wandering spiders, and the third only 20 percent snare-building and 80 percent wandering spiders. These differing percentages suggest that each species hunts in a different manner, one taking spiders directly from their webs, the second frightening them from the webs and seizing them on the ground where they also get a small number of wandering spiders, and the third hunting for its spiders on leaf litter or on vegetation where they obtain more wandering species.

Another interesting taxonomic finding was the determination that *Ancistrocerus catskill catskill* and *A. catskill albophaleratus*, hitherto considered to be discrete subspecies, were actually only color phases of the same taxon which occurred together in 13 percent of the nests, with the typical yellow-marked form occurring alone in 60 percent and the white-marked form alone in 27 percent of the nests.

In nests of the sphecid wasps belonging to *Isodontia*, subgenus *Murrayella*, I found a transition from *elegans*, which constructed individual cells separated from each other by thick partitions of grass stems and vegetable fiber, through *mexicana*, which sometimes made individual cells separated by flimsier, narrower partitions or else made just a larger brood cell in which several larvae developed without cannibalism, to *auripes*, in which there was always just a single large brood chamber.

I discovered that the bee *Megachile* (*Sayapis*) *policaris* Say usually stored a large mass of pollen and nectar in a brood cell and laid eggs at intervals in pockets in this mass. These bee larvae also developed without cannibalism. This is the first megachilid bee known to construct such a brood chamber.

In my study of the vespid wasps I determined that species belonging to genera primarily Holarctic in distribution, such as *Ancistrocerus* and *Symmorphus*, had shorter pupal periods than species of genera such as *Pachodynerus, Monobia, Euodynerus*, and *Stenodynerus*, which are primarily Austral or Neotropical in distribution.

This study also disclosed a number of previously unknown facts about life history, behavior, and host associations of a great many parasites and predators.

Almost all the mite-host associations were unknown previously. Two hypopial forms were discovered in the chaetodactylid mite *Chaetodactylus krombeini*, an apodous, encysted, overwintering form which developed within the skin of the first nymphal stage and the ordinary, 8-legged active form which developed from the apodous encysted form. The occurrence of an apodous encysted form was considered to be of profound evolutionary significance because the presence of encysted forms in an abandoned burrow provided the mite species with an opportunity to parasitize other species of bees which also nest in abandoned borings.

Considerable evidence was gathered which established a presumptive association of the dermestid beetle *Trogoderma ornatum* with spider-storing wasps of the genus *Trypargilum*. The newly hatched beetle larva appeared to be predatory on the wasp eggs or young larvae, and later larval instars fed on prey stored for the wasp larva or on wasp prepupae in adjacent cells.

A high parasitism rate of *Euodynerus foraminatus apopkensis* by the stylopid beetle *Pseudoxenos hookeri* provided abundant material which enabled me to determine that the beetles do not exsert from the abdomen of the host until several days after eclosion of the adult wasps. This is contrary to the conjecture of earlier workers who supposed that the stylopids exserted while the host wasps were in the pupal stage. Furthermore, I determined that penetration of the host egg by the triungulinid larvae of the stylopid might be the cause of the abnormally high mortality rate of eggs of this wasp.

Among the Bombyliidae *Lepidophora lepidocera* was unique in that the larva usually developed on the prey stored for the host wasp larva rather than on the resting wasp larva or pupa, as is normal in other genera attacking wasps and bees. Also, the *Lepidophora* larva usually had to feed on the contents of several cells in a series to develop to maturity.

Associations of parasitic *Coelioxys* bees with their megachilid hosts permitted me to hypothesize that the shiny black *Coelioxys* species, of which *dolichos* is the only North American representative, probably parasitize species of *Megachile*, subgenus *Melanosarus*. Another such hypothetical association is that of the group of *Coelioxys* species having an upturned spicule at the apex of the last visible abdominal tergum with resin-using species of *Chalicodoma*, subgenus *Chelostomoides*.

A final result of this project has been the acquisition for the collection of the U.S. National Museum of many thousands of specimens of wasps, bees, and their parasites in perfect condition. Some species were not represented previously and of others there were only a few specimens or series in relatively poor condition. Also preserved in the Museum collection are several hundred specimens of wasp and bee larvae for future taxonomic study, as well as several thousands of specimens of prey. All the reared and associated material bear identifying year, nest, and cell numbers so that they may always be associated with the original nest notes also on deposit in the Museum files.

ACKNOWLEDGMENTS

During the many years of these studies, I have had the appreciated cooperation of several collaborators in the field, who set out empty traps, ran the trap lines on a weekly or biweekly basis, and mailed the completed nests to me for study. My father, Louis H. Krombein, M.D., set out traps near his home at Derby, Erie County, N. Y., from 1956 to 1961. Richard Archbold, director of the Archbold Biological Station, Lake Placid, Highlands County, Fla., ran similar series at the station during 1957 and 1959 to 1962. Mont W. Cazier, during his term as director of the Southwestern Research Station, Portal, Cochise County, Ariz., ran trap lines on the desert floor near Portal in 1960 and 1961; in 1963, while at Arizona State University, he set out traps at Granite Reef Dam, Maricopa County, and again near Portal. Richard S. Beal set out traps in several localities in Arizona in 1957 while he was with the U.S. Department of Agriculture; in 1961, when he was at Arizona State University, he ran trap lines at Scottsdale, Granite Reef Dam, and Molino Camp in the Santa Catalina Mountains. The valued cooperation of these men enabled me to obtain life-history data on a number of species for which I would otherwise have had no information.

Identifications of prey and parasites required the assistance of many specialists. Particular mention should be made of the help of two individuals who identified not hundreds but thousands of specimens of prey, almost entirely immatures and frequently in less than perfect condition. These are my colleague Hahn W. Capps, U.S. Department of Agriculture, who identified all the lepidopterous larvae used as prey by vespid wasps, and Benjamin J. Kaston, Teachers College of Connecticut, who determined almost all the spiders used as prey by *Trypoxylon*, *Trypargilum, Dipogon,* and *Auplopus.* My friend Edward W. Baker, U.S. Department of Agriculture, not only identified all the Acarina but also determined that almost all of them required description as new genera and species, a task which he also performed. Other specialists who furnished identifications of prey or parasites are as follows: My colleagues, past and present, in the Insect Identification and Parasite Introduction Research Branch, U.S. Department of Agriculture, D. M. Anderson and W. H. Anderson (coleopterous larvae), P. H. Arnaud (Bombyliidae), R. S. Beal (Dermestidae), B. D. Burks (Chalcidoidea), A. B. Gurney (Orthoptera), C. F. W. Muesebeck (Braconidae), K. O'Neill (Thysanoptera), L. M. Russell (Aphidae), C. W. Sabrosky (Milichiidae, Conopidae, Tachinidae), M. R. Smith (Formicidae), T. J. Spilman (Rhipiphoridae), G. B. Vogt (Chrysomelidae), L. M. Walkley (Ichneumonidae), D. M. Weisman (Chrysomelidae), and W. W. Wirth (Bombyliidae, Phoridae); R. M. Bohart, University of California at Davis (Stylopidae); W. L. Downes, Jr., University of Illinois (Sarcophagidae); W. R. Enns, University of Missouri (Meloidae); W. J. Gertsch and W. Ivie, American Museum of Natural History (Araneae); C. G. Jackson, University of Richmond (Acarina); N. Marston, University of Kansas (Bombyliidae); R. B. Selander, University of Illinois (Meloidae, larvae); H. K. Townes, American Entomological Institute (Ichneumonidae); and H. K. Wallace, University of Florida (Araneae). P. W. Martin, Geochronology Institute of the University of Arizona, identified pollen from the nests of some southwestern bees. The identifications of wasps and bees are for the most part my own, although I have had help on a few difficult or puzzling species from the following: R. M. Bohart (Chrysididae, Vespidae); W. E. Ferguson, San Jose State College (Mutillidae); P. D. Hurd, Jr., University of California at Berkeley (Xylocopidae); A. Menke, University of California at Davis (Sphecidae); C. D. Michener, University of Kansas (Megachilidae); T. B. Mitchell, North Carolina State University (Megachilidae); and P. H. Timberlake, Citrus Experiment Station, California (Megachilidae).

Howard E. Evans, Museum of Comparative Zoology at Harvard University, kindly sent me a few spider prey records from nests of several species of *Trypargilum* and *Trypoxylon*.

C. D. F. Miller, Canadian Department of Agriculture, courteously made available for my examination many of the wasps reared and reported on by R. E. Fye (1965a). Prior to 1965 I had seen only a few specimens of *Euodynerus leucomelas* (Saussure) and of *Passaloecus ithacae* Krombein from Fye's material.

I am grateful to Paul W. Oman and William H. Anderson,

past and present chiefs of the Insect Identification and Parasite Introduction Research Branch, U.S. Department of Agriculture, for their support of this project during my employment with the Department, 1941-1965.

A special note of acknowledgment is due J. F. Gates Clarke, former chairman of the Department of Entomology, U.S. National Museum, for arranging the fabrication of some 3,500 traps in the cabinet shop of the Museum.

A generous grant from the American Philosophical Society enabled me to visit coastal North Carolina three times during the summer of 1955 to set out traps and retrieve the completed nests. A second grant from the Society permitted me to visit Arizona to study trap- and ground-nesting wasps and bees during the summer of 1959.

A final note of deep appreciation is due my wife for her enthusiastic interest in these life-history studies. Her patient and critical reading of the many manuscript pages in draft form and her cooperation in helping to check the final proofs have contributed substantially to the quality of the final report.

THE TRAP-NESTING TECHNIQUE

TOOLS

The traps used in my study were fabricated from straight-grained pieces of seasoned white pine. Borings of several diameters and of two lengths were made in these sticks. Twist drills were used for the drilling. These drills left the inner end of the boring obliquely angled and relatively smooth; the use of regular wood drills would have left the inner end very rough.

The smallest size drill was ⅛ inch (3.2 mm.) in diameter. The sticks used for borings of this diameter were 20 × 20 × 75 mm. The boring was drilled along the longitudinal midline to a depth of 64-70 mm. This was the shortest boring I used in this study.

The traps used most commonly were those made with drills having a diameter of 3/16 inch (4.8 mm.) or ¼ inch (6.4 mm.). These borings were drilled to a depth of 152 mm. in blocks of wood 20 × 20 × 165 mm.

A few traps used early in the study had ⅜ inch (9.5 mm.) borings drilled to a depth of 152 mm.

The largest size boring was ½ inch (12.7 mm.) in diameter,

drilled to a depth of 152 mm. in blocks of wood 25×25×165 mm.

Early in my study I tried inserting pieces of glass tubing in some of the larger borings. These were accepted by the wasps, and the clear sides made it possible to observe the nest during its construction. However, the impervious walls caused such an increase in moisture within the cells that the contents usually grew moldy within a few days. Also, reflections from the surface of the glass interfered with photography of the nests.

Other hollow tubular materials have been used by other investigators to attract these wasps and bees. Bamboo is excellent but has the obvious disadvantage of having a variable diameter so that cell sizes cannot be measured accurately. Soda straws also have been used, but one cannot split them open to make observations on the duration and activities of the immature stages.

Medler and Fye (1956), and Fye (1965a, b) used borings similar to mine, but they were drilled in sumac (*Rhus*) stems. These worked very successfully in Wisconsin and Ontario; but because sumac is not too abundant around Washington, I have not tested it.

Earlier, Medler used a domicile trap which consisted of a number of short boards bolted together with holes drilled along the interfaces. This trap attracted nesting individuals, but one could not readily make measurements and observations of an individual nest in this kind of setting. Most recently Nye and Bohart (1964) published plans for an improved domicile structure in which channels were routed out on boards and the latter then bound together to form many potential nesting sites. These structures are very useful for concentrating populations of desirable species of megachilid bees for transport and release of the progeny in areas where their pollination activities are needed; they are not satisfactory for the person who wishes to study individual nests, their occupants, and their development.

Matthews and Fischer (1964) used traps like mine but sawed them lengthwise along the upper edge of the boring; the lower half of the trap, containing most of the boring, was then covered with transparent film (Saran Wrap), and the two parts were fastened together with rubber bands. This technique offered an opportunity to observe development after completion of the nest by periodic removal of the top half of the trap.

PREPARING TRAPS FOR THE FIELD

Each trap was identified by a letter and number written on it with a black wax pencil. The same letter was used for all traps at a single locality in a given year. The numbers were assigned in sequence; thus, the traps used in a single season at Plummers Island, Md., for instance, might run from E 1 through E 190, whereas those at the Archbold Biological Station in Florida might run from B 1 to B 237 for the same season.

New traps were always set out unsplit. Frequently, I reused old traps when they split along the longitudinal axis of the burrow during the first season. The remnants of the old nests could be cleaned out with a narrow stiff brush and the two halves taped tightly together with friction tape. The early numbers on these old traps were scratched out and new ones assigned appropriate to the new season. I always sterilized these old traps before reuse by placing them in an oven at 200° F. for several hours.

Usually the traps needed no other preparation before being set out, except for those placed early in the season. During my first season of attempting to trap vernal bees, I experienced considerable loss from mold in the nests because of the frequent spring rains. I eliminated this difficulty in subsequent years by rolling the traps in a very shallow bath of melted paraffin so that the sides were coated with wax. This technique should be used on any early season nests in the United States. Only a shallow layer of melted paraffin should be used to prevent the wax from entering the boring itself.

PLACEMENT IN THE FIELD

Usually I made up a bundle of six traps to set at each station, two each of the 4.8- and 6.4-mm. borings and one each of the 3.2- and 12.7-mm. borings. Occasionally in special situations, such as when I trapped for vernal bees, I used only the 4.8- and 6.4-mm. borings. Sometimes I used only 3.2-mm. borings, as on an old cowshed wall that had had a heavy infestation of small anobiid beetles and a consequent abundance of small nesting Hymenoptera in the abandoned beetle borings.

In selecting stations in the field, I tried to set the traps where wood-nesting wasps and bees would be likely to search for nesting sites. Obvious sites for these were on or beneath dead branches, and on dead tree trunks or wooden structures that contained abandoned borings of other insects (figs. 3, 4, 7, 8).

In areas of open sandy scrub, such as Kill Devil Hills, N. C., and the Archbold Biological Station, Lake Placid, Fla., settings on live scrubby oaks bearing old cynipid galls were productive, as were settings on pine trunks with thick bark and beneath branches of live scrub hickory (figs. 1, 2, 9, 10). On the desert floor in Arizona the most productive settings were beneath dead branches of mesquite, palo verde, and desert willow; on dead agave and yucca stems; and on wooden fence posts (figs. 5, 6).

Usually settings in dense shaded areas in eastern woodlands were not satisfactory. Stations were more successful at the edges of woods or in areas of open woods where there was considerable sunshine during the day.

The traps were set so that the borings were in a horizontal position. Most of my traps were placed at elevations of 1-2 meters above the ground. Fye (1965c) noted the use of several devices to place traps at heights of 3-20 meters.

I found it preferable to check trap lines on a weekly basis whenever possible. Completed nests, signified by the boring entrances being plugged with mud or other substances, were picked up and empty traps were set out in their places. In the earlier years of the study, I picked up some traps as soon as it was evident that they were being used as nesting sites. Probing the borings delicately with a grass stem would identify those containing partially completed nests. Examination of incompleted nests provided data on egg size and hatch that were not usually available from completed nests.

METHODS OF NEST STUDY

When I received the nests at my office, I tried to open the unsplit traps by inserting a jack-knife at the blind end of the trap and, by twisting the blade, to split the trap with the grain of the wood along the longitudinal axis of the boring. Frequently the grain was at a slight angle necessitating that two or more splits be made before the entire length of the boring could be inspected. Presplit traps were easily opened by cutting the friction tape along the line of the previous split on one side so that the top of the trap could be folded back.

I then entered details of the nest architecture on standardized, mimeographed data sheets. The architectural information recorded included the following: Presence or absence of a preliminary plug at or near the end of the boring and length of empty cell if present; thickness of cell partitions and closing plugs and materials of which they were constructed; length of vestibular cell and of any intercalary cells present. A separate section contained notations of prey used by wasps. A table at the bottom of the data sheet provided columns for each cell. In these were recorded cell length and cocoon length as well as dates of egg hatch, larval maturity, cocoon spinning, pupation and adult emergence, and sex of cell occupant. The cells were numbered in sequence, cell 1 being at the inner end. Obviously, I could not record many of these developmental data because the nests already had passed the early stages. Also, upon first examination nests in early stages of development required one or more subsequent examinations to ascertain some of the desired data. The plain back of the data sheet allowed space to record additional supplemental data such as cocoon description, activities of the rightful nest occupants or their parasites, and so forth.

I considered that the stored or provisioned cell consisted of the space in which the food was stored plus the partition capping this space. Likewise, I considered that the vestibular and intercalary cells consisted of the empty space plus the closing plug or partition which capped them. Consequently, the measurements given in the specific accounts which follow should be interpreted accordingly. The mean cell length included the partition thickness so that the mean partition thickness, as given, should be subtracted from the mean cell length in determining the mean length of that part of the cell containing the store of food.

After recording the nest measurements and development, I reassembled the two halves of the nest and wound a rubber band near each end to keep the halves closely apposed. When I desired to reexamine the nest, I removed the rubber bands and top half of the nest and recorded the development. Occasionally I wrapped a piece of Cellophane or transparent film (Saran Wrap) tightly around the half of the trap containing the cells. This enabled me to observe and photograph the activities of the newly eclosed adult during the 2-5 day period before it left the cell.

After occupants of the nest pupated, it was necessary to affix some kind of a net around the nest entrance with a rubber band to confine the adults as they emerged. I tried Cellophane dialysis tubing; but many kinds of wasps, bees, and parasites chewed through it without difficulty. Next, I had small sleeves made from nylon organdy, about 85 mm. long and 65 mm. wide, with one end stitched shut. These kept in males and parasites, but females of many species were able to chew through them also. Finally, I settled on sleeves similar in size to those made from nylon organdy, but this time made from plastic mesh (Saran screening). These were objectionably stiff, but they kept the females from chewing through to the outside so they fulfilled the necessary function satisfactorily.

As adults emerged into these sleeves they were removed, killed, pinned, and labeled. It was necessary to examine the nests at frequent intervals daily once emergence began. Occasionally emerged adults would reenter the boring head first and fail to back out. If they were not removed by hand, these disoriented adults would block all further egress from the nest.

Frequently, when the cocoons were hard or tough, such as those of *Trypargilum* and *Megachile,* I placed each in a numbered glass vial to confine the adult upon emergence.

I had to keep a constant check on nests in my office to discover and eliminate infestations by two parasites, which are the bane of laboratory cultures. These parasites were the tiny eulophid wasp *Melittobia chalybii* and the grain itch mite, *Pyemotes ventricosus.* These parasites attack chiefly diapausing larvae and pupae of various insects in nature. In nature *Melittobia* apparently preys on solitary wasps and bees, but *Pyemotes* has a wider host range and attacks many kinds of terrestrial insects. I found both species in nests in the field and these were the likely sources of my laboratory infestations. Both parasites are slender, flattened animals. They had no difficulty in squeezing between the split halves of these traps, many of which did not fit tightly, or they entered the nests through the plastic mesh (Saran screen) emergence sleeves. Their development is so rapid that an infestation might spread through a number of nests if not discovered soon after it occurred.

Many nests, including all those stored later in the summer, had to be carried over the winter before adult emergence occurred. The nest occupants entered a prolonged larval diapause which could be terminated only after exposure to chilling temperatures for 2 or more months. In preparing the nests for overwintering I wound transparent adhesive (Scotch tape) around them lengthwise to cover the split. The purpose of this was to trap as many emerging *Melittobia* as possible and thus prevent their spread to other nests during warm periods in the late fall, winter, or early spring. The nests, except those from Florida, were then wrapped in bundles in manila paper and placed in a corrugated cardboard carton also wrapped in manila paper. This package was then hung outside an upstairs window at my home from mid-October or November through mid-March or early April. I treated the diapausing Florida nests differently only in that I exposed them to chilly weather for only 2 months and brought them indoors whenever temperatures went below freezing.

PHOTOGRAPHY

The trap-nesting technique is admirably adapted to still or motion-picture photography. A 35-mm. single-lens reflex camera with extension tubes and electronic flash can be mounted on a tripod to photograph the activities of the nesting females (figs. 14, 15, 70-77). After the traps have been opened, the same equipment can be used to record the nest architecture (*e.g.*, figs. 22, 23, 25) or the developmental details (figs. 30-38).

LOCALITIES

(Plate 1, Figures 1-4; Plate 2, Figures 5-8; Plate 3, Figures 9, 10)

The nests from Derby, Erie County, N. Y., came from a locality in western New York along the edge of Eighteen Mile Creek just a short distance from Lake Erie. Many of the settings were at the edges of wooded areas or along creek banks where the dominant trees were sycamore, willow, and elm. Other settings were made on the sides of wooden sheds or on windowsills, in crevices in a rock wall, and in piles of cut firewood.

Most of my nests from the metropolitan area of Washington, D. C., came from Plummers Island, Montgomery County, Md., the home of the Washington Biologists' Field Club. This island is in the Potomac River, a few miles northwest of the city and is 50-110 feet above sea level. Much of it is covered with deciduous woods, more or less open to sunlight at varying intervals during the day. The predominating trees are oak, hickory, elm, hop hornbeam, and sycamore. Many nests came from settings on dead branches or standing dead tree trunks in or at the edges of these wooded areas (figs. 7, 8). A large number also came from settings on the porch rafters (fig. 4) of the Club's cabin, Winnemana Lodge. These rafters contained abandoned borings of several different insects in which a number of species of solitary wasps and bees nested.

Elsewhere in the Washington area I ran a series of traps one year at Cropley, Montgomery County, Md., just a mile above Plummers Island and with similar habitats.

Most of the nests from Arlington County, Va., came from settings on the wall of an old wooden cowshed near my house. At one time the boards were badly infested with anobiid beetle larvae. A number of species of small wasps and bees nest in these old borings and some of them were induced to nest in 3.2-mm. borings in wooden traps. One year I ran a short series at Glencarlyn, Arlington County, in a rather densely wooded area of deciduous trees. Elsewhere in Virginia, I had a short series one year at Dunn Loring, Fairfax County, about 10 miles west of the District of Columbia, along the right of way of the Washington and Old Dominion Railroad.

At Kill Devil Hills, Dare County, in coastal North Carolina I trapped in two different habitats. One was the relatively barren, flat sandy area east of the line of dunes and parallel to the ocean. This was an area of sandy scrub characterized by scattered, scrubby live oak, Spanish oak, and bayberry (figs. 1, 2). The other area was on the lee side of the dunes where there were well-developed woods quite open to sunlight and with pine, oak, and hickory as the dominant trees (fig. 3).

All my Florida nests were from the Archbold Biological Station at Lake Placid, Highlands County. A few were from settings in an open concrete area beneath the laboratory building. Most of the nests were from the Highlands Ridge area of the Station at an elevation of about 200 feet. This is a sandy scrub area quite open to the sun and with oaks, scrub hickory, and pines as the principal trees (figs. 9, 10).

Most of the nests from Portal, Cochise County, Ariz., were from settings on the desert floor near the base of the Chiricahua Mountains at an elevation of about 4,000 feet (figs. 5, 6). There are no large trees in this area except for sycamores along the banks of intermittent streams. The dominant shrubs and plants are mesquite, acacia, yucca, agave, desert willow, and many kinds of cacti. The traps from Scottsdale and Granite Reef Dam in Maricopa County, Ariz., came from similar habitats.

SUPERSEDURE AND COMPETITION
(Plate 3, Figure 11)

In the specific accounts which follow I frequently mention that a wasp or bee was superseded by another wasp or bee. In the sense used here, the phenomenon of supersedure is interpreted as being the act of taking over by a second individual of the same or of a different species a boring partially stored by a first individual. This meaning does not imply that there was necessarily any competition in this succession. It sometimes happens that a female abandons a nest before completing it— she may become the prey of a larger predator or of an internal parasite, or she may simply die of old age. I have found a few nests with the mother dead inside. In one megachilid mother there was a conopid puparium filling the abdomen; in the other nests the mother may have died from old age. The remainder of the borings in these nests may have been used subsequently by another wasp or bee days or weeks after the first individual had used them.

Sometimes there was definite competition in this supersedure (fig. 11), as in a trap from Derby in which a trypoxylonine wasp placed a paralyzed spider at the inner end of the boring: *Ancistrocerus c. catskill* stored cell 1, *Trypargilum clavatum* stored cells 2-5, and *Trypoxylon frigidum* stored cells 6-7. I have also observed two females of *Osmia lignaria* both entering the same boring with pollen and nectar loads. Also there have been some evidences of competition between two different species in a single boring. I can recall one composite nest from Florida which contained a single completed cell of *Euodynerus foraminatus apopkensis* at the inner end, then a partially stored cell of a species of *Chalicodoma* (*Chelostomoides*) [identifiable because inner cell end and walls were coated with resin], and then several cells of *Stenodynerus saecularis rufulus*. Quite possibly taking over by *Stenodynerus* was the result of actual competition, because the bee cell was not completely stored and it had been sealed over by the wasp.

Competition between individuals for nesting sites is a problem that could be investigated in detail in these borings by marking nesting females and observing the day-to-day activities at a station with a number of borings. I have not had time for this kind of field endeavor, but it would certainly merit investigation by someone with the requisite time, patience, and inclination.

Actually, there are many fascinating facets of behavior which could be investigated by prolonged observation at these stations. One could determine the provisioning rates for prey, the number of pollen loads to store a bee cell, the number of visits with sealing materials to make a cell partition, and myriads of others.

NEST ARCHITECTURE

Two species, *Solierella affinis blaisdelli* and *Tracheliodes amu* (fig. 68), made nests without any division into cells. Several other species, *Megachile (Sayapis) policaris* (figs. 92-97), *Isodontia (Murrayella) auripes* (figs. 60, 61), and, occasionally, *I. (M.) mexicana,* made a large brood cell in which several larvae developed amicably without cannibalism. However, most of the wasps and bees made a series of linear cells in these borings, each cell being capped by a partition to separate it from the next cell in the series.

Text figure 1 illustrates two common types of serial nests. In nest A the wasp makes a preliminary plug of a small amount of mud or agglutinated sand at the inner end of the boring. Then she constructs a series of provisioned cells separated from each other by a narrow partition of the same material as the preliminary plug. Finally, at the outer end of the boring she leaves an empty space, the vestibular cell, which she seals with a thicker closing plug of the same material as the partitions between the provisioned cells.

Nest B is similar in most details. In this nest the wasp puts the preliminary plug some distance from the inner end of the boring and then constructs the first provisioned cell which she seals with the usual narrow partition. However, instead of making another provisioned cell, she leaves an empty intercalary cell which she seals with a somewhat thicker partition. Then she makes a second provisioned cell, and then another empty intercalary cell, and so forth, until she gets nearly to the end of the boring, where she makes the usual empty vestibular cell and thicker plug at the boring entrance.

PRELIMINARY PLUG

This preliminary plug was a constant feature in almost all nests of the several species of *Trypargilum* (figs. 53, 55). In nests of many other species this plug rarely occurred in more than a third of the nests of any one species. Such a plug was entirely

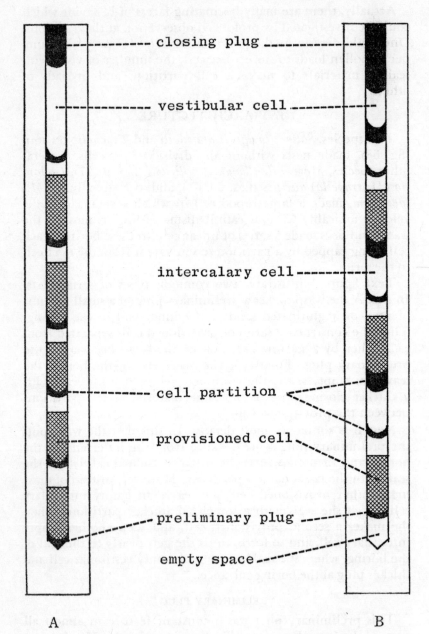

A   B

Text Figure 1.—Diagram of linear nests in borings.

lacking in nests of a few wasps. The sporadic occurrence of the plug in nests of most species suggests that it might be associated with the conformation of the inner end of the boring. Perhaps the plug was constructed to provide a smooth posterior end for the innermost cell in those borings where the inner end was roughened from protruding fibers. (See discussion below on the functions of the cell partitions.)

There was no apparent reason why this plug was made at the inner end of the boring in many nests (fig. 55) and at variable distances from the inner end in other nests of the same species (fig. 53). Individual idiosyncrasies of the nesting wasps and bees may have been the determining factor in the positioning of this partition some distance from the inner end, or the nesting females may have detected some adverse condition in the boring walls which caused them to set the preliminary plug some distance from the end.

CELL PARTITION

After the wasp or bee places a store of food in the first cell and lays an egg, or, lays an egg first and places a store of food in the cell as does the vespid wasp, she then constructs a partition to seal the cell and its contents. This partition is usually constructed several millimeters beyond the store of food. The material used in the partition varies with the individual species. Many of them use pellets of damp mud or of damp sand agglutinated by salivary secretions(?). These pellets are consolidated to form a lenticular partition. Other wasps and bees use resin, gum, leaf pulp, wood raspings from the boring walls, or even thick, compacted accumulations of various kinds of debris such as rotten wood, caterpillar droppings, small pebbles, spider webs, and earth.

Despite the disparity of materials used in their construction, these cell partitions exhibit two common features. The inner surface facing the stored cell is roughened and convex, whereas the outer surface is smooth and concave because the wasp can compact and form the material with her head. These features mean that each cell has a cylindrical form with a smooth, concave posterior wall toward the inner end of the boring and a roughened, convex anterior wall toward the nest entrance.

The cell partitions serve several obvious purposes. They offer the occupant a degree of protection from parasites and predators. They insure each larva an adequate amount of food. They prevent cannibalism between larvae in adjacent cells. An unexpected but very vital function was established by Cooper (1957) in a set of ingeniously devised experiments to determine what factors caused the larva to orient with its head toward the nest entrance, thus insuring the successful emergence of the adult wasp. Working principally with the vespid *Euodynerus f. foraminatus,* he was able to show that the larva oriented with its head toward roughness and convexity (i.e., the anterior end of the cell) and away from smoothness and concavity (the posterior end of the cell) so that the adult developed with its head toward the boring entrance and eventually could escape from the nest. Most mother wasps select nesting sites with a boring diameter snugly adjusted to their bodies. They cannot turn around inside the boring but must back in or back out. Consequently, their progeny must orient properly or they are doomed to death because they cannot chew through the inner blind end of the boring.

However, I found that mature larvae of two species usually or always oriented with their heads toward the blind inner end of the boring. Both species nested in 12.7-mm. borings and neither spun a cocoon. One was the large vespid wasp *Monobia quadridens* (Linnaeus) and the other the carpenter bee *Xylocopa virginica* (Linnaeus). Despite misorientation as larvae, the adults were able to orient themselves correctly. They always emerged successfully from the nests by chewing through the partitions between them and the nest entrance. Furthermore, I never observed a nest where the adult had first attempted to emerge toward the blind inner end before turning around and emerging toward the entrance.

Occasionally I found otherwise empty borings with just a closing partition at the entrance. For most of them it was impossible to determine the cause of this anomalous behavior. However, at one station I found four empty borings each plugged at the entrance by a spider wasp, *Dipogon s. sayi.* A possible explanation was disclosed in a fifth boring at this station. This boring contained two completed *Dipogon* cells at the inner end and then three vespid cells, the outermost still being stored with caterpillars. Apparently the supersedure by the vespid may have triggered the *Dipogon* female into this series of untimely and inappropriate nest closures. At times I have wondered whether some of this plugging of empty borings might not be analogous to the behavior of wrens in filling up all kinds of cavities with leaves or twigs to deny nesting sites to other birds, although I think that this explanation is rather implausible.

VESTIBULAR CELL

It is preferable to discuss the vestibular cell before the empty intercalary cells, because the vestibular type is a feature of nearly all nests whereas the intercalary is not, and because of the probable origin of the intercalary.

The vestibular cell is an empty space of varying length at or near the outer end of the boring (fig. 22). It is capped by a closing plug usually constructed of the same material as the cell partitions, although almost always twice or more as thick. Occasionally, the vestibular cell may be separated into two or more sections by narrow transverse partitions (fig. 23). It has been theorized that this cell functions to discourage penetration to the stored cells by parasites or predators. If it served this useful function at one period of nest evolution, it has now largely outlived such a purpose, because the parasites have timed their attacks to coincide with provisioning of the individual cells or they are persistent and resourceful enough to penetrate several partitions and empty spaces to get at a provisioned cell.

EMPTY INTERCALARY CELLS

In the nests of almost any species there may be an occasional empty intercalary cell between two stored cells. They occur sporadically and rarely in most species. For this reason they are of no significance in the nest architecture of most wasps, but they are probably the result of a behavioral response of the mother wasp to some factor such as the invasion of the preceding stored cell by a parasite, the discovery of mold spores or other contaminants on the boring walls in the section where the intercalary cell is made, and so forth. Conceivably, the occasional intercalary cell may actually be a vestibular cell, and may mark the spot where a second wasp superseded the maker of the first series of cells.

However, in certain wasps, particularly the vespids *Monobia quadridens* (fig. 29), *Pachodynerus erynnis* and *P. astraeus*, *Symmorphus c. cristatus* (fig. 21), and several species of *Euodynerus* (fig. 40), these cells were present in half or more of the nests. In some nests an intercalary cell was present between each pair of stored cells. However, these nests were in a minority, and most nests with intercalary cells had them between only some of the stored cells in a particular nest.

A peculiar but constant feature of these intercalary cells was that they were sealed by a thicker partition than the one sealing the stored cells. In other words, considered as a unit, the empty intercalary cell was indistinguishable architecturally (except for its position in a series of cells) from a vestibular cell at the nest entrance. I believe that the function of these intercalary cells has never been logically explained. Malyshev (1911, pp. 55-56) and Cooper (1953, p. 20) treated them as empty cells no different from the occasional empty cells at the inner end of the boring. I do not agree with this homology.

As I explained earlier, I consider that the plug at the inner end of the boring, whether it caps an empty space or not, serves as part of the orienting mechanism of the wasp larva in the first cell. I believe the probable explanation for the intercalary cell is that it is a relict of those days when the ancestors of these wasps may have made smaller nests consisting of just a single stored cell and a vestibular cell. During the evolution of nest building the wasps, when they found a cavity of sufficient length, put several of these single-celled nests together to form a linear series of stored cells with interspersed empty cells. As evolution progressed, more efficient use of the available space was made by the elimination of these intercalary cells, so now we find only some individuals of a few species of vespid wasps still clinging to the old habit of following each stored cell with an empty one.

OTHER TYPES OF LINEAR NESTS

All vespid wasps, most pompilid and sphecid wasps, and a few bees constructed nests such as described above with the partitions and closing plugs made of mud or agglutinated sand. However, some bees made different kinds of nests, also composed of cells in a linear series.

In the colletid bee *Hylaeus* the mother secretes a salivary substance which dries to form an extremely thin and delicate but impermeable transparent membrane over the inner walls of the cell. She fills this with a rather liquid pollen-nectar mix regurgitated from her crop, lays an egg on the outer surface of the mass, and then makes a transverse septum of the same diaphanous material. After constructing and storing a series of such cells, she leaves an empty vestibular cell and then seals the boring entrance with another partition of the salivary secretion.

In some megachilid bees the cell walls as well as the partitions between the cells and the closing plugs are made of vegetable material. The leaf-cutter bees of the genus *Megachile* (figs. 98-100) line the cell with a cup-shaped structure which they make by putting a number of rectangular leaf-cuttings, one within the other. A store of pollen and nectar is placed in the inner two-thirds of the cell, an egg is laid on the outer surface of this mass, and the cell is sealed by a number of circular leaf cuttings fitted down into the cell formed by the rectangular pieces. More rectangular cuttings are brought in to form the end and walls of the second cell, and so on, until there may be a series of a dozen cells in the boring. These species of *Megachile* do not make a vestibular cell as such, but they construct an equivalent by placing a number of very loosely fitted circular cuttings in the outer section of the boring.

The other genus of megachilid bees belonging to this category is *Anthidium* whose members are known as carder bees because they use cottony plant materials in the nest construction (figs. 79, 80). *Anthidium maculosum* lines the inner end of the boring and walls of the first cell with this matted cottony substance which it obtains from leaves of plants like cottonwood (*Populus*) or desert willow (*Chilopsis*). Then the female stores a rather liquid nectar-pollen mixture in the cell, lays an egg on the outer surface of the mass, makes a closing partition of the cottony material, and continues to store a series of cells in the same way. She does not construct a vestibular cell; instead, she makes a very thick plug consisting of a section of wadded cottony fibers, which is sometimes followed by a middle section of diverse materials such as small pebbles, and then an outer section of more wadded cotton.

LIFE CYCLE

The wasps and bees which use these traps exhibit the usual holometabolous development of egg-larva-pupa-adult. Most of them are multivoltine; that is, there are two or more generations a year. In nests of these species the occupants of overwintering nests pass the winter as resting or diapausing larvae, transform to pupae the following spring, and then to adults.

However, some species have only a single generation a year. The most abundant of these are the vernal bees of the genus *Osmia*. Occupants of their nests do not overwinter as resting larvae, but they transform to pupae the preceding summer and then to adults, which remain within the cocoons and do not chew their way out until the next spring. These *Osmia* bees are parasitized by species of the cuckoo wasp genus *Chrysura* and of the sapygid wasp *Sapyga*. These parasites have synchronized their development perfectly with that of their host bees. They transform to pupae and then to adults, concurrently with bee hosts, overwinter in their cocoons, and emerge concurrently with the bees the following spring.

A few species of vespid wasps are univoltine, having only a single generation, but the occupants of these nests overwinter as resting larvae and transform to pupae and adults late the following spring. In other words, no strictly vernal wasps nested in these borings.

When the mature larva finishes feeding, the body is plump and distended and has a more or less circular cross-section; the constrictions between the body segments are very weak (figs. 18, 21). The integument is transparent and glistening, and the tracheation, and frequently the oenocytes, may be seen through it. After the larva voids the accumulated fecal wastes and spins its cocoon, the body has a noticeably different appearance. The body always becomes somewhat flattened, the constrictions between the segments become very pronounced (cf. figs. 27, 28), the anterior end is usually bent downward and backward (fig. 20) although not so in *Monobia* (fig. 28) and *Euodynerus* (figs. 40, 41), and the integument becomes dull, opaque, and frequently finely wrinkled (fig. 19). The larva is usually quite flaccid, although in *Monobia* and some *Euodynerus* it is firm and leathery. This postdefecating larval stage, which is not preceded by a molt, is frequently called the prepupa. I have used the term prepupa in this report for the short period intervening between cocoon-spinning and pupation in larvae of the summer generation nests.

In nests of the overwintering generation (except in *Osmia* and its parasites), these postdefecating larvae enter a period of prolonged diapause during which development is inhibited. This diapause is broken by a period of exposure to chilly weather after which development is resumed. I have applied the terms diapausing or resting to larvae in these overwintering nests.

As the pupa develops within the larval integument, the body again becomes somewhat distended and the head end straightens out in those genera in which it was originally curved downward and backward. The darker posterior margin of the compound eye of the pupa is visible a day or two before the larval exuvia is shed.

The pupal stage is of variable duration depending upon the species. Figures 30-36 illustrate development of adult coloration within the pupal exuvia. Eclosion of the adult from this pupal cuticle occurs several days after the body becomes fully colored. After eclosion the adult remains in the cell for several days while the wings and integument harden.

Vespid nests are unique, differing from those of all other families of wasps and bees nesting in these borings in that the egg is laid in the inner end of the cell before any prey is stored in that cell. The other wasps and bees nesting in these borings first bring into the cell a store of food, paralyzed arthropods of various kinds for the wasps and a pollen-nectar mixture for the bees, before an egg is laid and the cell is sealed.

The deposition of the vespid egg is also unique among the wasps and bees in that it is suspended from a flexible thread several millimeters in length at a point several millimeters from the inner end of the cell (fig. 24). The eggs of other wasps are glued—loosely or firmly—to one of the individuals of prey stored for the waspling (*e.g.*, figs. 43, 52, 62), whereas those of bees are usually partly embedded in the pollen-nectar mixture (figs. 87, 91).

ADULT EMERGENCE

A question which intrigues many people is how the wasps in the inner cells are able to get out of the nest. They develop from eggs which are laid earlier and food must be provided before the cells in the outer end can be built and stored; sometimes several days elapse between provisioning the first and last cells in a nest. So one would imagine that the occupant of cell 1 should mature first and that the occupant of the last cell should mature last.

Several factors prevent this order of development. First, larval growth in a mixed vespid nest is a little slower in the inner, longer female cells where more food is stored. Second,

males tend to pupate in 1-2 days less than females after completion of larval feeding. Third, the pupal period is 2-4 days
shorter for male wasps. These different factors insure that in
mixed vespid nests of the summer generation the males in
the outer cells are ready to emerge several days earlier than their
sisters in the inner cells.

Newly eclosed adults usually spend 2-4 days in their cells
in order that the wings and integument can harden before they
emerge from the nest. This situation does not alter the fact
that males emerge before females, but it does operate to insure
that the males in an individual nest frequently emerge concurrently or within a day of each other, and the same is true
for the females several days later.

There are probably two signals that precipitate emergence
of a series of males from an individual nest. When the day
of emergence has arrived for the adult male in the outermost
cell, he starts to chew through the partition capping his cell.
He secretes salivary fluid which helps to moisten the partition
sealing the cell and to make egress easier. The vibrations from
his chewing are probably sensed by the wasp in the preceding
cell who commences to gnaw at the partition capping his cell.
His behavior is communicated to the wasp in the antepenultimate cell, and so forth, until each male is engaged in making
a hole through his own cell partition. But occasionally one of
the males, in the antepenultimate cell for example, decides it
is time to emerge before he gets such a signal. When he starts
to gnaw through the partition capping his cell, he would
initiate similar action by the wasp in the penultimate cell and
thence by the wasp in the outermost cell. I have actually seen
this second kind of emergence beginning in nests which have
been opened at just the appropriate time.

Occasionally it happens that the occupant of a cell near the
boring entrance may die in the cell, either as a prepupa, pupa,
or eclosed adult. This death requires the wasp in the cell
immediately preceding that one to chew through an extra
partition or two to emerge. Such effort is not always physically
possible, so that the death of an individual in an outer cell
may doom his or her predecessors in the earlier cells to a similar
fate.

The discussion thus far has been concerned with emergence
from nests of the summer generation. The occupants of overwintering vespid nests are all diapausing larvae. Using *Euody-*

nerus foraminatus apopkensis as an example, we find that when diapause is broken the males pupate 5 days before the females and have a shorter pupal period by 2 days. Consequently, their emergence from the nest takes place about a week before that of the females.

From overwintering nests emergence of various species in the laboratory followed a definite sequence corresponding to the first appearance of those species in nature. The earliest emergents were the vernal species such as the several species of *Osmia* and their parasites *Chrysura kyrae, C. pacifica,* and *Sapyga centrata.* Following these were several species of *Ancistrocerus* and *Trypoxylon, Symmorphus cristatus* and *S. albomarginatus,* and *Passaloecus cuspidatus.* In the next week or two many species of *Euodynerus* and *Stenodynerus, Symmorphus canadensis,* and *Isodontia* emerged. The species of *Trypargilum* and *Podium* emerged later, after most of the other wasps.

Another interesting discovery during this study was the demonstration that individuals of the same species emerged at the same time in Washington even though some nests came from western New York, others from the metropolitan area of Washington, D. C., and still others from coastal North Carolina. For example, in nests of *Trypargilum collinum rubrocinctum* held outdoors in Washington over the winter of 1957-58, adults emerged on May 15-16 from nests stored at Derby, May 16-24 from nests stored at Plummers Island, and May 17-22 from nests stored at Kill Devil Hills. Had these nests been kept in the localities in which they were stored, we could have expected that the North Carolina population would have emerged 1-2 weeks earlier than the population around Washington, D. C., and 3-4 weeks earlier than the population in western New York.

Two other aspects of adult emergence merit some discussion. I have termed these divided emergence and delayed emergence.

Divided emergence occurred when one or several individuals emerged the same summer that nests were constructed, about a month afterward, whereas the other individuals in the same nest overwintered as diapausing larvae, which next spring transformed to pupae and then to adults. This behavior occurred chiefly in *Trypargilum collinum rubrocinctum;* males and some females from the outermost cells emerged the preceding summer, and the remaining females from the inner cells the following spring. This type of emergence also occurred in one nest of *T. clavatum,* in two nests each of *T. t. tridentatum* and *T. t. archboldi,* and one nest each of *Euodynerus p. pratensis E. schwarzi, Stenodynerus lineatifrons,* and *Ancistrocerus c. catskill.*

Delayed emergence occurred when all but one or two occupants of an overwintering nest emerged as adults that spring, and one or two larvae continued in diapause all through a second winter and adults did not emerge until the next spring or summer. This phenomenon occurred most frequently, though still rarely, in 9 nests of *Trypargilum striatum.* The wasps which underwent this delayed emergence occurred at random in the nests and usually they died as fully colored pupae or newly eclosed adults in their cocoons. This delayed emergence also occurred in one nest of *Ancistrocerus t. tuberculiceps,* in my only nest of *Podium luctuosum,* and in six nests of the megachilid bee *Prochelostoma philadelphi.* The occupants undergoing delayed development in nests of the two wasps usually did not transform to viable adults. However, the occupants undergoing delayed development in the bee nests emerged at the proper season 2 years after their nests were constructed. In the bees this is probably a useful adaptation to insure that part of the progeny will be available for a second season in case the earlier emergents do not find good pollen and nectar sources the previous spring.

SEQUENCE OF SEXES IN NESTS

The sequence of sexes in multicelled nests is an important characteristic of species and even of genera and families. Insofar as possible I gave particular attention to determining this arrangement in all nests. There was no difficulty in determining the individual sexes from pupae in nests of the Vespidae, where the cocoons were so delicate that they usually split when the nest was opened. In nests of the other families, where the cocoons were usually opaque, and brittle or tougher, it was possible to make a large enough rip posteriorly in the cocoon to determine the sex. However, I usually put each cocoon of this type in a small glass vial with the associated nest and cell numbers. The sex of each wasp or bee could then be recorded when the adults emerged without the possibility of injury to the pupa by making a hole in the cocoon.

This phase of the study confirmed the already established

fact that, in nests of Vespidae in which both sexes develop, females are always in the cells in the inner end of the boring and males are in the cells in the outer end. The deviations from this arrangement were so rare that I suspected them to be occasioned by failure of the sperm to fertilize an egg with consequent development of a male wasp in a cell in which a female should have developed, or that the original nestmaker had been superseded by another female of the same species.

This pattern of females in the inner and males in the outer cells was usually found also in nests of the megachilid bees *Ashmeadiella, Prochelostoma, Osmia, Chalicodoma,* and the leaf-cutting species of *Megachile.* In 51 *Osmia lignaria* nests females were in the inner and males were in the outer cells in 75 percent of the nests. Under the specific heading I include an extended discussion of the arrangement in the other dozen nests in which I point out that the deviations from the normal sex sequence apparently fell into three groups. An occasional male cell in a sequence of female cells might have been caused by failure of the sperm to fertilize the egg; this hypothesis received some substantiation by the finding that these male cells actually were longer than normal male cells and that they had a larger store of food than was normal for male cells. In other nests, where there was a block of normal size male cells at the inner end or in the middle of the nest, their occurrence out of order might have been caused by the temporary "fatigue" of the muscles controlling egress of sperm from the spermetheca thus inhibiting release of sperm and resulting in deposition of unfertilized eggs. A third factor which perhaps accounted for the disarranged sequences in some nests might have been supersedure of the original nesting mother by another female of the same species, so that a sequence which started out as ♀-♀-♂-♂ or ♂-♂-♂ might end up as ♀-♀-♂-♂-♀-♀-♂ or ♂-♂-♂-♀-♀.

The megachilid bee *Anthidium maculosum* reversed the usual sequence by having males in the inner and females in the outer cells in all nests in which both sexes developed except in one where one male was out of place.

Wasps belonging to the genus *Trypargilum* demonstrated that sex sequence is an important taxonomic factor at the specific level. Except in a very few nests males were in the inner and females in the outer cells in both subspecies of *tridentatum* and in *striatum.* Females were in the inner and males in the outer cells in both subspecies of *collinum* in almost all nests.

In the two closely related species *johannis* and *clavatum* the situation was confused. Females were in the inner and males in the outer cells in five mixed nests of *johannis*, the reverse was true in two nests, and there was a random arrangement in three nests. Females were in the inner and males in the outer cells in five nests of *clavatum*, the reverse sequence occurred in four nests, and a random arrangement was found in four nests.

Pompilid wasps belonging to the genus *Dipogon* usually had a random sequence of sexes in their nests. It is possible that the size of the single spider placed in each cell was the factor which determined whether a female or male egg was laid.

Of other genera insufficient nests were available to permit any generalizations regarding sequence of sexes. I have mentioned the sequence under the specific treatments whenever any data were available, so that conclusions may be drawn as to the probable pattern when more nests are at hand.

This is the appropriate place to mention a phenomenon which could be inferred from the previous discussion. It is the ability of the female wasp or bee to know in advance, before storing the cell with food, the sex of the egg which she will place in the cell prior to sealing it. With the Vespidae, the only family in which the egg is laid before the cell is provisioned, the wasp still controls and knows the sex of the egg she has laid, because she brings in a large number of caterpillars if it is to be a female or a small number if it is to be a male.

In the wasps and bees males develop from unfertilized eggs and females from fertilized eggs. For many years it has been known that the queen bee controls the sex of her offspring, laying fertilized eggs in the smaller worker cells and unfertilized eggs in the larger drone cells. Several other examples of sex determination by female Hymenoptera are: In *Tiphia vernalis*, a wasp parasite of Japanese beetle larvae, Brunson (1938) found that usually female eggs are deposited on the larger third-instar grubs and usually male eggs on the smaller second-instar larvae; and in the chalcid parasite *Coccophagus ochraceus* Flanders (1962) has described different oviposition postures which forecast the sex of the egg to be laid. In *Osmia lignaria* nests I found that almost without exception males were produced in 4.8-mm. borings, and both sexes were produced in the larger borings. I theorized that the movement of the mother's abdomen in the smaller boring may have been so restricted as to prevent egress of the sperm from the spermatheca, thus insuring that only male eggs would normally be laid in these smaller borings. The few female eggs in the 4.8-mm. borings might have been laid by smaller than normal mothers.

Several nests of the megachilid bee *Megachile (Sayapis) policaris* Say offered striking proof that a female can lay some female eggs and then some male eggs, followed by additional series of female and male eggs. This bee is unique in that it constructs a series of brood cells in large borings. Each of these brood cells contains a large store of pollen and nectar and an average of 6.5 eggs (range 2-16). The larvae develop without cannibalism. In two *policaris* nests I found that both sexes developed in at least two or three consecutive brood cells.

Jayakar (1963) proposed the terms protothelytoky and protarrhenotoky for the phenomena of all female-producing eggs being laid before all male-producing eggs or all male-producing eggs being laid before all female-producing eggs. He observed the latter phenomenon in an Indian vespid mud-daubing wasp, *Eumenes esuriens* Fabricius. He obtained only a single 13-celled nest containing both sexes and found that all five eggs which produced males were laid before the seven eggs which produced females. (The egg died in the sixth cell.) Jayakar hypothesized that in this species a female produced a series of unfertilized male eggs followed by a series of fertilized female eggs. He also cited a 9-celled nest of the sphecid mud-dauber *Sceliphron madraspatanum* (Fabricius) in which four male eggs were laid before five female eggs.

Jayakar suggested that the phenomenon of protarrhenotoky could occur for three reasons: Delayed copulation so that some unfertilized eggs were laid first; the occurrence of a long interval between copulation and fertilization; and control of fertilization by a sphincter. His first suggestion is not substantiated by the large corpus of published observations, which indicate that mating takes place very shortly after emergence of the females and before there have been any nesting activities. I am not sure just what he means by his second reason, but he probably infers that the sperm may not be mature at the time of copulation; this hypothesis was not borne out by my nests of *Euodynerus foraminatus apopkensis* and *Osmia lignaria*, in which females developed in the innermost cells of some of the earliest nests stored by the mother wasps and bees. The third suggestion has already been proved for some of the parasitic and social Hymenoptera; there is no reason to suppose that it is not equally true in the solitary aculeates.

My observations show that females of all vespid wasps, and most sphecid wasps and bees, lay a series of female eggs before a series of male eggs in nests where both sexes are produced. Furthermore, although I have not worked with marked females, I am confident that a female is capable of alternating series of female and male cells. (See also my discussion several paragraphs above on sequence of sexes in the broodcell building *Megachile policaris*.) Consequently, during her life she may construct several nests each with females in the inner and males in the outer cells. However, the females of several sphecid wasps and bees, for example *Trypargilum tridentatum* and *Anthidium maculosum*, lay male eggs in the inner cells and female eggs in the outer cells. Here again, I do not doubt that a female can alternate these series so that several mixed nests built by the same female will each have males in the inner and females in the outer cells.

Jayakar stated that he could find no examples of *complete* protothelytoky, i.e., all female eggs laid before all male eggs, and I quite agree. However, I do not consider that he has established *complete* arrhenotoky on the basis of one nest each in *Eumenes esuriens* and *Sceliphron madraspatanum*. I believe that if marked females of these two species are kept under observation it will be found that in each of several nests constructed by a single individual there may well be first a series of male cells followed by a series of female cells.

CORRELATION OF SEX WITH CELL SIZE AND AMOUNT OF FOOD

In many species there was significant correlation between size of cell and amount of food stored in it with sex of the wasp or bee which developed therein. This correlation was especially noticeable in nests of almost all species of Vespidae and in nests of *Osmia* (fig. 84) and *Ashmeadiella* in the Megachilidae. In nests of these wasps and bees containing both sexes, the inner cells were longer and contained a proportionately larger amount of food than the shorter cells with less food in the outer section of the boring. Females developed in those longer inner cells and males developed in the shorter outer ones.

For example, in 6.4-mm. nests of the vespid wasp *Euodynerus foraminatus apopkensis,* 418 cells at the inner end of the borings from which female wasps emerged had a mean length of 17.5 mm., whereas 308 cells at the outer end from which males emerged had a mean length of only 13.4 mm. The cells in which females developed contained an average of 14 caterpillars, whereas male cells held an average of 8. *Osmia lignaria* provided another excellent example of this correlation: In 6.4-mm. nests of this bee, 235 cells at the inner end in which females developed had a mean length of 14.3 mm., and 255 male cells at the outer end of the borings had a mean length of 10.8 mm.; the pollen-nectar masses stored in female cells averaged 8.2 mm., but they averaged only 5.5 mm. in male cells.

This correlation was very rarely negative in vespid nests. It was negative in nests of *Stenodynerus saecularis rufulus* where male cells in both 4.8- and 6.4-mm. borings had a greater mean length than female cells. The sequence of sexes in mixed nests of this wasp was normal, that is females were in the inner and males in the outer cells. The anomaly occurred because the terminal stored cell in a nest frequently was considerably longer than any of the preceding stored cells, and most frequently males developed in these extra long cells.

The species of *Trypargilum* again provided interesting and anomalous data. The male cells of both subspecies of *tridentatum* had a greater mean length than female cells. Presumably a larger amount of prey was stored in male cells because male cocoons were longer than female cocoons and adult male wasps were a little larger than females. The situation was reversed in *johannis,* which constructed female cells and cocoons that were substantially longer than those of males.

PREY

Spider wasps of the family Pompilidae stored a single spider in each cell (figs. 43, 47), and wasps of the family Ampulicidae placed only a single cockroach in each cell (fig. 50). Wasps of the other families, Vespidae and Sphecidae, stored several to many specimens of prey per cell (*e.g.,* figs. 25, 52, 62).

Most of the vespid wasps preyed on externally feeding lepidopterous caterpillars, chiefly leaf rollers and tiers (*e.g.,* figs. 25, 39). However, the species of *Symmorphus* showed some diversity in that two of them preyed on externally feeding coleopterous larvae, *Chrysomela* species (fig. 22), while the third preyed chiefly on leaf-mining coleopterous or lepidopterous larvae (fig. 16).

The sphecid wasps showed the greatest diversity in prey selection. *Trypoxylon* and *Trypargilum* preyed on spiders (fig. 52), mostly immatures, and the other genera preyed on insects. The sphecine wasps stored nymphal and adult Orthoptera: Cockroaches by *Podium* (fig. 62) and snowy tree crickets and occasional tettigoniids by *Isodontia* (fig. 60). *Solierella* preyed on nymphal lygaeids. The pemphredonines *Passaloecus* (fig. 67) and *Diodontus* stored aphids, mostly immatures. The crabronine wasps all preyed on adult insects: *Tracheliodes* on worker ants (fig. 68), *Euplilis* on chironomid midges, and an unidentified wasp, possibly *Crossocerus,* on a mixture of true flies and caddisflies.

Spiders, whether stored by pompilid or by trypoxylonine wasps, were usually thoroughly paralyzed and exhibited only weak tremors of the mouthparts or tarsi. The aphids stored by *Diodontus* and *Passaloecus* were completely motionless; in addition to stinging them the wasps malaxated, or kneaded with their mandibles, the neck region of the aphids.

The lepidopterous and coleopterous larvae preyed upon by vespid wasps were more lightly paralyzed. They defecated and wriggled their legs, and sometimes caterpillars thrashed around if they were not confined by pressure of other caterpillars. Occasionally, full-grown caterpillars went on to pupate, and rarely adult moths emerged from the pupae; however, these adults were unable to leave and perished in the cell. Sometimes the caterpillars became cyanotic, presumably as a result of envenomation.

SEASONAL ABUNDANCE OF COMMON SPECIES

I obtained nests over a consecutive period of years from three localities: Derby, N. Y.; Plummers Island, Md.; and Lake Placid, Fla. In Table 1 I have listed those species for which I obtained 10 or more nests and the number of nests for each species in each season. The species in the upper section of the table are from Derby, those in the middle section from Plummers Island, and those in the lower section from Lake Placid. An *x* indicates that traps were not set out early enough in the season to provide nesting sites for vernal species (the two *Osmia* species at Plummers Island in 1956 and 1957, and

TABLE 1.—*Seasonal abundance of nests of common species.*

Locality and species	1954	1955	1956	1957	1958	1959	1960	1961	1962
DERBY, N. Y.:									
Ancistrocerus a. antilope	10	4	36	18	9	14	9	11	x
Symmorphus c. cristatus	0	4	28	11	1	0	17	3	x
Ancistrocerus c. catskill	0	7	9	5	6	4	5	8	x
Trypargilum striatum	2	2	0	0	3	2	11	7	x
Ancistrocerus t. tigris	2	4	4	0	2	8	3	2	x
Trypoxylon frigidum	0	6	3	3	1	1	0	3	x
Euodynerus f. foraminatus	0	1	1	10	5	0	0	0	x
Trypargilum c. rubrocinctum	1	0	4	2	0	6	1	2	x
Symmorphus canadensis	0	0	0	0	4	2	4	0	x
Passaloecus cuspidatus	0	0	1	1	0	5	3	0	x
PLUMMERS ISLAND, MD.:									
Trypargilum striatum	x	x	26	55	16	12	48	47	18
Osmia l. lignaria	x	x	x	x	20	60	7	32	21
Trypargilum clavatum	x	x	33	22	2	7	2	10	0
Osmia pumila	x	x	9	x	5	2	8	7	20
Trypargilum c. rubrocinctum	x	x	0	18	2	3	5	4	0
Monobia quadridens	x	x	0	27	1	2	1	2	1
Dipogon s. sayi	x	x	1	0	3	6	4	11	3
Ancistrocerus campestris	x	x	3	7	0	2	4	5	2
Euodynerus schwarzi	x	x	0	4	0	2	0	2	8
Symmorphus canadensis	x	x	1	2	4	5	3	2	0
Symmorphus albomarginatus	x	x	x	0	0	0	1	12	2
Osmia bucephala	x	x	0	x	2	3	2	6	0
Ancistrocerus a. antilope	x	x	0	6	0	0	2	2	2

TABLE 1.—*Seasonal abundance of nests of common species—Continued.*

Locality and species	1954	1955	1956	1957	1958	1959	1960	1961	1962
LAKE PLACID, FLA.:									
Euodynerus f. apopkensis	x	x	x	92	x	19	62	68	x
Pachodynerus erynnis	x	x	x	8	x	11	11	48	8
Monobia quadridens	x	x	x	4	x	18	8	24	24
Stenodynerus s. rufulus	x	x	x	7	x	7	5	40	17
Podium rufipes	x	x	x	27	x	3	12	15	0
Trypargilum johannis	x	x	x	15	x	0	2	7	17
Euodynerus megaera	x	x	x	1	x	10	5	15	0
Megachile mendica	x	x	x	4	x	2	10	8	0
Stenodynerus p. surrufus	x	x	x	2	x	0	2	15	4
Chalicodoma georgica	x	x	x	2	x	1	8	3	3
Trypargilum c. collinum	x	x	x	5	x	3	2	4	0
Trypargilum t. archboldi	x	x	x	4	x	0	0	4	4
Stenodynerus beameri	x	x	x	0	x	0	0	11	0
Stenodynerus lineatifrons	x	x	x	3	x	1	3	3	1

Euodynerus foraminatus apopkensis at Lake Placid in 1962) or that no traps were used at all (Derby in 1962, Plummers Island in 1954 and 1955, and Lake Placid in 1954-1956 and 1958). In each section the species are arranged in descending order according to the total number of nests stored.

From year to year the number of nests for any one species fluctuated. Some fluctuation was caused by the number of traps available from year to year. However, some was caused by a particular species being more common during one year than during the next one; or, at least, it used relatively more traps one year than it did in another. Only one species, *Euodynerus foraminatus apopkensis* at Lake Placid, was the most frequent user of traps in each year that traps were available to it. The wasp nesting most frequently at Derby was *Ancistrocerus a. antilope;* it provisioned more nests than other species in most years except 1955 and 1960, when it was the third most frequent user. *Trypargilum striatum* used more traps at Plummers Island than any other species, but it was the most frequent user only in 3 years (1957, 1960, 1961), the second most frequent in 3 years (1956, 1958, 1959), and the third in 1962. *Osmia lignaria* ranked first at Plummers Island in 3 of the 5 years in which traps were available to it, and second and third in 1 year each.

Most of the other species showed considerable fluctuation in their relative rank. For example, at Derby, the second most frequent user of traps, *Symmorphus cristatus,* had relative rank of 10, 3, 2, 2, 7, 10, 1, and 4 in the 8 years in which traps were available. At Plummers Island the third most frequent user of traps, *Trypargilum clavatum,* had relative rank of 1, 3, 6, 3, 8, 5, and 13. These rankings for the second and third most frequent species at Lake Placid, *Pachodynerus erynnis* and *Monobia quadridens,* were 4, 3, 3, 2, 4, and 7, 2, 5, 4, and 1, respectively.

Overtrapping was one other factor that caused some seasonal fluctuation. I was particularly aware of this condition at Plummers Island, where year after year I continued to set traps at the same or almost the same stations. I believe that overtrapping caused immediate decline of the *Monobia quadridens* population after 1957 and temporary reduction of *Trypargilum striatum* in 1958, 1959, and 1962; of *Osmia lignaria* in 1960; and of *T. clavatum* and *T. collinum rubrocinctum* after 1957.

MISCELLANEOUS OCCUPANTS OF TRAPS

Several other species of arthropods used these traps. The most serious of these from the standpoint of interfering with nesting by wasps and bees were *Crematogaster* ants (fig. 12). Colonies of these occasionally began in borings set on rotten wood. Although the ants nested in only one boring at first, their constant foraging into other borings in the same setting discouraged wasps and bees from attempting to nest. Ants belonging to *Camponotus* subgenus *Colobopsis*, which ordinarily nest in hollows in twigs and galls, nested in a few traps at settings on scrubby live and Spanish oaks on the barrens at Kill Devil Hills, N.C.

A grasshopper, *Melanoplus* sp. probably *punctulatus* (Scudder), deposited egg pods just within the entrance of a few traps set on pine trees in open woods at Kill Devil Hills.

Sowbugs occasionally entered traps placed in moist, shaded situations on dead fallen tree trunks at Plummers Island, Md.

In wooded areas snare-building spiders occasionally took over borings as retreats and spun snares in them.

Eleven caterpillars entered these borings to pupate, 9 of them at Kill Devil Hills, and 1 each at Plummers Island and Derby (fig. 13). Two moths were reared: The noctuid *Melipotis jucunda* Hübner, from one of the Kill Devil Hills nests, and the phycitid *Canarsia ulmiarrosorella* Clemens from the Derby nest. One caterpillar destroyed the contents of inner cells of an *Osmia ribifloris* nest at Portal, Ariz. I also found a caterpillar tunneling in the moldy pollen-nectar mass of a cell of the leaf cutter bee *Megachile mendica* Cresson in a nest from Lake Placid, Fla.; presumably the egg from which this caterpillar hatched was on one of the leaf cuttings brought into the nest by the female bee.

WASPS AND BEES

In the specific accounts of the wasps and bees which follow, I have listed in an introductory paragraph the number of nests available for study, the diameter of borings used, and the localities and particular stations from which the nests were obtained. After the introductory notes come several sections of original observations arranged under the side headings *supersedure and competition, nest architecture, prey* (for wasps only) or *larval food* (for bees only), *life history,* and *parasites and predators.* If no information was obtained for a particular section under a given species, that side heading is omitted. A final section, *previous observations,* summarizes earlier contributions on each wasp or bee, when any were published; literature published through 1965 has been included insofar as possible.

The arrangement is systematic insofar as possible and follows that of the catalog of North American Hymenoptera (Muesebeck, Krombein, Townes, *et al.,* 1951) to the subgeneric level. Arrangement of species and subspecies within the genus or subgenus is by species groups, when these are recognized, or alphabetical.

Superfamily VESPOIDEA

Family VESPIDAE

Nests of members of this family showed much less diversity in architecture than those of other families of wasps and bees that I found in the wood borings. At first glance the general architecture was so similar that it seemed monotonous, but upon detailed analysis some interesting differences became apparent.

Most of these species of wasps placed a preliminary plug of mud or agglutinated sand at the inner end of the boring or made a partition of one of these materials at varying distances from the inner end. This construction appeared in about a third to a half of the nests of each species. In the remaining nests the wasps laid an egg at the inner end of the boring without first bringing in sand or mud. However, several species did not follow this pattern. Some differences were not significant because those particular species stored only one or two nests. However, *Ancistrocerus spinolae* stored

4 nests and *Stenodynerus beameri* stored 11 nests, and neither put any sand at the inner end of the boring. Also, *Pachodynerus astraeus* in all 5 nests and *Euodynerus guerrero* in 7 of 8 nests did put some sand at the inner end before laying the first egg.

One of the most conspicuous features of the nests of a few vespid species was the presence of an empty intercalary cell between two stored cells. This cell was certainly of no significance when it occurred rarely, for example, in one of a dozen or so nests. However, with certain species one or several of these cells occurred in 10-90 percent of the nests. Since a gradient was found to exist in several genera, it will be preferable to discuss the occurrence of these cells by separate genus. In *Monobia quadridens* one or more intercalary cells were present in 124 of 140 nests. The cells were present in a large percentage of nests of the two species of *Pachodynerus;* namely, 21 of 86 nests of *erynnis* and 2 of 5 nests of *astraeus.* In *Symmorphus* these cells were lacking in nests of *canadensis* (45 nests) and *albomarginatus* (6 nests); the situation in *c. cristatus* was rather peculiar in that the cells were present in 13 of 24 nests in 4.8-mm. borings but lacking in all 7 nests in 3.2 and 6.4-mm. borings. In *Ancistrocerus* the cells were present in 31 of 122 nests of *a. antilope* (but usually only 1 per nest) and in 5 of 44 nests of *c. catskill* (2 per nest), and they were lacking in nests of *antilope navajo* (1 nest), *spinolae* (4 nests), *t. tuberculiceps* (10 nests), *durangoensis* (1 nest), *t. tigris* (39 nests) and *campestris* (21 nests). In *Euodynerus* intercalary cells were present in significant numbers in *guerrero* (7 of 8 nests), *p. pratensis* (6 of 7 nests), *schwarzi* (7 of 19 nests), *f. foraminatus* (15 of 28 nests), *foraminatus apopkensis* (24 of 241 nests), and *megaera* (8 of 51 nests), but were completely lacking in *m. molestus* (16 nests), *hidalgo boreoorientalis* (12 nests), and *oslarensis* (1 nest).

Another rather constant feature of most completely stored vespid nests was the presence of an empty vestibular cell at the outer end of the boring which was sealed by a plug thicker than the partitions capping the stored cells. I believe this vestibular cell may have been developed as a device to delude parasites and predators into abandoning attempts to break into the nest. Surprisingly enough, this cell was frequently lacking in a number of species. Disregarding those species with less than 5 nests, we find that the following species had vestibular cells in less than 80 percent of the completed nests: *Pachodynerus erynnis* (in only 49 of 69 nests), *Euodynerus foraminatus apopkensis* (134 of 221 nests), *E. hidalgo boreoorientalis* (5 of 10 nests), *E. megaera* (21 of 41 nests), *E. m. molestus* (7 of 10 nests), *E. schwarzi* (10 of 14 nests), *Ancistrocerus tuberculiceps* (4 of 7 nests), *Stenodynerus beameri* (6 of 11 nests), *S. lineatifrons* (12 of 18 nests), *S. fulvipes rufovestis* (5 of 8 nests), *S. toltecus* (10 of 15 nests), and *S. saecularis rufulus* (38 of 65 nests).

The closing plugs at the nest entrances were variable in thickness, but had a noticeably greater thickness in a few species. Normally, the mean thickness of these plugs was 2-5 mm. Again disregarding those species with less than five completed nests, we find that the following species usually had closing plugs with a mean thickness of greater than 5 mm.: *Monobia quadridens* (7 mm.), *Euodynerus f. foraminatus* and *E. guerrero* (6 mm.), *E. megaera* (3 mm. in 4.8-mm. borings, 4 mm. in 6.4-mm. borings, and 8 mm. in 12.7-mm. borings), *Pachodynerus erynnis* (7 mm.), *Stenodynerus ammonia histrionalis* (8 mm.), *Symmorphus canadensis* (4.8 mm. in 3.2-mm. borings, 8.6 mm. in 4.8-mm. borings), *S. c. cristatus* (9 mm.), and *S. albomarginatus* (10 mm.).

Stored cells per completed nest. There were significant differences in efficient use of nesting space. For example, of several species which nested frequently in 4.8- and 6.4-mm. borings, *Euodynerus foraminatus apopkensis* averaged 8.1 and 7.6 stored cells, respectively, in completed nests in borings of these two diameters. The absence of vestibular cells in 40 percent of the nests of this wasp more than offset the presence of intercalary cells in about 10 percent of the nests, so that *apopkensis* was able to make more efficient use of available space than any other vespid.

E. megaera and *Ancistrocerus a. antilope,* which were slightly larger wasps than *apopkensis,* made respectively 4.1 and 6.3, and 4.5 and 4.6 provisioned cells in borings of these two diameters.

Pachodynerus erynnis, a wasp of about the same size as *apopkensis,* provisioned only 3.2 and 4.1 cells, respectively, per nest. The cells of *erynnis* had a substantially greater mean length than *apopkensis* (more than twice as long for males and half again as long for females); also it made intercalary cells in 25 percent of the nests and vestibular cells in 70 percent of the nests.

Ancistrocerus c. catskill and *Symmorphus c. cristatus,* wasps of the same size but smaller than *apopkensis,* made 4.6 and 5.5, and 5.5 and 4.5 stored cells, respectively, in 4.8- and 6.4-mm. borings; the anomalous measurement for *cristatus* in 6.4-mm. borings was perhaps due to having only 7 cells available for measurement.

The most inefficient user of space was *Stenodynerus saecularis rufulus,* a wasp of about the same size as *Ancistrocerus c. catskill* and *Symmorphus c. cristatus.* It made only 3.3 stored cells in 4.8-mm. borings and 2.6 stored cells in 6.4-mm. borings. The stored cells of *s. rufulus* had mean lengths two to four times as long as those of *catskill and cristatus.* Also, *s. rufulus* more frequently had longer empty cells at the inner end of the boring than either of the other two species. However, its vestibular cells had a shorter mean length than those of *catskill* and *cristatus.*

Prey preferences. It is not possible to make many generalizations regarding the prey, because so many of the caterpillars stored were immatures or belonged to unknown genera whose closest identification could be obtained only to family. Except for *Symmorphus,* all the genera preyed upon external leaf-feeding caterpillars, leaf rollers or leaf tiers.

Most of the species of *Stenodynerus* preyed on Gelechioidea, although *pulvinatus surrufus, fulvipes rufovestis, toltecus,* and *saecularis rufulus* occasionally stored Pyraloidea also.

Other species using Gelechioidea only included *Euodynerus foraminatus apopkensis, Ancistrocerus t. tuberculiceps, A. t. tigris,* and *A. campestris.* Others using both Gelechioidea and Pyraloidea included *Ancistrocerus c. catskill, Monobia quadridens, Euodynerus schwarzi,* and *E. f. foraminatus.*

Ancistrocerus a. antilope used Gelechioidea, Pyraloidea, and Noctuoidea, as did *Pachodynerus erynnis* and *Euodynerus megaera.*

Euodynerus guerrero used Pyraloidea and Noctuoidea.

Euodynerus oslarensis stored Pyraloidea, Gelechioidea, and Cosmopterygidae.

The prey preferences noted for some of the species discussed above are probably much narrower than is actually the case. Some of my samples are based on the entire or partial contents of only a single cell. Samples from additional nests of these species in the future can be expected to contain caterpillars of one or more additional families or superfamilies.

The species of *Symmorphus* had more unusual prey preferences. *S. c. cristatus* and *albomarginatus* stored leaf-feeding *Chrysomela* larvae. The stench of salicylaldehyde, or a mixture of analogs and derivatives thereof, secreted by these beetle larvae was so strong when a fully stored nest was opened that it was difficult to see how the wasp larvae avoided suffocation. (Actually, the large amount of unexplained larval mortality in nests of these two species may be due to asphyxiation!) The third species, *canadensis,* preyed principally upon leaf-mining coleopterous larvae (*Chalepus dorsalis* in Chrysomelidae) and lepidopterous larvae (Gracillariidae and Walshiidae). Occasionally, very early in the season, it used *Apion* weevil larvae, which it may have obtained in *Betula* catkins.

Life history. Hartman (1944) provided a graphic description of a vespid depositing an egg in a piece of glass tubing. He described how the wasp touched the tip of its abdomen to the top of the glass tubing and spun out the flexible thread, and then the slow rhythmic pulsation of the wasp's abdomen as she "pumped" out the egg.

Authors who have written about the attachment of the vespid egg have mentioned that it was attached to the top of the cell. However, this does not always happen, because I observed some cells of *Symmorphus canadensis* in which the thread was attached occasionally to the bottom or to the side of the cell. The functional purpose of this suspensory thread is not to hang the egg above the mass of writhing, partially paralyzed prey, as supposed by some authors, but more likely to serve as a means of attaching the egg to a base, thus providing security against wind movements normally present in the natural twig-nesting habitat. The thread probably serves the additional useful purpose of anchoring the newly hatched larva when it begins to feed on the first specimen of prey. This thread appears to be homologous with the adhesive substance that other wasps use to attach their eggs to their prey.

In most of these nests the vespid wasps stuffed specimens of prey into the cell so closely that the egg was pushed back and rested along the top or side of the cell wall. The egg hung freely only in occasional cells of *Monobia* in 12.7-mm. borings (figs. 24, 25), in which the caterpillars sometimes filled no more than the bottom half of the cell. Apparently the eggs were rarely injured by being wedged between the cell wall and the prey, even though the prey were sometimes only lightly paralyzed and thus capable of wriggling about.

Only males were produced in some vespid nests, only females in others, and both sexes in still others. Occasionally, as in *Euodynerus foraminatus apopkensis*, the all-male nests were usually found in smaller borings (4.8 mm. for that wasp) and all-female nests in larger borings (6.4 mm.), with mixed nests occurring in the larger borings also. In the mixed nests a series of females developed in the longer inner cells in the boring and a series of males in the shorter outer cells. Exceptions to this rule were so infrequent as to merit special mention in the specific accounts which follow.

A sequence of sexes such as ♂-♀-♀-♀-♂-♂ might be due to several causes. If the first male cell was more or less equal in length to the female cells which followed and was distinctly longer than the male cells at the outer end of the boring, we might suspect that the mother wasp actually expected a female to develop in that first cell but that the sperm failed to fertilize the egg she laid therein. If the first male cell was significantly shorter than the female cells which followed it, we might suspect that there had been supersedure in this boring by another mother wasp of the same species. This superseder might have displaced a female that made a single male cell at the inner end, and then proceeded herself to lay first a series of female eggs and then a series of male eggs.

Cocoons. Most of the species spun complete but delicate, sub-opaque, silken cocoons. *Monobia quadridens* did not spin a cocoon, but it varnished over the cell walls and ends (fig. 29). Cocoons of *Symmorphus c. cristatus* (figs. 20, 21) and *S. albomarginatus* were opaque and denser and tougher than in the other species including *S. canadensis* (fig. 19).

Duration of pupal period. I was unable to determine the exact pupal period in most species because after eclosion the adults spent 2-4 days in the cells while the wings and integument hardened before they emerged from the nest. However, for most species I was able to record the elapsed time between pupation and adult emergence from the nest. Some significant differences were apparent. Listed below in decreasing amounts are the mean elapsed times for those species, each of which I observed a dozen or more times.

> *Pachodynerus erynnis:* ♀—22 days; ♂—20 days
> *Stenodynerus saecularis rufulus:* ♀, ♂—21 days each
> *Monobia quadridens:* ♀—18 days; ♂—17 days
> *Euodynerus foraminatus apopkensis:* ♀—18 days; ♂—16 days
> *Stenodynerus toltecus:* ♀—16 days; ♂—17 days
> *Stenodynerus ammonia histrionalis:* ♀—16 days; ♂—15 days
> *Stenodynerus krombeini:* ♀—17 days; ♂—12 days
> *Euodynerus megaera:* ♀—16 days; ♂—13 days
> *Ancistrocerus t. tuberculiceps:* ♂—15 days
> *Ancistrocerus a. antilope:* ♀—12 days; ♂—11 days
> *Ancistrocerus c. catskill:* ♀, ♂—9 days each

I did not measure this period for many individuals of *Symmorphus,* but the mean was 15 days each for 5 females and 2 males of *canadensis* and 12 and 10 days, respectively, for 3 females and 4 males of *c. cristatus.*

It is noteworthy that the species with the shortest pupal periods, those of *Ancistrocerus* and *Symmorphus,* are more northern in distribution or occur at higher altitudes (*A. tuberculiceps*) and belong to genera primarily of Holarctic distribution. The other species with the longer pupal periods are southeastern or southwestern in distribution and belong to genera which are primarily Neotropical or Austral and Sonoran in distribution.

Observations of several other species of *Ancistrocerus* indicated general support of the above data, although too few observations were involved for the information to be trustworthy. One northeastern form, *t. tigris,* had mean periods of 10 (♀) and 7 (♂) days for 7 individuals. A species somewhat more southern in distribution, *campestris,* had periods of 14 (♀) and 11 (♂) days for 2 individuals at Washington. A southwestern form, *antilope navajo,* had an 11-day period for 2 males. The rare species *spinolae* had longer periods of 17 days for 2 females and 14 days for 8 males at Kill Devil Hills.

Number of generations. Most of the species had two or more generations annually. However, a few were definitely or probably univoltine. The three species of *Symmorphus* had only a single generation with nesting occurring in late spring and early summer. Occasionally, *canadensis* had a very small summer emergence, and there was some indication that this might happen rarely in the other two species. The Floridian *Euodynerus foraminatus apopkensis* was strictly a vernal wasp. This finding was very surprising when one considers that the more northern subspecies, typical *foraminatus*, is multivoltine at Plummers Island and at Kill Devil Hills. Evidence from a single nest suggested that the rare Arizonan *Euodynerus oslarensis* was also a vernal univoltine species. The very rare eastern *Ancistrocerus spinolae* also appeared to have a single generation with nesting occurring in late spring and early summer at Kill Devil Hills. All the *Stenodynerus* were multivoltine, except that the Arizonan *bicornis cushmani* appeared to have a single summer generation based on the very late emergence of adults from an overwintering nest.

PSEUDODYNERUS QUADRISECTUS (Say)

I obtained only one nest of this relatively common southeastern wasp. It was in a 6.4-mm. boring attached to a dead standing tree trunk at the edge of a wooded area at Plummers Island, Md.

Nest architecture. There was an empty space of 60 mm. at the inner end of the boring and then a mud partition. Cells 1 and 2 were 28 and 25 mm. long, respectively, and capped by mud partitions 1.5 mm. thick. In the outer section of the boring was an empty vestibular cell 37 mm. long with one cross partition. The nest entrance was sealed by a mud plug 3 mm. thick.

Prey. Caterpillars were stored as prey.

Life history. The boring had been set out on July 11, but apparently the wasp did not begin to nest in it until the end of the month. I picked up the nest on August 3. When I opened it on August 5, the larva in cell 1 had just completed feeding, and the larva in cell 2 was half grown, and so the nest must have been completed about July 30-31. The nest occupants overwintered outdoors from November 5 to March 1 as diapausing larvae. A male wasp in cell 2 pupated in April and as an adult emerged from the nest on May 5. The female occupant of cell 1 pupated between May 1 and 5, eclosed on May 26, and left the nest on May 30.

P. quadrisectus has at least two generations a year in the Washington area. I have collected it at Plummers Island from June 6 to August 28.

Previous observations. Bequaert (1925, p. 78) reported *quadrisectus* nesting in galleries in a dead tree in New Jersey, and Rau (1935c, p. 111) found it nesting in abandoned borings of the carpenter bee in Missouri and using caterpillars as prey. Ashmead's (1894, p. 79) record of *Chrysis densa* Cresson as a parasite of *quadrisectus* in Florida is clearly erroneous, because the chrysidid occurs only in the western United States.

Source material.
Plummers Island, Md. 1962 series: M 87.
Identifications by the author.

MONOBIA QUADRIDENS (Linnaeus)

(Plate 7, Figures 24-29; Plate 8, Figures 30-38)

This is the largest vespid wasp which nested in the traps. It is unique in several other respects also. The chorion of the egg is tougher and less delicate than in any other wasp so far studied. The prepupa has a very leathery yellow integument in contrast to the white-to-creamy, more delicate integument of the prepupae of other wasps except *Euodynerus guerrero*. In a substantial number of cells the larva failed to orient itself properly after spinning the cocoon and rested with its head end inward instead of toward the boring entrance. This wasp is also quite leisurely, though not entirely unique, in its rate of provisioning.

It nested in 34 traps at 19 stations at Plummers Island, Md., from 1957 through 1962, 27 of them in 1957, and 1 or 2 in each of the following 5 years. Eleven nests were from settings on structural lumber, mostly on the rafters of the cabin porch, and on cut firewood; 21 were from settings on standing dead tree trunks; and 2 were from a setting on a live locust trunk. The stations on tree trunks were in open woods, while those on the cabin porch were completely shaded. Normally the wasp nested in old borings of the carpenter bee in the porch rafters.

At Kill Devil Hills, N. C., it nested in 28 traps at 24 stations, 1 in 1955, 8 in 1956, and the remainder in 1958. The stations were either at the edge of wooded areas or in open woods. Most of the nests were suspended from dead limbs of pine, oak, or hickory; but two were from a fallen tree trunk, one from beneath a thick plank on the sand, and one from a setting beneath the limb of a living tree.

It used a total of 78 traps at 38 stations in the Highlands Ridge sand scrub area of the Archbold Biological Station at Lake Placid, Fla., where there were 4 nests in 1957, 18 in 1959, 8 in 1960, and 24 each in 1961 and 1962. Most stations were beneath the limbs of living scrub hickory, oak, or pine; but 9 were on the side of pine trunks, 7 on the side of oak trunks, and a couple on dead limbs.

Almost all the nests were in 12.7-mm. borings. However, there were 2 nests at Plummers Island and 3 nests each at Kill Devil Hills and Lake Placid in 6.4-mm. borings. In every one of these exceptions there was no empty 12.7-mm. trap at the station at the time the 6.4-mm. boring was stored. Furthermore, it should be mentioned that most *Monobia* females are too large to enter a 6.4-mm. boring, which automatically restricted most of the nesting population to 12.7-mm. borings.

Supersedure and competition. There was very little supersedure in the *Monobia* nests, and no evidence indicated that this supersedure involved actual competition. At Plummers Island *Monobia* superseded *Trypargilum striatum* (Provancher) in 2 nests, and it was superseded by that wasp in 1 nest. A species of *Megachile* superseded *Monobia* in 1 Florida nest and was superseded by *Monobia* in another nest.

Nest architecture. The *Monobia* females at Plummers Island used mud to make the cell partitions and closing plugs. At Kill Devil Hills and Lake Placid the wasps used agglutinated sand for these purposes. The wasps began to store paralyzed caterpillars right at the inner end of the boring in 5 nests at Plummers Island, 2 at Kill Devil Hills, and 37 at Lake Placid. In 28 nests from Plummers Island, 17 from Kill Devil Hills, and 27 from Lake Placid, the wasps either first coated the inner end of the boring with mud or agglutinated sand or constructed a partition of one of these substances 5-17 mm. from the inner end. Sometimes the amount of mud or sand at the inner end was just enough to form a thin, smooth, concave coating; but occasionally there was a plug several millimeters thick (fig. 29). The same statement is true of the partitions capping an empty space at the inner end; occasionally the partitions were only 1-2 mm. thick, but sometimes they were as much as 10 mm. in thickness.

In table 2 appear the measurements of stored and empty intercalary and vestibular cells at each locality by sex in nests in 12.7-mm. borings. The cell lengths include the thickness of the partitions capping the stored and intercalary cells and of the closing plugs capping the vestibular cells.

This table shows that female cells are usually distinctly longer than male cells. On the whole the empty intercalary cells between stored cells show no significant differences in length either by sex or by station.

It will be noted that there were fewer intercalary cells than stored cells. Altogether * there were 84 stored cells and 58 intercalary cells in the Plummers Island nests, 60 stored and 19 intercalary at Kill Devil Hills, and 235 stored and 113 intercalary at Lake Placid. The values in the table suggest that intercalary cells are associated with female cells more frequently than with male cells. However, in most nests a male is produced in the outermost stored cell and beyond

---

* The figures given in this section, and in corresponding sections in other specific accounts, are greater than those given in the table. Figures in this section include cells in which adult wasps did not develop, so they could not be scored as to sex of the occupant.

that last stored cell there is usually a vestibular cell. In one nest from Florida there were two empty intercalary cells between stored cells 2 and 3; just possibly this anomalous behavior by the nesting female may have been due to cell 2 having been parasitized by *Chrysis smaragdula* Fabricius. In one Plummers Island nest there were three intercalary cells between two stored cells; there was no apparent explanation for this anomaly.

There were one or more intercalary cells in all multicelled nests at Plummers Island. At Kill Devil Hills there were 5 multicelled nests without intercalary cells and 10 with one or more such cells (fig. 29). Inasmuch as some of these nests were parasitized by *C. smaragdula* but others were not, omission of intercalary cells may be just a behavioral quirk of certain females rather than a reaction to

TABLE 2.—*Measurements (in mm.) of cells,* Monobia quadridens *(Linnaeus).*

Locality	Sex	STORED CELLS			INTERCALARY CELLS			VESTIBULAR CELLS		
		No	Range in length	Mean length	No.	Range in length	Mean length	No.	Range in length	Mean length
Md.	♀	32	18-46	28	26	9-32	17	19	6-116	39
	♂	18	13-30	21	5	12-32	18			
N.C.	♀	25	21-38	28	11	7-20	16	10	7-126	63
	♂	16	15-47	25	1	25	25			
Fla.	♀	63	18-40	26	36	8-42	17	56	7-118	44
	♂	65	7-29	20	14	12-32	19			

parasitism. At Lake Placid there were a dozen multicelled nests lacking intercalary cells (fig. 25).

Most completed nests had an empty vestibular cell at the entrance. Such a cell was missing in only 2 of 21 completed nests at Plummers Island, 6 of 17 at Kill Devil Hills, and 9 of 65 at Lake Placid. In 1 nest each at Plummers Island and at Kill Devil Hills, the vestibular cell was divided by 3 partitions, and in 1 nest at Plummers Island and in 3 at Lake Placid this cell was divided by 2 partitions. Equal numbers of the other nests at all three localities had a vestibular cell with a single partition or one without a partition. Four 5-celled completed nests at Kill Devil Hills and three 5-celled and one 6-celled nests at Lake Placid lacked both intercalary and vestibular cells.

Completed nests at Plummers Island contained an average of 3¼ stored cells (range 1-5) and 1¾ intercalary cells (range 0-3). Similar data for Kill Devil Hills were 3½ stored cells (range 1-5) and ¾ intercalary cell (range 0-2). At Lake Placid these figures were 3½ stored cells (range 1-6) and 1¼ intercalary cells (range 0-3). Three of the Florida nests contained 6 stored cells, no intercalary cells, and the vestibular cell was present or absent. Not all the occupants of these 6-celled nests reached maturity, but both sexes of *Monobia* developed in 2 of the nests.

Table 3 presents measurements in millimeters of the thickness of the partitions between the cells and of the closing plugs in nests in 12.7-mm. borings at all three localities. Note especially that the partitions capping empty intercalary cells were substantially thicker than those capping the stored cells (fig. 29).

Most of the 8 nests in 6.4-mm. borings consisted of only 1 stored cell and an empty vestibular cell. However, 1 nest at Lake Placid contained 2 stored cells and 1 at Kill Devil Hills had 5 stored cells. The 2 stored cells were each 30 mm. long in the Plummers Island nests, the partition of 1 cell was 2 mm. thick, and the 2 closing plugs

TABLE 3.—*Measurements (in mm.) of partitions and closing plugs*, Monobia quadridens (*Linnaeus*)

Locality	PARTITIONS				CLOSING PLUGS	
	Stored cells		Intercalary cells		Range in thickness	Mean thickness
	Range in thickness	Mean thickness	Range in thickness	Mean thickness		
Md.	0.5-2	1.3	1-6	4.2	2-7	4.4
N.C.	1-4	2.2	3-7	4.6	2-17	8.8
Fla.	1-5	1.5	0.5-9	4.1	2-17	6.1

were each 3 mm. thick. The 7 stored cells at Kill Devil Hills had a mean length of 27 mm. (range 22-47), the partitions were 1-2.5 mm. thick, and the closing plugs were 4-5 mm. thick. The 4 stored cells at Lake Placid had a mean length of 33 mm. (range 28-40 mm.), the partitions were 3-5 mm. thick, and the closing plugs were 4-5 mm. thick. Male *Monobia* emerged from all but four cells in nests in 6.4-mm. borings; the occupants of those four cells died as larvae.

In the multicelled nests in 12.7-mm. borings, 19 nests produced only females, 20 nests only males, and 45 nests both sexes. However, adults did not develop in all stored cells in most of these nests; and judging from the sequence of cells and their measurements most multicelled nests probably contained both sexes.

Prey. Consolidated identifications for the prey from several areas are presented below. These records are based on partial samples and on entire contents of completed cells.

PLUMMERS ISLAND, MD., 15 nests, 1957 and 1960:
    Phycitidae
        sp. in 15 cells in 7 nests
        Nephopteryx sp. in 6 cells in 3 nests

Epipaschiidae
  Epipaschia superatilis Clemens in 1 cell
Pyraustidae
  sp. in 13 cells in 4 nests
KILL DEVIL HILLS, N. C., 3 nests, 1956 and 1958:
Stenomidae
  Stenoma schlaegeri Zeller in 1 cell
Phycitidae
  Nephopteryx uvinella (Ragonot) in 1 cell
Epipaschiidae
  Tetralopha sp. in 3 cells in 2 nests
  Tetralopha asperatella (Clemens) in 1 cell
LAKE PLACID, FLA., 11 nests, 1957, 1959, 1960, 1961 and 1962:
Oecophoridae
  Psilocorsis sp. in 3 cells in 2 nests
  Psilocorsis sp. (near or *faginella* (Chambers)) in 1 cell
Stenomidae
  Stenoma sp. in 9 cells in 4 nests
  Stenoma sp. (near or *schlaegeri* Zeller) in 1 cell
Tortricidae
  spp. in 8 cells in 5 nests
  Platynota sp. in 5 cells in 3 nests
Epipaschiidae
  sp. in 3 cells in 2 nests
  Tetralopha sp. in 1 cell

The paralyzed caterpillars in the 12.7-mm. nests were usually arranged longitudinally with their heads inward in the lower half of the cell (fig. 25). In the 6.4-mm. nests the larvae were packed in more closely and filled the entire cell except for a small space near the closing partition.

The number of caterpillars stored per cell was variable, depending on the sex of the wasp occupant and on the size of the prey. The population at Plummers Island used only larger larvae, 10-18 mm. long, and stored from 4 to 7 (mean 5.4) per cell in 5 completed cells. There were 6 larvae in 1 female cell and 4 and 7 larvae, respectively, in 2 male cells. At Kill Devil Hills the wasps used either smaller larvae, 6-12 mm. long, or larger ones, 9-16 mm. long; one completed cell contained 19 smaller larvae. The wasps at Lake Placid used smaller larvae having a mean length of 11 mm. (range 6-16); they stored a mean of 14 caterpillars per cell (range 9-19). There were 17-19 larvae (mean 18) in 3 female cells at Lake Placid, and 9-15 (mean 13) in 6 male cells.

Apparently the wasps usually concentrated on storing a single species of caterpillar when they could find them in sufficient numbers. The wasps at Plummers Island stored only one species per cell in 29 cells in 14 nests. In a fifteenth nest one cell contained 5 caterpillars of a pyraustid species and 1 of a phycitid species. One cell at Kill Devil Hills was stored with 15 larvae of an epipaschiid species and 4 larvae of a phycitid species; another cell had a mixture of a stenomid species and an epipaschiid species; and a cell in a third nest contained only an epipaschiid species. Ten cells in 5 Florida nests contained only 1 species per cell, while 8 cells in 6 nests contained 2 or 3 species of prey. Two cells from different Florida nests contained, respectively, 2 stenomids, 11 tortricids, and 2 epipaschiids; and 2 stenomids, 6 oecophorids, and 6 epipaschiids. The greatest diversity of prey in a single nest was in one from Lake Placid, in which 2 adjacent cells contained 1 species each of Oecophoridae, Stenomidae, Tortricidae, and Epipaschiidae.

Life history. The egg is sausageshaped, 4.0-4.4 mm. long, 1.2-1.3 mm. wide, and has a very tough chorion (figs. 23, 24). A single observation suggests that the egg stage lasts at least 2 days. I found the mother wasp completing the closing plug of a nest at noon on July 30 at Plummers Island. The nest contained 4 stored cells, 3 intercalary cells, and a vestibular cell divided by a cross partition. Inasmuch as the wasp stored caterpillars in cell 4 and constructed mud partitions to seal this cell and a vestibular cell *after* laying the egg in cell 4, it seems probable that the egg must have been laid at least 24 hours earlier. It hatched at noon on the 31st, a minimum of 48 hours after its probable deposition.

The larval feeding period lasted 3-4 days in 5 larvae from as many nests from Plummers Island and Lake Placid (figs. 26, 27). Two observations establish a minimum of 5 days and a maximum of 8 days between deposition of the egg and completion of larval feeding.

The larvae did not spin silken cocoons, but they did varnish over the cell walls and ends. This process required 1-3 days. About 5 days after completion of larval feeding, the wasp entered the prepupal stage (figs. 28, 29). Pupation took place 8 days after completion of larval feeding in the summer generation. The period between pupation and emergence of the adult from the nest was 13 to 24 days for 21 females (figs. 30-38) and 12 to 22 days for 33 males. A period of 2-3 days elapsed between eclosion of the adults and emergence from the nest, and so the pupal period should be calculated accordingly. The exact elapsed time between egg hatch and emergence of the adult in Florida nests of the summer generation was 36 and 37 days for two females and 26 days for one male.

A substantial number of larvae in 12.7-mm. nests did not orient properly but transformed to pupae with their heads inward instead of toward the nest entrance. The borings were large enough to allow the adult wasps to turn around inside. These newly eclosed adults were able to orient themselves properly. They did not attempt to chew through the partitions between them and the inner end of the boring, but they always turned around and chewed through the partitions between themselves and the boring entrance. The larvae failed to orient properly in 27 of 38 cells in 15 nests at Plummers

Island, in 11 of 19 cells in 7 nests at Kill Devil Hills, and in 21 of 42 cells in 11 nests at Lake Placid. The larvae in 6.4-mm. nests oriented themselves with their heads toward the entrance.

Males always emerged before the females in each nest where both sexes were present. The emergence period for both sexes in individual nests of the summer generation was usually 2-7 days (mean 3.6), although 9 days were required in one nest and 12 in another. This same period was 4-17 days (mean 9) in overwintering nests. In these same individual nests the period between emergence of the latest male and the earliest female was 1-11 days (mean 4.1) for the summer generation nests and 0-11 days (mean 5.7) for overwintering nests. In individual nests all the males emerged on the same day or within a 3-day period (mean 0.4 day). Females usually emerged from individual nests within a 3-day period also (mean 0.9 day). However, in 2 nests of the overwintering generation 12 days elapsed between emergence of the first and last females, and in a third nest 68 days elapsed between emergence of the 2 females.

Developmental data from a few nests suggest that *Monobia* has a leisurely nesting rate. I took up one nest at Plummers Island on July 24, 1957, just as the mother completed the plug to seal the entrance. The nest contained 2 stored cells, 1 intercalary cell, and a vestibular cell. There was a half-grown larva in cell 1 and a newly hatched larva in cell 2; so it appears that completion of this 2-celled nest required a period of at least 4 days. I picked up a second nest at the same locality at noon on July 30, 1961, also just as the mother completed the closing plug. This nest had 4 stored cells, 3 intercalary cells, and a vestibular cell. On July 30 the larva in cell 1 was spinning, that in cell 2 had just completed feeding, there was a small larva in cell 3, and an egg in cell 4 which hatched on the 31st. This second nest must have required about a week to complete.

While I was in residence at the Archbold Biological Station in 1962, I checked the trap line daily. I first noted a female *Monobia* in a 12.7-mm. trap on the evening of June 27. On July 5, my last day in residence, I picked up this nest, which was not yet completed. There was a mature larva in cell 1, an intercalary cell between stored cells 1 and 2, a small larva in cell 2, an egg in completed cell 3, and an egg and five caterpillars in incompleted cell 4 (figs. 24, 25). If this wasp laid her first egg on June 28, which is not unreasonable, it must have taken her a week to provision and cap the first three cells and to construct the single intercalary cell.

Trap nests at Plummers Island were stored from late in June until late in August. However, females have been taken there from June 9 to October 13; so the actual nesting period may be longer than the trap nest data indicate. I judge that there is only a partial second generation because occupants of some nests stored between late June and July 24 emerged from July 21 to August 30; whereas occupants of other nests stored during the same period overwintered as diapausing larvae, as did occupants of all nests stored during August. I did not obtain exact information on the early nesting dates for the Kill Devil Hills population. Occupants of a few nests stored between June 1 and some time in July emerged from July 30 to August 4, but the occupants of most nests stored from July to early in September overwintered as diapausing larvae. I have collected *Monobia* females there as early as May 27.

Nests in Florida were provisioned from early in April until early in November. Adult emergence occurred from mid-May until mid-September from nests stored from early in April until mid-August. Overwintering larval diapause occurred in nests stored from mid-June until early in November.

There is perhaps a 1:1 sex ratio. I reared 32 females and 19 males from 77 stored cells at Plummers Island, 25 females and 21 males from 68 stored cells at Kill Devil Hills, and 63 females and 67 males from 239 stored cells at Lake Placid.

Parasites and predators. *Monobia* is not particularly troubled by parasites except for two species of symbiotic mites which occurred in a number of nests but did not injure the wasp occupants of infested cells. The symbiotic acarid mite *Tortonia quadridens* Baker was found in 2 nests from Kill Devil Hills and in 1 nest from Plummers Island. The symbiotic saproglyphid mite *Monobiacarus quadridens* Baker and Cunliffe was found in 3 nests from Kill Devil Hills and 8 from Lake Placid (fig. 27). In addition there were symbiotic mites, probably one or the other of these two species, in 2 nests from Plummers Island, 2 from Kill Devil Hills, and 28 from Lake Placid. In the laboratory, *Pyemotes* mites invaded 4 nests from Lake Placid.

The most injurious parasite was the cuckoo wasp *Chrysis* (*C.*) *smaragdula* Fabricius, which I believe to be host specific on *Monobia*. It occurred in 3 of 6 cells in 3 nests at Plummers Island, in 6 of 14 cells in 3 nests at Kill Devil Hills, and in 2 of 3 cells in a single nest at Lake Placid. In addition, what was undoubtedly this same species, as based on larval size or on the cocoon, was noted but not reared in 10 of 16 cells in 5 nests at Kill Devil Hills.

The chrysidid *Chrysis* (*C.*) *inaequidens* Dahlbom was reared from 1 cell of a 4-celled nest at Lake Placid.

Field infestations of the eulophid *Melittobia chalybii* Ashmead occurred in 1 nest each at Plummers Island and Lake Placid and in 2 nests at Kill Devil Hills. Secondary infestations in the laboratory occurred in 2 nests from Plummers Island, 4 from Kill Devil Hills, and 5 from Lake Placid.

I reared a male bombyliid *Anthrax aterrima* (Bigot) from a nest from Kill Devil Hills. Another bombyliid larva attacked a female

wasp pupa in a Plummers Island nest and was itself attacked by
Melittobia.

About 8 maggots of the miltogrammine sarcophagid fly *Amobia
erythrura* (Wulp) destroyed 3 of 4 cells in a Lake Placid nest. Another miltogrammine, undoubtedly also a species of *Amobia,* destroyed two 1-celled nests at Kill Devil Hills.

Phorid maggots, probably *Megaselia aletiae* (Comstock), were
present in one nest from Kill Devil Hills.

One 2-celled nest from Plummers Island contained a clerid larva
and a dermestid larva in cell 2 when I brought the nest in from the
field. I was unsuccessful in rearing adults from these. The dermestid
Trogoderma ornatum Say developed in one cell of another nest from
Plummers Island, but this infestation took place after some months
in the laboratory.

Previous observations. This large and conspicuously maculated
wasp has attracted the attention of a number of observers. Ashmead
(1894, p. 77) in Florida, Tandy (1908) in Illinois, Rau and Rau
(1918, pp. 346-354) and Rau (1922, p. 16; 1926, pp. 199-200; 1931a,
p. 200; 1931b; 1935d) in Missouri, Reinhard (1929, p. 86) in Maryland, Frost (1944) in Pennsylvania, and Krombein (1958d, p. 101) in
North Carolina published notes on various aspects of the biology
of *Monobia.* The most substantial contributions are those of the
Raus and Frost.

Ashmead and the Raus found it nesting in old carpenter-bee
borings, and the Raus also noted that it used abandoned borings of
mining bees in a clay bank as well as abandoned mud nests of *Sceliphron caementarium* (Drury). Tandy reported a nest in a groove
in a discarded window frame, and Frost induced a female to nest in
a series of glass tubes set in wooden borings. Reinhard found a nest
in a water-pump spout.

The Raus have a detailed account of its gathering damp mud to
make partitions and even of its bringing in water to moisten the
dry mud in the clay bank. Ashmead mentioned that it put a coating
of mud over the walls of the carpenter bee boring also, but as no
other observer reported this it is likely that Ashmead made some
error in his observation. Rau (1931b) reported double mud partitions in *Monobia* nests, *i.e.,* an empty intercalary cell between each
stored one; but Frost did not observe such empty cells in nests made
by his single wasp in glass tubing. Rau also mentioned the occurrence of an empty vestibular cell at the nest entrance.

Ashmead said that *Monobia* preyed on cutworms. This statement
is at such variance with prey records of later observers that one
wonders whether Ashmead's article was not written from memory
only, some years after the observations were actually made. The
Raus reported it as using a species of *Epipaschia* (?) and said that

they found 16 caterpillars in one cell and 18 in another; they timed two provisioning flights at 15 and 25 minutes, respectively. Rau (1922) found two species of Gelechiidae in a nest and reported a provisioning flight of 30 minutes. Frost's wasp used only *Desmia funeralis* (Hübner), the grape leaf folder, as prey; he found 7-13 larvae (mean 8) in 10 completely stored cells. Krombein reported a species of Stenomidae (?) as prey in North Carolina.

The Raus found *Monobia* active in Missouri from mid-May to October 3. Frost reported nesting in Pennsylvania from June 26 to July 20 and saw adults active as late as mid-August. Adults emerged from some of Frost's nests early in September, giving him the erroneous impression that *Monobia* adults hibernated.

In Pennsylvania Frost reported a total elapsed time of 52-56 days from egg deposition to adult emergence for two specimens in his nests; he did not mention the sex of these. This is much longer than the elapsed time I reported for Florida specimens of about 37-40 days for females and about 29 days for a male. Perhaps this difference was due to the high humidity in Frost's glass tube nests. Frost stated that the period between pupation and emergence of the adult was 26 days for one of his specimens. In Missouri Rau and Rau reported a total elapsed time of 34 days from egg deposition to emergence of an adult male.

Rau (1931b) stated that *Monobia* did not spin a cocoon but often deposited a "veneer of thin, paper-like material" on the cell walls.

Frost was the only author to provide some figures on the rate of provisioning of the cells. Working with what was quite clearly a single female, he reported a total of 10 completely stored cells over a period of 19 days. The provisioning was not done at a uniform rate but was more rapid early in the nesting cycle and much slower toward the end. The wasp stored 4 cells during her first 3 days of nesting. Only 2 cells were completed during the next 5 days when the weather was cooler with some rain. The next 3 cells were stored over a 4-day period of cool weather. Storing of the final completed cell required 4 days during a spell of warm weather.

Rau (1935d) reported courtship dances by the males beginning in May. They hovered in front of old carpenter-bee borings in which *Monobia* females were nesting and occasionally pounced on females returning with caterpillar prey. He did not observe actual mating. This dancing went on daily for a month. He observed mating in August, presumably by second generation adults. The female rested on the board near the nest entrance while the male dangled free, head downward. One female made a few short flights with the male dangling from the tip of her abdomen. Mating never lasted over 30 minutes.

Rau (1931a), reporting on a series of homing experiments, stated that males and females were unable to find their nests when liberated 2 miles away. Two other females were liberated a mile from their nests, and one returned the following day nearly 21 hours later.

Rau (1922) reared 3 specimens of *Chrysis* [recorded as cuckoo bees] from a 3-celled *Monobia* nest in a carpenter-bee boring.

Source material.

> Plummers Island, Md. 1957 series: P 25, 40, 45, 70, 75, 80, 85, 89, 100, 132, 142, 154, 156, 158, 166, 172, 175, 178, 187, 188, 189, 194, 204, 206, 219, 225, 228. 1958 series: S 97. 1959 series: Y 113, 114. 1960 series: E 85. 1961 series: K 127, 129. 1962 series: M 80.

> Kill Devil Hills, N. C. 1955 series: C 294. 1956 series: C 123, 203, 287, 288, 295, 706, 707, 727. 1958 series: T 171, 204, 206, 207, 211, 213, 217, 221, 222, 223, 224, 225, 227, 230, 234, 235, 240, 241, 247.

> Lake Placid, Fla. 1957 series: M 150, 170, 190, 268. 1959 series: V 49, 55, 56, 64, 68, 69, 70, 71, 72, 136, 145, 147, 148, 150, 151, 153, 155, 156. 1960 series: B 61, 62, 69, 72, 105, 108, 192, 208. 1961 series: F 61, 66, 68, 69, 72, 133, 134, 136, 137, 138, 139, 141, 142, 173, 247, 248, 249, 250, 251, 252, 325, 326, 327, 328. 1962 series: P 61, 62, 63, 64, 65, 66, 67, 71, 72, 127, 128, 132, 133, 134, 135, 220, 221, 222, 223, 224, 225, 226, 227, 228.

Identifications. Lepidopterous larvae by H. W. Capps; Acarina by E. W. Baker; Bombyliidae by W. W. Wirth; Miltogrammini by W. L. Downes; Dermestidae by R. S. Beal; Hymenoptera by the author.

EUODYNERUS FORAMINATUS FORAMINATUS (Saussure)

Some striking differences were noted in the biology and nest architecture of typical *foraminatus* from New York, Maryland, and North Carolina and the Floridian race *f. apopkensis* (Robertson). The typical race had two or more generations a year, but the Floridian race was univoltine. Typical *foraminatus* preyed principally on Gelechiidae, Oecophoridae, Tortricidae, and Pyraustidae; *f. apopkensis* preyed entirely on Olethreutidae, except toward the end of the nesting season when it occasionally used Tortricidae. The mean period between pupation and adult emergence in overwintering nests of *foraminatus* was a little shorter than that for *apopkensis,* 16 and 18 days, respectively, for females and 12 and 16 days for males.

I had 28 nests of typical *foraminatus* and 241 nests of *apopkensis.* The latter wasp was more efficient in its use of space and made a mean of 8.1 and 7.6 stored cells, respectively, in 4.8- and 6.4-mm. borings compared with 5.4 and 5.5 stored cells for typical *foraminatus.* The male cells of both races had the same mean length in both 4.8- and 6.4-mm. borings, but female cells were 2-3 mm. longer in nests of typical *foraminatus* than they were in *apopkensis.* A vestibular cell was present in all but one of the nests completed by typical *foraminatus;* such a cell was present in only 134 of the 221 nests completed by *apopkensis.*

Typical *foraminatus* was reared from 17 nests at 9 stations from Derby, N. Y., in 1955, 1956, 1957 and 1958; from 8 nests at 4 stations at Plummers Island, Md., in 1957 and 1960; from a single nest at Dunn Loring, Va., in 1954; and from 2 nests at Kill Devil Hills, N. C., in 1956 and 1958. It nested in 4.8- and 6.4-mm. borings with equal facility. Most of the stations were at the edge of wooded areas or in open woods. At Derby most nests were on structural lumber or on dead wood; *i.e.*, cut firewood and a dead stump. All the nests at Plummers Island were from settings on a dead tree trunk or a dead limb.

Supersedure and competition. E. f. *foraminatus* was superseded by *E. molestus* (Saussure) in 1 nest at Kill Devil Hills and by *Symmorphus* sp., probably *cristatus* (Saussure), in 1 nest at Derby.

Nest architecture. In 19 of the nests the wasp put a thin layer of mud at the inner end of the boring or constructed a thin partition of this material 10-124 mm. from the inner end before laying her first egg and bringing in prey. In the other 9 nests the wasp omitted this mud and laid an egg at the inner end of the boring.

The number of provisioned cells in completed nests varied because of the presence or absence of empty intercalary and vestibular cells and the diameter of the boring. The maximum number in a 4.8-mm. boring was 9 stored male cells and 1 vestibular cell. Similarly, in the largest nest in a 6.4-mm. boring there were 10 stored cells, from which I obtained 2 females and 6 males, and 1 vestibular cell; judged from the cell lengths the two individuals that escaped were females. Ten completed nests in 4.8-mm. borings averaged 5.4 stored cells and 1.7 intercalary cells per nest. Corresponding figures for 11 completed nests in 6.4-mm. borings were 5.5 stored cells and 2.3 intercalary cells.

Ten female cells in 4.8-mm. borings were 15-31 mm. long (mean 22) and 52 male cells were 8-31 mm. long (mean 16). In 6.4-mm. borings 24 female cells were 15-27 mm. long (mean 20) and 29 male cells were 9-22 mm. long (mean 13).

Empty intercalary cells were present in 15 nests, but there was 1 such cell between each stored cell in only 7 nests. The 42 intercalary cells were 1-23 mm. long (mean 5).

An empty vestibular cell was present in all but one of the 26 nests completed by *foraminatus*. In 11 nests the vestibular cell was divided by a cross partition, and in 1 nest this cell had 2 cross partitions. The vestibular cells were 3-133 mm. long (mean 38); these lengths include the thickness of the terminal plug at the nest entrance.

The partitions between cells and the terminal plugs were made of mud, except that sand was used in the two nests from Kill Devil Hills. The partitions between cells were 0.5-7 mm. thick (mean

1.6); usually those capping the empty intercalary cells were thicker than those capping the stored cells. The terminal plugs of 24 nests were 0.5-8 mm. thick (mean 3.6).

In nests containing both sexes the females were in the innermost cells and males in the outermost except in one 4.8-mm. nest from Plummers Island where the arrangement beginning with the innermost cell was ♀-♂-♀-♂-♂-♂ ♂. Perhaps another *foraminatus* female superseded at cell 3 in this nest. However, cell 2 was so long (23 mm.) that one would expect a female to develop in it; possibly the sperm failed to fertilize this egg so a male developed.

Only males were reared from 7 multicelled nests in 4.8-mm. borings, and both sexes were reared from 6 nests. In multicelled nests in 6.4-mm. borings, only males were reared from 4 nests, only females from 3, and both sexes from 5. The overall ♀:♂ ratio was 27:69 from 133 stored cells. However, at Derby this ratio was 13:41 from 83 cells and at Plummers Island it was 11:19 from 37 cells.

Prey. Consolidated identifications of prey from two areas are presented below. The records are based both on entire cell contents and on partial samples.

> Derby, 6 nests, 1957 and 1958:
>   Gelechioidea—probable sp. in 1 cell
>   Gelechiidae—sp. in 1 cell
>   Oecophoridae—sp. in 6 cells in 3 nests
>   Tortricidae—sp. in 2 cells in 2 nests
> Plummers Island, 7 nests, 1957 and 1960:
>   Gelechiidae—sp. in 2 cells in 2 nests
>   Tortricidae—sp. in 2 cells in 2 nests
>   Pyralidae—sp. in 1 cell
>   Epipaschiidae—*Epipaschia superatilis* Clemens in 1 cell
>   Pyraustidae—sp. in 2 cells in 2 nests
>   *Desmia funeralis* (Hübner) in 3 cells in 1 nest

This wasp stored 3 to 9 caterpillars per cell (mean 6) in 10 cells. Unfortunately the number per cell could not be correlated with the sex, but it may be assumed that fewer caterpillars were stored in cells in which males were destined to develop. Usually only a single species was stored in each cell, but at least one cell in each of three nests contained two species belonging to two different families.

Life history. No data were obtained on duration of the egg and larval stages. A male larva which hatched from the egg on June 8 emerged as an adult on the 24th; a female larva in this same nest, which completed feeding on the 9th, emerged as an adult on the 25th. This nest was stored between June 1 and 8. The period between pupation and adult emergence in overwintering nests was 14-21 days (mean 16) for 3 females and 10-14 days (mean 12) for 7 males.

The cocoons were of delicate, whitish, subopaque silk. Seven female cocoons in 4.8 mm. borings were 11-14 mm. long (mean 12), and 17 male cocoons were 8-13 mm. (mean 10); 6 female cocoons in 6.4-mm. borings were 11-16 mm. (mean 14), and 18 male cocoons were 7-13 mm. (mean 9).

Except for 4 individuals, the prepupae were properly oriented in their cocoons with their heads directed toward the boring entrance. The misorientation of some individuals in these two nests from Plummers Island may have been due to possible damage to some of the cell partitions before the cocoons were spun.

Males emerged before females in almost all multicelled nests containing both sexes. However, the period between emergence of the two sexes was only 1-2 days in two summer generation nests and 1-5 days in four overwintering nests.

Data from 6 nests at Plummers Island suggest that an individual wasp may provision 2-3 cells per day. One nest, completed in 2-3 days, contained 7 stored cells, and one vestibular cell divided by a cross partition. Another nest, completed in 3-4 days, had 8 stored cells, 6 intercalary cells, and 1 vestibular cell.

Data from these nests and from occurrence of the adults in the field indicate that typical *foraminatus* has at least two generations a year, a noticeable contrast to the condition in *foraminatus apopkensis* which is definitely univoltine. Adults emerged June 30 to July 24 from nests stored at Derby from about June 1 through early July; occupants of nests stored later in July overwintered as diapausing larvae. Two Plummers Island nests were stored between late May and early June and adults emerged from them late in June; in nests stored between July 10 and late August the occupants overwintered as diapausing larvae. I collected adults from May 19 to September 9 at Plummers Island. The two nests at Kill Devil Hills were stored in July and the occupants overwintered as diapausing larvae. I have collected females at Kill Devil Hills as early as May 30.

Parasites and predators. The cuckoo wasp *Chrysis (C.) coerulans* Fabricius parasitized 6 of 11 cells in 2 nests at Derby. The ichneumonid *Pimpla spatulata* Townes was reared from the outermost cell of a nest from Derby. The eulophid *Melittobia chalybii* Ashmead infested 1 nest in the field at Derby.

A male puparium of the stylopid *Pseudoxenos hookeri* (Pierce) was found protruding from the abdomen of a *foraminatus* female from a nest at Plummers Island.

Previous observations. Biological notes have been made on this species by Hungerford and Williams (1912, p. 255) in Kansas, by Rau and Rau (1918, pp. 334-340) and Rau (1922, pp. 17-18; 1928, pp. 398-400; 1932; 1935c, pp. 110-111; 1944) in Missouri, by Medler (1964a) in Wisconsin, by Cooper (1954, pp. 281-282) in New York, by Hartman (1944) in Connecticut, and by Markin (1965) in Idaho.

In many of these notes the wasp was called *rugosus* (Saussure), now recognized as a synonym of *foraminatus*.

Hungerford and Williams reported it as nesting in a boxelder stump. The Raus found nests in borings in old logs and in an elderberry twig; later Rau found nests also in borings in twigs of sumac and elder, in old cells in a *Polistes* comb, and in the flutings of corrugated cardboard. Hartman induced it to nest in glass tubes inserted into bamboo sections, and Cooper and Medler used trap nests in white pine and in sumac respectively. Markin induced the wasp to nest in soda straws. All observers noted the use of mud to form partitions and closing plugs.

Only the Raus, Medler and Markin mentioned the presence of double partitions or empty spaces (*i.e.*, intercalary cells) between some of the stored cells. The Raus found that this space was usually very narrow, though ocasionally it was as much as 6 mm. long. Later, Rau (1932) reported intercalary cells 3-11 mm. long in a twig nest. Medler reported a range of 1-38 mm. (mean 6-8) for intercalary cells in borings 6.4 and 8.0 mm. in diameter. Medler also found that occasionally there were two intercalary cells between two stored cells, and, more rarely, that intercalary cells were lacking.

Only Rau (1932), Medler, and Markin presented data on the length of stored cells. In a single twig nest Rau found two female cells 19 and 25 mm. long, and eight male cells 10-13 mm. long. Medler reported a mean length of 16.5 mm. for 197 female cells (range 6-53) and of 13 mm. for 137 male cells (range 6-51), based on combining measurements of nests in 4.8-, 6.4-, and 8.0-mm. borings. Markin observed that male cells averaged 11.4 mm. in length in 6-mm. straws, and that female cells were 17.8 mm. long.

Rau (1932) reported a vestibular cell of 38 mm. in one nest. Medler merely stated that a typical nest had a vestibular cell of variable length correlated with the number of stored and intercalary cells in the remainder of the nest. Medler found that partitions between cells were 1-3 mm. thick, and that the terminal plugs were 5-10 mm. thick.

Rau (1932) found 10 cells in a nest in a twig boring of unspecified diameter. Cooper found 27 stored cells in 6 nests in 6-7 mm. borings. Medler reported 4.45 stored cells per summer generation nest (range 1-10 cells) and 4.76 stored cells per overwintering nest (range 1-11 cells), but he did not give separate figures by boring diameter.

Rau (1932), Cooper, Medler, and Markin reported that in nests containing both sexes females almost always developed in the innermost cells and males in the outermost. However, Cooper and Medler found three nests in which the arrangement of sexes did not follow this pattern as indicated below (x=larval mortality):

Cooper No. 6: ♂-♀-♂-♀-♂-♂
Medler No. 12: x-♀-♂-♀-♀
Medler No. 16: ♂-♂-♀-♀-♂-♀-♂

Cooper commented that the over-all sex ratio did not differ significantly from equality, although in an individual nest the ratio might be extreme. Medler reared 331 females and 224 males. I obtained a 27:69 ratio in my nests. The discrepancy possibly may be explained by the fact that more males are produced in 4.8-mm. borings. Most of Medler's nests were in 6.4- or 8.0-mm. borings, whereas half of mine were in 4.8-mm. borings and half in 6.4-mm.

The Raus reported as prey a tortricid, *Enarmonia* sp; a gelechiid, *Gnorimoschema gallaesolidaginis* Riley; and a pyralid, *Loxostege* sp. probably *similalis* Guenée. Cooper found *foraminatus* preying on small Pyralidae and Gelechioidea and storing 8-14 caterpillars per cell. Medler reported as prey a species each of Gelechiidae, Oecophoridae, Olethreutidae, Pyralidae (*Acrobasis* sp.), Pyraustidae, Thyridae (*Thyris maculata* Harris), and several species of Tortricidae including *Archips* sp. He found as many as 4 different families in a single nest. He also stated that 139 and 107 mg. of caterpillars were stored respectively in 2 cells in which male wasps developed. Basing his judgment on the length of the cells, he determined that 2 cells in which females would have developed held 160 and 189 mg. of caterpillars, respectively. He counted 4-23 caterpillars (mean 9) in 5 female cells and 3-16 (mean 9) in 9 male cells.

Medler reported the egg to be 1.5-2 mm. long. He found that in the field the eggs hatched in 2-3 days and that larvae matured in 6-7 days. He said that there were 5 larval instars, the first 3 being completed in less than 48 hours at 27° C, the fourth in about a day, and the fifth in 36-48 hours. He mentioned that the larva was only half grown after the fourth instar. The prepupal stage was 4-5 days in nests of the summer generation and was followed by a pupal period of 10-12 days. Adults remained in the nest at least 3 days after eclosion. Rau (1944) reported a life cycle of 3-4 weeks in Missouri.

Rau (1935c) stated that *foraminatus* of the summer generation spun only a vestigial cocoon, consisting at most of a cap or partial sheet; but neither Medler, Markin, nor I found that cocoons of the summer generation were incomplete. Earlier Rau (1928) also thought that the cocoon was a network of silk threads into which material from the alimentary canal was injected. Medler noted that the silk was sometimes tinted green, yellow, or brown and that the cocoon was spun against the cell walls.

Rau (1932) noted that a female stored 10 cells in a week. Rau,

Medler, and Markin reported two generations a year in Missouri, Wisconsin, and Idaho, respectively. The wasps nested as early as May 27 in Missouri.

Cooper reared the bombyliid *Anthrax irroratus* Say and the trigonalid wasp *Lycogaster pullata* Shuckard from pupae of *foraminatus*. Medler reared two cuckoo wasps, *Chrysis (C.) coerulans* Fabricius and *C. (C.) nitidula* Fabricius, from nests of *foraminatus*, and also found the scavenger phorid fly *Megaselia aletiae* (Comstock) in some nests. The Raus found *Chrysis (C.) inaequidens* Dahlbom [incorrectly identified as *C. (Hexachrysis) intricata* Brullé] flying around the woodpiles where *foraminatus* was nesting.

Source material.
> Derby, N. Y. 1955 series: D 1b. 1956 series : J 137. 1957 series: G 9, 10, 42, 44, 52, 55, 58, 66, 78, 92. 1958 series: R 11, 17, 21, 36, 39.
> Plummers Island, Md. 1957 series: P 47, 51, 54, 144, 254, 271. 1960 series: E 7, 43.
> Dunn Loring, Va. 1954 series: C 13.
> Kill Devil Hills, N. C. 1956 series: C 179. 1958 series: T 199.

Identifications. Lepidopterous larvae by H. W. Capps; Stylopidae by R. M. Bohart; Ichneumonidae by H. K. Townes; wasps by the author.

EUODYNERUS FORAMINATUS APOPKENSIS (Robertson)

(Plate 25, Figure 119)

This univoltine vernal wasp was the most frequent nester in wooden traps at the Archbold Biological Station, Lake Placid, Fla., in 1957, 1960, and 1961. It was reared from 92 nests at 34 of the 48 stations in the Highlands Ridge sand-scrub area of the Station in 1957, from 19 nests at 8 of 12 stations in 1959, from 62 nests at all 12 stations in 1960, and from 68 nests at all 12 stations in 1961. The traps at most of these stations were suspended beneath the limbs of living or dead hickory and oak. The rest were beneath live or dead limbs of pine, or tied to pine trunks. The wasp nested with equal facility in borings either 4.8 or 6.4 mm. in diameter, 118 of the nests being in traps of the smaller size, and 123 in traps with the larger boring. There were available 236 borings 4.8 and 6.4 mm. in diameter in 1957, so *apopkensis* occupied at least 39 percent of the available nesting sites.

There were also 4 nests from the Station from which I reared intermediates between *foraminatus apopkensis* and *f. parvirudis* Bohart). Two of these were in 4.8-mm. borings and 2 in 6.4-mm. borings. These nests came from three different stations, 2 on the side of a pine trunk and 1 on a dead oak. In 1 nest there was supersedure by a leaf-cutting species of *Megachile*.

In addition to the nests noted above there were 28 almost certainly stored by *apopkensis*, either because they contained the same species of prey that *apopkensis* used almost exclusively, or because they contained prepupae which did not die until late summer or fall (*apopkensis* was the only Florida vespid with such a prolonged larval diapause), or because of the excessive egg mortality, also characteristic of nests of *apopkensis*.

Supersedure and competition. There was supersedure by other species of wasps or bees in 8 of 92 nests of *apopkensis* in 1957, none in 1959, 3 of 62 nests in 1960, and 6 of 68 nests in 1961. Two nests were taken over by *Euodynerus megaera* (Lepeletier), 2 by *Stenodynerus saecularis rufulus* Bohart, 1 by *S. pulvinatus surrufus* Krombein, 1 by an unidentified vespid, 4 by *Podium rufipes* (Fabricius), 1 by *Trypargilum johannis* (Richards), 3 by *Chalicodoma georgica* (Cresson), and 3 by *Megachile mendica* Cresson. *E. apopkensis* did not supersede any other wasp or bee in 1957 or 1960, but it superseded *Pachodynerus erynnis* (Lepeletier) in 1 nest in 1959, and in 1961 it superseded *Stenodynerus pulvinatus surrufus* in 1 nest, *S. saecularis rufulus* in 1 nest, *Trypargilum c. collinum* (Smith) in 1 nest, and an unidentified species of *Megachile*, possibly *mendica* in 1 nest. It seems probable that most of this supersedure was due to actual competition rather than to abandonment of the nests for some other reason, because none of the nests in the inner sections of the borings was capped by an empty vestibular cell.

Nest architecture. The details of nest architecture were somewhat variable in the completely stored borings. In half of the nests the wasps began by storing a cell right at the inner end, and in the other half the females constructed a plug of firmly agglutinated sand particles before storing a cell. The plug varied from 1 to 8 mm. in thickness and was placed at the inner end of the boring or at a variable distance from the inner end.

The number of provisioned cells per nest was quite variable, since this depended on the presence or absence of empty intercalary cells or vestibular cells, and on the sex of the developing wasps. The maximum number of cells in a nest with a 6.4-mm. diameter was 13. In one nest there were 3 female cells, 10 male cells, and 1 empty cell. In the other nest there were 13 male cells. The maximum number of cells in a nest with a 4.8-mm. diameter boring was 12, all of them containing males. The number of provisioned cells in 97 completed nests in 4.8-mm. borings ranged from 1 to 12 with a mean of 8.1 cells per nest. In 104 completed nests in 6.4-mm. borings, there were 2-13 stored cells with a mean of 7.6 per nest. The almost identical ranges and means for these two sets of nests reflected the preponderance of larger female cells in the 6.4-mm. borings and of smaller male cells in the 4.8-mm. borings.

Table 4 summarizes measurements of stored cells. There were only a few oversize cells. Most of them were the terminal cells in nests that lacked empty vestibular cells, which may explain why these particular cells were so long.

Empty intercalary cells were present in 24 nests. There was one such cell between each stored cell in only 7 nests; in each of the other nests there were more stored cells than empty intercalaries. The 57 intercalary cells were 4-34 mm. long with a mean of 13.2 mm.

An empty vestibular cell was present in 134 of the 221 completely stored nests. Usually this cell was undivided, but there was a single cross partition in 20 vestibular cells, and 2, 4, and 5 such partitions in 1 cell each. The range in length of the 134 vestibular cells

TABLE 4.—*Measurements (in mm.) of stored cells*, Euodynerus foraminatus apopkensis (*Robertson*)

Boring diameter	Sex	Number of cells	Range in length	Mean length
4.8	♀	53	11-30	20.3
	♂	772	7-44	15.3
6.4	♀	418	8-46	17.5
	♂	308	7-45	13.4

including the terminal sand plug was 4 to 130 mm. with a mean of 27.3 mm.

The partitions between cells and the terminal plugs were made from grains of sand firmly agglutinated to form a solid wall. The range in thickness of cell partitions in 212 nests was 0.5 to 5 mm. with a mean of 1.8 mm. The terminal plugs at the entrances of 226 nests ranged from 1.5 to 22 mm. with a mean of 6 mm.

In nests containing both sexes the females were always in the innermost cells, males in the outermost. Thirty nests produced only females, about 100 of the remaining nests produced only males, and the rest contained both males and females. Both sexes were produced throughout the nesting period from the end of February to the end of April. There was a significant correlation between the length of the cell and sex of the wasp, females always being produced in longer cells as noted above. Furthermore, there appeared to be significant correlation between the diameter of the boring and sex of the wasp, about 90 percent of the females being produced in borings with a diameter of 6.4 mm., and two-thirds of the males in 4.8-mm. borings. The actual production of adult wasps from the 241 nests was 776 males and 361 females.

The 4 nests from which I reared *apopkensis-parvirudis* intergrades fell within the range of variation noted for typical *apopkensis* nests. There were 4 stored and 2 vestibular cells in the single completed 4.8-mm. nest. Both of the 6.4-mm. nests were completely provisioned; 1 contained 1 vestibular and 7 stored cells, while the other held only 9 stored cells. The 6 male cells in 4.8-mm. borings were 18-22 mm. long (mean 19.3 mm.). Ten male cells in 6.4-mm. borings were 12-24 mm. long (mean 16.4 mm.), and 6 female cells were 16-24 mm. long (mean 19.5). There were no empty intercalary cells in these nests. Vestibular cells were present in 2 of the 3 completely stored nests; there was 1 vestibular cell of 10 mm. in 1 nest, and 2 cells of 22 and 28 mm. in the other nest. The cell partitions were 2-7 mm. thick (mean 3.5 mm.), and closing plugs were 5-10 mm. thick (mean 7.7 mm.).

Prey. Most of the prey that I preserved came from cells in which the wasp eggs died. The prey stored by *apopkensis* consisted almost entirely of small larvae, 6-8 mm. long, of a species of Olethreutidae. This particular species was not stored by any other vespid at Lake Placid. It was stored entirely in 67 of the 78 nests from which I preserved prey, and it appeared to be stored also in most of the other nests that still contained prey when I opened them. The nests containing olethreutids had 2 to 24 larvae per cell with a mean of 10 larvae per cell (based on 138 cells). Limited data indicate that an average of 14 larvae are placed in a cell in which a female wasp is to develop (based on 22 cells), and 8 larvae in a cell in which a male is to develop (based on 55 cells).

Rarely, one or a few larvae of a species of Tortricidae or of a species of *Platynota* in the Tortricidae were found in a cell that otherwise contained nothing but olethreutids. The tortricids seemed to be stored later in the nesting season, perhaps when the olethreutids may have become scarce. One or two cells in several nests actually contained more tortricids than olethreutids, and two nests may have been provisioned entirely with a species of *Platynota*. One of the latter, an 8-celled nest completed about April 25, contained 2 to 3 larvae of a species of *Platynota*, 8 to 10 mm. long, in each of cells 1-7; a male *apopkensis* developed in cell 8. In the other 7-celled nest, completed about April 26, wasps developed in 6 cells, and the seventh contained 3 larvae of *Platynota* sp.

I preserved the prey in one cell of a nest of the *apopkensis-parvirudis* intergrade. It contained 4 tortricid larvae, 3 of one species and one of a second.

Life history. Since most occupants of the nests were in the late larval or early prepupal stages when I received the nests, I have no data on duration of the egg and larval stages or on the number of larval instars. There was a substantial egg mortality of 12 percent in 1957, some of it probably due to parasitism by first instar larvae of *Pseudoxenos hookeri* (Pierce) as it was in 1959 when 2 of 14 dead eggs had been entered by stylopid larvae (fig. 119).

Most of the cocoons were spun from delicate, semitransparent white silk; but occasionally they were light tan and subopaque. The larval feces were voided at the inner end of the cell before the cocoon was spun, and the larva completely encased itself in the cocoon. The cocoons showed less variation in length than did the cells. Lengths of the cocoons by sex in borings of the two diameters were as follows: 257 male cocoons in 4.8-mm. borings ranged from 7 to 22 mm. with a mean of 10.9 mm., and 17 female cocoons ranged from 12 to 19 mm. with a mean of 14.4 mm.; in 6.4-mm. borings 103 male cocoons ranged from 6 to 21 mm. with a mean of 9.1 mm., and 155 female cocoons ranged from 9 to 18 mm. with a mean of 12.9 mm.

Except for 20 individuals, all of the prepupae were oriented in the cocoons with the head end toward the nest entrance. The misorientation of all but 3 of these may have been due to the nests having been opened before the cocoons were spun with a possible resultant damage to the cell partitions which indicate to the wasp larva how it should orient. The 3 exceptions were already misoriented prepupae when the nests were first opened.

This is the only vespid from Florida with such a prolonged larval diapause. The wasps remained in diapause from early spring until fall in my office except that some of the nests were chilled for a month at 42° F. in 1957 in an unsuccessful attempt to break the diapause. During the winter the nests were exposed outside for about 2 months except during freezing temperatures. This period proved sufficient to break diapause and pupation began about a week after the traps were brought in.

In 1957 there were 167 entirely pale male pupae on December 30; 62 additional males pupated on December 31; and the last 25 had pupated by January 2. Three females pupated on December 31; 78 more by January 2; 13 more on the 3d; an additional 13 by January 6; 2 on the 7th; and 1 each on the 8th, 13th, and 20th. Coloration of the pupae occurred as in the following timetable in one nest: pale violet eyes developed in 3 days and black eyes on the 4th day; the thorax and base of abdomen began to darken 3 days later; the body was entirely dark except appendages by the 9th day after pupation; the adults eclosed a day later and left the nest 4 to 5 days after eclosion.

The dates of pupation and emergence of the adults from the nest (*not eclosion of the adult*) were noted for 184 males and 108 females in 1957. This period ranged from 13 to 22 days for the males with a mean of 16.1 days, and the largest number of males (78) emerged on the 16th day after pupation. For the females this period ranged from 14 to 22 days with a mean of 18.2 days and emergence of the largest number of females (36) took place on the 18th day after pupation.

I placed Cellophane over the cells in the 1959 nests in order to obtain precise data on dates of eclosion of the wasps and of extrusion of the stylopid parasites. Male wasps pupated January 9 to 12, eclosed January 21 to 27, and emerged from the nests January 26 to 29; female wasps pupated January 13 to 18, eclosed January 30 to February 5, and emerged February 4 to 10. The mean elapsed time between pupation and eclosion was 13.3 days for males and 18.2 days for females. The mean elapsed time between eclosion and emergence from the nest was 3.8 days for males and 3.5 days for females.

Emergence of 215 males from the 1957 nests occurred from January 13 to 21 with a peak emergence of 71 on the 14th, and emergence of 101 females was from January 16 to 29 with a peak emergence of 26 on the 20th. Dates of emergence from individual nests were variable. In some nests all males emerged on the same date, but in other nests as much as 6 days elapsed between the emergence of the first and last males. An average period of 1.9 days elapsed between emergence of the first and last males in an individual nest in the 46 nests scored. The females exhibited the same spread of emergence dates in individual nests, but the average period between emergence of the first and last females in an individual nest was 2.4 days for the 29 nests scored. Males emerged an average of 5.8 days ahead of the females in a single nest when both sexes were present; the range was from 3 to 12 days between the emergence of the last male and the first female in the 27 nests scored.

Developmental data were similar for the 4 nests of the *apopkensis-parvirudis* intergrades.

There were two cases of accelerated development and one case of delayed emergence in the 241 nests. In one 1957 nest that produced 9 males, the one in the outermost cell eclosed sometime between October 2 and December 22 and was found dead and desiccated in the nest on December 30; the other occupants of this nest emerged from January 13 to 17. The 1957 nest in which delayed development occurred yielded 4 females; those in cells 1, 2, and 4 pupated between January 2 and 6 and left the nest on January 23; the occupant of cell 3, which I placed in a separate empty nest after I noted its delayed development, did not pupate until January 20 and died on February 6 after failing to shed all of the pupal exuvia. In the one 1959 nest in which accelerated development occurred, the male occupants of cells 1, 5, and 9 of a 10-celled nest transformed to adults and died in the cells between the end of May and January 3; the other occupants of this nest transformed to adults January 24 to 27.

The data from these nests indicate that there is only a single generation a year. There is a prolonged larval diapause that is initiated by a long period of aestivation followed by a shorter period requiring exposure to chilly weather.

Parasites and predators. The most abundant parasite was the endoparasitic stylopid *Pseudoxenos hookeri* (Pierce). In 1957 it parasitized at least 25 percent of the available nests, 10 percent of the total available adult wasps, and 33 percent of the adults in stylopized nests. It parasitized a lesser number of nests and individuals in subsequent years. In addition, it was probably responsible for some of the excessively high egg mortality (figs. 119-122), which was not found in the nests of other vespids. This stylopid was also found in one vespid in a nest of the *apopkensis-parvirudis* intergrade.

The cuckoo wasp *Chrysis (C.) inaequidens* Dahlbom was reared from 7 nests in 1957, 5 in 1959, 6 in 1960, and 4 in 1961. An unidentified chrysidid, probably this same species, occurred in 2 other nests in 1957. *C. inaequidens* parasitized 25 percent of the available vespids in the 22 parasitized nests. The development of these parasites was not synchronized with that of the host, for the adult cuckoo wasps emerged from the nests during April and May of the same year in which the nests were stored.

A variant of *Chrysis (C.) coerulans* Fabricius was reared from 22 nests in 1960, in which it parasitized 24 percent of the available vespids. An unidentified chrysidid, possibly this same species, occurred in one cell of another 9-celled nest in 1960.

The chrysidid *Chrysis (C.) derivata* Buysson was reared from 1 cell of a 3-celled nest in 1960.

Amobia floridensis (Townsend), the sarcophagid predator, was present in 2 nests in 1957, in which its maggots destroyed the contents of 6 out of 16 cells. Adult flies emerged several weeks after the nests were infested.

Amobia erythrura (Wulp) was reared from 1 nest in 1957, from 3 nests in 1959, and from 1 nest in 1961. The maggots destroyed the contents of 19 out of 37 cells. Adult flies emerged from these nests several weeks after the latter were infested.

Miltogrammine maggots were found in 3 other nests in 1957 and 1961, in which they destroyed 10 out of 15 cells. No adult flies were reared, but I suspect that the species involved was one or both of the *Amobia* listed above.

The rhipiphorid beetle *Macrosiagon c. cruentum* (Germar) developed in cell 1 of a 10-celled nest and emerged as an adult on February 3, 1958, 2 weeks after the last wasp had left the nest.

A museum pest, the dermestid beetle *Thylodrias contractus* Motschulsky, infested 2 cells of a 6-celled nest in 1960. An unidentified dermestid, possibly the same species, infested a cell in another 6-celled nest in 1960. Probably both of these infestations arose in the laboratory. The beetle larvae destroyed the wasp prepupae in the infested cells.

The bombyliid *Lepidophora lepidocera* (Wiedemann) is possibly predaceous on *apopkensis*. One female was reared in April 1957 from a nest that contained paralyzed larvae of the species of olethreutid stored exclusively by *apopkensis*. There was only 1 wasp prepupa in this nest, and it died between October 2 and December 20.

The bombyliid *Toxophora* sp. parasitized the prepupae in 2 of 15 cells in 2 nests in 1961. Both of these parasites died after transforming to the characteristic pupa of *Toxophora*. It is quite likely that the species was *amphitea* Say, which was reared from nests of other wasps in these borings at Lake Placid in 1961. It was the only species of *Amphitea* reared from these traps in Florida.

The grain itch mite *Pyemotes* sp. infested 2 of 18 cells in 2 nests in the field in 1961. Additional infestations by this mite occurred in the laboratory in 3 other nests.

I reared several parasites of the species of olethreutid used most commonly as prey by *apopkensis*. One was the tachinid *Leskiella brevirostris* James which emerged from several puparia in 4 nests. Only 1 of these parasites developed within each host larva and pupated within the host larva; the adult flies emerged several weeks after I received the nests. The braconid *Macrocentrus instabilis* Muesebeck was reared from 2 larvae in 2 nests; the 2 parasite females emerged April 12, 2 weeks after I received the nests. The ichneumonid *Temelucha grapholithae* Cushman (?) was reared from 1 larva; the female parasite emerged from her cocoon on the host larva on April 13, 2 weeks after I received the nest. The bethylid *Goniozus platynotae* Ashmead was reared from an olethreutid larva in each of 2 nests in 1957 and 1960. In the earlier nest 4 of the parasite cocoons were attached to the host larva when I opened the nest on March 19; *platynotae* females emerged from each of these on April 1. In the 1960 nest there were 5 cocoons on an olethreutid larva when I opened the nest on April 14; 2 females and 3 males of *platynotae* emerged on April 21.

Several parasites of tortricid larvae were also reared from these nests. The tachinid *Nemorilla floralis* (Fallén) was reared from the larva of a tortricid species in a nest of the *apopkensis-parvirudis* intergrade; the adult fly emerged May 31, 2 weeks after the nest was mailed to me. The bethylid *Goniozus hubbardi* Howard parasitized a tortricid larva, possibly *Platynota* sp., in a nest of *apopken-*

sis; 3 females and 2 males emerged from the cocoons on April 27, 2 weeks after I opened the nest.

Source material.

Lake Placid, Fla. 1957 series: M 1, 2, 3, 4, 6, 7, 8, 11, 12, 13, 14, 26, 27, 28, 29, 42, 43, 56, 57, 58, 59, 61, 62, 64, 66, 67, 68, 69, 71, 73, 74, 79, 83, 84, 86, 87, 88, 93, 96, 97, 99, 104, 112, 114, 122, 123, 126, 129, 133, 134, 139, 143, 147, 149, 151, 153, 157, 158, 166, 167, 169, 176, 177, 181, 182, 183, 184, 193, 196, 197, 198, 199, 206, 207, 208, 212, 213, 214, 218, 221, 223, 224, 229, 236, 238, 239, 267, 269, 272, 275, 281, 283. 1959 series: V 1, 2, 4, 8, 12, 21, 24, 32, 45, 46, 48, 79, 80, 84, 88, 95, 97, 98, 103. 1960 series: B 14, 15, 18, 19, 20, 21, 22, 23, 24, 25, 26, 29, 31, 34, 35, 36, 37, 38, 39, 40, 42, 45, 46, 47, 48, 50, 51, 53, 54, 55, 57, 60, 80, 83, 85, 87, 88, 89, 90, 91, 94, 96, 97, 98, 101, 102, 112, 115, 116, 117, 121, 122, 123, 124, 126, 129, 135, 137, 140, 151, 162, 163. 1961 series: F 13, 15, 19, 20, 25, 26, 27, 30, 31, 32, 33, 34, 35, 36, 37, 39, 40, 41, 42, 43, 47, 49, 54, 57, 59, 90, 91, 92, 98, 100, 101, 102, 103, 104, 106, 111, 113, 114, 115, 116, 118, 119, 120, 122, 123, 126, 127, 128, 131, 147, 154, 158, 160, 162, 165, 166, 167, 170, 171, 172, 174, 175, 176, 177, 181, 184, 185, 191.

f. apopkense-f. parvirudis intergrades. 1960 series: B 157. 1961 series: F 132, 155, 161.

probable *f. apopkense* nests, but no data from them included in text. 1957 series: M 9, 31, 32, 44, 72, 111, 116, 168, 179, 217, 237. 1959 series: V 19, 26. 1960 series: B 13, 16, 17, 30, 43, 56, 58, 82, 84, 99, 100, 110, 133. 1961 series: F 55, 253.

Identifications. Coleoptera by R. M. Bohart and T. J. Spilman; Diptera by P. H. Arnaud, W. W. Wirth, C. W. Sabrosky, and W. L. Downes, Jr.; Hymenoptera by R. M. Bohart, C. F. W. Muesebeck, and the author.

EUODYNERUS MEGAERA (Lepeletier)

(Plate 9, Figure 40; Plate 26, Figures 123, 124)

This wasp nested in 20 nests at 14 stations at Kill Devil Hills, N. C., in 1954, 1955, 1956, and 1958, and in 31 nests at 14 stations in the Highlands Ridge sand-scrub area of the Archbold Biological Station, Lake Placid, Fla., in 1957, 1959, 1960, and 1961. The nests were in open wooded areas or at the edges of denser woods. Seventeen of the Kill Devil Hills nests were from stations on dead tree trunks or suspended from dead limbs of hickory, pine, oak, or willow, and 3 nests were from limbs of living trees. At Lake Placid most of the nests were from stations suspended from limbs of living oak or scrub hickory, and 4 were from stations on the sides of pine trunks. At Kill Devil Hills there were 4 nests in 4.8-mm. and 16 in 6.4-mm. borings; at Lake Placid there were 10 in 4.8-mm. borings, 16 in 6.4-mm. borings and 5 in 12.7-mm. borings.

Supersedure and competition. Only 3 examples of supersedure were observed in *megaera* nests, all at Lake Placid. *E. megaera* superseded *E. foraminatus apopkensis* (Robertson) in 2 nests and was superseded by the same species in the third nest.

Nest architecture. In half the nests the wasp laid an egg at the inner end of the boring and began to store prey immediately; in the other nests the wasps put a narrow plug of agglutinated sand at the inner end or a sand partition some distance from the inner end.

The number of stored cells per completed nest was variable depending on the diameter of the boring, the presence or absence of empty intercalary and vestibular cells, and the sex of the developing wasps. Nine completed nests in 4.8-mm. borings averaged 4.1 stored cells (range 1-6), 0.2 intercalary, and 0.3 vestibular; corresponding figures for 24 nests in 6.4-mm. borings were 6.3 stored cells (range 5-10), 0.5 intercalary, and 0.5 vestibular; and in 5 nests in 12.7-mm. borings there were 9.4 stored cells (range 8-11), no intercalary, and 0.2 vestibular.

There were no significant differences between length of stored

TABLE 5.—*Measurements (in mm.) of cells,* Euodynerus megaera *(Lepeletier)*

Boring diameter	Sex	STORED CELLS			INTERCALARY CELLS			VESTIBULAR CELLS		
		No.	Range in length	Mean length	No.	Range in length	Mean length	No.	Range in length	Mean length
4.8	♀	3	33-35	34	1	—	14	7	13-114	35
	♂	38	16-45	25						
6.4	♀	103	14-40	23	16	4-16	8	13	4-35	13
	♂	51	11-36	17						
12.7	♀	38	9-18	13	0	—	—	1	—	12
	♂	7	8-13	10						

cells by sex and by boring diameter at the two localities. Consequently, in Table 5 I have consolidated the measurements for North Carolina and Florida nests and shown the mean length and range by sex and by boring diameter of the stored cells, and by boring diameter of intercalary and vestibular cells.

Intercalary cells were present in only 5 nests from Kill Devil Hills (fig. 40) and 3 from Florida. Most of these cells were in 6.4-mm. borings. Vestibular cells were present in only 7 of 12 completed nests at Kill Devil Hills and in 14 of 29 completed nests at Lake Placid. In one nest the vestibular cell was divided by a cross partition.

The partitions between cells and the terminal plugs were made of agglutinated sand except in several nests at Kill Devil Hills for which mud was used. The partitions were 0.5-3 mm. thick (mean 1.5). In the few nests where intercalary cells were present the partitions capping those cells were thicker than those capping the stored cells in the same nest (fig. 40). The terminal plugs at the boring entrances were 1-7 mm. thick (mean 3) in 4.8-mm. nests, 0.5-15 mm. (mean 4) in 6.4-mm. nests, and 3-12 mm. (mean 8) in 12.7-mm. nests.

In nests containing both sexes, females were in the innermost and males in the outermost cells. Males only were reared from 12 nests in 4.8-mm. borings, females only from 1 nest, and both sexes from a single nest. In 6.4-mm. nests females only were reared from 14 nests, both sexes from 14 nests, and males only from 4 nests. In 12.7-mm. nests both sexes were reared from 3 nests and females only from 2 nests.

The over-all sex ratio was 3:2, as based on my rearing of 144 females and 96 males from a total of 277 stored cells. At Kill Devil Hills 53 females and 27 males emerged from 99 cells, and at Lake Placid 91 females and 69 males emerged from 178 cells.

Prey. Consolidated identifications of prey from these two localities are presented below. They are based both on entire cell contents and on partial samples from a total of 25 cells.

> Kill Devil Hills, 3 nests, 1954 and 1956:
>> Tortricidae
>>> *Archips* sp. in 1 cell
>>> sp. in 1 cell
>> Pyraustidae
>>> *Desmia funeralis* (Hübner) in 2 cells in 1 nest
>>> *Framinghamia helvalis* (Walker) in 1 cell
>> Epipaschiidae, *Tetralopha* sp. in 2 cells in 2 nests
>> Phycitidae
>>> *Nephopteryx nyssaecolella* (Dyar) in 1 cell
>>> *Nephopteryx uvinella* (Ragonot) in 1 cell
>>> sp. in 1 cell
> Lake Placid, 11 nests, 1959-1961:
>> Oecophoridae, *Psilocorsis* sp. in 1 cell
>> Tortricidae
>>> *Platynota* sp. in 1 cell
>>> sp. in 15 cells in 9 nests
>> Olethreutidae, sp. in 10 cells in 4 nests
>> Epipaschiidae, sp. in 2 cells in 1 nest
>> Noctuidae, *Palthis angulalis* Hübner in 1 cell

E. megaera stored 3-18 larvae per cell (mean 7) in 23 cells. The sex of the wasp which would have developed in some of these cells could be predicted from the sex of wasps in the adjoining cells. As based on these inferences, 6-18 larvae (mean 9.5) were present in 4 female cells and 3-8 larvae (mean 5.4) in 5 male cells. Just a single species of caterpillar was stored in 11 cells, 2 species of 2 families in 13 cells, and 3 species representing 3 families in 1 cell. In a 4-celled nest from Kill Devil Hills caterpillars from 3 adjacent cells belonged to 6 different species and 4 families.

Life history. I did not obtain any data on the duration of the egg stage or the larval feeding period. Data from Florida nests suggest that adults of the summer generation usually emerged 28-35 days after the nest was stored. The period between completion of larval feeding and pupation was 7-17 days (mean 10). The period between pupation and emergence of the adults from the nest was 10-16 days (mean 13) for 5 males, and 14-20 days (mean 16) for 17 females. Three females spent 2-5 days (mean 3) in the nest after eclosion from the pupal exuvia.

The cocoons were spun of delicate, opaque whitish silk. Female cocoons averaged 15 mm. long both in 4.8-and 6.4-mm. borings; male cocoons averaged 14 mm. long in 4.8-mm. and 12 mm. long in 6.4-mm. borings.

Except for 7 individuals, the prepupae were properly oriented in the cocoons with their anterior ends toward the entrance. Five of the 7 misoriented individuals were in a 12.7-mm. boring where the adult wasps could turn around inside the boring and orient in the proper direction to escape from the nest.

Males usually emerged before females in all multicelled nests containing both sexes. The period between emergence of the last male and the first female in a single nest ranged from 0-6 days (mean 3). All the males in a single nest emerged on the same day, except for 1 nest where their emergence took place over a 2-day period. The females in a single nest also emerged on the same day in most nests, although there were 8 nests in which their emergence took place over a period of 2-4 days.

Data from 3 nests at Kill Devil Hills and from Lake Placid indicate that an individual wasp stores on the average about 2⅓ cells per day. The maximum appeared to be 8 stored cells and 1 vestibular cell in a period of 2-3 days.

Emergence dates establish that *megaera* is bivoltine at both localities. At Kill Devil Hills wasps emerged August 11-12 from 2 nests probably stored the first half of July; occupants of the other nests, stored from about July 1 to early August, overwintered as diapausing larvae, and emerged as adults the next spring. I have collected *megaera* females at Kill Devil Hills from June 1 to August 7. The species must be active well into September, however, judged from the August 11-12 emergence dates from the 2 nests reported above. At Lake Placid occupants of nests, stored between mid-March and early in May, emerged from April 17 to May 29; occupants of a single nest stored around June 1 overwintered as diapausing larvae and emerged the following spring.

Parasites and predators. The cuckoo wasp *Chrysis (C.) coerulans* Fabricius was reared from 4 of 11 cells in 2 nests from Lake Placid. At Kill Devil Hills *Chrysis (C.) inaequidens* Dahlbom parasitized 4 of 13 cells in 2 nests; this same species parasitized 1 of 2 cells in a nest at Lake Placid. The eulophid *Melittobia chalybii* Ashmead infested 1 nest in the laboratory.

Bombyliid flies were also parasites of minor importance. *Anthrax aterrimus* (Bigot) was reared from 2 of 9 cells in 2 nests at Kill Devil Hills. *Toxophora amphitea* Walker was reared from 3 of 10 cells in 2 nests at Lake Placid. An unreared bombyliid killed the occupant of 1 cell in another nest from Lake Placid.

Previous observations. I published a brief note (Krombein, 1955b, pp. 146-147) on the first nest I obtained at Kill Devil Hills. Data from that nest are included in the account presented above.

Source material.
>   Kill Devil Hills, N. C. 1954 series: F 4. 1955 series: C 138, 142, 275, 276, 373, 408. 1956 series: C 120, 243, 259, 260, 430, 618, 673, 674, 675, 694, 695. 1958 series: T 62, 162.
>   Lake Placid, Fla. 1957 series: M 184. 1959 series: V 18, 20, 43, 44, 47, 85, 92, 104, 110, 116. 1960 series: B 49, 68, 79, 95, 111. 1961 series: F 14, 16, 38, 43, 51, 62, 63, 64, 65, 87, 89, 105, 122, 124, 125.

Identifications. Lepidopterous larvae by H. W. Capps; Bombyliidae by W. W. Wirth; wasps by the author.

EUODYNERUS SCHWARZI (Krombein)
(Plate 9, Figure 39)

I described this species from Plummers Island, basing the description largely on reared specimens from trap nests. *E. schwarzi* nested in 19 nests at or near the Island, 5 in 4.8-mm. borings, 12 in 6.4-mm. borings, and 2 in 12.7-mm. borings. Three nests came from the mainland woods adjacent to the Island, 2 from a station on an old mule shed, and 1 from a station on a decaying tree trunk. Fifteen of the nests on the Island were from 9 stations on dead tree trunks or limbs, and 1 was from the limb of a living tree. The nests were in shade for part of the day. The wasps obviously preferred the 6.4-mm. traps, and it is possible that the few nests in 4.8- and 12.7-mm. borings were made because no empty 6.4-mm. borings were available at the time.

Nest architecture. The wasps used mud to fashion the partitions closing the cells and the closing plug at the nest entrance. In half the nests the wasps put a thin coating of mud at the inner end of the boring or constructed a mud partition 11-102 mm. from the inner end of the boring. In the other nests the wasps laid an egg at the inner end and then began to bring in paralyzed caterpillars.

Table 6 presents measurements of stored and empty intercalary and vestibular cells by sex in nests in these 3 sizes of borings.

Several anomalies in table 6 require comment. Several abnormally long female and male cells in 6.4-mm. borings resulted in male cells being almost as long and in female cells being longer than those in

4.8-mm. borings. Except for these, the stored cells followed the usual pattern of being progressively shorter as the boring diameter increased.

This species was not as prone as *Monobia quadridens* to construct empty intercalary cells. There was 1 intercalary cell in a 4.8-mm. boring; but since the wasp was not reared from the preceding stored cell, I could not enter the measurement in table 6. There were intercalary cells in only 6 of the 6.4-mm. borings; not all of them could be scored in table 6 because of larval mortality in the stored cells preceding some of them.

All but 4 of the completed nests had a vestibular cell. In 2 nests the vestibular cell had a cross partition. Five nests were not completely stored when they were picked up.

TABLE 6.—*Measurements (in mm.) of cells*, Euodynerus schwarzi (*Krombein*)

Boring diameter	Sex	STORED CELLS			INTERCALARY CELLS			VESTIBULAR CELLS		
		No.	Range in length	Mean length	No.	Range in length	Mean length	No.	Range in length	Mean length
4.8	♀	4	20-25	23	0	—	—	2	13-16	15
	♂	10	12-23	18	0	—	—			
6.4	♀	23	18-79	28	7	3-7	5	7	3-38	18
	♂	17	11-30	17	4	3-6	5			
12.7	♀	11	11-19	14	0	—	—	1	—	23

Three completed nests in 4.8-mm. borings averaged 5 stored cells. Nine such nests in 6.4-mm. borings averaged 5 stored cells and 2 intercalary cells. The maximum number of stored cells in a 6.4-mm. nest was 8; I reared males from 6 of the cells and the other 2 larvae died. The two 12.7-mm. nests contained 3 and 10 stored cells, respectively (fig. 39).

The mud partitions capping stored cells were 1-2 mm. thick. When intercalary cells were present, the partitions capping them were usually at least a millimeter thicker than those capping the adjacent stored cells. The mud plugs at the boring entrance were 1-6 mm. thick (mean 3).

Prey. The following species of caterpillars were preserved from nests of *schwarzi:*

Gelechiidae
  Gelechia albisparsella (Chambers) in 1 cell
Oecophoridae
  Psilocorsis sp. in 1 cell
Tortricidae
  sp. in 11 cells in 4 nests
Pyraustidae
  Loxostege mancalis (Lederer) in 1 cell

The number of larvae stored per cell varied with the size of the caterpillar and the sex of the wasp which was to develop on them. In 5 cells in which females were to develop there were 5-10 larvae per cell (mean 8), and in 6 male cells there were 3-4 larvae per cell (mean 3.5).

Usually only 1 species of prey was stored per cell, but in 1 cell there appeared to be larvae of 3 or 4 species. In 1 cell there were larvae of both Tortricidae and Oecophoridae, although only 1 of the latter was found in 6 cells in that nest. Occasionally the wasp venom caused the development of a cyanotic appearance in the paralyzed caterpillars.

Life history. The egg was sausageshaped, 2.4-3.0 mm. long, and 0.8-1.0 mm. wide. Two eggs in the outer cells hatched July 31 in a nest picked up on July 28. Six larvae required 3-5 days (mean 4) to consume the store of caterpillars provided for each. Spinning of the cocoon required 2 days. Pupation occurred 4-6 days later in the summer generation. The period between pupation and emergence of the adult was 9 days for a male and 11 days for 2 females of the summer generation, and 12-13 days for 3 females of the overwintering generation. The total elapsed time between egg hatch and emergence of the adult was 24 and 26 days, respectively, for 2 females of the summer generation.

The cocoons were spun of delicate, subopaque unvarnished silk and were white to light tan. Female cocoons averaged 14.8 mm. long in 4.8-mm. nests and 16.8 mm. long in 6.4-mm. nests; male cocoons averaged 13.8 mm. in 4.8-mm. nests and 17.0 in 6.4-mm. nests.

Males emerged before females in all nests where both sexes were present. The period between emergence of the first male and the last female from individual nests of the overwintering generation was 4-17 days (mean 9). All occupants emerged on the same day from overwintering nests which contained only males. In those nests which contained only females, the emergence from individual nests required 4-7 days (mean 5).

E. schwarzi had a reasonably rapid rate of provisioning. Estimates based on egg hatch from 6 nests suggest that from 1½ to 3 cells (mean 2) may be stored per day.

Nesting occurred at Plummers Island from about June 20 until at least the end of July. However, I have collected males there as early as June 2 and females as late as August 28; so the actual nesting period may be somewhat longer. There appeared to be only a partial second generation which emerged July 17 to August 11 from nests stored from late in June until mid-July. Occupants of most nests stored after early July overwintered as diapausing larvae. There was divided emergence in 1 nest stored between

July 5 and early in August; a male emerged from 1 cell during September and occupants of the other cells overwintered as resting larvae.

I reared 37 females and 28 males from 84 stored cells.

Parasites and predators. I reared a female of *Chrysis* (*C.*) *nitidula* Fabricius from one nest. A single chrysidid occurred in each of two other nests, but I did not rear adults.

The chalcidoid *Melittobia chalybii* Ashmead infested 1 nest in the field, and secondarily invaded 2 nests in the laboratory.

A male and a female of the bombyliid *Toxophora amphitea* Walker were reared from a single nest.

Source material.
Plummers Island, Md. 1956 series: H 29, 37, 59. 1957 series: P 3, 63, 123, 148. 1959 series: Y 141, 144. 1961 series: K 46, 104. 1962 series: M 51, 71, 82, 89, 90, 95, 100, 107.

Identifications. Lepidopterous larvae by H. W. Capps; *Toxophora* by W. W. Wirth; Hymenoptera by the author.

EUODYNERUS HIDALGO BOREOORIENTALIS (Bequaert)

I obtained 4 nests of this wasp from a single station at Kill Devil Hills, N. C., in 1958, and 8 nests from 4 stations in the Highlands Ridge sand-scrub area of the Archbold Biological Station, Lake Placid, Fla., in 1957, 1961, and 1962. The Kill Devil Hills nests were from a setting beneath a dead branch of a scrubby oak on the barrens in open sun. The Florida nests also were in full sun in open areas, most of them suspended from limbs of scrub hickory but a few from the trunk of a pine tree. Half of the nests in each locality were in 4.8- and half in 6.4-mm. borings.

Supersedure and competition. This wasp superseded a species of *Stenodynerus* subg. *Parancistrocerus* in a 4.8-mm. nest at Lake Placid.

Nest architecture. In half of the nests the wasps began storing prey at the inner end of the boring, and in the other borings they placed some agglutinated sand at the inner end or made a partition of that material 50-110 mm. from the inner end.

Two cells of male wasps in 4.8-mm. borings at Kill Devil Hills were 22 and 35 mm. long; measurements were not made on 6.4-mm. nests from that locality. In 4.8-mm. nests from Lake Placid 11 female cells were 15-23 mm. long (mean 18) and 4 male cells were 15-27 mm. (mean 21); in 6.4-mm. nests 9 female cells were 13-20 mm. (mean 16) and 15 male cells were 9-18 mm. (mean 13).

There were no intercalary cells, and only 5 of the 10 completed nests had a vestibular cell 12-84 mm. long (mean 64).

The partitions capping the cells and the terminal plugs at the nest entrances were made of firmly agglutinated sand. The former were 1-1.5 mm. thick, the latter 1-6 mm. (mean 3).

At Kill Devil Hills the 2 nests in 4.8-mm. borings contained only a single cell each, and the 2 in 6.4-mm. borings contained 8 and 11 cells, respectively. At Lake Placid 3 nests in 4.8-mm. borings averaged 5 stored cells (range 3-8) and 1 vestibular cell, while 4 nests in 6.4-mm. borings averaged 8 stored cells (range 5-10) and 0.5 vestibular cell (range 0-1).

Males were always in the outer and females in the inner cells in mixed nests. The over-all sex ratio is probably 1:1, as based on my rearing 24 females and 22 males from a total of 71 stored cells.

Prey. Cell 8 of an 8-celled nest, probably that of a male wasp, contained 7 phycitid caterpillars, *Homoeosoma electellum* (Hulst).

Life history. Undoubtedly 2 or more generations develop each year. All my nests were of the summer generation. The period between storing the nest and emergence of adults was about 5 weeks for the summer generation. Duration of combined egg and larval feeding stages was probably 7-9 days. The period between completion of larval feeding and pupation was 7-9 days for 6 individuals. The period between pupation and emergence of adults was 13-16 days (mean 14) for 5 males and 19 days for 2 females.

Cocoons were subopaque, delicate and white, and in some cells coextensive with cell walls and ends. One male cocoon in a 4.8-mm. boring was 33 mm. long. In 6.4-mm. borings 8 female cocoons were 10-19 mm. long (mean 14) and 10 male cocoons 9-17 mm. (mean 13).

All larvae oriented properly with their heads toward the nest entrance except for 1 specimen in a 1-celled 4.8-mm. nest at Kill Devil Hills. When I opened this nest on July 28 I found a dead male wasp at the inner end. It had emerged some days earlier and chewed some wood fibers from the inner end in a vain attempt to escape.

The 4 nests at Kill Devil Hills were probably stored by the same female during June. When I picked up the nests and opened them on July 28 the two 1-celled nests in 4.8-mm. borings each contained a dead male wasp. One of the 6.4-mm. nests contained 5 dead wasps (4 ♀, 1♂), but 6 others had emerged successfully. The other 6.4-mm. nest contained 8 cells from which all occupants had already emerged. The nests at Lake Placid were provisioned from early in June until early in July, and adults emerged July 13 to August 6.

Previous observations. No notes on *h. boreoorientalis* have been published before these. However, several authors have published brief notes on typical *hidalgo* (Saussure). Bequaert (1939, pp. 68-69) reported a mud cell of typical *hidalgo* from an old *Polistes* nest in Oklahoma, and Rau (1943b, p. 533) found its cells in an old mud nest of *Sceliphron caementarium* (Drury) in southern Texas. Isely (1913, pp. 296-299) found it nesting in what were probably the old mud cells of an anthophorid bee in a burrow in a clay bank in Kansas early in July. He said that the wasp preyed on relatively small caterpillars which it gathered on provisioning flights of 1.5-8 minutes (mean 5). There were 18 caterpillars in one fully stored cell. The mud cells were 16 mm. long and 9.6 mm. wide. A male wasp emerged 10 weeks after one of the cells was stored.

Source material.
   Kill Devil Hills, N. C. 1958 series: T 1, 2, 101, 102.
   Lake Placid, Fla. 1957 series: M 279. 1961 series: F 156, 190, 206, 217, 234, 277. 1962 series: P 154.

Identifications. Lepidopterous larvae by H. W. Capps; wasps by the author.

EUODYNERUS PRATENSIS PRATENSIS (Saussure)

I received 8 nests of this wasp in 1961, 7 from Portal and 1 from Scottsdale, Ariz. All nests were from stations in full sun on the desert floor, 3 from a single station on the side of a dead agave stem, 4 beneath limbs of cedar, ironwood, and mesquite, and 1 from a fallen log. Six nests were in 6.4-mm. and 2 in 12.7-mm. borings.

Supersedure and competition. E. *pratensis* superseded *Trypargilum tridentatum* (Packard) in 1 nest from Portal. However, the *Trypargilum* had completed its nest and left an empty space of 40 mm. at the outer end of the boring, and so there was no actual competition for the remaining space.

Nest architecture. In 4 nests the wasps put a little mud at the inner end of the boring before laying an egg, and in 3 nests they did not.

Five completed nests in 6.4-mm. borings had an average of 4.4 stored cells (range 3-6) and 1.6 intercalary cells. The 2 nests in 12.7-mm. borings had an average of 4.5 stored cells (range 4-5) and 3.0 intercalary cells.

In 6.4-mm. borings 6 female cells were 19-26 mm. long (mean 22) and 6 male cells 14-27 mm. (mean 21). In 12.7-mm. borings 2 female cells were each 16 mm. long and 5 male cells were 9-13 mm. (mean 11).

Intercalary cells were present in 4 of 5 completed nests in 6.4-mm. borings. Eight of them were 7-11 mm. long (mean 8). Six intercalary cells 9-14 mm. long (mean 10) were present in the two 12.7-mm. borings.

A vestibular cell 36 mm. long, divided by a cross partition, was present in the single completed nest in a 12.7-mm. boring. Vestibular cells 9-91 mm. long (mean 53) were present in 4 of the 5 completed nests in 6.4-mm. borings; one of these vestibular cells had 1 cross partition and one had 2 such partitions.

The partitions and closing plugs were made of mud. The partitions were 1-4 mm. thick in 6.4-mm. nests, and 1 mm. thick for the partitions closing stored cells in a 12.7-mm. nest and 2-3 mm. thick for those closing the empty intercalary cells. Seven terminal plugs at the boring entrances were 2-7 mm. thick (mean 4).

In mixed nests males were in the outermost cells and females in the innermost, except in 1 nest where the sequence was ♂-♀-♀-♂-x-♂. I reared 10 females and 11 males from 32 stored cells in the 8 nests, 8 females and 6 males from 6.4-mm. nests, and 2 females and 5 males from 12.7-mm. nests.

Prey. No specific prey determinations were made, but head capsules of caterpillars were present in some of the cells.

Life history. No data were available on the duration of the early stages. The period between pupation and emergence of the adult in the laboratory from overwintering nests was 11-18 days (mean 15) for 6 males, and 16-22 days (mean 19) for 3 females. This same period was 20 days for 1 male from a nest stored about May 1.

There are several generations a year with the nesting period running from at least May 1 until at least mid-September. The Scottsdale nest was stored early in May and picked up on the 4th. The occupant of cell 1 was already a prepupa and those in cells 2 and 3 had almost finished spinning their cocoons when I opened the nest on the 15th. A male wasp pupated in cell 1 on the 19th and another in cell 3 on the 23d, and so apparently this 3-celled nest with a vestibular cell was provisioned over a period of 4 days. As a male emerged from cell 3 on June 12, the period between storing the nest and emergence of the progeny is approximately 40-43 days during the spring.

The other nests were stored later in the season. One of them was stored July 13-25, and adult females emerged in the shipping carton prior to September 5. Three nests were stored between July 25 and September 3; occupants of one emerged prior to September 22, occupants of another overwintered as prepupae, and in the third there was divided emergence with females in cells 1 and 2 transforming to adults September 29 and males in cells 3 and 4 overwintering as resting larvae. I removed the females from the nest before they could emerge normally. The last 3 nests were provisioned between September 3 and October 19; all occupants overwintered as diapausing larvae.

The 3 nests from the single station on the agave stem may have been stored by the same female wasp. A 5-celled nest was stored between July 25 and September 3, and 5- and 6-celled nests between September 3 and October 19. All 3 nests could have been stored during a consecutive period from late in August until mid-September. The occupants of all cells were diapausing larvae when I opened the nests on September 21, and November 3 and 6, and all of them overwintered in that stage. The three nests had 2, 4, and 2 intercalary cells, respectively, and the latter two also had a vestibular cell. They might have been stored in this sequence (x = mortality, / = end of one nest and beginning of another): x-♀-♀-x-x/ ♂-x-♂-♂-♂/♂-♀-♀-♂-x-♂. (Or, perhaps, the sequence given for nest 2 should actually be for nest 3 in order of storing, and vice versa.)

Two male cocoons in a 6.4-mm. nest were each 16 mm. long. As usual they were of delicate, subopaque whitish silk.

Males emerged before or concurrently with the females in all mixed nests except in the one with divided emergence where the females emerged from the inner cells in the fall and males from the outer cells in the spring.

Parasites and predators. The cuckoo wasp *Chrysis* (*Trichrysis*) *mucronata* Brullé was reared from 1 cell of a 6-celled nest from Portal. All my other host records for this cuckoo wasp are of *Trypargilum t. tridentatum* (Packard). However, the specimen from this *pratensis* nest definitely had the vespid as a host because the chrysidid cocoon bore caterpillar remains. In the 3-celled nest from Scottsdale 1 cell was parasitized by another chrysidid, which was attacked and killed in the laboratory by *Pyemotes* mites.

A pupa of the bombyliid fly *Toxophora*, probably *virgata* Osten Sacken, was destroyed in a 5-celled nest from Portal when a *pratensis* female emerged from an earlier cell.

Cell 4 in a 5-celled nest from Portal was parasitized by a rhipiphorid beetle, possibly *Macrosiagon c. cruentum* (Germar). I first noticed the small bettle larva curled around the thorax of a *pratensis* prepupa on April 3. It finished feeding on the 7th but was killed a few days later when a female *pratensis* emerged from an earlier cell.

Source material.
Portal, Ariz. 1961 series: G 88, 132, 223, 329, 340, 343, 409.
Scottsdale, Ariz. 1961 series: H 85.

Identifications by the author.

EUODYNERUS GUERRERO (Saussure)
(Plate 9, Figure 41)

This wasp nested in 8 borings at 5 stations at Portal, Ariz., in 1961, 7 in 6.4-mm. borings and 1 in a 4.8-mm. boring. All nests were from settings in direct sun on the desert floor, 3 from wooden or barbed wire fences, 3 from limbs of desert willow, and 2 from branches of a dead mesquite.

Supersedure and competition. E. guerrero built 1 cell at the outer end of a 6.4-mm. boring in which *Megachile (Sayapis) policaris* Say had used the inner 122 mm.

Nest architecture. The inner end of the boring lacked mud in only 1 nest. In the other borings the wasps put 1-7 mm. of mud at the inner end or constructed a partition of that material 22-25 mm. from the inner end.

Nine female cells in 6.4-mm. borings were 22-33 mm. long (mean 26), and 10 male cells were 17-27 mm. (mean 20). Two male cells in the 4.8-mm. boring were 30 and 32 mm. long.

Intercalary cells were present in all nests except the one where *guerrero* superseded the megachilid bee. Fifteen of these cells were 4-10 mm. long (mean 7). Six nests each had a vestibular cell with a mean length of 10 mm. (range 6-13).

The partitions between cells and the terminal plugs at the nest entrances were made of mud. The stored cells were capped by partitions 1-2 mm. thick, whereas the intercalary cells had partitions 3-5 mm. thick. The terminal plugs were 5-8 mm. thick (mean 6). One of them had a thick rounded button at the outer end (fig. 41).

The nest in the 4.8-mm. boring had 3 stored cells, 2 intercalary cells, and a vestibular cell. The 6 multicelled nests in 6.4-mm. borings had an average of 4 stored cells (range 3-4), 2 intercalary (range 1-3), and 1 vestibular (range 0-1).

Prey. The caterpillars in one cell, in which the newly hatched wasp larva died, were identified as 8 specimens of a species of Noctuidae and 1 specimen of a species of Pyraustidae. It is probable that this was a male cell because it was only 18 mm. long.

Life history. The nests were stored between September 3 and October 18. I opened them early in November, by which time all the occupants were resting larvae. They overwintered outdoors from November 17 to March 3. Adults emerged from mid-April to mid-May. The period between pupation and emergence was 21-23 days for 4 females, and 13-20 days for 3 males. Emergence of individuals from a single nest took periods ranging from 1 to 25 days.

Certainly two or more generations of *guerrero* develop annually, considering the early emergence dates from these nests. A specimen in the U.S. National Museum was captured early in June in the Chisos Mountains of southwestern Texas.

I reared 9 females and 12 males from 27 stored cells.

The prepupa is yellow and has a tough leathery integument, as does that of *Monobia quadridens* (Linnaeus). The cocoons were delicate, white, and subopaque. Two female cocoons in 6.4-mm. borings were 15 and 17 mm. long, and 1 male cocoon was 12 mm.

Parasites and predators. Chrysis (C.) arizonica Bohart was reared from 2 of 7 cells in 2 nests, and *Chrysis (C.) inflata* Aaron was reared from 1 cell in a 3-celled nest.

Source material.

  Portal, Ariz. 1961 series: G 80, 203, 257, 259, 313, 341, 342, 390.

Identifications. Lepidopterous larvae by H. W. Capps; wasps and bees by the author.

EUODYNERUS MOLESTUS MOLESTUS (Saussure)

I reared this vespid from 16 nests at 11 stations at Kill Devil Hills, N. C., 11 in 6.4-mm. and 5 in 4.8-mm. borings. Five of the nests were on the barrens and 11 at the edges of or in open woods. Most of the nests were suspended from dead limbs of oak or pine, but 2 were in a tree hole in a sweetgum, and 1 was suspended from a live branch of oak.

Supersedure and competition. E. molestus superseded *E. f. foraminatus* (Saussure) in a 6.4-mm. nest.

Nest architecture. The inner end of the boring was empty in 8 nests, and in 6 nests the wasp placed some agglutinated sand at the inner end or made a partition of this material 31-106 mm. from the inner end.

Two female cells in 4.8-mm. borings were 31 and 37 mm. long, and 22 cells in 6.4-mm. borings were 17-50 mm. long (mean 25). Six male cells in 4.8-mm. borings were 17-40 mm. long (mean 31) and 7 cells in 6.4-mm. borings 15-18 mm. long (mean 17).

Nests contained no intercalary cells. Seven of 10 completed nests had a vestibular cell. The vestibular cell in 1 nest had 2 cross partitions, and in another a single cross partition. The vestibular cells were 2-98 mm. long (mean 27).

Partitions between cells and terminal plugs at nest entrances were of firmly agglutinated sand. Those between cells were 1-2 mm. thick, and terminal plugs 1.5-3 mm. thick.

Two completed nests in 4.8-mm. borings had 2-4 stored cells, and 5 completed nests in 6.4-mm. borings had 2-8 stored cells (mean 5).

Prey. The following species of caterpillars were found in 7 nests:

Pyraustidae
  sp. in 1 cell
  Desmia funeralis (Hübner) in 4 cells in 3 nests
  Framinghamia helvalis (Walker) in 1 cell
Epipaschiidae
  sp. in 1 cell
  Tetralopha sp. in 1 cell
  possibly *Tetralopha* sp. in 1 cell

The number of larvae stored per cell ranged from 6 to 14 (mean 9 for 4 cells). Usually I found only a single species per cell, but

1 cell contained 13 specimens of a species of Pyraustidae and 1 *Tetralopha* species (Epipaschiidae).

Life history. Duration of egg and larval feeding stages was not observed. Eighteen days elapsed between completion of larval feeding and emergence of an adult male in a nest of the summer generation. The period between pupation and adult emergence in the summer generation was 10 days for a male and 14 for a female. The adult wasps remained in the cells 2-3 days after their eclosion from the pupal skin.

The cocoons were light tan, delicate, and subopaque. In 6.4-mm. nests 23 female cocoons were 8-25 mm. long (mean 15) and 6 male cocoons 9-20 mm. (mean 13). Prepupae and pupae were noticeably yellow rather than creamy.

Males emerged before females in all nests containing both sexes. The period between emergence of the last male and first female was only a day in 1 summer generation nest, and 4-5 days in 2 overwintering nests.

Adults emerged July 29-August 17 from nests stored during July. In nests stored from the latter part of July until early in September, the occupants overwintered as resting larvae and adults emerged the following spring. Data from 3 nests suggested that 2 cells per day may be stored. I have collected *molestus* females at Kill Devil Hills from May 28 to September 10; so the species is certainly multivoltine.

I reared 24 females and 13 males from 50 stored cells.

Parasites and predators. A rhipiphorid beetle *Macrosiagon c. cruentum* (Germar) was reared from 1 cell in a 3-celled nest.

A chrysidid parasitized 1 cell in an 8-celled nest, but I did not rear it.

The eulophid *Melittobia chalybii* Ashmead infested 1 nest in the laboratory.

Previous observations. Earlier I published a brief note (Krombein, 1958d, p. 101) recording a female carrying a *Desmia funeralis* larva 15 mm. long to her nest in a thick plank on the sand at Kill Devil Hills.

Source material.
    Kill Devil Hills, N. C. 1956 series: C 234, 236, 330, 331, 480, 485, 658, 659, 680, 681, 682, 711. 1958 series: T 178, 184, 186, 199.

Identifications. Lepidopterous larvae by H. W. Capps; Rhipiphoridae by T. J. Spilman; wasps by the author.

EUODYNERUS OSLARENSIS (Cameron)

I obtained only 1 nest of this rare univoltine species in a 4.8-mm. boring set beneath a small palo-verde tree on a desert mountainside at Granite Reef Dam, Ariz., in 1961.

Nest architecture. The inner end of the boring had a thin coating of mud. Then there were 7 cells, 17, 22, 15, 14, 13, 14, and 24 mm. long, respectively, each capped by a mud partition 1-1.5 mm. thick. There was a vestibular cell 30 mm. long, and the closing plug of mud at the boring entrance was 3 mm. thick.

Prey. Nine caterpillars were stored in each of 2 cells, those in cell 4 a single species of Phycitidae, and those in cell 5 consisting of 1 larva of a species of Gelechiidae and the others of a species of Cosmopterygidae.

Life history. The nest was stored during May, and I opened it on June 7. The occupants of cells 1-3 and 6-7 were already resting larvae in cocoons; the eggs in cells 4-5 failed to hatch.

The cocoons in cells 1-3 and 6 were 15, 18, 13, and 12 mm. long; they were of delicate, white, subopaque, unvarnished silk. Occupants of all cells entered the winter as diapausing larvae. All of them died during the winter except the occupant of cell 1. It transformed to a pupa March 23-24, 3 weeks after the nest was brought in from outdoors. A female of *oslarensis* eclosed early in April but died in her cell before April 7 without attempting to emerge.

Source material.
Granite Reef Dam, Ariz. 1961 series: H 75.

Identifications. Wasp by R. M. Bohart; caterpillars by H. W. Capps.

PACHODYNERUS ASTRAEUS (Cameron)

(Plate 24, Figures 115-118)

I received 5 nests of this species in 1961, 4 from Granite Reef Dam and 1 from Scottsdale, Ariz. One was in a 4.8-mm. boring and 4 were in 6.4-mm. borings. Each was from a different station, 2 suspended from branches of mesquite and 3 from branches of palo verde. The stations were located on the desert floor or mountainside and along a stream.

Supersedure and competition. The vespid superseded *Trypargilum tridentatum* (Packard) in one boring after *tridentatum* had built one cell (figs. 115-118), and it superseded a *Megachile* in another boring after the bee had placed a few leaf cuttings at the inner end.

Nest architecture. In all nests the vespid placed a little mud at the inner end of the boring or made a partition of this material 7-111 mm. from the inner end.

There were few stored cells per nest because the females either constructed an unusually long vestibular cell or put a long empty space at the inner end of the boring. The nest in the 4.8-mm. boring had 3 stored cells and a vestibular cell. The nests in 6.4-mm.

borings averaged 2.25 stored cells (range 1-4), 1.0 intercalary cell, and a vestibular cell.

Two female cells in the 4.8-mm. boring were 34 and 22 mm. long. In the 6.4-mm. borings a male cell was 12 mm. long, and 6 female cells 13-15 mm. long (mean 14).

Two 6.4-mm. nests containing 7 stored cells had 4 intercalary cells each 4 mm. long.

There was a single vestibular cell 45 mm. long in the 4.8-mm. boring. Four vestibular cells in 6.4-mm. borings were 9-123 mm. long (mean 78). In 2 of the 6.4-mm. nests the vestibular cell was divided by a cross partition.

The partitions and closing plugs were made of mud. The partitions in the 4.8-mm. nest were 2-11 mm. thick, and the closing plug was 2 mm. In the 6.4-mm. nests the partitions capping the stored cells were 0.5 mm. thick, whereas those capping the intercalary cells were 2-4 mm. The closing plugs of the 6.4-mm. nests were 1-4 mm. thick (mean 2.4).

The single male was in the outermost cell. I reared 8 females and 1 male from the 12 stored cells.

Prey. The remains of caterpillars were found in some cells, but no identifications were made.

Life history. The wasp larvae had already entered diapause when I received the nests. These borings were empty as late as July 19, 1961. Presumably they were stored between that date and late in September, although they were not picked up until the latter part of November. Consequently, I obtained no data on the duration of the egg and larval feeding periods. The nests were placed outdoors from January 9 to March 3, 1962. Pupation took place 3-13 days after the nests were brought back into the laboratory. The period between pupation and emergence of the adult was 11-16 days (mean 13.5) for 5 of the females and 20-26 days for the only male.

The species is undoubtedly multivoltine. Other specimens in the U.S. National Museum were taken in southern Arizona and California during May, June and August.

The cocoons were delicate, subopaque, and spun of whitish silk (figs. 115-118).

Parasites and predators. The rhipiphorid beetle *Macrosiagon c. cruentum* (Germar) parasitized the prepupa in the innermost cell in a 4-celled nest (figs. 115-118). One cell in another nest was infested in the laboratory by a dermestid beetle larva.

Previous observations. Rau (1940, p. 592) found *astraeus* (recorded as *acuticarinatus* (Cameron)) nesting in abandoned mud nests of *Sceliphron caementarium* (Drury) in Jacala, Mexico. He found up to 3 vespid cells per *Sceliphron* cell. Davis (1964, p. 13) reported 4-8 cells of the wasp in a few larval cases of the bagworm *Oiketicus toumeyi* Jones from Arizona.

Source material.
    Scottsdale, Ariz. 1961 series: H 88.
    Granite Reef Dam, Ariz. 1961 series: H 92, 187, 201, 279.

Identifications. Rhipiphoridae by T. J. Spilman; Hymenoptera by the author.

PACHODYNERUS ERYNNIS (Lepeletier)

This wasp is the earliest to nest at Lake Placid, Fla. Adults were reared from 8 nests in 1957, 11 in 1959, 11 in 1960, 48 in 1961, and 8 in 1962. Twenty-five were in 4.8-mm. borings and 61 in 6.4-mm. borings. Nests came from 34 different stations in the Highlands Ridge sand-scrub area. Ten were suspended beneath dead branches, 74 beneath branches of live hickory, oak, and pine, and 2 were tied to pine trunks.

Supersedure and competition. P. erynnis superseded Chalicodoma (*Chelostomoides*) *georgica* (Cresson) in 3 nests and a species of *Megachile* in 1 nest. It was superseded by *Euodynerus foraminatus apopkensis* (Robertson) in 2 nests, by *Stenodynerus (Parancistrocerus) saecularis rufulus* Bohart in 1 nest, and by a species of *Chalicodoma (Chelostomoides)* in 1 nest.

Nest architecture. The wasps began 51 of the nests by making a partition of firmly agglutinated sand particles about 1.5 to 9 mm. thick at or near the inner end of the boring. In the other nests there was no such plug at the inner end. Nearly all nests were completed, but the number of stored cells varied owing to the presence or absence of an empty cell at the inner end, of empty intercalary cells, and of vestibular cells. Eighteen completed nests in 4.8-mm. borings contained from 1 to 5 stored cells with a mean of 3.2; 41 completed nests in 6.4-mm. borings contained from 1 to 8 stored cells with a mean of 4.1. Table 7 gives the dimensions of stored cells in 4.8-and 6.4-mm. borings.

Twenty-four nests had empty intercalary cells, but such a cell was present between *each* of the stored cells in only 9 of these nests. The 53 intercalary cells ranged from 4 to 35 mm. long with a mean length of 11.9 mm.

Vestibular cells were present in 55 of the 78 completed nests. Including the terminal sand plug, the vestibular cells ranged from 4 to 110 mm. in length with a mean of 45 mm. Five of the vestibular cells were divided by a cross partition.

The partitions between cells, and the terminal plugs, were made from firmly agglutinated sand grains. The partitions were 0.5 to 7 mm. thick with a mean of 2.1 mm. In nests where empty intercalary cells were present, the partitions capping the stored cells were usually 0.5 to 1.5 mm. thick, while those capping the empty cells were about 4 mm. thick. The terminal plugs ranged from 2 to 16 mm. in thickness, with a mean of 7.0 mm.

Prey. Consolidated identifications for 18 completely or partially provisioned cells from 13 nests are given below. The number in parentheses following the family name indicates the number of larvae taken as prey in that family.

Stenomidae (6): 6 sp. or spp.
Blastobasidae (6); 6 sp.
Tortricidae (3): 2 *Platynota* sp.; 1 sp.
Oecophoridae (13): 7 *Psilocorsis* sp.; 6 sp. or spp.
Phycitidae (42): 10 *Acrobasis* sp.; 9 *Etiella zinckenella* (Treitschke); 23 sp. or spp.
Chrysaugidae (1): 1 sp.
Noctuidae (34): 27 *Palthis angulalis* Hübner; 7 sp.

TABLE 7.—*Measurements (in mm.) of stored cells,* Pachodynerus erynnis *(Lepeletier)*

Sex	Boring diameter	Number of cells	Range in length	Mean length
♂	4.8	27	17-109	37.0
♂	6.4	73	13-116	27.3
♀	4.8	24	22-79	32.1
♀	6.4	116	14-125	25.2

There were 5 to 10 lepidopterous larvae per cell (mean 7.3) in 11 fully provisioned cells from 7 nests. Eight of these cells contained larvae of 2 different species, and in 6 of those 8 cells the larvae belonged to 2 different families of Lepidoptera.

Life history. No data were obtained on the duration of the egg and larval stages because the occupants of all nests were in the late larval, prepupal, or pupal stages when I received the nests.

The cocoons are complete, semitransparent, and of delicate silk. In 4.6-mm. borings 16 female cocoons were 12-17 mm. long (mean 13.8 mm.), and 16 male cocoons were 10-17 mm. long (mean 11.7 mm.). In 6.4-mm. borings 57 female cocoons were 11-17 mm. long (mean 13.7 mm.), and 26 male cocoons were 10-17 mm. long (mean 12.8 mm.). Only one larva was misoriented, that is, with its head end toward the inner end of the boring.

A limited number of observations indicate that about 7 days elapse between the time a male larva finishes feeding and its pupation, and about 7 to 10 days (mean 9 days for 12 larvae) for a female larva. The elapsed time between pupation and emergence of the adult was more variable. In March this period ranged from 19 to 33 days for females, and 18 to 28 for males. Later, April through November, these periods were more uniform and ranged from 20 to 25 days for females (mean 22 days for 23 females) and from 15 to 25 days for males (mean 20 days for 16 males).

Males were always in the outermost cells in nests containing both sexes, and they normally emerged from 1 to 8 days (average 2 days) before their sisters. In a single nest individuals of the same sex emerged on the same day or within a day of one another.

P. erynnis is definitely multivoltine; the available data suggest that breeding is probably continual during all but a short period of 1 to 3 months during the winter. It is possible that the species normally overwinters as an adult rather than as a resting larva. The earliest provisioned nest was received in Washington on February 4; a female wasp emerged from it on March 13. Other recently provisioned nests received from February through December produced adults not more than a month after receipt of the nests in Washington. One nest received early in January contained a prepupa which pupated by the 11th; a female wasp died after eclosion on February 6. Another nest received early in January contained a resting larva in the one provisioned cell and the mother was dead but still limp near the entrance; this nest was placed outdoors for 8 weeks and a male wasp pupated early in March and emerged on March 22.

A limited number of observations of the dates on which larvae completed feeding in several nests suggest that the mother wasp probably stores and caps 2-3 cells a day.

The over-all sex ratio, females to males, was about 4:3. I reared 119 females and 83 males from a total of 303 provisioned cells during the 5 seasons that I obtained nests from Florida.

Parasites and predators. One cell in each of 2 nests was infested by phorids belonging to the genus *Megaselia.*

One cell was destroyed by 2 miltogrammine maggots of *Amobia erythrura* (Wulp). One cell in another nest was destroyed by an unidentified miltogrammine maggot.

Three males and 2 females of the bombyliid *Toxophora amphitea* Walker parasitized prepupae in 5 nests. Four first instar bombyliid larvae, possibly this same species, were found on prepupae in 4 cells of 3 other nests. Another full-grown bombyliid larva, probably a species of *Lepidophora,* was found in a cell with the shrunken lepidopterous larvae stored by the mother wasp.

Three nests were infested in the field by the chalcidoid *Melittobia,* and 1 nest was infested in the laboratory by the same parasite.

Three cells of a 4-celled nest and 1 cell of a 3-celled nest were parasitized by the chrysidid *Chrysis* (*C.*) *inaequidens* Dahlbom.

Two males, from 2 nests having a combined total of 5 cells,

contained exserted puparia of the stylopid *Pseudoxenos erynnidis* Pierce.

One nest was infested, probably in the laboratory, by the mite *Pyemotes*.

Several cocoons of an unidentified braconid parasitic on *Palthis* sp. were found in 1 cell in each of 2 nests.

A tachinid, *Stomatomyia floridensis* (Townsend), was reared from one of the lepidopterous larvae stored as prey.

Previous observations. Ashmead (1894, p. 77) recorded *erynnis* as nesting in a door lock, in old holes in a board fence, and in abandoned galls of *Amphibolips cinerea* Ashmead.

Source material.

> Lake Placid, Fla. 1957 series: M 23, 34, 38, 51, 52, 53, 54, 263. 1959 series: V 4, 28, 40, 41, 42, 96, 106, 107, 109, 114, 141. 1960 series: B 146, 160, 178, 197, 201, 204, 210, 211, 222, 224, 225. 1961 series: F 21, 23, 24, 45, 46, 48, 53, 55, 56, 58, 60, 85, 86, 95, 97, 109, 110, 112, 117, 121, 130, 148, 149, 151, 169, 179, 180, 187, 192, 205, 224, 230, 235, 236, 244, 256, 257, 269, 271, 287, 313, 320, 324, 332, 333, 340, 342, 348. 1962 series: P 37, 38, 45, 53, 97, 98, 153, 173.

Identifications. Larvae of Lepidoptera by H. W. Capps; Phoridae and Bombyliidae by W. W. Wirth; *Amobia* by W. L. Downes; Tachinidae by C. W. Sabrosky; *Pseudoxenos* by R. M. Bohart; Hymenoptera by the author.

ANCISTROCERUS ANTILOPE ANTILOPE (Panzer)

(Plate 6, Figure 23)

This wasp was an extremely common user of traps at Derby, N. Y., whence I obtained 111 nests during the period 1954-1961. It also used 12 traps at Plummers Island, Md., from 1957 to 1962. About two-thirds of the nests were in 6.4-mm. and a third in 4.8-mm. borings, but there were also 2 at Derby in 12.7-mm. borings. Most of the settings were at the edges of wooded areas or in areas of open woods. Most nests were from stations on structural lumber or suspended from limbs of living trees, but 10 were from settings on dead standing tree trunks or on cut firewood, and 8 were from a wall of rock slabs.

Supersedure and competition. Typical *antilope* superseded other wasps and bees in 9 nests at Derby. The species superseded included *Symmorphus c. cristatus* (Saussure), *S. albomarginatus* (Saussure), *Ancistrocerus c. catskill* (Saussure), *A. t. tigris* (Saussure), *Trypargilum* sp., and *Megachile* sp. It superseded *Trypargilum collinum rubrocinctum* (Packard) in one nest at Plummers Island and *Trypargilum* sp. in another nest.

Nest architecture. In about a third of the nests the wasps placed a little mud at the inner end of the boring or constructed a partition of this material some distance from the inner end. In the other nests the wasps laid an egg at the inner end and began to store prey without first bringing in mud.

In table 8 I have summarized measurements of stored, intercalary, and vestibular cells at the two localities. The cell lengths include the thickness of the partitions capping the cells and of the closing plugs at the nest entrances. (See also fig. 23 of a typical nest.)

It is noteworthy that at both localities male cells in 4.8-mm. borings were somewhat longer than female cells, the reverse of the

TABLE 8.—*Measurements (in mm). of cells in nests of* Ancistrocerus a. antilope *(Panzer)*

Locality and boring diameter	Sex	STORED CELLS			INTERCALARY CELLS			VESTIBULAR CELLS		
		No.	Range in length	Mean length	No.	Range in length	Mean length	No.	Range in length	Mean length
N.Y. 4.8	♀	14	13-29	19	2	10-26	18	32	15-125	67
	♂	91	13-44	21						
N.Y. 6.4	♀	104	15-42	22	30	3-56	17	70	8-140	53
	♂	129	8-58	16						
N.Y. 12.7	♀	5	8-11	9	1	—	32	1	—	115
Md. 4.8	♀	2	10-14	12	1	—	27	2	9-83	62
	♂	9	14-22	17						
Md. 6.4	♀	5	15-22	19	1	—	21	4	14-109	77
	♂	16	11-22	15						

usual pattern. It will be recalled that *antilope* preferred borings of 6.4 mm. to borings of 4.8 mm. by a ratio of 2:1. Data in Table 8 also suggest that females developed rather infrequently in 4.8-mm. borings. Consequently, this abnormal cell length ratio in 4.8-mm. nests may have been due to having data from too few nests.

Empty intercalary cells between stored cells were of infrequent occurrence, being present in only 29 nests from Derby and 2 from Plummers Island. Only 35 intercalary cells were present, so each of these nests usually had only one such cell.

Vestibular cells were present in 109 of the 112 completed nests. In 62 nests the vestibular cell was not divided, but in 42 nests the cell was divided by 1 cross partition (fig. 23), 4 nests had 2 such partitions, and a single nest had 3 such partitions.

The cell partitions and terminal plugs at the nest entrances were made of mud. The former were 0.5-4 mm. thick (mean 1.5), the latter 1-10 mm. (mean 4.5).

Fourteen completed nests in 4.8-mm. borings and 34 in 6.4-mm. borings lacked an empty cell at the inner end of the boring. In these particular nests there were 2-8 stored cells (mean 3.9 ♂ and 0.6 ♀ cells) in 4.8-mm. borings, and 1-8 stored cells (mean 2.8 ♂ and 1.8 ♀ cells) in the 6.4-mm. borings. The largest nests yielded 6 ♀, 2 ♂ from a 4.8-mm. nest and 4 ♀, 4 ♂ from a 6.4-mm. nest.

Prey. Consolidated identifications for the prey from Derby and Plummers Island are listed below. These records are based both on partial samples and on the contents of completely stored cells.

> Derby, N. Y., 20 nests, 1954, 1956-1960
> Oecophoridae, sp. in 9 cells in 6 nests
> Gelechiidae, sp. in 3 cells in 3 nests
> Tortricidae
> sp. in 3 cells of 3 nests
> *Archips* sp. in 2 cells of 1 nest
> Phycitidae, sp. in 2 cells in 2 nests
> Noctuidae
> sp. in 2 cells in 2 nests
> sp. in Hypeninae in 2 cells of 2 nests
> *Epizeuxis aemula* Hübner in 3 cells in 2 nests
> Plummers Island, Md., 4 nests, 1957
> Oecophoridae, *Psilocorsis* sp. in 2 cells in 2 nests
> Gelechiidae, sp. in 3 cells of 3 nests
> Olethreutidae, sp. in 1 cell

Usually only a single species of caterpillar was stored in an individual cell. There was a mixture in only 2 cells of 2 nests from Derby of those which I preserved. One of them, stored early in June, contained a single specimen of a species of Tortricidae and several specimens of a species of Noctuidae. The other, stored in mid-August, contained several larvae each of a species of Gelechiidae and of a species of Phycitidae. Occasionally the wasps preyed on mature caterpillars; the caterpillars had partially transformed to pupae in 9 cells whose contents were preserved.

I found 3-10 larvae stored per completed cell. There were 6-10 caterpillars (mean 7.4) in 5 cells in which females should have developed, judged from the sex of wasps which developed in cells on each side of these 5. Similarly, there were 4-8 caterpillars (mean 6.1) in a dozen cells in which males should have developed.

Life history. The egg was sausageshaped, creamy white, 2.5-2.7 mm. long, and 1.0-1.2 mm. wide. It was suspended by a thread from the ceiling of the cell, about 3.5 mm. from the inner end of the cell; the thread suspending it from the ceiling was about 0.6 mm. long. I did not ascertain the duration of the egg stage. Several wasp larvae required only 3 days to consume the caterpillars stored for them. The period between completion of larval feeding and pupation for the summer generation was 7 days for 1 female and 5 days for 4 males. The pupal stage was 6-9 days (mean 8) for 23 males and 7-11 days (mean 9) for 14 females. The adults left the nests 2-4 days after eclosion.

The cocoons were delicate, subopaque, and white to yellowish or light tan (fig. 23). In 4.8-mm. borings 13 female cocoons were 9-17 mm. long (mean 13) and 66 male cocoons 8-15 mm. (mean 11). In 6.4-mm. borings 63 female cocoons were 11-19 mm. long (mean 14) and 81 male cocoons 7-15 mm. (mean 11). Only 3 larvae were misoriented in their cocoons with their heads toward the inner blind end of the boring instead of toward the entrance. One was in the innermost cell of a 6.4-mm. nest; the inner end of the boring was not coated with mud so its comparative roughness may have led to this misorientation. The other 2 were each in cell 1 of nests which did have an empty cell at the inner end of the boring.

There were 2 generations a year at Derby. Adults emerged 20-45 days (mean 25) after the nests were stored from 35 nests of the summer generation. Adults emerged June 22 to August 3 from nests stored from the latter part of May through the end of June. Occupants of the 4 nests stored from early in July until early in September overwintered as diapausing larvae and adults emerged the following spring.

One 5-celled nest from Plummers Island was completed about June 10, and an adult male emerged from cell 1 on June 30. The other nests from that locality were stored during September, one of them as late as the 30th, and their occupants overwintered as diapausing larvae.

In mixed nests the males always emerged before females except in 2 nests where there was some concurrent emergence. The period between emergence of the last male and first female from an individual nest of the summer generation was 1-5 days (mean 3) in 16 nests. This same period in 4 overwintering nests was 4-29 days (mean 12). In an individual nest all males emerged on the same day or within a 2-day period (mean 0.4), and all females on the same day or within a 3-day period (mean 0.4).

Females were in the inner and males in the outer cells of all mixed nests except 2 from Derby where the sequences were ♂-x-♀-♂ and ♀-♂-♀.

The rate of provisioning probably varies with the weather conditions and availability of prey. Evidence from several nests suggests that 3-4 cells may be stored per day under optimum conditions. An 8-celled nest at Derby was completed in 1-2 days; it contained 6 female cells, 2 male, and 1 vestibular. A 7-celled nest from Plummers Island was also completed in 1-2 days, as based on egg hatch data; only 2 males were reared from it.

Apparently the female:male ratio is 1:2. I obtained 106 females and 203 males from a total of 460 stored cells. The ratio approached equality in the 6.4-mm. nests, where there were 89 females and 107 males; but it was 1:8 in the 4.8-mm. nests.

Parasites and predators. The most common parasite was the symbiotic saproglyphid mite *Kennethiella trisetosa* (Cooreman), which occurred in 77 nests, 69 from Derby and 8 from Plummers Island. It developed only in cells in which males were produced because the female wasp larvae destroyed any mites in their cells before spinning their cocoons.

The cuckoo wasp *Chrysis (C.) coerulans* Fabricius parasitized 12 of 33 cells in 8 nests at Derby. *Chrysis (C.) nitidula* Fabricius parasitized 3 of 9 cells in 3 nests at Derby and 3 of 13 cells in 3 nests at Plummers Island. Chrysidids also parasitized 4 of 8 cells in 3 nests at Derby, but as they were not reared to maturity specific identification was impossible.

The eulophid *Melittobia chalybii* Ashmead infested 3 nests in the field, 2 at Derby and 1 at Plummers Island. In the laboratory it invaded 2 additional nests from Derby.

The miltogrammine fly *Amobia distorta* (Allen) destroyed 5 of 8 cells in a nest at Derby. Other miltogrammines, almost certainly this same species, destroyed 23 of 33 cells in 7 nests at Derby and 1 of 7 cells in a nest at Plummers Island.

Previous observations. A number of workers have published biological notes based on North American specimens of this Holarctic wasp as follows: Ashmead (1894, p. 77); Peckham and Peckham (1900, pp. 91-93; 1905, pp. 92-94) and Medler and Fye (1956) in Wisconsin; Strand (1914) and Taylor (1922, pp. 56-60) in Massachusetts; Rau and Rau (1918, pp. 345-346) and Rau (1928, p. 405) in Missouri; Blackman and Stage (1924, p. 195), Reinhard (1929, pp. 86-91), and Cooper (1953) in New York; Buckle (1929) in Quebec; and Fye (1965a, pp. 729-731) in northwestern Ontario. In some of these accounts the wasp is called *capra* (Saussure), a synonym of *antilope;* Fye's account was published in error under the name *Ancistrocerus c. catskill* (Saussure).

The Raus reported a nest in an elder twig, and later Rau found one in a sumac twig. Blackman and Stage reared it from a boring in dead hickory. Reinhard observed nests in the channels between and under shingles, and Cooper also saw *antilope* nesting in a similar situation. Cooper also found a 2-celled nest in an old mud cell of *Sceliphron caementarium* (Drury). Taylor, Cooper, and Medler and Fye induced the wasps to nest in artificial sites in glass tubes, or in borings in pine sticks and sumac stems. Most of these observers mentioned that the cell partitions and closing plugs were made of mud. Strand reported rearing *antilope* from a mud nest; it is probable that the mother appropriated the mud cell of another wasp and that she did not build the mud cell herself as Strand supposed. The Peckhams reported a nest in the mouthpiece of a tin horn; since they neither observed the maker nor reared progeny, it cannot be certain that their wasp was actually *antilope*.

Several authors presented cell measurements. The Raus' nest in elder had cells with a range in length of 6-32 mm.; their shortest cell was 1.5 mm. shorter than any of mine; there was a single intercalary cell 19 mm. long, but they did not report a vestibular cell. Rau's later nest in sumac was in a boring 6.4 mm. wide and had two cells 13-19 mm. long; it apparently lacked intercalary and vestibular cells.

Taylor obtained 2 nests in glass tubes with an inner bore 6 and 7.5 mm. wide, respectively. The stored cells were 26 and 28 mm. long in the smaller boring and there was an empty cell at the inner end and a vestibular cell. The other nest had an empty inner cell, a single stored female cell 25 mm. long, and a vestibular cell.

Reinhard reported 10 stored cells each about 13 mm. long and a vestibular cell of 64 mm. in a channel 6.4 mm. high. These cells are substantially shorter than the mean length reported for male cells in 6.4-mm. borings, and possibly he observed a species other than *antilope*.

Cooper reported that 10 female cells in 6- to 7-mm. borings were 17-32 mm. long (mean 23) and that 3 male cells were 10-19 mm. (mean 14). He found a vestibular cell 3-56 mm. long (mean 21) in 16 of 17 completed nests. He also reported 8 empty cells other than vestibular cells in 19 nests. Three of these were at the inner end of the boring and 5 near the outer end, between the last stored cell and the terminal vestibular cell.

Medler and Fye reported that 40 female cells in 6.4-mm. borings were 11-31 mm. long (mean 18) and that 42 male cells were 9-25 mm. (mean 14). In 8-mm. borings 12 female cells were 10-20 mm. (mean 15) and 5 male cells were 9-21 mm. (mean 15). They reported 60 empty nonvestibular cells in 44 nests; but only 11 of these, 6-32 mm. long, were true intercalary cells. They found vestibular cells 4-95 mm. long in all but one of the nests.

Cooper stated that the cell partitions were 0.8-1.5 mm. thick and that the terminal plugs were 1.5-10 mm. thick (mean 5.5). Medler and Fye reported comparable data of 0.5-3.5 mm. and 1-8 mm.

Cooper found an average of 2.7 provisioned cells each in nests having a mean length of 96 mm. for 6-mm. borings and 124 mm. for 7-mm. borings. Medler and Fye also reported an average of 2.7 stored cells in completed nests in 6.4- and 8-mm. borings 150 mm. long. However, the data provided in their table 1 show an average of 2.7 stored cells in 6.4-mm. borings and 2.2 cells in 8-mm. borings. Disregarding those nests in which there was an empty cell at the inner end of the boring, I have calculated that

Cooper obtained 2.4 stored cells in 6-mm. borings 96 mm. long and 3.3 stored cells in 7-mm. borings 124 mm. long, and that Medler and Fye found 2.8 stored cells in 6.4-mm. borings 150 mm. long and 2.4 stored cells in 8-mm. borings 150 mm. long. Cooper's largest nest had 5 stored cells, while Medler and Fye reported a 9-celled nest in a 6.4-mm. boring.

Cooper found 4 different species of pyralids and probably gelechiids being used as prey, the gelechiids comprising 80 percent of the 700-900 caterpillars examined. He stated that cells stored with more than a single species were found later in the season, and that the caterpillars in any one cell might represent several different instars. He found 4-15 caterpillars (mean 9) in completely provisioned cells.

Medler and Fye obtained caterpillars representing a dozen species of Gelechiidae, Tortricidae, Epipaschiidae, Phycitidae, and Noctuidae. They found that 3-13 larvae (mean 7) were stored per completed cell. They also reported a significant correlation between cell length and number of caterpillars stored.

Several erroneous prey records have been reported. Ashmead quoted Fyles as stating that the prey of *antilope* was the larch sawfly, *Pristiphora erichsonii* (Hartig); this anomalous record was not published by Fyles himself, nor has it been substantiated by subsequent observers. Buckle stated that *antilope* preyed on larvae of the silver-spotted skipper, *Epargyreus tityrus* (Fabricius), on locust. Cooper suggested that Buckle's wasps actually may have been preying on other caterpillars and discarding (or disregarding) those of the skipper. If Buckle's identification was based on these discarded specimens, this would explain his impression that the skipper was the prey. Cooper himself observed *antilope* extracting gelechioid caterpillars from nests in locust leaves.

Cooper stated that the egg was about 2.8 mm. long and 0.9 mm. wide and that it was suspended by a thread about 0.7 mm. long attached about 5.5 mm. from the inner end of the cell. Cooper reported that the egg hatched in 2-4 days (mean 2.5) and that the larva fed for 5-7 days (mean 6), there being 3-5 molts; Medler and Fye reported a period of 7.3 days for the combined egg and larval feeding stages. Cooper said that a day elapsed between completion of feeding and beginning of the cocoon and that spinning the latter required 2-4 days; Medler and Fye reported 1.3 days for the period between completion of feeding and completion of the cocoon. Cooper reported excretion of the feces 1-2 days after completion of the cocoon and that pupation took place 3.5-4.5 days later in the summer generation. Cooper found that the adult wasps eclosed 11-17 days (mean 15) after pupation occurred. Medler and Fye reported 18.8 days for the period from completion of the cocoon to eclosion of the adult. The period between deposition of the egg and eclosion of the adult was given as 29-35 days by Cooper, and the period between egg hatch and eclosion of the adult was stated to be 27.4 days by Medler and Fye. Probably 2-3 days more should be added to these figures to calculate the actual date of emergence of the adults. Taylor reared a single female and gave 2 days for the egg stage, 15 days for the larva, and 16 days for the pupa.

Cooper as well as Medler and Fye reported 2 generations a year, and Cooper thought that there might possibly be a third. Occupants of most second generation nests overwintered as diapausing larvae.

The Raus described the cocoon as being light tan, thin, and papery; but Rau described his later nest as having only varnished walls and no cocoons. The latter observation is at variance with data reported by other observers. Cooper reported cocoons as I have described and stated that the feces were usually excreted after completion of the cocoon.

Neither Cooper nor Medler and Fye reported any nests with an abnormal sequence of sexes. Females were in the inner and males in the outer cells. Cooper reared 10 females and 3 males from 51 provisioned cells, and Medler and Fye got 50 females and 43 males from 117 provisioned cells.

Cooper reported that it took more than a week to provision 3 stored cells during a cold spell early in September and that the most rapid rate was the storing of 5 cells in the first 2 days of July. He considered about a cell a day as the average rate. He also conjectured that the average female provisioned about 2 dozen cells during her lifetime.

Both the Raus and Reinhard reported *Chrysis* sp. (or spp.) as parasites of *antilope*. Medler and Fye found parasites in their nests but did not list them specifically. Cooper reared *Chrysis* (*C.*) *nitidula* Fabricius from 2 nests and found an infestation of *Melittobia chalybii* Ashmead in 2 nests. In a later contribution Medler (1946d) reported rearing *C.* (*C.*) *nitidula* Fabricius and *C.* (*C.*) *coerulans* Fabricius from nests of *antilope*.

I have seen progeny from 11 nests which Fye (1965a, pp. 729-731) reported erroneously as *Ancistrocerus c. catskill* (Saussure). All the specimens I examined were *antilope*, and so Fye's account, his tables I, III, IV, and VI, and figure 5 should be corrected accordingly. He obtained 11 nests in 6.4-mm. borings in elderberry and chinaberry stems and 7 nests in 8.0-mm. borings. In 6.4-mm. borings female cells were 24.3 ± 1.8 mm. long and male cells 21.8 ± 1.1 mm.; corresponding measurements in 8.0-mm. borings were 19.7 ± 1.8 and 12.2 ± .5 mm., respectively. Fye noted that empty intercalary cells were rare. He stated that the cell partitions and closing plugs were made of clay; the former were 0.8-1.6 mm. and the latter 1.6-8.0 mm. thick. Five vestibular cells were 17.6-52.6 mm. long; only 1 of these was divided by a cross partition. One nest in a 6.4-mm. boring contained 4 provisioned cells; 4 nests in 8.0-mm. borings had 2-6 stored cells (mean 4.5). Fye reported the most commonly stored caterpillar prey as *Rheumaptera* sp., probably *hastata* Linnaeus, *Tetralopha* spp., unidentified Phycitinae, *Acleris variana* Fernald, and *Anacampsis niveopulvella* Chambers (?); usually 2-6 caterpillars were stored per cell. The larval feeding period was 11-14 days. Fye reported both univoltine and bivoltine strains of the wasp. He reared 8 females and 4 males from summer generation nests and 5 females and 26 males from overwintering nests. He reported as parasites *Amobia distorta* Allen, *Chrysis* (*C.*) *coerulans* Fabricius, and *C.* (*C.*) *nitidula* Fabricius (?). He did not mention the mite *Kennethiella trisetosa* (Cooreman), but I found hypopi on most of his reared wasps, and so undoubtedly most, if not all, of his nests were infested.

Source material.

Derby, N. Y. 1954 series: 3 unnumbered nests and I A, V B, IX A, IX B, IX C, X A, X B. 1955 series: D 6c, 7b, 8c, 12d. 1956 series: J 1, 2, 3, 4, 6, 10, 12, 13, 16, 17, 20, 24, 26, 29, 30, 35, 38, 41, 44, 50, 51, 53, 56, 59, 60, 63, 65, 68, 73, 78, 80, 82, 91, 94, 95, 97. 1957 series: G 1, 6, 7, 12, 41, 46, 51, 56, 59, 65, 68, 75, 77, 81, 89, 96, 99, 100. 1958 series: R 7, 9, 12, 16, 31, 32, 34, 40, 42. 1959 series: W 21, 23, 37, 39, 40, 47, 49, 53, 54, 56, 57, 59, 60, 64. 1960 series: D 21, 43, 49, 51, 57, 58, 59, 60, 69. 1961 series: L 25, 38, 42, 55, 62, 63, 88, 89, 90, 91, 92.

Plummers Island, Md. 1957 series: P 31, 170, 285, 286, 288, 289. 1960 series: E 23, 168. 1961 series: K 114, 253. 1962 series: M 59, 101.

Identifications. Lepidopterous larvae by H. W. Capps; Acarina by E. W. Baker; Miltogrammini by W. L. Downes, Jr.; wasps and bees by the author.

ANCISTROCERUS ANTILOPE NAVAJO (Bequaert)

I received a single nest of this wasp from a setting on a tree trunk at Oak Creek Canyon, Ariz., in 1957. It was in a 6.4-mm. boring.

Nest architecture. There was an empty space of 25 mm. at the inner end of the boring and then a mud partition 3 mm. thick. Then there were 2 male cells 21 and 23 mm. long and a vestibular cell 79 mm. long divided by a transverse partition. The partitions and closing plug were of mud and were 3-4 mm. thick. The cocoons were 11-12 mm. long and spun of delicate, white, subopaque silk.

Life history. The occupants were already resting larvae when I received the nest on October 3, and I do not know when it was stored. They overwintered outdoors, transformed to pupae about April 20, and adult males left the nest on May 1.

Source material.
 Oak Creek Canyon, Ariz. 1957 series: Q 23.

Identification by the author.

ANCISTROCERUS SPINOLAE (Saussure)

This wasp is very closely related to *antilope* (Panzer). I reared it from 4 nests from 3 stations at Kill Devil Hills, N. C., in 1956 and 1958. The nests were in 6.4-mm. borings and were from settings at the edges of or in open woods. Two were beneath dead pine limbs and 2 beneath a dead limb of sassafras.

Nest architecture. In all nests the females laid an egg and began to store paralyzed caterpillars at the inner end of the boring. Three female cells were 17-19 mm. long and 24 male cells 11-26 mm. long (mean 16). All the nests were completely stored, but only 2 of them had an empty vestibular cell, 9 and 15 mm. long, respectively. The partitions capping the stored cells and the closing plugs at the nest entrances were made of agglutinated sand; the former were 1-3 mm. thick and the latter 5-12 mm. thick (mean 8).

There were 7-10 stored cells per nest (mean 8.5). Females developed in the innermost cells in the only nest containing both sexes. I reared 3 females and 23 males from 34 stored cells.

Life history. I suspect that *spinolae* may be a vernal species with only a single generation a year. I have collected females at Kill Devil Hills only early in the season, May 30-June 1; it has been taken in May in Missouri and in June in Michigan. I picked up these 4 nests on July 29, but they had been completed some time previously because the occupants were already resting larvae in cocoons on that date. Despite this early nesting the occupants overwintered outdoors as diapausing larvae and pupated the following spring. The period between pupation and emergence from the nest was 13-16 days (mean 14) for 8 males and 17 days for each of 2 females.

The cocoons were moderately tough and spun of light tan silk. Three female cocoons were 13-14 mm. long and 15 male cocoons 7-12 mm. long (mean 10).

Males emerged 5 days earlier than females from the single nest in which both sexes developed.

Parasites and predators. All the nests were infested by the symbiotic saproglyphid mite, *Kennethiella trisetosa* (Cooreman), which occurred in 17 of 24 male cells but in none of the female cells.

Miltogrammine maggots destroyed cells 1-5 in a 7-celled nest, but were themselves destroyed by mold. The bombyliid fly *Anthrax aterrimus* (Bigot) developed on the wasp prepupa in cell 7 of this same nest.

Previous observations. Rau (1946, p. 10) reported that a female of *spinolae* had probably emerged from an old mud nest of *Sceliphron caementarium* (Drury) in Missouri.

Source material.
Kill Devil Hills, N. C. 1956 series: C 379. 1958 series: T 151, 167, 168.

Identifications. Acarina by E. W. Baker; Bombyliidae by W. W. Wirth; wasps by the author.

ANCISTROCERUS CAMPESTRIS (Saussure)

Although this wasp is widely distributed, I obtained nests only at Plummers Island, Md. There were 15 nests in 4.8-mm. borings and 6 in 6.4-mm. borings at 11 stations during every year in the period 1956-1962 except 1958. A dozen nests were from settings on the rafters of the cabin porch, and 9 were on standing or fallen dead tree trunks.

Supersedure and competition. *A. campestris* superseded *Trypoxylon clarkei* Krombein in a 4.8-mm. boring.

Nest architecture. In 7 nests the mother wasps placed an egg at the inner end of the boring without first bringing in mud. Before laying an egg in the other nests the females either plastered a thin layer of mud at the inner end or constructed a mud partition 8-80 mm. from the inner end.

Fourteen female cells in 4.8-mm. borings were 17-27 mm. long (mean 21), and 33 male cells were 11-23 mm. (mean 15). In 6.4-mm. borings 11 female cells were 14-22 mm. long (mean 17) and 7 male cells 6-13 mm. long (mean 10).

There was a single empty intercalary cell 10 mm. long in a 4.8-mm. nest. Vestibular cells were present in 11 of 13 completed nests. They were 7-80 mm. long (mean 48).

The partitions capping the stored cells and the closing plugs at the boring entrances were made of mud. The former were 1-4 mm. thick (mean 1.7) and the latter 2-5 mm. thick (mean 3.4).

Ten completed nests in 4.8-mm. borings contained 2-7 stored cells (mean 4.9), and 3 completed nests in 6.4-mm. borings contained 4-11 stored cells (mean 6.3).

Males only were produced in 7 multicelled nests in 4.8-mm. borings and both sexes in 6 nests. In multicelled nests in 6.4-mm. borings females only were produced in 2 nests and both sexes in 2 nests.

Prey. Samples of the caterpillar prey were preserved from 6 nests in 1957 and 1961. These were identified as follows:

Oecophoridae, *Psilocorsis* sp. in 6 cells in 5 nests
Gelechiidae
    sp. in 1 cell
    Gelechia albisparsella (Chambers) in 1 cell

About 15 specimens of the *Psilocorsis* sp. were stored in a cell in which a female *campestris* developed. In 2 cells in which males developed there were 5 and 7-8 specimens of the *Psilocorsis* sp., respectively. There were 6 specimens of *Gelechia albisparsella* in a cell in which a male probably would have developed. Most of the cells from which I preserved samples contained only a single species of caterpillar, but 1 cell had 5 *Psilocorsis* and 1 gelechiid.

Life history. The egg was sausage-shaped, 2.2 mm. long and 0.6 mm. wide. It hatched about 3 days after it was laid. Four larvae required 4-5 days to consume the caterpillars stored for each.

Two larvae spent 2 days each spinning the delicate, white, sub-opaque cocoons. Ten female cocoons were 9-13 mm. long (mean 12), and 25 male cocoons were 7-9 mm. (mean 8).

In nests of the summer generation 1 female pupated 8 days after spinning her cocoon. The period from pupation to adult emergence was 11 days for 1 male, 14 days for a female. The newly eclosed adult spent 1-2 days in the cocoon before leaving the nest. The period from completion of larval feeding until adult emergence was 17-23 days (mean 19) for 3 males and 20-25 days (mean 23.5) for 4 females.

Males emerged 1-4 days before females from nests which contained both sexes. In individual nests all of the males emerged on the same day or within a day of each other, and female emergence was similarly timed.

Data from 5 nests suggest that in midsummer a wasp stored 2-3 cells per day. In 3 nests 4 cells were stored in 1+ days, and 5 cells in each of 2 nests were stored in 2-3 days.

There are probably 3 generations a year at Plummers Island, because nesting took place from early in June until mid-September. Adults emerged July 2 to August 31 from nests stored from early in June until the end of July. Occupants of nests stored from early in August until mid-September overwintered as diapausing larvae and adults emerged the following spring. I have collected *campestris* at the Island from June 2 until September 23.

I reared 26 females and 40 males from a total of 87 stored cells. In the 21 cells in which adults did not develop, there were probably at least 4 female cells and 13 male cells. Consequently, the sex ratio appears to be about 1:2.

Parasites and predators. I reared a bombyliid fly, *Toxophora amphitea* Walker, from 1 cell. The eulophid *Melittobia chalybii* Ashmead infested 1 cell in the field.

Pyemotes mites invaded 4 cells in a 7-celled nest after it was brought into the laboratory.

Previous observations. Rau and Rau (1916, p. 43) reported that in Missouri *campestris* nested in abandoned mud-dauber nests,

Sceliphron caementarium (Drury), and provisioned the cells with caterpillars.

Source material.
    Plummers Island, Md. 1956 series: H 82. 1957 series: P 16, 17, 18, 104, 167, 238, 265. 1959 series: Y 116, 118. 1960 series: E 1, 27, 70, 162. 1961 series: K 5, 36, 49, 126, 191. 1962 series: M 22, 47.

Identifications. Lepidopterous larvae by H. W. Capps; Bombyliidae by W. W. Wirth; wasps by the author.

ANCISTROCERUS DURANGOENSIS Cameron

I obtained only 1 nest of this vespid. It was in a 6.4-mm. boring at a station beneath the limb of a dead tree at about 8,200 feet elevation in the Chiricahua Mountains near Portal, Ariz.

Nest architecture. There was a little mud at the inner end of the boring. Cell 1, 19 mm. long, was capped by a thin mud partition. Cell 2 was not capped. The vespid cocoon was 11 mm. long.

Prey. Head capsules of caterpillars, the prey of the vespid, were attached to the cocoons.

Life history. When I picked up the nest on July 20, the occupants of the two cells were already pupae. Both adults eclosed by July 28. A female of *durangoensis* emerged from cell 2 on July 31.

Parasites and predators. A female of the cuckoo wasp *Chrysis* (*C.*) *inflata* Aaron emerged from cell 1 on August 3.

Source material.
    Portal, Ariz. 1959 series: X 237.

Identifications. Wasps by the author.

ANCISTROCERUS TUBERCULICEPS TUBERCULICEPS (Saussure)

I obtained 10 nests of this vespid, 9 from 4 stations at Portal, Ariz., in 1959 and 1961, and 1 from Molino Camp, Santa Catalina Mountains, Ariz., in 1961. Four nests were in 4.8-mm. borings, 5 in 6.4-mm. borings, and 1 in a 12.7 boring. Most of the nests were from stations in full sun on the desert floor on dead or living mesquite, desert willow, and ocotillo, but 2 were in full shade on the side of a wooden shed.

Nest architecture. In 6 of the nests the mother wasp laid an egg near the inner end of the boring without first bringing in mud. In the other 4 nests the wasps put a little mud at the inner end of the boring, or constructed a partition of this material 5-57 mm. from the inner end before laying an egg.

In 4.8-mm. nests 1 cell from which a female was reared was 20 mm. long and 13 male cells were 11-17 mm. (mean 14). Three female cells in 6.4-mm. borings were 18-20 mm. long (mean 19) and 19 male cells were 8-16 mm. (mean 11). The cells in the 12.7-mm.

boring were irregularly arranged, and no measurements were made. Some were short and arranged transversely, and others were in irregular pairs along the boring axis. One female and 11 males were reared from this 16-celled nest.

There were no empty intercalary cells. There were vestibular cells 3-23 mm. long (mean 13) in only 4 of the 7 completed nests.

The cell partitions and closing plugs were made of mud. The former were 1-2.5 mm. thick (mean 1.3) and the latter 1.5-4 mm. thick (mean 3.1).

Four completed nests in 4.8-mm. borings had 6-10 stored cells (mean 8); 2 such nests in 6.4-mm. borings had 8 and 13 stored cells, respectively; and the single nest in a 12.7-mm. boring, which filled only half of the boring, had 16 stored cells.

Prey. Typical *tuberculiceps* stored only a single species of Gelechiidae in the 9 completed cells from 5 nests whose contents were preserved for identification. Caterpillars were preserved from 4 nests from Portal in both years and from the single Molino Camp nest. There were 5-11 caterpillars (mean 8) in these 9 cells. Male wasps probably would have developed in 2 of the cells which held 5 and 11 caterpillars, respectively.

Life history. I can report very little on the developmental cycle of this wasp because the occupants of all nests were diapausing larvae, pupae, or newly emerged adults when I opened the nests for study. The period between pupation and emergence from overwintering nests was 12-17 days (mean 15) for 15 males.

The cocoons were dirty white and subopaque; 7 male cocoons from 4.8- and 6.4-mm. nests were 8-10 mm. long. One of the larvae misoriented after spinning its cocoon and lay with its head toward the inner end. It was in cell 1 of a nest where the mother had not placed mud at the inner end of the 4.8-mm. boring; this may explain the misorientation.

The occupants of individual nests usually emerged on the same day or within a period of 2 days. However, in 1 nest emergence of all occupants required more than a year. Males in cells 4-6 pupated March 17-19, 1962, but were killed by *Pyemotes* mites; the resting larvae in cells 3 and 7-10 died during the winter; a male in cell 2 pupated May 19-22 and emerged on June 3; the larva in cell 1 remained in diapause outdoors during the next winter, and an adult female emerged April 2, 1963.

The two nests in 1959 must have been stored about mid-June, because adults emerged from them July 18-24. Four of the 1961 nests were stored between September 4 and October 18; occupants overwintered outdoors in Virginia as diapausing larvae and emerged as adults the following spring except in the 1 nest where there was delayed emergence. The other nests also may have been stored between September 4 and October 18, but they were not picked up until the period December 24-29. When I opened them on January 13, the occupants were already in the pupal stage and adults emerged during the next 10-12 days. It is most unlikely that these wasps would be emerging in Arizona during January. The most probable explanation for this anomalous development is that the nests had received sufficient exposure to cold in the field in Arizona to break diapause, so that when they were brought indoors into warmer conditions late in December pupal development was initiated. (Occupants of the earlier nests pupated 14-16 days after they were brought into the laboratory after overwintering outdoors.)

I reared 5 females and 43 males from 86 stored cells. Males probably would have developed in most of the cells where there was larval mortality, judged from the length of the cells and their position in the nests.

Parasites and predators. The cuckoo wasp *Chrysis* (*C.*) *inflata* Aaron parasitized 5 of 11 cells in 2 nests from Portal. A bombyliid fly parasitized the occupant of a cell in a Portal nest, but I was unable to rear the parasite. A clerid larva fed on the resting larvae in the outer 2 cells of another nest from Portal.

Several parasites were secondary invaders of *tuberculiceps* nests in the laboratory. A dermestid larva destroyed the occupant of 1 cell, and *Pyemotes* mites attacked and killed the occupants of 6 cells in 2 nests.

Previous observations. Rau (1940, p. 593) reared this wasp [recorded as *tuberculocephalus*] from old pipe-organ nests of *Trypargilum mexicanum* (Saussure) in Mexico. He noted that the cocoons were more substantial than in the species of *Ancistrocerus* he observed in Missouri.

Source material.
   Portal, Ariz. 1959 series: X 118, 218. 1961 series: G 50, 100, 138, 328, 366, 371, 372.
   Molino Camp, Santa Catalina Mountain, Ariz. 1961 series: H 285.

Identifications. Lepidopterous larvae by H. W. Capps; wasps by the author.

ANCISTROCERUS CATSKILL CATSKILL (Saussure)
(Plate 3, Figure 11)

One of the interesting taxonomic results obtained during this study was the proof that the taxon formerly referred to as *catskill albophaleratus* (Saussure) is actually just a white-marked color phase of the normal yellow subspecies *catskill catskill.* Both yellow- and white-marked individuals were reared from 6 nests from Derby. All yellow-maculated individuals were bred from 25 nests from

Derby, N. Y., and 3 nests from Plummers Island, Md., and all white-marked individuals from 13 nests from Derby.

The sequence of individuals in 5 of the mixed nests from Derby was as follows, where y = yellow-marked adults, w = white-marked individuals, and x = larval mortality. (In the sixth mixed nest I was unable to record the sequence of individual wasps.)

> D 3d: ♂w-♂w-♂y
> J 33: ♀w-♂w-♂w-♂w-♂y
> J 62: ♀w-♀w-♂y
> R 20: ♀w-♀y-♀y-♀y-x-♀y-♀y-♀y-♀y
> L 69: ♀w-♀w-x-x-x-x-x-x-♂w-♂y

It is noteworthy that the white-maculated specimens were always in the inner cells in mixed nests. This finding suggests one of two possibilities which would need to be checked by field observation or by laboratory experimentation. The more plausible is that a female's early eggs all develop into white-marked individuals. The other possibility is that white-marked individuals develop as a result of the decreased oxygen gradient in the inner cells. The latter explanation does not seem very plausible when one looks at the sequence of individuals in nests R 20 and L 69, which had mostly white-marked or mostly yellow-marked individuals, respectively. Also, if this hypothesis is valid, why should there be entirely white-marked individuals in all of the cells in some other nests?

The occurrence of white-marked individuals also appears to be associated with locality. None of them developed in nests from Plummers Island, but they occurred in almost half the nests from Derby. The white-marked phase (*albophaleratus*) is more northern in distribution; Bohart (*in* Muesebeck, *et al.*, 1951, p. 893) reported it as being transcontinental in the Canadian and Transition Zones, whereas typical *catskill* occurs in the Transition and Austral Zones.

I obtained 44 nests from 21 stations at Derby, 1955-1961, and 3 nests from 2 stations at Plummers Island, 1957 and 1962. Four of the nests were in 3.2-mm., 26 in 4.8-mm., and 17 in 6.4-mm. borings. Thirty-two nests were from settings on structural lumber, 2 on a dead tree trunk, 3 in crevices in a rock wall, and the remainder on branches of living trees and piles of cut firewood.

Supersedure and competition. *A. catskill* superseded a species of *Trypargilum* in one nest at Derby. It was superseded by *T. clavatum* (Say) and *Ancistrocerus a. antilope* (Panzer) in 1 nest each at Derby. The supersedure of and by *Trypargilum* occurred in the same nest and may have been actual competition. There was a dead spider at the inner end of this boring, a mud partition 18 mm. from the inner end, and then a single *catskill* cell followed by several *T. clavatum* cells. The supersedure by *antilope* may not have been the result of competition, because in that nest there was a single *catskill* cell, then an empty cell (the vestibular cell?), and then an *antilope* cell.

Nest architecture. In two-thirds of the nests the wasps did not bring in any mud first but laid an egg near the inner end of the boring and then began to store caterpillars. In the other nests the wasps either plastered a thin layer of mud at the inner end or made a thin partition of mud 3-107 mm. from the inner end.

In table 9, I summarize the dimensions of stored and vestibular cells in nests from Derby only.

There was a vestibular cell in all but 2 of the completed nests at

TABLE 9.—*Measurements (in mm.) of cells in nests of* Ancistrocerus c. catskill
(*Saussure*)

Boring diameter	Sex	STORED CELLS			VESTIBULAR CELLS		
		No.	Range in length	Mean length	No.	Range in length	Mean length
3.2	♂	4	13-31	19	4	28-54	38
4.8	♀	47	11-25	16	21	11-130	71
	♂	41	9-19	12			
6.4	♀	33	7-21	12	15	14-136	59
	♂	22	6-15	9			

Derby. Ten of these cells were divided by a single partition, and 4 cells had 2 such partitions.

Five of the nests had 1 or more empty intercalary cells between stored cells. Altogether there were only 9 such empty cells among a total of 20 stored cells.

There were too few cells in Plummers Island nests to provide significant measurements. Six male cells in 4.8-mm. borings were 10-18 mm. long (mean 14). In 6.4-mm. borings a single male cell was 19 mm. long, and 2 female cells were 16 and 19 mm. long. There were no intercalary cells in these nests. The 2 completed nests had vestibular cells 60 and 87 mm. long, the latter being divided by a cross partition.

The partitions capping the stored cells and the closing plugs at the nest entrances were made of mud. The partitions were 0.5-2 mm. thick (mean 1.0), and the closing plugs were 1-10 mm. thick (mean 3.6).

The 2 completed nests in 3.2-mm. borings had 1-2 stored cells (mean 1.5). There were 1-9 stored cells (mean 4.6) in 23 completed nests in 4.8-mm. borings and 2-11 cells (mean 5.5) in 15 completed nests in 6.4-mm. borings.

In multicelled nests in 4.8-mm. borings both sexes were reared from 8 nests, males only from 10 nests and females only from 7 nests. In 6.4-mm. nests both sexes were reared from 8 nests, males only from 3 nests and females only from 5 nests.

Prey. I preserved samples of prey from a dozen cells in 11 nests from Derby during the several years in which I obtained nests. Consolidated identifications were as follows:

Oecophoridae
    sp. in 3 cells in 3 nests
    probable sp. in 2 cells in 2 nests
Olethreutidae, sp. in 2 cells in 2 nests
Gelechiidae, sp. in 4 cells of 3 nests
Phycitidae, *Salebria fructella* Hulst in 1 cell
Pterophoridae, *Pterophorus delawaricus* (Zeller) in 1 cell

In 4 completely stored cells from Derby in which males would have developed there were, respectively, 3 and 5 specimens of a gelechiid, 3 specimens of an oecophorid, and 10 specimens of the phycitid *Salebria fructella*. In one cell in which a female would possibly have developed there were 6 specimens of the pterophorid *Pterophorus delawaricus*. Usually only a single species of caterpillar was stored in each nest, but one nest did contain a few olethreutids interspersed among a number of speckled gelechiids.

Plummers Island samples from 1 cell each in 2 nests were determined as Tortricidae, *Archips* sp. from 1 nest and an unknown species of that family from the other nest.

Life history. Not much information was obtained on the immature stages. One larva consumed its store of caterpillars in 3-4 days, and another larva spun its cocoon in 1-2 days.

The cocoons were delicate, white, and subopaque (fig. 11). Three male cocoons in 3.2-mm. borings were each 9 mm. long. In 4.8-mm. nests 31 female cocoons were 9-12 mm. long (mean 10) and 40 male cocoons 7-12 mm. (mean 8). In 6.4-mm. nests 22 female cocoons were 8-11 mm. (mean 10) and 19 male cocoons 6-13 mm. (mean 8). One larva misoriented in its cocoon and lay with its head toward the inner end of the 3.2-mm. boring.

Pupation occurred 4-6 days after the larvae completed feeding. The period between pupation and adult emergence was 7-12 days (mean 9) for 16 females and 6-11 days (mean 9) for 23 males.

The period between egg hatch and adult emergence was 22-23 days for one female; so the entire life cycle of egg to adult probably was 25-26 days for a female in midsummer and somewhat shorter for a male.

In nests containing both sexes males usually emerged 1-3 days before females in the same nest, although in one nest both sexes emerged on the same day. In individual nests all males emerged on the same day or within a day of each other, and female emergence was similarly timed.

Limited data indicate that the wasps may provision 2-3 cells a day during midsummer. In one of the Plummers Island nests stored in mid-September the provisioning rate was apparently a cell a day in a 4-celled nest.

Adults emerged June 25 to August 18 from nests stored at Derby from early in June until late in July, and so there are probably 2 generations a year at that locality. In one nest stored at Derby between July 20 and August 8, the occupants of cells 2 and 3 emerged late in August; but the occupant of cell 1 overwintered as a resting larva and transformed to an adult the following spring. The 4 nests from Plummers Island were stored during September. Their occupants also overwintered as diapausing larvae and transformed to adults the following spring. However, there are probably three generations a year at Plummers Island where I have collected adults from June 2 to August 12.

I reared 82 females and 70 males from 219 stored cells. In the 67 cells from which I failed to rear wasps, there would probably have been a minimum of 14 females and 23 males, judged from the size of the cells and sex of wasps in adjacent cells. These data suggest a sex ratio of 1:1.

Parasites. The cuckoo wasp *Chrysis* (*C.*) *coerulans* Fabricius parasitized 4 of 15 cells in 3 nests at Derby. The eulophid *Melittobia chalybii* Ashmead attacked the occupants of 1 cell in a 3-celled nest in the field at Derby.

One maggot of the miltogrammine fly *Amobia distorta* (Allen) destroyed 1 cell in a 6-celled nest at Derby. Other miltogrammine maggots, most likely this same species, destroyed 4 cells each in a 6- and an 8- celled nest at Derby. At Plummers Island the bombyliid fly *Anthrax argyropyga* Wiedemann parasitized 1 cell in a 5-celled nest.

The saproglyphid mite *Kennethiella* species near *trisetosa* (Cooreman) infested 1 cell of a 2-celled nest at Derby. Two nests at Plummers Island had infestations of the saproglyphid mite *Vespacarus tigris* Baker and Cunliffe, a species which normally has as its host *Ancistrocerus t. tigris* (Saussure.)

Previous observation. Myers (1927) reported a mud cell of *catskill* in a cavity between the top of the wainscot and the foot of the wall of a room in Massachusetts. Rau (1935c, p. 111) said that in Missouri it nested in abandoned mud-dauber nests, old nail- and key-holes about a house, and in old burrows of the mining bee, *Anthophora abrupta* Say, in a clay bank. Later Rau (1945) found nests in smooth hollow stalks of bamboo (*Arundinaria*) in Tennessee. Hobbs *et al.* (1961, p. 144) reported that *catskill* nested in the abandoned clay cells of *Anthophora occidentalis* Cresson at the end of burrows in a clay bank in southern Alberta. Fye (1965a, pp.723-729) reared it from borings in sumac stems in northwestern Ontario.

Rau (1945) discovered that there was correlation between the cell size and sex of the wasp which developed therein. He reared 4 females from the bottom cells in one stalk and 2 males from the upper cells; female cells were 10 mm. long and male cells 6 mm. long.

Hobbs *et al.* reared the cuckoo wasp *Chrysis (C.) nitidula* Fabricius from cells of *catskill.* Medler (1964d) reared *C. (C.) nitidula* and *C. (C.) coerulans* Fabricius from nests of *catskill.* Myers reared a miltogrammine fly which was identified for him as *Pachyophthalmus signatus* (Meigen); probably this was the same species identified for me as *Amobia distorta* (Allen).

Fye (1965a, pp. 723-729) published a detailed account of the bionomics of this wasp under the name *catskill albophaleratus* (Saussure); the observations he reported (pp. 729-731) under the same *catskill catskill* (Saussure) should be referred to *a. antilope* (Panzer), *q. v.* I examined the progeny from 82 of Fye's nests and found that all of it represented the white-marked color phase (*albophaleratus*) except for 2 of 11 individuals from 1 nest which were of the yellow-marked color phase (*catskill*). He reared the wasp from 69 nests in 6.4-mm. borings in elderberry and chinaberry stems, and from 18 nests in 8.0-mm. borings. In 6.4-mm. borings female cells were 12.3±.6 mm. long and male cells 9.3±.2 mm.; corresponding measurements in 8.0-mm. borings were 12.5±.5 mm. and 8.6±.5 mm., respectively. He stated that empty intercalary cells were rare. The cell partitions were 0.8-1.6 mm. thick, and the closing plugs were 0.8-9.6 mm.; both were made of clay. Vestibular cells were 17.6-77.8 mm. long; occasionally these cells were divided by 1 or 2 cross partitions. He reported 2-8 provisioned cells per nest in 6.4-mm. borings. The wasps usually used smaller caterpillars as prey, especially those belonging to the genera *Recurvaria, Eucordylea,* and *Pulicalvaria*; usually about 20 caterpillars were stored per cell. Fye noted that the provision masses were 0.025-0.50 g. for male and 0.051-0.12 g. for female cells. He noted a larval feeding period of 7-10 days for occupants of nests during the summer; this period was 5-18 days for larvae during September. The period from egg hatch to adult emergence was about 40 days for members of the summer generation. Fye noted that the wasp had both univoltine and bivoltine strains. He reared 178 females and 76 males from summer generation nests and 6 females and 34 males from overwintering nests. He reported as parasites *Chrysis (C.) coerulans* Fabricius and *C. (C.) nitidula* Fabricius (?); he also reported *Glypta* spp. as questionable parasites, but these undoubtedly were parasites of the caterpillar prey.

Source material.

Derby, N. Y. 1955 series: D 1d, 1e, 2b, 2c, 3d, 4a, 11d. 1956 series: J 15, 33, 57, 62, 66, 67, 69, 75, 108. 1957 series: G 5, 8, 19, 28, 90. 1958 series: R 20, 24, 27a, 62, 63, 63a. 1959 series: W 25, 47, 52, 74. 1960 series: D 15, 22, 23, 73, 83. 1961 series: L 30, 36, 46, 49, 53, 54, 68, 69.

Plummers Island, Md. 1957 series: P 111, 199, 290.

Identifications. Lepidopterous larvae by H. W. Capps; Miltogrammini by W. L. Downes, Jr.; Bombyliidae by W. W. Wirth; Acarina by E. W. Baker; wasps by the author.

ANCISTROCERUS TIGRIS TIGRIS (Saussure)

A. tigris nested in 25 nests at Derby, N. Y., 11 in the metropolitan area of Washington, D. C., 2 at Lost River State Park, W. Va., and 1 at Kill Devil Hills, N.C. Eight nests were in 3.2-mm. borings, 22 in 4.8-mm., and 8 in 6.4-mm.; the boring diameter was not noted for one nest. Most of the nests were from the edges of wooded areas or in open woods. About two-thirds of them were from stations on structural lumber, cut firewood, and dead trunks or limbs, and the rest were suspended from limbs of living trees.

Supersedure and competition. *A. tigris* was superseded by *Ancistrocerus a. antilope* (Panzer) in 2 nests at Derby and by *Trypargilum collinum rubrocinctum* (Packard) in a nest at Cropley, Md.

Nest architecture. The wasps began most nests by laying an egg near the inner end of the boring and then bringing in prey. However, in eight nests the mothers either placed a thin layer of mud at the inner end or made a thin partition of that material 27-60 mm. from the inner end.

There were no significant differences in cell lengths from the various localities. Consolidated measurements of the stored and vestibular cells are presented in table 10.

Vestibular cells were present in 28 of the 31 completed nests. In most of the nests this cell was not divided by a cross partition; but in 3 nests there was such a partition, and in 2 others there were 2 and 3 such partitions, respectively.

There was an empty intercalary cell 35 mm. long between 2 stored cells in 1 of the 4.8-mm. nests.

The cell partitions and closing plugs at the nest entrances were made of mud. The former were 0.5-3 mm. thick (mean 1.0), and the closing plugs were 1-6 mm. thick (mean 3.0).

Seven completed nests in 3.2-mm. borings averaged 3.1 stored cells (range 1-5), 19 completed nests in 4.8-mm. borings averaged 5.3 stored cells (range 1-13), and 3 completed nests in 6.4-mm. borings averaged 5.0 stored cells (range 1-12).

TABLE 10.—*Measurements (in mm.) of cells in nests of* Ancistrocerus t. tigris *(Saussure).*

Boring diameter	Sex	STORED CELLS			VESTIBULAR CELLS		
		No.	Range in length	Mean length	No.	Range in length	Mean length
3.2	♀	3	18-20	19	4	3-41	16
	♂	19	10-40	16			
4.8	♀	79	8-82	14	19	6-137	66
	♂	13	9-21	13			
6.4	♀	13	8-13	11	5	9-87	40

Prey. Consolidated identifications for the prey from Derby and from the metropolitan area of Washington are tabulated below. These records are based on partial samples and on complete cell contents.

Derby, N. Y., 5 nests, 1956, 1958, 1960
 Oecophoridae, probable sp. in 1 cell
 Gelechiidae, sp. in 7 cells in 2 nests
 Olethreutidae, sp. in 2 cells in 2 nests
 Olethreutidae *or* Phaloniidae, sp. in 3 cells in 1 nest
 Torticidae, sp. in 1 cell
Washington, D. C., 5 nests, 1954, 1956, 1959, 1960
 Oecophoridae, *Psilocorsis* sp. in 1 cell
 Gelechioidea, probable sp. in 1 cell
 Gelechiidae, sp. in 2 cells in 2 nests
 Olethreutidae, sp. in 2 cells in 2 nests
 Phaloniidae, sp. in 1 cell

One completed cell at Lost River State Park contained 7 larvae of an olethreutid, 1 of a gelechiid, and 4 head capsules not identifiable to family.

Most of the cells sampled contained only a single species of caterpillar, but 1 cell held 1 oecophorid, 1 olethreutid, and 14 gelechiids.

Fifteen completely stored cells contained 2-18 larvae (mean 5.7). Females probably would have developed in 3 of these cells which held 3-18 larvae (mean 9.3) and males in 6 cells containing 2-3 larvae each (mean 2.8).

Life history. The egg was sausage shaped and creamy white, and one of them was 2.1 mm. long. This egg was attached 2.5 mm.

from the inner end of the cell. I did not ascertain the duration of
the egg stage. One larva required 4 days to consume its store of
caterpillars. Pupation occurred 5 days after the larva finished feeding in the summer generation. The pupal period lasted 6 days for
2 males and 8-10 days for 9 females. Several adults emerged from
the nest only a day after their eclosion from the pupal exuvia.
These data suggest that the cycle of egg deposition to adult emergence required 19-23 days in nests of the summer generation.

The cocoons were opaque, white to light tan, and delicate.
In 4.8-mm. borings female cocoons were 8-12 mm. long (mean
10) and male cocoons were 7-8 mm. Two larvae were misoriented
and lay with their heads toward the inner end of the boring.
This reversal was probably due to damage to the cell partitions
during my inspection of the nest prior to pupation of the occupants.

Undoubtedly there were 3 generations a year at Derby. Adults
emerged June 15 to August 27 from nests stored from the latter
part of May until early in August. The occupant of only 1 nest
from Derby overwintered as a diapausing larva. This nest was
stored between July and early August; the wasp was already in
larval diapause when I opened the nest on August 18.

In the Washington area *tigris* adults emerged July 15 to August
18 from nests stored from late in June until late in July. However,
in 3 nests from Plummers Island stored early in June of 1960 and
1963 the occupants overwintered as diapausing larvae. These were
the only trap nests stored during those 2 years in the Washington
area, and I can offer no explanation for the anomalous development
of their occupants. In 1960 I collected females at Plummers Island
on June 21, July 5, and October 1, 17, and 22; and in 1963 I
caught females on May 19, June 28, July 21, September 28, and
October 26. The earliest date of capture for a female at Plummers
Island was May 10, 1914. The extended flight period and short
developmental cycle suggest that there may be at least four generations in the Washington area.

The two nests at Lost River State Park were stored early in July.
An adult female developed in only 1 of the nests and emerged by
August 1. I have collected *tigris* at Lost River from June 19 to
August 30, and so it appears that there are at least 2 generations
a year.

A. tigris is a rare wasp at Kill Devil Hills, where the only specimens I collected were taken on June 1. The single nest from that
locality was completed during the period from early spring until
mid-July. The larvae in the nest were already in diapause when I
opened it on July 29. They overwintered in that stage and transformed to pupae and then to adults the following spring.

There were only 4 nests in which both sexes developed; females were in the inner cells, males in the outer. The males emerged 1-3 days before females in 2 nests, and there was concurrent emergence in the other 2. In most of the other nests all the occupants emerged on the same date, even though there were as many as 13 females in 1 of these nests. However, in 1 nest 3 females emerged over a 7-day period, and in another nest a female emerged from cell 3 on March 14 in the laboratory and occupants of cells 1 and 2 were still viable prepupae as late as June 20.

Scarcely any data were obtained on the rate of provisioning. In 1 nest at Plummers Island 4 cells may have been provisioned in 1-3 days, because there were eggs in these cells when I opened the nest for study.

I reared a total of 90 females and 24 males from 154 stored cells in the 39 nests. At Derby there were 65 females and 17 males from 111 cells. These figures indicate a probable 4:1 sex ratio.

Parasites and predators. The most common parasite was the symbiotic saproglyphid mite *Vespacarus tigris* Baker and Cunliffe, which was found in 8 nests, 4 from Derby, 2 from Plummers Island, and 1 each from Dunn Loring and Kill Devil Hills.

The cuckoo wasp *Chrysis* (*C.*) *coerulans* Fabricius was reared from 8 of 24 cells in 4 nests from Derby. The eulophid *Melittobia chalybii* Ashmead infested 3 nests in the field at Plummers Island.

One miltogrammine fly *Amobia distorta* (Allen) was reared from 1 cell of a nest from Derby. Four maggots of an unidentified miltogrammine fly destroyed a 1-celled nest at Lost River State Park.

Previous observations. A. *tigris* has been the subject of published observations by Rau and Rau (1918, pp. 344-345) in Kansas; Bequaert (1925, p. 106; 1944, p. 260) in Massachusetts, New York, Pennsylvania, Georgia and Illinois; Boyce (1946) and Fye (1965a, pp. 731-734) in Ontario; Krombein (1954, pp. 2-3) in West Virginia; and Coppel (1961) and Medler (1965b) in Wisconsin.

The Raus found 3-celled nests in abandoned mud-dauber nests (*Chalybion* or *Sceliphron*). Bequaert reared it from a boring in the pith of a brier and from old cynipid galls on oak. Boyce found as many as 4 cells in completed nests in old golden-rod galls caused by *Epiblema* and *Gnorimoschema*. Krombein, Medler, and Fye induced it to nest in traps in white pine sticks, sumac, elderberry and chinaberry stems, rubber tubing, and bamboo. Coppel found 1-celled nests in cocoons of *Diprion similis* from which the adult sawflies had emerged.

Only Krombein, Medler, and Fye presented precise measurements of the various details of nest construction. My notes on the West Virginia nests have been included in the preceding account. Most of Medler's data were from female cells in borings 150 mm. long. A dozen cells in 4.8-mm. borings were 8-20 mm. long (mean 11) and 35 cells in 6.4-mm. borings were 5-21 mm. (mean 10). In one 6.4-mm. nest a dozen female cells averaged 8 mm. long and 6 male cells averaged 6 mm. Medler noted an empty vestibular cell in completed nests, but gave no measurements on these nor on the thickness of the mud partitions and closing plugs. Medler found 3-5 stored cells in three 4.8-mm. borings, and 1-18 stored cells (mean 6) in six 6.4-mm. borings. He stated that females were in the inner cells and males in the outer, and he reared 28 females and 2 males from 47 stored cells in sumac stems. Fye reported an average length of 11.0 ± 1.3 mm. for 7 female cells in 6.4-mm. borings, and of 10.1 ± 1.4 mm. for 4 female cells in 8.0-mm. borings. The clay partitions were 0.8-1.6 mm. thick, and the closing plugs 1.6-3.2 mm. thick. He noted 2 vestibular cells 59 and 74 mm. long, the latter divided by a cross partition.

Boyce reported as prey mostly *Spilonota ocellana* (Denis & Schiffermüller), the eye-spotted bud moth, with occasional specimens of *Coleophora fletcherella* Fernald, the cigar casebearer. He found 4-11 caterpillars per completed cell. Medler and I reported Olethreutidae and Gelechiidae as prey. Fye found mostly *Eucordylea* sp., fair numbers of *Acleris variana* Fernald, and a few larvae of *Griselda radicana* Walsingham.

Boyce found the life cycle to be 34-40 days in duration, with eggs hatching 1-3 days after the nests were found, the larvae feeding for the next 6-11 days, pupation occurring a week later, and adults emerging in about 11 days. Apparently his earliest nests in Ontario were provisioned during the first week in June, and adults emerged as early as July 16. Fye reported 9 days in the larval stage, 8-14 days in the prepupal stage, and 19-30 days in the pupal stage. Emergence from Fye's nests was August 16-28, 41-45 days after eclosion. (I presume he means nest completion or egg hatch, not eclosion.) One of Medler's nests must have been stored about mid-June; the *tigris* adults had all emerged from it by July 5.

Bequaert and Medler both recorded *Chrysis* (*C.*) *nitidula* Fabricius as a parasite, and the latter author also reared *C.* (*C.*) *coerulans* Fabricius from *tigris* cells. Bequaert noted the ichneumonid *Acroricnus junceus* (Cresson) as a parasite, Boyce reared *Calliephialtes notandus* Cresson from *tigris,* and Coppel found that 3 sawfly parasites successfully parasitized *tigris* in sawfly cocoons, namely, *Ephialtes* sp., *Agrothereutes lophyri,* n. subsp., and *Monodontomerus dentipes* (Dalman). Bequaert mentioned that the stylopid *Pseudoxenos tigridis* Pierce was described from parasitized specimens of *tigris* and said that he had often seen stylopized adults; Medler recorded an undetermined stylopid as a parasite. Fye reported *Ephialtes* (*Pimpla*) *decumbens* (Townes) as a parasite. Fye did not mention finding mites in any of his *tigris* nests. However, at least

2 of them were infested with *Vespacarus tigris* Baker and Cunliffe because I noted hypopi clustered beneath the apex of the third tergum of each of 2 females from different nests.

Source material.
> Derby, N. Y. 1954 series: VII A, XVII B. 1955 series: D 5a, 7a, 8b, 9b. 1956 series: J 40. 77, 84, 90. 1958 series: R 6, 15. 1959 series: W 5, 15, 17, 31, 32, 36, 53, 54. 1960 series: D 74, 81, 82. 1961 series: L 31, 37.
> Cropley, Md. 1955 series: B 2.
> Plummers Island, Md. 1956 series: H 92, 93. 1959 series: Y 98, 127. 1960 series: E 73, 98. 1962 series: M 1. 1963 series: U 4.
> Glencarlyn, Va. 1954 series: D 23, 27.
> Lost River State Park, W. Va. 1953 series: 7253 D, 7453 C.
> Kill Devil Hills, N. C. 1956 series: C 424.

Identifications. Lepidopterous larvae by H. W. Capps; Acarina by E. W. Baker; Miltogrammini by W. L. Downes, Jr.; Hymenoptera by the author.

SYMMORPHUS CANADENSIS (Saussure)

(Plate 4, Figures 14, 15; Plate 5, Figures 16-18; Plate 6, Figure 19)

This smallest of our native *Symmorphus* is unique in that it preys mostly on coleopterous and lepidopterous leaf-mining larvae. I received 10 nests from 7 stations at Derby, N. Y., 1958-1960; 16 nests from 13 stations at Plummers Island, Md., 1957-1961; and 19 nests from an old cowshed wall at my home in Arlington, Va., in 1954, 1955, 1956, and 1962. The traps from Derby were at stations on wooden buildings or in piles of cut firewood, and those at Plummers Island were mostly on wooden buildings, except for a few on dead standing or fallen tree trunks. Thirty-seven nests were in 3.2-mm. borings, 7 in 4.8-mm., and 1 in a 6.4-mm.

Supersedure and competition. At Derby *canadensis* superseded *Passaloecus ithacae* Krombein in 1 nest. At Plummers Island it superseded *Trypoxylon* sp., *T. johnsoni* Fox, and *Passaloecus* sp. in 1 nest each, and was superseded in 1 nest by *T. johnsoni*.

Nest architecture. In about a dozen nests the wasps smeared a small amount of mud at the inner end of the boring or made a mud partition 6-44 mm. from the inner end. However, in most nests the wasps did not bring in mud first but laid an egg near the inner end of the boring and then began to store prey.

The single nest in the 6.4-mm. boring was abnormal. It contained a single stored cell 108 mm. long whose occupant I failed to rear. There was no vestibular cell. The maker was identified by the *Chalepus* larvae stored as prey.

Consolidated measurements for stored and vestibular cells in 3.2- and 4.8-mm. nests from the 3 localities are presented in table 11.

There was an empty intercalary cell 4 mm. long between the 2 stored cells in a 3.2-mm. nest from Derby. A vestibular cell was present in all but 6 of the completed nests. Five of the completed nests lacking a vestibular cell were from Arlington, and 1 was from Plummers Island.

The partitions capping the stored cells were made of mud and were 0.5-7 mm. thick (mean 1.7). The closing plugs at the nest entrances were usually also of mud and somewhat thicker in the 4.8-mm. borings. The closing plugs in 3.2-mm. nests were 0.25-12 mm. thick (mean 4.8) and 5-11 mm. thick (mean 8.6) in 4.8-mm. nests. One plug in a 4.8-mm. nest had 8 mm. of mud and 3 mm. of red-cedar fiber at the outer end.

Twenty-nine completed nests in 3.2-mm. borings had 1-4 stored

TABLE 11.—*Measurements (in mm.) of cells in nests of* Symmorphus canadensis *(Saussure)*

Boring diameter	Sex	STORED CELLS			VESTIBULAR CELLS		
		No.	Range in length	Mean length	No.	Range in length	Mean length
3.2	♀	9	11-23	16	24	5-43	20
	♂	24	10-27	18			
4.8	♀	17	12-19	16	5	20-90	41
	♂	5	10-15	13			

cells (mean 2.4), and 5 completed nests in 4.8-mm. borings had 7-10 stored cells (mean 8.2).

Both sexes were reared from 3 of the multicelled nests in 3.2-mm. borings, females only were obtained from 5 nests and males only from a dozen nests. In the 4.8-mm. borings both sexes were reared from 2 nests and females only from 1 nest. It is not surprising that so few of the 3.2-mm. nests produced both sexes, because of the small number of cells per nest in those short borings.

Prey. S. canadensis preyed almost entirely on coleopterous leaf-mining larvae (Chrysomelidae) or on lepidopterous leaf-miners (Gracillariidae and Walshiidae). The beetle larvae used most commonly were *Chalepus dorsalis* Thunberg, the locust leaf-miner (figs. 14, 16). Larvae of the gracillariid *Lithocolletis* were used most frequently among the Lepidoptera, although the caterpillar prey also included another gracillariid and the walshiid *Aeaea ostryaeella* (Chambers). Occasionally, weevil larvae belonging to the genus *Apion* were used. Unfortunately the latter could not be identified specifically, although one specimen was determined as being near *walshi* Smith, which has been found in *Betula catkins* in May.

The larvae though paralyzed were capable of bending the abdomen and voiding feces. Some of the mature beetle larvae were able to pupate after being stung by the wasps.

At Derby I found only *Chalepus* larvae in the 6 nests which reached me before the prey was consumed. Two cells stored early in July contained a total of a dozen larvae, 11 in the last instar and 1 in the penultimate instar.

At Plummers Island lepidopterous caterpillars were stored commonly, perhaps because many of my settings were not in close proximity to locust trees, so that the wasps could not obtain *Chalepus* larvae. I found *Chalepus* in 10 nests and preserved entire cell samples from 8 cells in 3 nests stored at the end of June and the beginning of July. One cell in the first nest held 9 last instar and 2 penultimate instar *Chalepus;* another cell in a second nest contained 9 last instar and 8 pupating larvae; and 4 cells in the third nest had 10-15 larvae (mean 12) per cell, 4 in the penultimate instar, 16 in the last instar, and 29 pupating larvae or pupae.

The prey in 6 other nests from Plummers Island was lepidopterous except for a weevil (*Apion*) larva mixed in with the caterpillars in 1 cell. The earliest nest was completed about June 10; cell 2 contained 17 paralyzed but moderately active caterpillars of a species of Gracillariidae, a pupa of the same species, and a tiny *Apion* larva near *walshi* Smith about 2 mm. long. In another nest completed about June 15 there were 39 specimens of a species of Gracillariidae in cell 3; a male wasp developed subsequently in this cell. A partially completed cell in a third nest, stored about June 20, contained 7 larvae of a species of Gracillariidae, and 2 larvae of the gracillariid *Lithocolletis* sp. Another nest, completed the first week in July, contained 32 *Lithocolletis* larvae in cells 3 and 4. The fifth nest was completed during the last week in September; cells 3 and 4 each held about a dozen caterpillars, all *Lithocolletis* except for 1 walshiid *Aeaea ostryaeella* (Chambers) which mines leaves of hop hornbeam (*Ostrya*).

At my home in Arlington *Chalepus* larvae were stored in at least 14 nests between June 13 and July 12. In a nest completed on June 14, 2 cells had 17 and 19 *Chalepus*, 4.5-5.8 mm. long, mostly in the third instar. The beetle larvae in nests stored from June 23 to July 12 were larger, and were mostly in the last instar with a few in the penultimate instar. Seven cells from 6 nests contained 7-13 *Chalepus* (mean 11) per cell. A single nest was completed May 23 and was entirely stored with *Apion* larvae about 2.7 mm. long, perhaps because *Chalepus* larvae were not available so early in the season. Cells 2 and 3 of this 3-celled nest contained 21 and 24 beetle larvae, respectively; a female wasp developed subsequently in the cell with 24 specimens of prey.

Life history. The eggs were fastened by a thread attached 3-5 mm.

from the inner end of the cell. Usually the eggs of Vespidae are suspended by this thread from the top of the cell, but observations of Arlington nests showed that this is not true for *canadensis*. I scored the attachment of eggs in 15 cells in 9 nests: 7 eggs were attached to the top of the cell, 7 on the floor of the cells, and 1 on the side of the cell. The eggs were 1.84-2.15 mm. long. They hatched in 1+-2+ days.

The larval feeding period was 3-5 days (mean 4) for 8 larvae (figs. 17, 18). One larva required 1-2 days to spin its cocoon. Usually there was only a single generation. However, on the rare occasion when there was a small summer emergence, pupation occurred about 4 days after the larva completed its cocoon.

The cocoons were very delicate, white, and subopaque (fig. 19). In 3.2-mm. nests 11 male cocoons were 8-12 mm. long (mean 10) and 7 female cocoons were 9-11 mm. (mean 10). The length of cocoons in the 4.8-mm. nests averaged about 2 mm. less.

The pupal period was 9-10 days for a female which emerged early in July. In overwintering nests the period between pupation and adult emergence was 15 days for 2 males and 12-20 days (mean 15) for 5 females. One male and 1 female each spent 4 days in the cocoon after eclosion before leaving the nest.

In mixed nests males and females emerged concurrently from 2 nests, and males emerged 2 and 6 days before females in 2 other nests. In 2 Plummers Island nests 10 days elapsed between emergence of the first and last females in a single nest, and 7 days between emergence of the first and last males in another nest. Four days elapsed between the emergence of 2 males in a nest from Arlington.

Some interesting data were obtained on the rate of provisioning. At Arlington I set out one 3.2-mm. trap at 1830 hours on June 23. A wasp completed a nest in this boring within 24 hours; it contained 2 stored cells, one of them with a dozen *Chalepus* larvae (contents of the other cell not counted), and 1 vestibular cell. A 7-celled nest with vestibular cell at Plummers Island was probably completed in 3 days; one cell contained 17 mature *Chalepus* larvae. Judged from egg hatch data, 2 cells were stored per day in 2 or 3 other nests at Plummers Island.

There was only a single generation a year at Derby, where nests were stored from late in June until late in July. I found only 1 generation also at Arlington, where nests were provisioned from May 23 until July 2. However, at Plummers Island there was an occasional small midsummer emergence. Most nests were stored there from mid-June to mid-July and their occupants overwintered as diapausing larvae. However, 1 female eclosed about July 2 or 3 from a nest completed before June 14, and a female and 2 males eclosed before July 11 in a nest completed about June 15. All these adults died without leaving the nests. However, some adults must emerge successfully in midsummer, because I have collected *canadensis* at Plummers Island from May 19 to October 17, and I obtained 1 trap nest which was not completed until the last week in September. Although I did not obtain trap nests from Lost River State Park, W. Va., I have collected *canadensis* there from June 19 to August 28; so there must be at least a small second generation in that area also.

I reared 26 females and 29 males from 124 stored cells, and so there is probably a 1:1 sex ratio.

Parasites and predators. The cuckoo wasp *Chrysis* (*C.*) *cembricola* Krombein was reared from 1 cell at Arlington. Probably this same species parasitized 2 cells in another Arlington nest; 1 of these larvae was lost and the other was preserved as a mature larva for taxonomic study. The eulophid *Melittobia chalybii* Ashmead infested 1 Arlington nest in the field, and 1 nest each from Arlington and Plummers Island in the laboratory.

Maggots of an unidentified miltogrammine fly, almost certainly *Amobia distorta* (Allen), destroyed 2 cells in a nest at Derby. Phorid larvae, undoubtedly *Megaselia aletiae* (Comstock), infested 1 cell of a Plummers Island nest.

A dermestid larva, probably *Trogoderma ornatum* Say, destroyed the wasp egg and some of the prey in 1 cell of a Plummers Island nest.

The grain itch mite *Pyemotes ventricosus* (Newport) occurred in 2 nests at Arlington; I do not know whether the infestations originated in the field or after the nests were brought into the laboratory. An unknown saproglyphid mite occurred in 2 nests at Plummers Island.

Previous observations. Reinhard (1929, pp. 72-83) in Maryland was the first to publish biological notes on this species under the name *debilis* (Saussure), a synonym. He reported finding nests of it in a wooden post in abandoned tunnels of a wood-boring beetle grub, *Tenebroides.* His wasps cleaned out the beetle borings, built a clay partition at the bottom, put in a store of paralyzed prey, attached an egg to the side wall, and then above this placed a clay ceiling, which became the floor of the next cell. His reporting that the egg was laid after the prey was stored is certainly erroneous. His wasps stored leaf-mining caterpillars, *Antispila nyssaefoliella* Clemens, which they obtained from leaves of sour gum. Reinhard found a series of 9 cells in 1 nest, 2 of which contained 24 and 26 caterpillars, respectively. He stated that the egg stage lasted 5 days in September, and that the wasp larvae completed feeding 8-9 days after hatching and overwintered as diapausing larvae. He reported that *canadensis* was parasitized by the torymid wasp, *Monodontomerus*.

Some years ago (Krombein, 1952, p. 91) I reported *canadensis* as nesting in borings in logs of a cabin in Virginia and storing as prey chrysomelid leaf-miners, *Chalepus* sp., and a weevil leaf-miner, *Prionomerus calceatus* (Say). Later (Krombein, 1954, p. 3) in West Viginia I found it nesting in an identical situation and using larvae of *Chalepus dorsalis* Thunberg as prey. Two years after that in West Virginia (Krombein, 1956b, p. 155) I reported two provisioning flights of 10 and 15 minutes, and *Chalepus* again being used as prey.

Source material.
> Derby, N. Y. 1958 series: R 22, 61, 62a, 65. 1959 series: W 1, 82. 1960 series: D 12, 46, 77, 80.
> Plummers Island, Md. 1957 series: P 1, 2. 1958 series: S 1, 7, 19, 87. 1959 series: Y 1, 5, 8, 11, 12. 1960 series: E 79, 103, 104. 1961 series: K 78, 149.
> Arlington, Va. 1954 series: A 12, 14. 1955 series: A 5. 1956 series: K 1, 4, 5, 6, 7, 8, 9, 10, 11, 13, 14, 16, 18, 21, 22. 1962 series: N 3.

Identifications. Coleopterous larvae by D. M. and W. H. Anderson; lepidopterous larvae by H. W. Capps; wasps by the author.

SYMMORPHUS ALBOMARGINATUS (Saussure)

I reared *albomarginatus* from 2 nests from 2 stations at Derby, N. Y., in 1957, and from 4 nests from 3 stations at Plummers Island, Md., in 1960-1962. Five nests were in 6.4-mm. borings, and 1 was in a 4.8-mm. boring. The Derby nests were from settings on windowsills, and the Plummers Island nests were from settings on standing dead tree trunks or beneath dead limbs.

This wasp probably nested at Plummers Island in 6 additional 4.8-mm. borings and in 6 more 6.4-mm. borings in 1956 and 1961. I failed to rear adults, but the prey and nest architecture were consistent with those features in *albomarginatus* nests.

Supersedure and competition. S. *albomarginatus* superseded a species of *Megachile* in one nest at Derby and *Osmia pumila* Cresson in a nest at Plummers Island. It was superseded by *Ancistrocerus a. antilope* (Panzer) in one nest at Derby. In one of the nests, supposedly stored by *albomarginatus*, the vespid was superseded by the pompilid *Dipogon s. sayi* Banks.

Nest architecture. In the *albomarginatus* nests the wasps left the inner end empty in 4 borings and placed a little mud at the inner end or constructed a mud partition 34 mm. from the inner end in the other borings. In the probable *albomarginatus* nests the inner end was free of mud in 3 nests, 7 nests had a mud plug at the inner end, and 2 had a mud partition 35-41 mm. from the inner end.

The male cells in 4.8-mm. borings were 13-14 mm. long, and 2 male cells in 6.4-mm. borings were 11-15 mm. Thirteen female cells in 6.4-mm. borings were 13-22 mm. long (mean 16). There were no empty intercalary cells. Vestibular cells 16-36 mm. long were present in 4 of the 5 nests completed by *albomarginatus;* the fifth completed nest lacked such a cell. The partitions capping the cells were of mud and were 1-4 mm. thick (mean 2). The closing plugs were also of mud and were quite substantial, being 8-12 mm. thick (mean 10).

The single completed nest of *albomarginatus* in a 4.8-mm. boring had 9 stored cells; a probable nest in the same size boring had only 5 stored cells. In 6.4-mm. borings there were 7 stored cells in each of the 2 nests completed by *albomarginatus;* 3 probable nests had 2, 5, and 7 stored cells, respectively.

Only males were reared from the 4.8-mm. nest, and only females from all the 6.4-mm. nests, except one from which both sexes were reared.

Prey. Larvae of one or more species of *Chrysomela* were stored in 5 *albomarginatus* nests. All the prey had been consumed in the sixth nest when I received it. No counts were made of the prey per cell.

The same prey was stored in all the nests presumed to have been stored by *albomarginatus* also. There were 5-20 larvae (mean 11) per cell in 10 cells.

Life history. The following data on the early stages are from nests of supposed *albomarginatus.* The egg was sausage shaped; 1 of them measured 1.9 mm. by 0.6 mm. It was suspended 5 mm. from the inner end of the cell. It hatched in 3-4 days. Eight larvae required 6-8 days to consume the prey stored for them. A period of 4-6 days lapsed between completion of larval feeding, spinning of the cocoon, voiding of the feces, and assumption of the flaccid diapausing form.

The cocoons of *albomarginatus* were white, opaque, and tougher than in most vespids. Nine female cocoons in 6.4-mm. borings were 8-12 mm. long (mean 10).

The period from pupation to emergence of the adult was 11-13 days for one overwintering female. Less precise data for this same period are 14-24 days for 5 males and 18-26 days for 1 female. Pupation of these 6 individuals took place during an 8-day period, and it is probable that the actual duration was much closer to the minimum than to the maximum interval.

Two males emerged 3 days earlier than the female in the single nest which contained both sexes. Emergence from the other nests did not require more than a 2-day period.

Egg-hatch data from 2 supposed nests of *albomarginatus* suggest that 2-3 cells may be stored per day.

Occupants of the 6 *albomarginatus* nests overwintered as diapausing larvae, and adult emergence occurred the following spring. Inasmuch as these nests were stored during June, it appears that there is only a single generation a year. However, there may be either a small emergence in July from nests stored during June or else the females may nest over a long period. One probable 3-celled nest was not opened until August 20. On that date the *Symmorphus* larvae were almost full grown, and so the cells could not have been stored before early in August.

I reared 13 females and 5 males from 39 stored cells in 6 nests.

Parasites and predators. The following parasites were reared from *albomarginatus* nests: The cuckoo wasp *Chrysis* (*C.*) *coerulans* Fabricius was reared from 3 cells in a 7-celled nest from Plummers Island. The eulophid *Melittobia chalybii* Ashmead infested 1 cell in a Derby nest in the field. The miltogrammine fly *Amobia distorta* (Allen) destroyed 3 cells in this same nest. The grain itch mite *Pyemotes ventricosus* (Newport) infested a Plummers Island nest in the laboratory.

The following parasites occurred in the nests thought to have been stored by *albomarginatus* at Plummers Island: *Amobia distorta* destroyed 5 cells in a 7-celled nest. A dipterous maggot, possibly a phorid, destroyed the wasp egg in 1 cell. In the laboratory 7 nests were infested by *Pyemotes* and 2 by *Melittobia*.

Source material.

Derby, N. Y. 1957 series: G 51, 53.

Plummers Island, Md. 1956 series: H 14 (?). 1960 series: E 65. 1961 series: K 34 (?), 50 (?), 59 (?), 67 (?), 96 (?), 101 (?), 102 (?) 113 (?), 115 (?), 121 (?), 157 (?), 170. 1962 series: M 61, 75.

Identifications. *Chrysomela* larvae by D. M. Weisman; Miltogrammini by W. L. Downes, Jr.; wasps by the author.

SYMMORPHUS CRISTATUS CRISTATUS (Saussure)
(Plate 6, Figures 20-22)

I reared this wasp from 30 nests from 18 stations at Derby, N. Y., 1955-1958 and 1960, and from a single nest at Arlington, Va., in 1962. Five nests were in 3.2-mm. borings (1 of them from Arlington), 24 nests were in 4.8-mm. borings, and 2 were in 6.4-mm. borings. Nine nests at Derby were from settings on structural lumber, 11 from those in a pile of cut firewood, 9 from those on branches of live trees, and a single one from a rock wall. The single nest from Arlington was on an old cowshed wall.

S. cristatus probably stored 34 additional nests at Derby, as based on the finding of *Chrysomela* larvae stored as prey in these nests, from which I did not rear adult wasps. Six of them were in 3.2-mm., 17 in 4.8-mm., 10 in 6.4-mm. borings, and 1 in a 9.5-mm. boring. These nests were from the same or similar stations from which I obtained *cristatus* nests.

Supersedure and competition. S. *cristatus* superseded a species of *Osmia*, probably *pumila* Cresson, in 1 nest at Derby, and it was superseded by a caterpillar-storing vespid wasp in another nest at Derby. A species of *Passaloecus* put a plug of resin at the entrance of a nest being stored by *cristatus* at Derby, apparently mistaking the vespid nest for her own. In the nests possibly stored by *cristatus* that wasp superseded a caterpillar-storing vespid and a *Hylaeus* bee in 1 nest each, and was superseded in 1 nest each by *Ancistro-*

TABLE 12.—*Measurements (in mm.) of cells in nests of* Symmorphus c. cristatus *(Saussure).*

Boring diameter	Sex	STORED CELLS			INTERCALARY CELLS			VESTIBULAR CELLS		
		No.	Range in length	Mean length	No.	Range in length	Mean length	No.	Range in length	Mean length
3.2	♀	5	13-16	14	0	—	—	5	22-32	27
	♂	5	11-13	12						
4.8	♀	32	10-21	15	34	2-18	5	20	25-99	63
	♂	47	8-22	14						
6.4	♀	7	11-19	15	0	—	—	2	31-112	72

cerus a. antilope (Panzer), *Euodynerus f. foraminatus* (Saussure) and a species of *Megachile*.

Nest architecture. In 13 nests the wasps put a thin layer of mud at the inner end of the boring or made a mud partition 11-63 mm. from the inner end. In 17 nests the wasps laid the first egg near the inner end without first bringing in mud. In the nests supposedly built by *cristatus,* 9 had mud at or near the inner end, and 15 lacked this preliminary mud plug.

Consolidated measurements for stored cells, empty intercalary cells, and vestibular cells are presented in table 12.

Every completed nest had an empty vestibular cell at the entrance (fig. 22). A dozen of these cells were not divided by cross partitions, but 13 had a single partition dividing the vestibular cell into 2 parts, and 1 each had 2 and 3 partitions, respectively.

There were no empty intercalary cells between stored cells (fig. 20) in nests in 3.2- or 6.4-mm. borings. Thirteen of the 24 nests in 4.8-mm. borings had 1-7 such cells between the stored cells (fig. 21). In 8 nests there was an intercalary cell between each stored cell, but there were only 1 or 2 intercalary cells each in 5 nests having 4-8 stored cells.

The partitions capping the cells were made of mud, and were 0.3-3 mm. thick (mean 1). The closing plugs of mud were much thicker than usual (fig. 22), 27 of them being 3-20 mm. thick (mean 9).

The 34 nests presumed to have been built by *cristatus* showed similar architectural details. Each of the 25 completed nests had a vestibular cell. Intercalary cells were present in 15 of 17 nests in 4.8-mm. borings, but there was none in 3.2-or 6.4-mm. borings. However, there was an intercalary cell of 1-4 mm. thickness between each stored cell in the 9.5-mm. nest. The closing plugs were abnormally thick also.

Eight completed nests of *cristatus* in 3.2-mm. borings had 2-3 stored cells (mean 2.8), 22 in 4.8-mm. borings had 2-8 stored cells (mean 5.5) (fig. 22), and 9 in 6.4-mm. borings had 2-7 stored cells (mean 4.5).

Both sexes were bred from two 3.2-mm. nests, females only from 1 nest, and males only from 2 nests. In 4.8-mm. nests both sexes were reared from 8 nests, females only from 8 nests, and males only from 7 nests. Only females were reared from the two 6.4-mm. nests.

Prey. S. *cristatus* preyed on external leaf-feeding larvae of one or more species of *Chrysomela*. The larvae in 1 cell were identified as belonging to a species in the *scripta* (Fabricius) complex. Other specimens were identified just as *Chrysomela* sp. (or spp.).

The number of beetle larvae stored per cell was dependent upon the instar of the larvae and the sex of the wasp which was to develop in a particular cell. In cells in which male wasps probably would have developed there were 10-14 probable second instar beetle larvae per cell (mean 12.5). There were 4, 5, and 8 larvae stored in 3 other probable male cells; these beetles undoubtedly were of later instars. In cells in which female wasps should have developed, there were 16 beetle larvae probably in the third instar in 1 cell, 10 of an unspecified instar in another cell, and 7 in the last instar in a third cell.

In the nests presumed to have been made by *cristatus*, the species and numbers stored were the same or nearly so. There were 15 probable second instar *Chrysomela* larvae in one cell, 8-15 probable third instar larvae (mean 11) in 9 cells, and 7-9 last instar larvae in 2 cells.

Life history. One egg hatched in 3 days. No observations were made on the length of time required for the larvae to consume the prey. One larva needed 1-2 days to spin its cocoon.

The cocoons of *cristatus* were tough, dense, opaque, and white to light tan in color (figs. 20, 21). In 4.8-mm. nests 18 female cocoons were 7-14 mm. long (mean 10.4) and 28 male cocoons 7-12 mm. long (mean 9.6). The few cocoons measured in 3.2 and 6.4 mm. nests fell within the above ranges.

The occupants of all nests overwintered as diapausing larvae and transformed to pupae the following spring. The period between pupation and emergence from the nest was 8-11 days (mean 10) for 4 males and 9-14 days (mean 12) for 3 females.

Males emerged 3-6 days before females in nests in which both sexes developed. In nests in which only one sex developed the occupants usually emerged on the same day, or within a day of each other, except in 2 nests where the emergence period required 2 and 5 days, respectively.

Limited data suggest that 2-3 cells per day may be stored under normal conditions.

There was only a single generation a year at Derby, where nests were stored throughout June. The single nest from Arlington was completed about July 15, suggesting the possibility of 2 generations there.

I reared 44 females and 52 males from 132 stored cells. Females would probably have developed in at least 12 and males in at least 6 of the 36 cells from which I failed to rear adult wasps. Consequently, it appears that there is a 1:1 sex ratio.

The sequence of sexes in the nests was normal, with females in the inner and males in the outer cells, except in one nest where the arrangement in cells 1-5 was ♂-♀-♀-♂-♂.

Parasites and predators. The following parasites were found in *cristatus* nests from Derby. Maggots of the miltogrammine fly *Amobia distorta* (Allen) destroyed 4 cells in a 5-celled nest. Another miltogrammine, undoubtedly this same species, occurred in 1 cell of another nest. A cuckoo wasp, probably a species of typical *Chrysis,* parasitized 1 cell in a third nest; it was preserved as a mature larva for taxonomic study.

The other nests presumed to have been stored by *cristatus* were more heavily parasitized. Maggots, probably of *Amobia distorta,* destroyed almost all the cells in 3 nests. Cuckoo wasps parasitized 3 of 6 cells in 2 nests. The eulophid *Melittobia chalybii* Ashmead infested 5 nests in the field. The grain itch mite *Pyemotes ventricosus* (Newport) infested 3 nests in the laboratory.

Previous observations. Fye (1965a, pp. 734-735, tables I, IV, VII) published an account of 5 nests which he obtained in traps made from elderberry and chinaberry in northwestern Ontario. I examined reared material from each of these nests and found that progeny from 2 nests (13, 104) was misidentified; these specimens are actually the white color phase of *Ancistrocerus c. catskill* (Saussure). Accordingly, Fye's data require reinterpretation, and the summary below reflects this. The data in table I are properly credited to *cristatus;* the data for *cristatus* in table IV have to be disregarded inasmuch as they are based on consolidated records from all 5 nests; similarly the data in table VII relating to *cristatus* must be disregarded—the 1961 data include 1 *catskill* nest, and the single 1962 nest was made by *catskill.* The nest dimensions given in the discussion must be disregarded; based on the admissible data for 2 nests in table I, female cells in 6.4-mm. borings were 14.4-19.9 mm. long (mean 16.8) and male cells were 9.6-14.4 mm. (mean 12.8); vestibular cells were 51 and 76 mm. long, and each was divided by 2 cross partitions; the 3-celled nest had no empty intercalary cells and the 4-celled nest had 2 such cells; the closing plugs near or at the boring entrances were 4.8 and 6.4 mm. thick. Larvae of the external leaf-feeding chrysomelid *Gonioctenus americanus* Brown were stored, 2-7 in male cells and 5-7 in female cells; Fye also mentioned that a correspondent had found *cristatus* preying on larvae of *Chrysomela crotchi* Brown in another area of northwestern Ontario. There was only 1 generation, adults emerging late in June. The larval feeding period was 11-14 days. Fye reared *Chrysis (C.) coerulans* Fabricius from 1 cell.

Source material.
    Derby, N. Y. 1955 series: D 5c, 13b, 13c (?), 14b (?). 1956 series: J 14 (?),
        19 (?), 28 (?), 31 (?), 32 (?), 36 (?), 46 (?), 47, 48 (?), 49, 52, 53 (?), 54 (?),
        55(?), 58, 64, 70, 81 (?), 83, 87, 92, 93, 99 (?), 100, 115 (?), 124, 126 (?),
        133 (?). 1957 series: G 3 (?), 4, 7 (?), 15 (?), 40, 44 (?), 45 (?), 47 (?), 48 (?),
        49, 150 (?). 1958 series: R 3. 1960 series: D 1, 2, 6, 14, 18 (?), 20, 25, 28,
        29, 30 (?), 31, 32, 35, 36, 40 (?), 76 (?), 79 (?). 1961 series: L 20 (?), 29 (?),
        36 (?).
    Arlington, Va. 1962 series: N 10.

Identifications. Coleopterous larvae by G. B. Vogt; Miltogrammini by W. L. Downes, Jr.; wasps and mites by the author.

STENODYNERUS (STENODYNERUS) BEAMERI Bohart

I received 11 nests of this species from 4 stations in the Highlands Ridge sand-scrub area of the Archbold Biological Station, Lake Placid, Fla., in 1961. Ten were from settings beneath the limbs of live scrub hickory, and 1 was from the limb of a live oak. Eight nests were in 3.2-mm. and 3 in 4.8-mm. borings.

Supersedure and competition. An unidentified vespid superseded *beameri* in one of the 4.8-mm. nests. There was no actual competition in this nest, because the female of *beameri* stored 3 cells and then made a vestibular cell which ended 40 mm. from the outer end of the boring. The unknown vespid came along subsequently and in the remainder of the boring made 1 cell whose occupant was parasitized by a bombyliid.

Nest architecture. *S. beameri* females placed an egg at the inner end of each boring without first bringing in some agglutinated sand.

In 4.8-mm. borings 5 female cells were 15-25 mm. long (mean 18) and 9 male cells 12-43 mm. (mean 22). Five male cells in 6.4-mm. borings were 12-19 mm. long (mean 15).

There were no empty intercalary cells. Vestibular cells 11-30 mm. long (mean 19) were present in only 3 of the 8 completed nests in 3.2-mm. borings. Each of the 3 nests in 4.8-mm. borings had a vestibular cell 15-121 mm. long (mean 69).

The partitions capping stored cells and the closing plugs at the nest entrances were made of agglutinated sand. The former were 1-3 mm. thick (mean 2) and the latter 2-9 mm. thick (mean 4).

There were 2-3 stored cells (mean 2.5) in eight 3.2-mm. nests and 1-5 stored cells (mean 3) in three 4.8-mm. nests.

Males only were produced in 3 nests each in 3.2- and 4.8-mm. borings. Both sexes were produced in 4 nests in 3.2-mm. borings and a female only in 1 nest.

Prey. Lepidopterous head capsules were attached to some of the cocoon walls, but even family identifications were impossible. At Kill Devil Hills *S. krombeini* Bohart, the closest relative of *beameri*, used larvae of Olethreutidae and Gelechiidae.

Life history. No information was obtained on the duration of the egg and larval feeding stages. Two males pupated 5 and 7 days after the larvae completed feeding. The period between pupation and emergence of the adults was 16 days for a female and 15-17 days for 3 males. These meager data suggest that the complete life cycle requires about 28-30 days.

The cocoons were delicate, white, and subopaque. In 3.2-mm. nests 1 female cocoon was 11 mm. long, and 2 males were 8 and 12 mm.

There was concurrent emergence in the few nests in which both sexes developed and emerged.

The dates of completion of larval feeding in 3 nests suggest that 1-2 cells may be stored per day.

Adults emerged June 12 to September 18 from nests stored from mid-May until the latter part of August. There are probably at least 3 generations annually.

I reared 5 females and 14 males from 29 stored cells. Males would probably have developed in at least 3 of the 10 cells from which I failed to rear adults; so these few nests indicate a possible sex ratio of 1:3.

Parasites and predators. The bombyliid *Anthrax argyropyga* Wiedemann parasitized 2 cells in a 3-celled nest. The bombyliid

Toxophora amphitea Walker parasitized 1 cell in a 3-celled nest, and another *Toxophora,* most likely this same species, parasitized 1 of 2 cells in a third nest; the *Toxophora* pupa was killed when the wasp emerged from the preceding cell.

Source material. Lake Placid, Fla. 1961 series: F 8, 12, 77, 78, 79, 193, 197, 198, 199, 306, 307.

Identifications. Bombyliidae by W. W. Wirth; wasps by the author.

STENODYNERUS (STENODYNERUS) KROMBEINI Bohart

This wasp nested in 23 nests at 15 stations on the barrens at Kill Devil Hills, N. C., 1954-1956. Ten nests were in settings suspended from live or dead branches of scrubby live oak, 8 in similar

TABLE 13.—*Measurements (in mm.) of cells in nests of* Stenodynerus (S.) krombeini *Bohart*

Boring diameter	Sex	STORED CELLS			VESTIBULAR CELLS		
		No.	Range in length	Mean length	No.	Range in length	Mean length
4.8	♀	29	11-24	15	6	8-97	42
	♂	24	10-27	15			
6.4	♀	6	8-14	11	0	—	—
	♂	6	11-15	13			

settings on Spanish oak, 3 on branches of pond pine, and 2 on branches of *Myrica.* Eighteen nests were in 4.8-mm. and 5 were in 6.4-mm. borings.

Nest architecture. In 8 nests the wasps put some agglutinated sand at the inner end of the boring or made a partition of that material 10-73 mm. from the inner end before laying the first egg. In the other nests the wasps laid an egg at the inner end without first bringing in sand.

Measurements of the stored and vestibular cells are presented in table 13.

There were only 6 completed nests and each of them had a vestibular cell. One of the vestibular cells was divided by a transverse partition. There were no empty intercalary cells.

The partitions capping the stored cells and the closing plugs at the nest entrances were made of firmly agglutinated sand. The former were 0.5-2 mm. thick (mean 1.1) and the latter 1-6 mm. thick (mean 2.5).

Six completed nests in 4.8-mm. borings had 5-10 stored cells (mean 7.3). There were no completed nests in 6.4-mm. borings, but one of them had 7 stored cells, the outermost of which was not capped by a thicker plug than usual or by a vestibular cell.

In 4.8-mm. nests both sexes were reared from 4 nests, females only from 10 nests and males only from 4 nests. Both sexes were reared from 3 nests in 6.4-mm. borings and males only and females only from 1 nest each.

Prey. Samples of the caterpillar prey were preserved from 4 nests during 1955 and 1956. These consisted of a species of Gelechiidae and a species of Olethreutidae. Mixtures of these 2 species were found in 4 cells in 3 nests. The gelechiid species only was found in 2 cells in the fourth nest.

A male developed in a cell containing 11 caterpillars of 2 different species; no samples were kept from this cell. Two adjacent cells in another nest contained, respectively, 3 of the gelechiid and 7 of the olethreutid, and a dozen of the gelechiid and 4 of the olethreutid; the sex of the wasps in these cells could not be predicted.

Life history. One larva required 4 days to consume the caterpillars stored for it. It spun a cocoon and pupated 6 days after it finished feeding. The period between pupation and adult emergence was 10-14 days (mean 12) for 6 males and 15-19 days (mean 17) for 6 females. The adults remained 2-3 days in the cocoons after eclosion before they emerged from the nest.

The cocoons were delicate, light tan, and subopaque. Seventeen female cocoons in 4.8-mm. borings were 9-19 mm. long (mean 12) and 22 male cocoons 8-18 mm. (mean 12). Two male cocoons in 6.4-mm. borings were 11 and 12 mm. long. The pupa in 1 cocoon lay with its head inward toward the blind inner end of the boring. It was in cell 1 of a nest where the mother had put some sand at the inner end of the boring. The misorientation took place before I opened the nest.

Adults emerged July 24 to September 26 from nests presumably stored from late in June until late in August. Probably there are 2 or 3 generations a year at Kill Devil Hills, where I have collected adults from May 26 to September 11.

Occupants of 1 nest stored during the first week of August, and of several nests stored from mid-August through the first week in September, overwintered as diapausing larvae and transformed to adults the following spring.

The dates on which 5 male larvae completed feeding in 1 nest indicated that these 5 cells were stored during a period of 2-3 days.

The occupants of most mixed nests were arranged in the normal sequence with females in the inner and males in the outer cells. However, in 2 nests the sequence was irregular as follows beginning with the innermost cell (x = larval mortality): x-♂-♀ and ♂-♂-♀-♂-♀-♀-♂.

In 2 mixed nests the first female emerged 5 days after the last male, but in 2 other mixed nests there was concurrent emergence. Emergence of all occupants in multicelled nests required periods of 1-13 days (mean 3.3).

I reared 35 females and 30 males from 83 stored cells. At least 2 females and 2 males probably would have developed in the 18 cells from which I failed to rear adults. It appears that there is a 1:1 sex ratio.

Parasites and predators. The cuckoo wasp *Chrysis* (*C.*) *stenodyneri* Krombein parasitized 4 of 11 cells in 3 nests.

A miltogrammine fly, probably a species of *Amobia,* parasitized 1 cell.

The grain itch mite *Pyemotes ventricosus* (Newport) infested 2 nests in the field and 1 in the laboratory.

Previous observations. I published a few biological notes on this species several years ago (Krombein, 1955b, p. 148). These notes were based on the single nest from Kill Devil Hills in 1954.

Source material.
>   Kill Devil Hills, N. C. 1954 series: E 17. 1955 series: C 5, 21, 23, 30, 41,
>   71, 74, 75, 355, 363, 455, 478, 479. 1956 series: C 32, 37, 40, 61, 188, 307,
>   364, 612, 614.

Identifications. Lepidopterous larvae by H. W. Capps; wasps and mites by the author.

STENODYNERUS (STENODYNERUS) PULVINATUS
SURRUFUS Krombein

I reared this wasp from 23 nests from 11 stations in the Highlands Ridge sand-scrub area of the Archbold Biological Station, Lake Placid, Fla., in 1957, and 1960-1962. Eighteen of the nests were from settings beneath limbs of live scrub hickory, 2 each from beneath limbs of live pine and oak, and 1 from the side of an oak trunk. Six nests were in 3.2-mm., 15 in 4.8-mm., and 2 in 6.4-mm. borings.

Supersedure and competition. It superseded *Euodynerus foraminatus apopkensis* (Robertson) in 1 boring and was superseded by that species in another boring at the same station.

Nest architecture. In 8 nests the wasps put a plug of agglutinated sand at the inner end of the boring or constructed a partition of that material 15-35 mm. from the inner end. In the other nests the wasps laid an egg at the inner end without first bringing in sand.

The lengths of stored and vestibular cells are presented in table 14.

Only 2 completed nests lacked vestibular cells; both of these were in 3.2-mm. borings. Only 1 vestibular cell was divided by a cross partition. There was an empty intercalary cell 8 mm. long between 2 stored *surrufus* cells in 1 of the 4.8-mm. nests. This was in the nest which was superseded by *Euodynerus*.

The partitions capping the stored cells and the closing plugs at the nest entrances were made of firmly agglutinated sand. The partitions were 1-4 mm. thick (mean 2.2), and the closing plugs 1.5-7 mm. (mean 3.8). One of the closing plugs in a 4.8-mm. boring had a small median nipple of sand projecting from the outer surface.

Six completed nests in 3.2-mm. borings had 1-2 stored cells (mean 1.5), 13 completed nests in 4.8-mm. borings had 1-6 stored cells (mean 3.2), and 2 in 6.4-mm. borings had 2-3 stored cells.

TABLE 14.—*Measurements (in mm.) of cells in nests of* Stenodynerus (S.) pulvinatus surrufus *Krombein*

Boring diameter	Sex	STORED CELLS			VESTIBULAR CELLS		
		No.	Range in length	Mean length	No.	Range in length	Mean length
3.2	♀	3	16-27	22	4	9-49	21
	♂	5	18-37	28			
4.8	♀	18	15-62	25	14	13-125	60
	♂	14	15-45	23			
6.4	♀	4	11-15	13	2	49-128	89
	♂	1	—	8			

Both sexes were bred from one 3.2-mm. nest, males only from 3 nests and females only from 2 nests. In 4.8-mm. nests both sexes were reared from 7 nests, males only from 3 and females only from 5. Both sexes and females only were bred from 1 nest each in 6.4-mm. borings.

Prey. The caterpillars stored for prey were identified in 1 cell from each of 4 nests in 1961. One cell in which a female probably would have developed contained 10 caterpillars of a species of Gelechiidae and 2 of a species of Olethreutidae. A male developed in 1 cell which contained 10 specimens of a species of Gelechiidae. A male probably would have developed in a cell which held 5 larvae of Phycitidae, 3 of a species doubtfully belonging to the genus *Salebriaria* and 2 of another genus and species. The fourth cell contained 5 caterpillars of a species of Olethreutidae and 1 of a species of Gelechiidae; the sex of the wasp occupant could not be forecast with certainty.

Life history. No information was obtained on the duration of the egg stage or larval feeding period. The period between completion of larval feeding and pupation in the summer generation was 6-8 days (mean 7) for 3 females and 7-9 days (mean 8.5) for 5 males. The period between pupation and adult emergence was 16-21 days (mean 19) for 5 females and 15-19 days (mean 18) for 5 males. Allowing 7 days for the combined egg stage and larval feeding period would give a period of 29-36 days for the complete life cycle during the summer generation. The complete life cycle was 30-31 days in a nest first occupied by the mother on June 26 from which 2 females and a male emerged on July 27.

The cocoons were the usual delicate, silken, white, subopaque structures. Twelve female cocoons in 4.8-mm. borings were 11-22 mm. long (mean 15), and 7 male cocoons were 11-25 mm. (mean 16). A female cocoon in a 3.2-mm. boring was 19 mm. long, and 3 male cocoons were 11-21 mm. (mean 14). Three female cocoons in 6.4-mm. borings were 9-12 mm. (mean 10).

Data from several nests indicate that 1-2 cells may be stored per day.

Adults emerged from late in April until September 21 from nests provisioned between the latter part of March and the latter part of August. In 3 nests stored throughout November the resting larvae had to be subjected to 2 months of chilling weather in Arlington to break the larval diapause.

The traps were stored during late March, April, May, June, July, August, and November. The nesting and life history data obtained during this study suggest the possibility of a minimum of 6 generations a year with probably continuous breeding from late March into November.

I reared 25 females and 20 males from 58 stored cells. A minimum of 4 females and 3 males probably would have been bred from the 13 cells from which I failed to rear adult wasps, and so it appears that there is a 1:1 sex ratio.

Females developed in the inner and males in the outer cells in all mixed nests except one 3-celled nest where the sequence was ♂-♀-♂.

Parasites and predators. The cuckoo wasp *Chrysis* (*C.*) *inaequidens* Dahlbom parasitized 4 of 10 cells in 2 nests.

A bombyliid fly *Anthrax argyropyga* Wiedemann parasitized the prepupae in 2 of 6 cells in 2 nests.

Maggots of a miltogrammine fly, undoubtedly a species of *Amobia,* destroyed 3 cells in a 4-celled nest.

Previous observations. The only published biological data on this wasp are those I included with my original description (Krombein,

1959a, p. 150) based on the first two nests I received. Data from these have been incorporated in the account given above.

Source material.
    Lake Placid, Fla. 1957 series: M 286, 287. 1960 series: B 147, 153. 1961
        series: F 1, 2, 5, 74, 80, 99, 100, 147, 157, 258, 262, 292, 297, 299, 300.
        1962 series: P 5, 88, 149, 197.

Identifications. Lepidopterous larvae by H. W. Capps; Bombyliidae by W. W. Wirth; wasps by the author.

STENODYNERUS (STENODYNERUS) AMMONIA
AMMONIA (Saussure)

This vespid stored a single cell in a 3.2-mm. boring at Lake Placid, Fla., in 1962. The trap was suspended from the branch of a live scrub hickory in the Highlands Ridge sand-scrub area of the Archbold Biological Station.

Nest architecture. The nest contained a single cell 60 mm. long capped by a partition of agglutinated sand 1.5 mm. thick. There was not a preliminary sand plug in the inner end of the boring.

Prey. The single stored cell contained 15 paralyzed caterpillars of a species of Blastobasidae of which I preserved 2.

Life history. As I had this boring under observation during a period of residence at the Station, I can furnish some notes on the nesting activity. I first noted the female entering the boring at 0904 hours on June 20. She made several flights from the boring between 0914 and 0937, though she did not bring in prey. I worked elsewhere for the next 2 hours. It was overcast when I came back at 1135, and the wasp was resting just inside the boring entrance with her head outward. There was a heavy shower from 1200-1300, and the wasp was not in the boring at 1410. Ten minutes later she returned, entered head first, backed out immediately, and then backed into the boring (to oviposit?). She flew off at 1423 and flew back 26 minutes later carrying a paralyzed caterpillar. She backed out a minute later and flew off. She returned 44 minutes later, at 1534, with another paralyzed caterpillar. Again, she backed out of the boring within a minute and flew off. She returned at 1652, this time without a caterpillar, entered the boring head first, backed out almost at once, and then backed in. She remained in this position until 1737 when she flew out and did not return by 1740 when I left. She was back in the boring, head outward, at 1930.

I saw her fly in and out several times on the 21st, but I made no detailed notes. On the 22d she was not in the boring when I checked it at 0758 and 1112. The next time I checked the trap was at 1130 on June 23. By this time she had constructed a partition of agglutinated sand just within the entrance.

I opened the nest at 1230 on June 23 and found a newly hatched vespid larva in the single cell. If oviposition took place when I surmised, at 1420 on June 20, the egg must have hatched in a few hours less than 3 days. The wasp larva finished feeding on the 13 caterpillars June 28, and spun a delicate cocoon 10 mm. long of subopaque white silk. Pupation occurred on July 8, and an adult female wasp died during eclosion about the 23rd.

Parasites and predators. A female phorid fly, *Megaselia aletiae* (Comstock), flew out when I split open the nest, and I removed 3 of her larvae from the cell.

Source material.
    Lake Placid, Fla. 1962 series: P 8.

Identifications. Lepidopterous larvae by H. W. Capps; Diptera by W. W. Wirth; wasp by the author.

STENODYNERUS (STENODYNERUS) AMMONIA HISTRIONALIS (Robertson)

I reared this subspecies from 19 nests from 13 stations on the barrens at Kill Devil Hills, N. C., 1954-1956. Eleven nests were in 4.8-mm. and 8 were in 6.4-mm. borings. Eleven nests were from settings beneath live or dead branches of scrubby Spanish oak, 7 beneath branches of scrubby live oak, and 1 beneath the limb of a pond pine.

Nest architecture. In 9 nests the wasps laid an egg at the inner end of the boring without first making a plug of agglutinated sand. In the other nests the wasps first placed some agglutinated sand at the inner end or made a partition of this material 28-75 mm. from the inner end.

In 4.8-mm. borings 26 female cells were 11-70 mm. long (mean 18), and 4 male cells were 15-21 mm. (mean 17). Eleven female cells were 11-27 mm. long (mean 16) in 6.4-mm. borings, and 7 male cells were 14-30 mm. (mean 18).

There was a single empty intercalary cell 40 mm. long between 2 stored cells in a 4.8-mm. boring. Vestibular cells 8-105 mm. long (mean 42) were present in 10 of 11 completely stored nests. Three of the vestibular cells were divided by a transverse partition.

The partitions capping the stored cells and the closing plugs were made of firmly agglutinated sand. The former were 1-4 mm. thick (mean 2), and the latter were 2-17 mm. long (mean 8).

Six completed nests in 4.8-mm. borings had 1-9 stored cells (mean 4.7), and 5 in 6.4-mm. borings had 2-7 stored cells (mean 4.6).

Both sexes were reared from 3 nests in 4.8-mm. borings, females only from 7 nests and males only from 1 nest. In 6.4-mm. borings both sexes were reared from 3 nests and females only from 5 nests.

Prey. Partial or complete samples of the caterpillar prey were preserved from 7 nests during these 3 years. Consolidated identifications were as follows:

> Olethreutidae, sp. in 4 cells in 3 nests
> Gelechiidae, sp. in 3 cells in 3 nests
> Tortricidae, sp. in 3 cells in 3 nests

A female wasp probably would have developed in a completely stored cell containing 5 larvae of a tortricid. Male wasps developed in 2 adjacent cells of another nest containing respectively 7 and 8 olethreutid larvae.

Usually only a single species of caterpillar was stored in an individual cell, but I preserved an olethreutid and a tortricid from one cell, and an olethreutid and a gelechiid from a single cell in another nest.

Life history. No information was obtained on the size of the egg or on the length of time required for it to hatch. A female larva required 4 days to consume its store of prey. Two females of the summer generation pupated 5-6 days after they completed larval feeding. The period from pupation to adult emergence was 15-18 days (mean 16) for 11 females and 13-18 days (mean 15) for 8 males; these figures are for both summer and overwintering nests. Adults usually spent 3-4 days in the cocoons after eclosion from the pupal exuvia.

This wasp made the usual delicate, white, subopaque cocoon. Thirteen female cocoons in 4.8-mm. borings were 11-15 mm. long (mean 13), a male cocoon 12 mm. In 6.4-mm. nests 3 female cocoons were 9-15 mm. long (mean 11), and 6 male cocoons were 8-17 mm. (mean 12).

Most of the larvae were properly oriented in their cocoons with their heads toward the entrance. However, 1 individual in each of 3 nests misoriented and lay with its head toward the blind inner end of the boring. One specimen may have misoriented because of damage to the partitions when I opened that nest for examination, but the other 2 specimens misoriented before the nests were opened. One was a dwarf individual which had left 6 of its caterpillars untouched when it spun its cocoon.

Data from two 4-celled nests indicate that they were stored during a period of 2-3 days.

Adults emerged July 17 to September 5 from nests stored between late June and early August. Occupants of nests stored later in August and early in September overwintered as resting larvae and transformed to adults the following spring. Data from these nests and from my collecting at Kill Devil Hills, where I have netted *ammonia histrionalis* from May 24 to September 13, suggest that there may be three generations a year.

I reared 37 females and 11 males from 74 stored cells. Inasmuch as a minimum of 6 females and 1 male might have been expected from the 26 cells from which I failed to rear adults, it appears that the sex ratio is probably 3:1.

The sequence of sexes in mixed nests was the normal one of females in the inner cells and males in the outer, except for one nest where the sequence in cells 1-7 was ♂-♂-x-♀-♂-♂-♂.

Parasites and predators. The cuckoo wasp *Chrysis* (*C.*) *stenodyneri* Krombein was reared from 1 cell. Miltogrammine maggots, *Amobia erythrura* (Wulp), destroyed 6 cells in a 7-celled nest. Another miltogrammine, possibly the same species, was found in a cell in another nest. The mite *Pyemotes ventricosus* (Newport) infested 1 nest, probably after it was brought into the laboratory.

Previous observations. Several years ago (Krombein, 1955b, pp. 147-148) I published some biological notes on *ammonia histrionalis* based on the 1954 nest from Kill Devil Hills.

Source material.
> Kill Devil Hills, N. C. 1954 series: E 25. 1955 series: C 10, 17, 49, 50, 76, 348, 442, 458. 1956 series: C 22, 346, 443, 444, 445, 456, 457, 467, 482, 609.

Identifications. Lepidopterous larvae by H. W. Capps; Miltogrammini by W. L. Downes, Jr.; wasps by the author.

STENODYNERUS (STENODYNERUS) LINEATIFRONS Bohart

This wasp nested in 15 borings at 11 stations on the barrens at Kill Devil Hills, N. C., in 1955, 1956 and 1958, and in 11 borings from 8 stations in the Highlands Ridge sand-scrub area of the Archbold Biological Station, Lake Placid, Fla., in 1957 and 1959-1962. The nests at Kill Devil Hills were suspended from living and dead branches of scrubby live and Spanish oaks and bayberry. The nests at Lake Placid were from similar settings beneath the limbs of scrub hickory and oaks. Two nests were in 3.2-mm., 19 in 4.8-mm., and 5 in 6.4-mm. borings.

Nest architecture. In 5 nests the wasps placed some agglutinated sand at the inner end of the boring, or constructed a partition of that material 11-18 mm. from the inner end before laying any eggs. In the other nests the wasps laid an egg near the inner end without first bringing in sand.

The cells in the Florida nests were usually longer than those in North Carolina nests, and so I have tabulated them separately in table 15. It is possible that these differences are not significant because of the rather small number of cells measured.

Vestibular cells were lacking in the only 2 completed nests in 3.2- and 6.4-mm. borings. Such a cell was present in all but 2 of 14 completed nests in 4.8-mm. borings. One of them was divided by a cross partition.

There was 1 intercalary cell of 11 mm. between 2 stored cells in a 4.8-mm. nest from Lake Placid, and 1 of 15 mm. in a 6.4-mm. nest from Kill Devil Hills.

The partitions capping the stored cells and the closing plugs at the nest entrances were made from firmly agglutinated sand.

TABLE 15.—*Measurements (in mm.) of cells in nests of* Stenodynerus (S.) lineatifrons *Bohart*

Boring diameter	Locality	Sex	STORED CELLS			VESTIBULAR CELLS		
			No.	Range in length	Mean length	No.	Range in length	Mean length
3.2	Fla.	♀	1	—	24	0	—	—
		♂	2	32-40	35			
4.8	N. C.	♀	23	12-26	15	4	8-50	26
		♂	3	—	14			
	Fla.	♀	11	14-31	23	8	7-85	40
		♂	10	15-54	28			
6.4	N. C.	♀	10	12-31	17	0	—	—
		♂	4	25-32	29			
	Fla.	♀	4	12-18	15	0	—	—
		♂	2	13-60	37			

The partitions were 0.5-4 mm. thick (mean 1.3) and the closing plugs were 3-11 mm. thick (mean 5.0).

There were 2 stored cells in each of the 3.2-mm. nests. In completed nests in 4.8-mm. borings there were 5-9 stored cells (mean 7.3) in 4 nests from North Carolina and 2-4 (mean 3) in 6 completed nests from Florida. In the 2 completed nests in 6.4-mm. borings there were 5 and 7 stored cells, respectively, in nests from North Carolina and Florida.

In the 3.2 mm. nests both sexes were reared from 1 nest and a male only from the other. There were both sexes in 7 nests in 4.8-mm. borings, females only in 9 nests, and males only in 3 nests. In 6.4-mm. nests both sexes were reared from 2 and females only from 3 nests.

Prey. Consolidated identifications of prey from the two areas are as follows:

> Kill Devil Hills, N. C., 6 nests, 1955, 1956, 1958
>> Olethreutidae, sp. in 7 cells in 5 nests
>> Tortricidae
>>> sp. in 1 cell
>>> *Rhyacionia frustrana* (Comstock) in 1 cell
>> Gelechiidae, sp. in 1 cell
>
> Lake Placid, Fla., 3 nests, 1957, 1960
>> Olethreutidae, sp. in 3 cells in 3 nests
>> Gelechiidae, sp. in 2 cells in 2 nests

Four completely stored cells of undetermined sex in 2 nests at Kill Devil Hills contained a total of 32 larvae of a species of Olethreutidae. Most cells at that locality from which I preserved samples were stored with this single species. However, one cell contained both this olethreutid species and the tortricid *Rhyacionia frustrana,* and a cell in another nest contained a gelechiid species and a tortricid species.

At Lake Placid 1 cell contained an olethreutid species only, but 1 cell each in 2 other nests contained this olethreutid and a gelechiid. A male cell contained 8 olethreutid caterpillars and a small pink gelechiid larva.

Life history. A male larva in one of the Florida nests required 6 days to consume its store of caterpillars. The period between pupation and adult emergence was 14-19 days (mean 16.5) for 4 females and 12-16 days for 2 males. The period between completion of larval feeding and adult emergence was 29-43 days for 2 early spring females from Florida and 19-20 days for a Florida female in midsummer.

The cocoons were delicate, subopaque, and varied in color from white to light tan. A male cocoon in a 3.2-mm. boring was 11 mm. long. In 4.8-mm. borings 28 female cocoons from both localities were 8-13 mm. long (mean 10) and 10 male cocoons were 8-15 mm. (mean 10). Nine female cocoons in 6.4-mm. borings were 10-12 mm. (mean 11), and 6 males were 8-12 mm. (mean 10). One larva misoriented in its cocoon and lay with its head toward the blind inner end of the boring. This misorientation was possibly due to my having damaged the partitions before the larva spun. One cocoon was anomalous in that it was covered on the outside with sand grains; apparently the partition capping the cell was not made of firmly agglutinated sand grains and the wasp larva covered the outside of its cocoon with the loose sand.

At Kill Devil Hills adults emerged July 24-August 30 from nests provisioned from the latter part of June until August 10. Occupants of nests stored from the latter part of July through August overwintered as diapausing larvae.

There was divided emergence in one 3-celled nest being stored on August 10. On that date cell 1 contained a prepupa in its cocoon, cell 2 contained a larva just completing its feeding (this larva preserved on this date), cell 3 contained a wasp larva half-grown, and what would have been cell 4 contained a wasp egg and a few caterpillars. The occupant of cell 1 pupated in mid-August and an adult female was removed on August 30 as she began to chew through the partition capping her cell. The occupant of cell 3 over-wintered as a diapausing larva and an adult female emerged the following spring. It may be that there was supersedure and that cell 1 was stored by a different mother from cell 3. However, there was no empty cell between stored cells to indicate this. There appear to be only 2 generations annually in coastal North Carolina.

Adult wasps emerged April 3 to August 21 from nests stored at Lake Placid between the first of March and the latter part of July. Nests were stored in Florida during March, April, June, and July, and it appeared that there were several generations a year with more or less continual breeding during the warmer months.

Data from 4 nests at Kill Devil Hills suggest that 1.5-3 cells may be stored per day. However, 2 nests stored early in the season in Florida showed a probable provisioning rate of ¾-1 cell per day.

In nests in which both sexes developed, emergence of the last male and first female was concurrent in 4, and in 4 others a period of 3-9 days elapsed. Emergence of all occupants from 13 multi-celled nests required periods of 1-16 days (mean 4.5), but took place on a single day in 3 other nests.

I reared 36 females and 13 males from 70 stored cells at Kill Devil Hills, and 16 females and 14 males from 40 cells at Lake Placid. Females probably would have developed in at least 10 of the 21 cells from which I failed to rear adults at Kill Devil Hills, and so the sex ratio there would appear to be at least 3:1. At Lake Placid at least 1 female and 2 males would have developed in the 10 cells from which I failed to rear adults, and so the sex ratio in that locality may be 1:1.

Parasites and predators. The cuckoo wasp *Chrysis* (*C.*) *stenodyneri* Krombein was reared from 2 of 13 cells in 2 nests at Kill Devil Hills. Probably the same species parasitized 1 of 4 cells in another nest at the same locality.

The bombyliid *Toxophora amphitea* Walker parasitized 5 of 8 cells in 3 nests at Lake Placid. I failed to rear adult bombyliids from 4 of 9 parasitized cells in a nest at Kill Devil Hills.

The grain itch mite *Pyemotes ventricosus* (Newport) infested 1 nest from Kill Devil Hills in the laboratory.

Previous observations. A few years ago (Krombein, 1953, p. 115) I reported capturing a female *lineatifrons* climbing over foliage of a scrubby live oak on the barrens at Kill Devil Hills, carrying a paralyzed caterpillar 6.6 mm. long of a species of *Rhyacionia*, possibly *frustrana* (Comstock), in her mandibles.

Source material.

Kill Devil Hills, N. C. 1955 series: C 52, 55, 56. 1956 series: C 39, 59, 60, 62, 86, 357, 486, 608, 649, 700. 1958 series: T 5, 90.

Lake Placid, Fla. 1957 series: M 127, 131, 132. 1959 series: V 100. 1960 series: B 8, 27, 52. 1961 series: F 211, 290, 296. 1962 series: P 7.

Identifications. Lepidopterous larvae by H. W. Capps; Bombyliidae by W. W. Wirth; wasps by the author.

STENODYNERUS (STENODYNERUS) VANDUZEEI Bohart

I obtained 2 nests of this relatively rare species from 2 stations on the desert floor at Portal, Ariz., in 1960 and 1961. Both were in 3.2-mm. borings, one being on a support beneath a bridge, and the other from a setting on a mesquite trunk.

Nest architecture. There was no mud at the inner end of the borings. One nest contained 2 stored cells 32 and 25 mm. long, and the other 3 cells 18, 17, and 23 mm. long. Males emerged from all but cell 3 in the second nest; the occupant of that cell was probably a male also. Neither nest had intercalary or vestibular cells. The partition capping cell 1 in the first nest was 2 mm. thick and made of mud. The closing plug of this nest was 4 mm. thick and consisted of some tiny pebbles mixed with the mud.

Prey. Caterpillar remains were attached to some of the cocoons.

Life history. Both nests were presumably stored late in the season, perhaps during September. All the occupants were diapausing larvae in cocoons when I opened the nests in December 1960 and November 1961. The 5 cocoons were delicate, white, opaque, and 10-14 mm. long (mean 12).

I kept both nests outdoors in Arlington over the winter. In the first nest the occupant of cell 2 pupated between May 12 and 18, and an adult male emerged June 7; the occupant of cell 1 pupated later, and that male emerged June 20. In the second nest the occupants of cells 1 and 2 pupated between June 2 and 8, and adult males emerged from the nest on the 22d.

Source material.

Portal, Ariz. 1960 series: X 11. 1961 series: G 298.

Identifications by the author.

STENODYNERUS (PARANCISTROCERUS) PEDESTRIS
PEDESTRIS (Saussure)

I received 2 nests of this wasp from Derby, N. Y., in 1955. One was in a 3.2-mm. and one in a 4.8-mm. boring. Both were from the same station, a rocky cliff along a stream, and both were provisioned at the same time and probably by the same female.

Nest architecture. There was no mud at the inner end of either boring. The wasp laid her first egg in each boring near the inner end.

The 3.2-mm. nest had 3 stored cells 15, 20, and 16 mm. long; females developed in the first 2 cells and the occupant of the third cell died as a larva. There was a vestibular cell 9 mm. long with a closing mud plug 2 mm. thick.

The 4.8-mm. nest had 5 stored cells 16, 15, 17, 18, and 16 mm. long; females developed in cells 1-3, a male in cell 4, and the occupant of cell 5 died before maturity but was probably a male. There were 2 empty intercalary cells 21 and 22 mm. long between stored cells 2 and 3. There was a vestibular cell 25 mm. long with a mud closing plug 3 mm. thick. The cocoons in this nest were delicate, white, subopaque, and a couple of millimeters shorter than the cell lengths.

Prey. Two caterpillars remaining in cell 5 of the second nest were identified as a species of Gelechiidae.

Life history. The nests were stored between June 19 and July 5, presumably closer to the earlier date because adult females were already eclosed in a couple of the cells on July 20 when I opened the nests. The occupants of the other cells eclosed and died in the nests between that date and August 1.

Parasites and predators. All but 1 cell in each nest was infested with the saproglyphid mite *Vespacarus pedestris* Baker and Cunliffe.

Previous observations. Rau (1928, pp. 388-395; 1935c, p. 110) reported that *pedestris* nested in Missouri in abandoned borings of other insects in twigs of sumac and elder. In his earlier account he used the synonymous name *Odynerus conformis* Saussure in describing the nests of *pedestris.*

He found 3-5 stored cells 8-22 mm. long per nest. He did not correlate the cell length with the sex of the occupant. Vestibular cells 5-51 mm. long were present in only 2 of the nests. However, he mentioned empty spaces above the terminal stored cells in several nests, and perhaps the closing plugs in these nests were lost during transport from the field to the laboratory. There was an empty intercalary cell 29 mm. long between 2 stored cells in one nest. The cell partitions were of mud and usually quite thin, although he recorded a range of thickness of 1.6-6.4 mm. in one nest.

As adult wasps emerged early in May, during June, and in mid-August, there are assuredly at least two generations in Missouri.

He reared the bombyliid fly *Toxophora amphitea* Walker from a cell in 1 nest.

The Raus' (1918, pp. 332-334) earlier notes on *pedestris* nesting in a clay bank were based on a misidentification of the wasp, according to an annotation by S. A. Rohwer in his personal copy of the publication.

Source material.

Derby, N. Y. 1955 series: D 11a, 12b.

Identifications. Acarina by E. W. Baker; lepidopterous larvae by H. W. Capps; wasps by the author.

STENODYNERUS (PARANCISTROCERUS) PEDESTRIS BIFURCUS (Robertson)

I received 2 nests of this wasp in 3.2-mm. borings from the Archbold Biological Station, Lake Placid, Fla., in 1960. The nests were from 2 different stations in the Highlands Ridge sand-scrub area, 1 beneath the limb of a live scrub hickory, the other beneath an oak limb.

Nest architecture. In the first nest the inner end lacked a sand plug, there was a single female cell 24 mm. long, and a vestibular cell 39 mm. long. The partition capping the stored cell was 2 mm. thick and the closing plug 4 mm. thick; both were of firmly agglutinated sand.

In the second nest there was a partition of agglutinated sand 5 mm. from the inner end of the boring. Then there were 3 male cells 13, 13, and 19 mm. long, respectively. There was no vestibular cell. The partitions capping cells 1 and 2 were 1-2 mm. thick, and the partition capping cell 3 was 3 mm. thick.

Prey. No identifiable prey remains were left; but this wasp most certainly preys on caterpillars, as does the typical subspecies *p. pedestris* (Saussure).

Life history. The first nest must have been stored early in June. The prepupa in the only cell was ready to pupate when I opened the nest on June 23. It pupated by the 27th and a female emerged from the nest on July 7.

The dates of storing of the other nest are not known. The occupants were all resting larvae in cocoons when I received the nest on December 30. The cocoons were delicate, white, subopaque and 10, 9, and 15 mm. long, respectively. I kept these nests outdoors in chilly weather in Arlington from January 7 to March 24. The occupants were already pale dark-eyed pupae on March 30. Males failed to eclose in cells 1 and 3; the male in cell 2 eclosed successfully but was dead and dry in its cell on April 14.

Source material.

Lake Placid, Fla. 1960 series: B 6, 75.

Identifications by the author.

STENODYNERUS (PARANCISTROCERUS) BICORNIS
CUSHMANI Bohart

I received 2 nests of this species from Portal, Ariz., in 1960. Both were from a station beneath a dead branch of live acacia on the desert floor, and may have been stored by the same female. One nest was in a 4.8-mm. and 1 in a 6.4-mm. boring.

Nest architecture. The 4.8-mm. nest had the remains of an old *Trypargilum* nest in the inner end from which the occupants had emerged before the *cushmani* female used the boring. The latter wasp made a transverse partition of mud 73 mm. from the inner end to seal off the *Trypargilum* nest. Then, she stored 3 cells 14, 13, and 28 mm. long with prey; the first cell was that of a female wasp. The mud partitions capping the cells were 1.5-2 mm. thick. There was no vestibular cell.

The 6.4-mm. nest had an old bee nest in the inner end from which the occupants had emerged before the *cushmani* female used the boring. The wasp sealed off the old bee nest by a mud partition 35 mm. from the inner end. She then stored 2 female cells 13 and 19 mm. long capped by mud partitions 1.5-2 mm. thick. There was a vestibular cell of 62 mm. with a closing mud plug of 4 mm.

Life history. These nests were not mailed to me until mid-December. Presumably they had been stored during the latter part of the summer. The vespid occupants of cell 1 in the 4.8-mm. nest and cells 1 and 2 in the 6.4-mm. nest were diapausing larvae in cocoons when I opened the nests on December 23. Chrysidid wasps had parasitized cells 2 and 3 in the 4.8-mm. nest and had emerged during the summer.

The nests were kept outdoors in Arlington during the rest of the winter until April 16. The 3 female *cushmani* did not pupate until early in June and emerged toward the end of the month. The period between pupation and adult emergence was 17-18 days for the 3 individuals.

It is possible that *cushmani* may have only a single generation a year with nesting occurring during the summer. In a nest of *Stenodynerus r. rectangulis* (Viereck) kept under identical conditions during the winter, the female wasp pupated about April 18 and the adult emerged about May 2, more than 7 weeks earlier than emergence occurred in the *cushmani* nests.

Parasites and predators. An undescribed saproglyphid mite, presumably a species of *Vespacarus*, occurred on all 3 vespids in the 2 nests.

An unknown cuckoo wasp, presumably a species of *Chrysis* subg. *Chrysis*, parasitized 2 cells in a 3-celled nest.

Source material.
   Portal, Ariz. 1960 series: X 123, 223.

Identifications by the author.

STENODYNERUS (PARANCISTROCERUS) TEXENSIS (Saussure)

I received 1 nest in a 4.8-mm. boring from a setting beneath a dead mesquite branch on the desert floor at Portal, Ariz., in 1960. Another nest was in a 3.2-mm. boring, also beneath a mesquite limb, at Granite Reef Dam, Ariz., in 1961.

Supersedure and competition. S. texensis superseded a species of *Ashmeadiella* in the 3.2-mm. nest.

Nest architecture. In the 4.8-mm. nest from Portal the wasp laid an egg at the inner end of the boring without first bringing in mud. The completed nest contained a dozen cells 9-13 mm. long (mean 11); 5 cells containing dead female wasps were 10-11 mm. (mean 11). The mud partitions capping the cells were 1-1.5 mm. thick. The presence of a vestibular cell and closing plug was not noted. This nest was not sent to me until mid-December; the occupants of the 2 outer cells had emerged some time earlier, and there were dead prepupae and fully colored pupae in the other cells.

In the 3.2-mm. nest from Granite Reef Dam there were 2 *Ashmeadiella* cells in the inner 15 mm. of the boring. The *texensis* female then made 3 cells 19 (♀), 8 (♂), and 8 (♂) mm. long, and a vestibular cell 7 mm. long. The mud partitions capping the *texensis* cells were 1 mm. thick and the closing plug was 1.5 mm.

Life history. Very little information is available. There are probably 2 or more generations a year. The Granite Reef Dam nest was stored between May 29 and July 19. The 2 males left the nest while it was in transit, July 20-27, and I removed an eclosed female from cell 1 when I opened the nest on the 28th.

The date of storing the 12-celled nest from Portal could not be ascertained. The occupants of cells 11 and 12 emerged probably several months before the trap was picked up in mid-December. There were dead dry prepupae in cells 1, 2, 5, 7, and 10, and dead, dry, fully colored female pupae in cells 3, 4, 6, 8, and 9. The cocoons were delicate, white, subopaque and 8-10 mm. long.

Parasites and predators. An undescribed saproglyphid mite presumably belonging to the genus *Vespacarus* was found in the acarinarium of the female from the Granite Reef Dam nest.

Previous observations. I recorded this species (Krombein *et al.*, 1958, p. 168), as *lacunus* (Saussure) a synonym, as having been reared from abandoned mud dauber cells, *Sceliphron*.

Source material.
    Portal, Ariz. 1960 series: X 88.
    Granite Reef Dam, Ariz. 1961 series: H 19.

Identifications by the author.

STENODYNERUS (PARANCISTROCERUS) HISTRIO (Lepeletier)

This wasp nested in 5 nests from 5 stations at Kill Devil Hills, N. C., 1954-1956, and in 1 nest from the Highlands Ridge sand-scrub area of the Archbold Biological Station, Lake Placid, Fla., in 1961. The nests at Kill Devil Hills were all in 4.8-mm. borings and from an area of open woods. They were suspended from dead branches of oak, pine, hickory, and *Myrica*. The Florida nest was in a 3.2-mm. boring from a setting beneath the limb of a scrub hickory.

Nest architecture. In 3 nests the wasps laid an egg at the inner end of the boring without first bringing in sand. In the other 3 nests the wasps put some agglutinated sand at the inner end or made a partition of that material 17-43 mm. from the inner end.

In the 3.2-mm. nest there was an empty cell 43 mm. long at the inner end, a male cell 16 mm. long, and a vestibular cell of 6 mm. Seven female cells in 4.8-mm. borings were 14-26 mm. long (mean 20) and 5 male cells were 15-20 mm. (mean 18).

There were no empty intercalary cells between stored cells. There were no completely stored nests in 4.8-mm. borings, and so the only vestibular cell was the 6-mm. cell in the 3.2-mm. boring.

The partitions capping the stored cells were 1-2 mm. thick and the single closing plug was 3 mm. thick. Both partitions and plug were made from firmly agglutinated sand.

One incompleted nest in a 4.8-mm. boring contained 7 stored cells, 4 female and 3 male, in the inner 132 mm. The outer 15 mm. was empty. Presumably the wasp would have made this portion into an empty vestibular cell had she completed the nest. All the cell partitions in this nest, even that capping cell 7, were 1 mm. thick.

In multicelled nests both sexes were present in 1 nest, and males only and females only in 1 nest each.

Prey. None of the caterpillars used as prey was preserved for identification.

Life history. An egg in an incompletely stored cell hatched in 2-3 days. In 3-4 days this larva consumed the 1 caterpillar in the cell with it as well as 8 other caterpillars which I transferred to it from a cell of an unidentified vespid. The pupal period was 21 days in 2 females in an overwintering nest. These females remained in their cocoons for 3 days after shedding the pupal exuvia before they emerged from the nest.

The cocoons were delicate, white, subopaque, and lined the walls and ends of the cells. In 1 nest they were incomplete and covered only the anterior fourth of each cell.

In the single Florida nest the adult male emerged July 18 from a nest presumably completed the latter part of June. Probably there are 3 or more generations a year in Florida.

Adults emerged from the Kill Devil Hills nests the latter part of July from nests presumably stored the latter part of June. Occupants of 2 nests stored early in August overwintered as diapausing larvae and adults emerged the following spring. It is presumed that there are 2 generations a year at Kill Devil Hills, where I have collected adults from May 25 to August 9.

The provisioning rate at Kill Devil Hills was about a cell a day in a 4-celled nest stored early in August.

I reared 7 females and 6 males from 14 completely stored cells.

Parasites and predators. The symbiotic saproglyphid mite *Vespacarus histrio* Baker and Cunliffe was present in all 5 nests from Kill Devil Hills, but it was lacking in the single nest from Lake Placid.

The grain itch mite *Pyemotes ventricosus* (Newport) infested one of the Kill Devil Hills nests. The infestation probably arose in the laboratory.

Previous observations. Some years ago (Krombein, 1955b, pp. 148-149) I published biological notes on *histrio* based on the single nest of this species obtained at Kill Devil Hills in 1954.

Source material.

> Kill Devil Hills, N. C. 1954 series: F 5. 1955 series: C 281. 1956 series: C 117, 238, 367.
> Lake Placid, Fla. 1961 series: F 4.

Identifications. Acarina by E. W. Baker; wasps by the author.

STENODYNERUS (PARANCISTROCERUS) SAECULARIS RUFULUS Bohart

This was the most frequent user of trap nests in this subgenus in Florida. I received 76 nests from 27 stations in the Highlands Ridge sand-scrub area of the Archbold Biological Station at Lake Placid in 1957 and 1959-1962. Fifty-one nests were from setting beneath limbs of live scrub hickory, 19 were in similar settings beneath live limbs of oak, 3 from a setting on an oak trunk, 2 from settings on pine trunks, and 1 from a basement area beneath the laboratory. One nest was in a 3.2-mm., 49 in 4.8-mm., and 26 in 6.4-mm. borings.

Supersedure and competition. Several supersedures were involved in these nests. This wasp superseded one or more species of *Chalicodoma* (*Chelostomoides*) in 4 traps, *Euodynerus foraminatus apopkensis* (Robertson) in 2 nests and *Pachodynerus erynnis* (Lepeletier) in 1 nest. It was superseded by the *Euodynerus* and by *Chalicodoma* in 1 nest each.

Nest architecture. In 44 nests the wasps placed some agglutinated sand at the inner end of the boring or made a partition of that material 2-112 mm. from the inner end before laying the first egg. In the other nests the wasps laid an egg at the inner end without first bringing in sand. There were rather long empty spaces at the inner end of the boring in a number of nests. These coupled with rather long vestibular cells in other nests resulted

TABLE 16.—*Measurements (in mm.) of cells in nests of* Stenodynerus (Parancistrocerus) saecularis rufulus *(Bohart)*

Boring diameter	Sex	STORED CELLS			VESTIBULAR CELLS		
		No.	Range in length	Mean length	No.	Range in length	Mean length
3.2	♂	1	—	42	0	—	—
4.8	♀	65	17-75	30	27	2-76	30
	♂	41	17-109	37			
6.4	♀	33	11-53	25	11	9-120	42
	♂	18	13-75	37			

in a very low number of stored cells per nest, one of the diagnostic features of this wasp.

Consolidated measurements of stored and vestibular cells are tabulated in table 16.

The greater mean length of male cells was unique and anomalous. It was occasioned by the peculiarity that the terminal stored cell frequently was considerably longer than any of the other stored cells, and these terminal cells more frequently housed males than females.

Another peculiarity of these nests was the rather frequent lack of the vestibular cell. Sometimes this lack was associated with an abnormally long terminal stored cell, but these long terminal stored cells occurred occasionally also in nests with a vestibular cell. Sixty-five nests were completely stored, but only 38 had vestibular cells. One of the vestibular cells was divided by a cross partition.

There was an empty intercalary cell 52 mm. long between 2 stored cells in a 4.8-mm. nest.

The partitions capping the stored cells and the closing plugs at the nest entrances were made of firmly agglutinated sand. The partitions were 1-4 mm. thick (mean 2.2) and the plugs were 1-10 mm. (mean 5.1).

The single nest in a 3.2-mm. boring had only 1 stored cell. There were 1-7 stored cells (mean 3.3) in 52 completed nests in 4.8-mm. borings, and 1-6 stored cells (mean 2.6) in 17 completed nests in 6.4-mm. borings.

A male was reared from the 3.2-mm. nest. In 4.8-mm. nests both sexes were reared from 21 nests, females only from 17 and males only from 9. Both sexes were reared from 11 nests in 6.4-mm. borings, females only from 10 and males only from 3.

Prey. Samples of prey were preserved from a number of cells in 17 nests during all 5 years. Consolidated identifications are as follows:

Olethreutidae, sp. in 11 cells in 6 nests
Gelechiidae, sp. in 4 cells in 2 nests
Tortricidae
    sp. in 3 cells in 2 nests
    Rhyacionia sp. in 1 cell
    Platynota sp. in 5 cells in 4 nests
    Platynota rostrana (Walker) in 1 cell
Phaloniidae, sp. in 1 cell
Pyraustidae
    sp. in 12 cells in 5 nests
    Pyrausta tyralis (Guenée) in 7 cells in 5 nests
Phycitidae
    sp. in 7 cells in 6 nests
    Homoeosoma sp. in 1 cell
    Homoeosoma (?) sp. in 1 cell (same cell as line above)
Epipaschiidae, sp. in 1 cell

Some cells and even nests contained only a single species of caterpillar. Other cells had a mixture of 2 to 7 species representing as many as 5 families. Undoubtedly only a single species was preyed upon when the wasp found a plentiful supply, and several species would be stored when caterpillars were less common. The most diverse mixture was in cell 6 from one of the 1957 nests which contained 7 larvae and 1 pupa of a species of Pyraustidae, 4 pupae of a species of Tortricidae, 2 larvae of the tortricid *Platynota* sp., 1 larva of a species of Phaloniidae, 1 pupa of a species of Gelechiidae, 1 pupa of a species of Phycitidae, and 2 pupae of one or two unidentified species. (Undoubtedly pupation of the prey occurred after the mature paralyzed caterpillars were brought into the nest.) Cells 4 and 8 from this same nest also contained a mixture of some of the same species, but only 3 species each.

More caterpillars were stored in cells in which females were to develop. One 3-celled nest was stored with a single species of Pyraustidae of which I preserved 2 caterpillars from each cell for identification. Female wasps developed in cells 1 and 2 which originally held 15 and 10 caterpillars when stored. A cell in another nest in which a female developed had 5 larvae of a species of Epipaschiidae and 6 larvae of a species of Phycitidae. One cell in still another nest in which a female wasp should have developed contained 3 larvae and 4 pupae of a pyraustid, 1 larva and 2 pupae of a gelechiid, and 2 larvae and 1 pupa of a tortricid. A cell from a fourth nest in which a male developed had 10 caterpillars mostly of a single species of Pyraustidae. Two cells in a fifth nest in which male wasps should have developed contained, respectively, 5 and 3 larvae of *Pyrausta tyralis*.

I watched the nesting activities of one female in a 6.4-mm. boring at the Archbold Biological Station on June 18, 1962. I timed 3 provisioning flights at 1½, 2, and 4½ minutes. Each time that the wasp returned with a caterpillar she entered the boring head first with it, remained inside for periods of 1-2½ minutes, then backed out of the boring and flew off. On the following she left the nest for the first time between 0810 and 0825 and returned at 0843 with a caterpillar. Her prolonged absence may not have been due to the difficulty of finding a caterpillar, because she may have fed first before hunting for prey. She abandoned the nest soon after, because I disarranged the contents by probing the boring with a grass stem to determine how much of the boring had been used.

Life history. The eggs were sausage shaped; 2 were 2.5-2.8 mm. long and 0.8-0.9 mm. wide. One of them hatched in 2-3 days on June 27. The larva completely consumed the 11 phycitid and epipaschiid caterpillars stored for it in 6 days. It pupated 8-9 days later, and a female wasp emerged from the nest in another 15-16 days, and so the entire life cycle for this 1 female in midsummer was 33 days.

No other information was obtained on the early stages. In nests of the summer generation 14 female larvae pupated 8-16 days (mean 12) after they completed feeding, and 6 male larvae pupated 9-11 days after completion of feeding. The period between pupation and emergence of the adult was 13-26 days (mean 21) for 29 females and 16-25 days (mean 21) for 13 males.

The cocoons were delicate, white, and subopaque. In 4.8-mm. nests 38 female cocoons were 10-29 mm. long (mean 16) and 21 male cocoons 11-38 mm. (mean 16). In 6.4-mm. nests 14 female cocoons were 9-24 mm. long (mean 15) and 6 male cocoons 11-67 mm. (mean 22).

Most of the larvae came to rest in the cocoon with their heads toward the boring entrance. I noted only two cases of misorientation. One may have been due to damage to cell partitions when I examined the nest prior to spinning of the cocoon. However, the other was already misoriented in its cocoon when I first opened the nest.

The dates of larval maturity in several nests suggest that 2-3 cells may be stored per day under normal conditions.

Adults emerged April 20 to October 24 from nests completed between the second week in March and mid-September. I received a nest which might have been stored about the end of November, because it contained a male pupa when I opened it on January 5. I also received several nests stored during October for which 2 months of chilling weather outdoors in Washington was required to break the larval diapause.

There appeared to be continual storing of nests from mid-March through at least mid-September, and so there are probably a minimum of 5 generations a year.

I reared 77 females and 51 males from 188 stored cells. In the 60 cells from which I failed to rear adults, females would probably have developed in at least 11 cells and males in at least 10.

Parasites and predators. The symbiotic saproglyphid mite *Vespacarus saecularis* Baker and Cunliffe was found in 73 of 76 nests and in most of the cells in those nests.

The cuckoo wasps *Chrysis* (*C.*) *coerulans* Fabricius and *C.* (*C.*) *inaequidens* Dahlbom parasitized 1 cell each in 2 nests.

A female *Melittobia chalybii* Ashmead was found in 1 nest in the field, and the same species infested another nest in the laboratory.

Miltogrammine maggots, undoubtedly belonging to one or more species of *Amobia,* infested 6 of 14 cells in 3 nests.

Phorid maggots, undoubtedly *Megaselia aletiae* (Comstock), occurred in 1 cell each in 2 nests.

Several species of bombyliid flies parasitized this wasp. *Anthrax argyropyga* Wiedemann was reared from 1 cell each in 2 nests. *Lepidophora lepidocera* (Wiedemann) was reared from another nest. A specimen of *Toxophora amphitea* Walker was reared from a fourth nest, and another specimen of *Toxophora,* possibly the same species, parasitized 1 cell in a fifth nest.

I reared the tachinid *Stomatomyia floridensis* (Townsend) from a caterpillar of *Pyrausta tyralis* (Guenée) which was stored for prey.

Previous observations. Bohart (*in* Muesebeck, *et al.,* 1951, p. 903) noted that *saecularis rufulus* had been reared from oak galls on scrub oak in Florida.

Source material.

Lake Placid, Fla. 1957 series: M 142, 143, 171, 186, 242, 251, 285. 1959 series: V 76, 83, 121, 123, 133, 137, 138. 1960 series: B 86, 92, 114, 118, 149.

1961 series: F 22, 28, 29, 30, 52, 93, 94, 115, 145, 150, 159, 166, 168, 178, 182, 183, 195, 200, 203, 205, 208, 209, 212, 216, 222, 237, 243, 255, 263, 264, 280, 281, 288, 291, 294, 312, 320, 334, 336, 350. 1962 series: P 20, 51, 87, 94, 96, 103, 107, 114, 164, 175, 179, 180, 185, 199, 200, 201, 215.

Identifications. Acarina by E. W. Baker; lepidopterous larvae by H. W. Capps; Bombyliidae by W. W. Wirth; Tachinidae by C. W. Sabrosky; wasps and bees by the author.

STENODYNERUS (PARANCISTROCERUS) VOGTI Krombein

This species was described from the single female reared from this nest; no additional specimens have been collected. The nest was constructed in a 4.8-mm. boring at a station on the side of a dead standing tree trunk in open woods at Plummers Island, Md., in 1957.

Prey. Three species of caterpillars were stored in the cell, 2 species of Gelechiidae and 1 of Tortricidae.

Life history. The nest was only partially constructed, when I picked up the trap on August 22. However, apparently it had been abandoned by the mother, because there was a small vespid larva near the inner end with some paralyzed caterpillars. The mother had made a mud partition 3 mm. from the inner end of the boring, then laid an egg and began to bring in prey. She had not made a closing partition for the cell, but there were enough caterpillars for the larva to reach maturity and start to spin a cocoon on August 26.

The wasp larva entered diapause and overwintered outdoors from mid-October until mid-April. It pupated on May 7 and an adult female emerged from the nest on the 23d.

Parasites and predators. The wasp was infested with a saproglyphid mite presumably representing a new species of *Vespacarus.* There were 3 adult mites in the cell when the larva spun its cocoon. They laid eggs on the wasp pupa in May, but none of the eggs developed into hypopi. I preserved one adult, but it could not be identified specifically.

Source material.
    Plummers Island, Md. 1957 series: P 155.

Identifications. Lepidopterous larvae by H. W. Capps; wasp by the author.

STENODYNERUS (PARANCISTROCERUS) PERENNIS ANACARDIVORA (Rohwer)

I received 2 nests of this wasp from the Archbold Biological Station, Lake Placid, Fla., in 1961. Both were in 4.8-mm. borings from a single station beneath the limb of a live scrub hickory in the Highlands Ridge sand-scrub area.

Nest architecture. The wasp (or wasps) laid eggs at the inner ends of both borings without first bringing in agglutinated sand.

The earlier nest had 5 stored cells 15, 13, 14, 14, and 41 mm. long, respectively; females developed in cells 1 and 3 and males in cells 4 and 5. There was a vestibular cell 44 mm. long. The partitions capping the stored cells were 1.5-2 mm. thick, and the closing plug at the nest entrance was 3 mm. thick; both were made of firmly agglutinated sand.

The second nest had 4 stored cells 8, 28, 17, and 10 mm. long, respectively; females developed in cells 1 and 2 and a male in cell 3. There was an empty intercalary cell 84 mm. long between cells 3 and 4. Actually, this may have been a vestibular cell, because the occupant of cell 4 was a nearly mature larva on April 6, when adults were ready to eclose in cells 1 and 2 and the occupant of cell 3 was a pale black-eyed pupa. There was a vestibular cell 4 mm. long. The partitions capping the cells were 1-2 mm. thick and the closing plug was 2 mm. thick; both were made of agglutinated sand.

Prey. A cell in which a female wasp probably would have developed contained 13 caterpillars of a species of Olethreutidae.

Life history. Both nests were sent to me on the same date, and they may have been stored by the same mother. The females in the inner cell in both nests were fully colored pupae when I opened the nests on April 6. Two females and 2 males emerged from 1 nest on April 14. The 2 females and 1 male in the other nest died without being able to cut through the entrance plug. They killed the occupant of cell 4 as they attempted to emerge.

The cocoons were delicate, white, and subopaque. Four female cocoons were 6-11 mm. long (mean 9) and 3 male cocoons 9-12 mm. (mean 10).

Parasites and predators. Both nests were infested by the symbiotic saproglyphid mite *Vespacarus anacardivorus* Baker and Cunliffe.

Previous observations. Krombein and Evans (1955, pp. 228-229) reported on a nest of *perennis anacardivora* found in a dead twig at Paradise Key in the Everglades National Park, Fla. The twig was 6 mm. in diameter and contained a boring 50 mm. long and 1.8 mm. wide made by another insect. There were 3 cells 15, 11, and 14 mm. long, respectively; the egg in cell 1 was dead, and 2 males developed in cells 2 and 3. A partition at the inner end of the boring and those capping the stored cells were 0.5-1.0 mm. thick at the center and as much as 3 mm. thick at the sides; they were made of fragments of pith and other vegetable matter and particles of earth. The outer end of the boring was empty, and there was no closing plug. One cocoon was a complete silken sheath, and in the other cell the larva had made only a vestigial cocoon at the anterior end and had varnished the cell walls. The outer 2 cells were infested with a symbiotic saproglyphid mite, determined subsequently as *Vespacarus anacardivorus*.

Source material.

Lake Placid, Fla. 1961 series: F 17, 18.

Identifications. Lepidopterous larvae by H. W. Capps; Acarina by E. W. Baker; wasps by the author.

STENODYNERUS (PARANCISTROCERUS) RECTANGULIS RECTANGULIS (Viereck)

I obtained 3 nests of this vespid from the desert floor at Portal, Ariz., in 1959 and 1960. The nests came from 3 stations beneath branches of mesquite, hackberry, and juniper. Two were in 4.8-mm. borings and one was in a 3.2-mm. boring.

Supersedure and competition. Trypargilum t. tridentatum (Packard) superseded *rectangulis* in 1 nest.

Nest architecture. In one of the 4.8-mm. nests the wasp put a mud partition 25 mm. from the inner end, and in the other nests the wasps laid eggs at the inner end without first bringing in mud. The former nest was not completed and had just a single female cell 12 mm. long capped by a mud partition 1 mm. thick.

The other nest in a 4.8-mm. boring had 3 female cells 10, 14, and 14 mm. long capped by mud partitions 1 mm. thick. This nest was superseded by *Trypargilum*.

The nest in the 3.2-mm. boring had a single female cell 45 mm. long. This cell was capped by a tough, flexible, transverse partition 0.1 mm. thick which, since it was not made of mud, could not have been made by the mother wasp.

Prey. No whole caterpillars were left in the cells, but one cocoon had an adherent head capsule and shriveled skin which were lepidopterous.

Life history. These nests contained either eclosed dead adults, a pupa, or a diapausing larva; so I obtained no information on duration of the early stages.

The earliest nest must have been stored about mid-June. I opened it on July 20 and found dead adult females of *rectangulis* in the first 3 cells and *Trypargilum* prepupae in cocoons in the next 3 cells. The *Trypargilum* prepupa in cell 4 had been killed by one of the vespids in her attempts to leave the nest. The *Trypargilum* in cells 5 and 6 pupated on July 21. Inasmuch as 12-14 days elapse between spinning of the *Trypargilum* cocoon and pupation, the vespids must have attempted to emerge between July 10 and 20.

The second nest was also opened on July 20 and must have been stored about the first of that month. The single cell contained a pale, dark-eyed pupa. The female wasp eclosed successfully but did not emerge. It was found dead in the trap the next time I opened it on August 27.

The third nest was not sent to me until mid-December and must have been stored some months earlier. It contained a diapausing larva. I kept the nest outdoors for several months until April 16. This female pupated about April 18 and eclosed about May 2.

Two female cocoons in 3.2- and 4.8-mm. borings were each 9 mm. long.

Source material.

   Portal, Ariz. 1959 series: X 75, 102. 1960 series: X 302.

Identifications by the author.

STENODYNERUS (PARANCISTROCERUS) FULVIPES FULVIPES (Saussure)

(Plate 21, Figures 102, 104-107; Plate 22, Figures 109, 110)

I first reared this wasp from a single nest in a 4.8-mm. boring set in a pile of cut firewood at Dunn Loring, Va., in 1954. Later, in 1955 and 1956, I obtained 6 nests from Kill Devil Hills, N. C. Three of the later nests were in 4.8-mm. and 3 in 6.4-mm. borings. They were from 5 different stations on the barrens and at the edge of woods. Four were beneath living and dead branches of scrubby live oak, and 1 each on a dead pine limb and on a wooden fence post.

Nest architecture. In 2 nests the wasps made a partition of agglutinated sand 37-58 mm. from the inner end of the boring before laying the first egg. In the other nests the wasps laid an egg near the inner end without first bringing in sand or mud.

Three female cells in 4.8-mm. borings were 25-35 mm. long (mean 29), and 1 male cell was 36 mm. long. In 6.4-mm. borings 3 female cells were 16-22 mm. long (mean 20).

There was an empty intercalary cell 7 mm. long between 2 stored cells in one of the 4.8-mm. nests from Kill Devil Hills. The 5 completed nests each had a vestibular cell 19-99 mm. long (mean 55). Two of the vestibular cells were divided by a transverse partition.

The partitions capping the stored cells, and the closing plugs at the nest entrances were made of mud in the Dunn Loring nest and of firmly agglutinated sand or mud in the Kill Devil Hills nests. The partitions were 2-3 mm. thick and the closing plugs 3-5 mm.

Two completed nests in 4.8-mm. borings had 2 and 3 stored cells, respectively; and 3 such nests in 6.4-mm. borings had 1, 2, and 3 stored cells, respectively.

In multicelled nests females only emerged from 4 nests and males only from 1.

Prey. A cell in a Kill Devil Hills nest, in which a female probably would have developed, contained 8 caterpillars of a species of Tortricidae, 4 of them partially transformed to pupae.

Life history. I did not obtain any information on the duration of the early stages. The period between pupation and adult emergence from over-wintering nests was 24-28 days for 3 females and 26 days for a male. A similar period was only 13 days for a single female of the summer generation. Adults spent 3-6 days (mean 4) in the nest after eclosion before they left the nest.

The cocoons were delicate, white, and subopaque. Two female cocoons in 4.8-mm. borings were each 15 mm. long, and two female cocoons in 6.4-mm. borings were 15 and 18 mm. long.

It is presumed that there are at least 2 generations annually in each locality. An adult emerged August 11 from a nest stored probably before mid-July. Occupants of nests stored during August and early in September overwintered as diapausing larvae and emerged as adults the following spring.

I reared 6 females and 3 males from 15 stored cells. At least 1 female and 2 males would probably have developed in the 6 cells from which I failed to rear adults.

Parasites and predators. The symbiotic saproglyphid mite *Vespacarus fulvipes* Baker and Cunliffe was found in all 7 nests (figs. 102, 104-107, 109, 110).

The bombyliid fly *Anthrax argyropyga* Wiedemann parasitized 1 of 2 cells in the Dunn Loring nest.

Maggots of an unidentified miltogrammine fly, undoubtedly a species of *Amobia*, destroyed 2 of 3 cells in a nest at Kill Devil Hills.

Previous observations. Rau and Rau (1916, p. 43) found nests of *fulvipes* in old mud dauber nests from Kansas. Later the Raus (1918, pp. 341-344, fig. 68) reported that in Missouri it nested in logs and also that it dug its own tunnels in the vertical face of a clay bank by moistening the earth with water brought in for that purpose; this latter observation requires confirmation. Rau (1935c, p. 112) also found that it nested in an abandoned bee burrow in a clay bank.

The Raus (1918) excavated 4 nests in the clay bank and found the tunnels to be 6.4 mm. in diameter. There were 1-3 stored cells per nest with a length of 13-19 mm. Two nests had vestibular cells 19 mm. long, and 2 nests lacked these cells. They noted that the closing plugs were thicker than the cell partitions.

In a 2-celled nest they found 7 and 8 caterpillars, respectively. Some of these were so lightly paralyzed that they pupated and normal adults emerged. These were identified as the noctuid *Chara-*

coma nilotica Rogenhofer; they mistakenly termed this a butterfly in their book. In a 1-celled nest they found 13 larvae of the tortricid *Cymolomia* [recorded as *Exertema* (!)]. In 4 other cells they counted 6-10 caterpillars, which were not identified for them. Later, Rau (1935c, p. 112) reported on a female which had such a long caterpillar that she alighted on a leaf, folded the prey in half and flew off with the ends tucked against her thorax with her hind-legs.

The Raus (1918) saw a cuckoo wasp enter a cell, but they did not rear the parasite.

Source material.
Dunn Loring, Va. 1954 series: C 34.
Kill Devil Hills, N. C. 1955 series: C 90, 92, 105, 255, 477. 1956 series: C 617.

Identifications. Lepidopterous larvae by H. W. Capps; Acarina by E. W. Baker; *Anthrax* by W. W. Wirth; wasps by the author.

STENODYNERUS (PARANCISTROCERUS) FULVIPES RUFOVESTIS Bohart

This wasp nested in 9 traps at Lake Placid, Fla., in 1957, 1959, and 1962, 5 times in 4.8-mm. borings, and 4 times in 6.4-mm. borings. Eight of the nests were from a station in an open area beneath the laboratory building at the Archbold Biological Station, and one was suspended beneath a limb of a live hickory tree in the High-lands Ridge sand-scrub area of the Station.

Supersedure and competition. This wasp superseded *Trypargilum johannis* (Richards) in 1 nest and a species of *Chalicodoma* (*Chelostomoides*) in another; it was superseded by *T. johannis* in 1 nest.

Nest architecture. The wasps began 5 of the nests by constructing a partition of agglutinated sand grains or mud at or near the inner end of the boring. There were 2 to 4 provisioned cells per nest. In borings of 4.8-mm. diameter 3 male cells were 24 to 54 mm. long and 8 female cells 23 to 69 mm. long. In 6.4-mm. borings 3 male cells were 17 to 41 mm. long, and 2 female cells were 17 to 30 mm. long. Intercalary cells were lacking. Vestibular cells were present in 5 nests and ranged from 7 to 114 mm. in length; one of these cells was divided by a cross partition.

The cell partitions and closing plugs were made from agglu-tinated sand or mud. The partitions were 1 to 3 mm. thick and the closing plugs were 3 to 5 mm. thick.

Prey. Eleven lepidopterous larvae were present in 1 cell in-fested with Miltogrammini. These consisted of 8 specimens of a species of Pyraustidae and 3 specimens of 2 species of Gelechiidae. A cell in another nest contained 13 specimens of the pyraustid

Pyrausta tyralis (Guenée) and 1 specimen of the gelechiid *Trichotaphe* sp.

Life history. Occupants of the nests were in the prepupal or pupal stage when I opened the nests. The cocoons ranged from 13 to 22 mm. long. In 5 nests received from June 30 to September 27, adults emerged from July 18 to October 25. Occupants of 4 nests received from October to December did not transform immediately to pupae but had to be placed outdoors for 2 months of chilly weather to break the diapause. The wasps pupated several weeks after the nests were brought back into the laboratory. The period between pupation and emergence of the adults was 14 to 15 days for 2 individuals, 18 for a third, and 24 for a fourth.

Parasites and predators. Sixteen of the 21 stored cells contained specimens of the symbiotic saproglyphid mite *Vespacarus rufovestis* Baker and Cunliffe.

One cell was infested by Miltogrammini and contained 3 puparia of the fly and remains of the prey stored by the wasp. One adult was reared, a specimen of *Senotainia trilineata* (Wulp) (?).

An adult female of *Melittobia chalybii* Ashmead infested 1 cell in each of 2 nests in the laboratory.

Source material.
    Lake Placid, Fla. 1957 series: M 297, 302, 306, 313. 1959 series: V 129. 1962 series: P 83, 84, 111, 189.

Identifications. Acarina by E. W. Baker; Miltogrammini by W. L. Downes, Jr.; lepidopterous larvae by H. W. Capps; wasps by the author.

STENODYNERUS (PARANCISTROCERUS) TOLTECUS (Saussure)

I received 19 nests of this species from Arizona, 10 from Portal in 1959 and 1961, 3 from Scottsdale in 1961, 5 from Granite Reef Dam in 1961, and 1 from Molino Camp in the Santa Catalina Mountains in 1961. Three nests were in 3.2-mm. borings, 10 in 4.8-mm., and 6 in 6.4-mm. The Portal nests came from 6 stations, 1 on a dead yucca stalk, 1 on a barbed wire fence (4 nests), 1 on dead and 1 on live mesquite, and 2 on desert willow. The Scottsdale nests were from a single station attached to a fence post beneath a palo-verde tree on the desert floor. The Granite Reef Dam nests were from 4 stations on the desert floor, 2 on palo verde, 1 on a dead mesquite limb, and 1 on a blooming ocotillo. The Molino Camp nest was under an *Arbutus* (?) tree on the desert mountainside.

Supersedure and competition. S. *toltecus* superseded an *Ashmeadiella* (?) in 1 nest at Portal; the latter had smeared a little leaf pulp at the inner end of the boring. Later this *toltecus* nest was susperseded by *Trypargilum t. tridentatum* (Packard) in the same boring. This species of *Trypargilum* also superseded *toltecus* in a nest at Scottsdale. An *Ashmeadiella* (?) started to supersede *toltecus* in a nest at Granite Reef Dam but did no more than to plaster a little leaf pulp over the mud partition capping the fifth *toltecus* cell.

Nest architecture. In a dozen nests the wasps laid an egg at the inner end without first bringing in mud. In the other 7 nests the wasps smeared a little mud at the inner end or made a mud partition 20-88 mm. from the inner end before laying the first egg.

Consolidated measurements for the stored and vestibular cells are presented in table 17.

TABLE 17.—*Measurements (in mm.) of cells in nests of* Stenodynerus (Parancistrocerus) toltecus *(Saussure)*

Boring diameter	Sex	STORED CELLS			VESTIBULAR CELLS		
		No.	Range in length	Mean length	No.	Range in length	Mean length
3.2	♀	1	—	20	1	—	12
	♂	5	10-26	17			
4.8	♀	25	10-16	14	5	11-60	29
	♂	19	9-15	12			
6.4	♀	18	8-16	12	4	62-112	79
	♂	7	7-13	10			

There were no empty intercalary cells between stored cells. Vestibular cells were lacking in 2 completed nests in 3.2-mm. borings and in 3 such nests in 4.8-mm. borings.

The partitions capping the stored cells and the closing plugs at the nest entrances were made of mud. The partitions were 0.5-1.5 mm. thick, and the closing plugs 1-5 mm. thick (mean 2). A closing plug in one 4.8-mm. nest had a slender nipple of mud 3 mm. long projecting from the outer surface, and another had a small button of mud on the outer surface.

Three completed nests in 3.2-mm. borings had 1-3 stored cells (mean 2), 7 such nests in 4.8-mm. borings had 6-12 stored cells (mean 8.9), and 4 nests in 6.4-mm. borings had 3-7 stored cells (mean 5.5).

Both sexes were reared from one 3.2-mm. nest, and males only from 2 nests. In 4.8-mm. borings both sexes were reared from 6 nests and only females from 3. In 6.4-mm. borings both sexes were reared from 3 nests and females only from 3.

Prey. S. *toltecus* was very partial to Gelechiidae and stored caterpillars of that family in most cells from which I preserved samples.

One or more species of Gelechiidae were stored in 3 nests each from Portal, Scottsdale, and Granite Reef Dam.

One completed cell in a 6.4-mm. nest from Portal contained 7 larvae of a species of Gelechiidae and 2 of a species of Phycitidae. Another 4.8-mm. nest from Portal, being stored on July 22, contained 81 small gelechiid caterpillars 3-5 mm. long (mean 3.5) in a cell 12 mm. long; there were 76 of a pale-green species and 5 of a black-speckled species. A completed cell in a third nest at Portal held 10 larvae of a species of Gelechiidae.

At Granite Reef Dam 2 cells from 2 nests in which females would probably have developed contained respectively 10 and 16 larvae of a species of Gelechiidae. A cell from a third nest contained 9 larvae of a gelechiid species.

I was unable to preserve the entire contents of any completed cells from Scottsdale nests. Remains from 10 cells in these 3 nests were all of a species of Gelechiidae.

Life history. I picked up one nest in the field on July 22, 1959, while it was being stored and captured the female as she flew back to the nest. The egg was sausage-shaped, 2.2 mm. long and 0.6 mm. wide. That in cell 1 was attached by a thread from the top of the cell about 2 mm. from the inner end of the boring. The egg died before hatching. I obtained no data on the duration of the larval feeding period.

The period between completion of feeding and emergence of the adult was 29 days for a single male in a nest stored about May 1. Inasmuch as the period between pupation and emergence for 12 males was 13-22 days (mean 17), and 15-17 days (mean 16) for 8 females, it is probable that the period between completion of larval feeding and pupation was about 2 weeks.

The cocoons of *toltecus* were delicate, white, subopaque shrouds. In 3.2-mm. nests 1 female cocoon was 17 mm. long and 4 males 12-20 mm. (mean 14). Thirteen female cocoons in 4.8-mm. nests were 8-14 mm. long (mean 11) and 11 males 8-12 mm. (mean 10). In 6.4-mm. nests 7 female cocoons were 6-14 mm. long (mean 10) and a single male cocoon was 11 mm. long.

Adults emerged June 7 to September 29 from nests completed between early May and early September. These data suggest the possibility of at least 3 generations a year. The occupants of the Molino Camp nest overwintered as diapausing larvae and adults emerged the following spring; this nest was completed on an undetermined date between August 10 and October 21.

There was concurrent emergence on a single day from all nests in which both sexes developed. Occupants of the other nests emerged on the same day or within a day of each other.

I reared 44 females and 31 males from 107 stored cells. There should have been at least 4 females and 4 males from the 32 cells from which I did not rear adults; so the sex ratio probably is 1:1.

Parasites and predators. The symbiotic saproglyphid mite *Vespacarus toltecus* Baker and Cunliffe was present in all nests.

The cuckoo wasp *Chrysis (C.) arizonica* Bohart parasitized 8 of 16 cells in 2 nests from Granite Reef Dam. Unidentified chrysidids parasitized a single cell in another nest from Granite Reef Dam and 1 from Portal.

The eulophid *Melittobia chalybii* Ashmead was a primary parasite in a nest from Portal.

The bombyliid fly *Toxophora virgata* Osten Sacken parasitized 2 of 18 cells in 2 nests from Portal. An unreared species of *Toxophora,* undoubtedly this same species, parasitized 4 of 19 cells in 2 other nests at Portal and 2 of 5 cells in a nest from Molino Camp.

The Molino Camp nest was infested in the laboratory by the grain itch mite *Pyemotes ventricosus* (Newport).

Source material.

> Portal, Ariz. 1959 series: X 68. 1961 series: G 9, 43, 52, 60, 87, 92, 250, 321, 323.
>
> Scottsdale, Ariz. 1961 series: H 4, 32, 83.
>
> Granite Reef Dam, Ariz. 1961 series: H 13, 60, 74, 91, 194.
>
> Molino Camp, Santa Catalina Mts., Ariz. 1961 series: H 124.

Identifications. Lepidopterous larvae by H. W. Capps; Acarina by E. W. Baker; wasps by the author.

Superfamily POMPILOIDEA

Family POMPILIDAE

Only a few species of spider wasps nested in these traps. They belonged to the genera *Dipogon* (subgenera *Dipogon* and *Deuteragenia*) and *Auplopus.* The species of *Auplopus* were unique among all the wasps and bees nesting in these borings in that they constructed free mud cells within the boring (figs. 42, 44, 45). In *mellipes* these cells were occasionally separated from each other by a mud partition, but the nests of *caerulescens subcorticalis* lacked these partitions. In one nest, the cells of the latter wasp were placed end to end like a string of beads, and in the other nest each was separated from the next by a few millimeters.

The species of *Dipogon* built a series of linear cells in the borings, which were separated by partitions of various materials. In the single nest of the subgenus *Dipogon* these partitions were narrow and composed entirely of tiny wood chips rasped from the boring wall by the mother wasp. In the subgenus *Deuteragenia* the plugs capping the cells were much thicker and were composed of a great variety of debris gathered from the ground or from rotten wood and occasionally with some intermixed wood chips from the boring walls (figs. 46, 48).

The spider wasps differed from those of other families in these traps except Ampulicidae in that only a single specimen of prey was stored per cell. This meant that the wasps had to prey on an arthropod much larger in relation to the wasp's size than did those species which stored several specimens of prey in a single cell. The species of *Auplopus* usually amputated all, or almost all, of the spider's legs which undoubtedly made it easier to transport and to store the spider in the mud cell. It was very unusual for the species of *Dipogon* to amputate the spider's legs, although sometimes they did so.

DIPOGON (DEUTERAGENIA) SAYI SAYI Banks
(Plate 10, Figures 46 (♀), 47 (♀), 48)

I reared this species from five 6.4-mm. borings from Derby and Rochester, N. Y., and from seventeen 6.4- and thirteen 4.8-mm. borings from the metropolitan area of Washington, D. C. All the traps had been placed along the edges of woods or in wooded areas. Twenty-six nests were in traps suspended from dead branches or tied to dead tree trunks, 7 from branches or trunks of living trees, and 2 from structural timber on an old shed or porch. Thirteen of 18 nests in the period 1960-1962 came from 1 station on the side of a dead, standing barked tree in dense shade.

Supersedure and competition. In 1 Derby nest an unidentified vespid provisioned 1 cell between a *sayi* cell at the inner end of the boring and 3 *sayi* cells at the outer end of the boring. At Plummers Island *sayi* superseded the megachilid bee *Osmia lignaria* Say in 1 nest, and a vespid wasp *Symmorphus* sp. in another nest; it was superseded by the sphecid wasp *Trypargilum clavatum* (Say) in 1 nest and by an unidentified spider wasp belonging to the genus *Auplopus* in another nest.

Nest architecture. In most of the nests the mother wasp placed no barrier at the inner end of the boring. However, in 2 nests *sayi* coated the inner end with a thin layer of mud, in 1 nest the female left the inner 75 mm. empty and then constructed a plug of debris before provisioning the first cell, and in still another nest the female put a little trash at the inner end.

Data from nests in 6.4-mm. borings suggested that male and female cells may be of equal length when an adequate sample is available for measurement. Twenty-three cells of male *sayi* in 6.4-mm. borings were 10 to 49 mm. long (mean 17.4), and 54 female cells were 9 to 78 mm. long (mean 17.7). In 4.8-mm. borings where there were only a few male cells, 8 cells of that sex were 9 to 19 mm.

long (mean 15), and 24 female cells were 11 to 43 mm. (mean 21). The cells of *sayi* were variable in length because the partitions capping them were so variable in thickness, as may be seen from Table 18.

About half of the 25 completely stored nests had an empty vestibular cell near the entrance. These cells were 34 to 75 mm. long in 4.8-mm. nests and 28 to 130 mm. long in 6.4-mm. nests. One vestibular cell was divided into 2 sections by a cross partition. The closing plugs were usually quite short in these nests with a vestibular cell. An empty intercalary cell was present in only 1 *sayi* nest.

The partitions capping the cells were complicated affairs of variable thickness as noted above. The inner part of the partition was

TABLE 18.—*Measurements (in mm.) of cells and partitions in nests of*
Dipogon s. sayi *Banks*

Boring diameter	Number of cells	Range in cell length	Mean cell length	Number of partitions	Range in partition thickness	Mean partition thickness
4.8	51	7-57	20.2	42	2-44	10.3
6.4	106	9-78	17.5	104	1-47	6.1

made of a variety of substances, but the outer end was usually of earth with the external face formed into a concave surface (figs. 46, 48). The partitions in 3 Derby nests were composed respectively of rotted wood bark and other debris, bits of wood and debris, and debris. In the 1 *sayi* nest from Rochester, the partitions were made up of some loose leaf fill at the inner end beyond which was an outer section of densely packed soil mixed with bits of wood and leaf fragments and a little silk. In the Washington area the inner part of the partitions in 12 nests was made of debris of unspecified composition. In several nests this debris consisted of leaf fragments, bits of soil, caterpillar frass, and some silk. Two other nests had the inner section of the partition composed entirely of bits of wood fiber rasped off the boring walls or of these fibers mixed with bits of bark, leaves, and caterpillar frass. In 1 nest all partitions except one were of debris; the exception was made of wood fibers from the boring wall. Two other *sayi* nests had bits of punky wood, in one mixed with caterpillar frass, and in the other with wood fibers from the boring wall, bits of earth, and even a tiny live snail.

The closing plugs at the boring entrances were 10 to 44 mm. long (mean 19) in 4.8-mm. nests, and 4 to 72 mm. long (mean 26) in 6.4-mm. nests. In general they were rather similar in composition to the partitions, but there were several interesting exceptions. In 2 nests the outside of the plug was smeared with a thin layer of a dark, hard, gummy substance. In the Rochester nest the closing plug consisted of 33 mm. of packed mud at the inner end, then 11 mm. of packed wood fibers rasped from the inside of the boring, and then a thin layer of mud smeared over the outer end of the plug.

I observed 1 female fashioning the closing plug of her nest on July 30, 1961. She compacted the material by rubbing it with the bent-under apex of her abdomen. Iwata (1939, p. 24) described similar behavior by one of the Japanese species, *nipponica* (Yasumatsu).

Occasionally, females plug an otherwise empty boring. I watched one doing so on June 28, 1961, at the entrance of an empty 4.8-mm. boring. On that same date I found at this station 2 empty 6.4-mm. borings and 1 empty 3.2-mm. boring, each of which had a closing plug recently fashioned by a *Dipogon*, probably by this same female. The possible explanation for this bizarre behavior was discovered when I opened still another 4.8-mm. boring from this same station on June 28. There were newly hatched *Dipogon* larvae in cells 1 and 2; cells 3-5, the latter not yet complete, were stored with caterpillars by a vespid wasp. Apparently the act of supersedure was enough to trigger this *sayi* female into a series of untimely and inappropriate nest closures.

The number of cells in completed nests ranged from 3 to 11 in 4.8-mm. borings and from 1 to 9 in 6.4-mm. borings. The mean number of stored cells in completed nests in borings of both sizes was 4 per nest when a vestibular cell was present and 8 per nest when a vestibular cell was lacking.

Prey. In my nests *sayi* used only crab spiders (Thomisidae) belonging to the genus *Xysticus* (fig. 47). In the samples mature enough for sex determination these were all females. Normally the wasp did not amputate any of the spider's legs, but a half-grown *Xysticus* sp. from a Derby nest had 2 of the legs amputated beyond the coxae. The wasp may have done this in order to feed on the exuding blood. One spider from the Rochester nest was an adult female of *Xysticus fraternus* Banks. A spider from the Cropley nest was an immature *Xysticus* sp. Spiders from 3 cells of a single nest from Plummers Island were a female *X. funestus* Keyserling, a female *X. ferox* (Hentz), and a juvenile *Xysticus* sp. In 3 other Plummers Island nests a sample from one was a juvenile *Xysticus* sp., from a second a female *Xysticus* sp., and from a third a female *X. ferox*. One cell in the Dunn Loring nest contained an immature female *X. funestus*. Kaston (1948, pp. 424-427) noted that *funestus* and *ferox* are found under bark and stones and *fraternus* under leaf litter on the ground.

The spider was usually stored in the cell on its back with its head toward the entrance. Presumably, then, the female wasp drags it into the boring by the spinnerets. Each cell contained a single, permanently paralyzed spider.

Precise figures are not available on the rate of provisioning. Data from egg hatch and emergence of adults suggest that as many as 3 cells may be stored in a single day.

Life history. The egg was deposited anteriorly on either the right or left side of the spider's abdomen. Usually it was placed somewhat obliquely, but occasionally it was placed vertically. The eggs were sausage-shaped and creamy white; two of them measured 1.4-1.5 × 0.5 mm.

The data in this paragraph are from Plummers Island nests. Three eggs hatched in 2 days each. The larvae completed feeding in 5 to 7 days and then spun their cocoons. During the summer the elapsed time between egg hatch and emergence of the adults was 14-20 days for males (mean 17) and 17-22 days for females (mean 20). The elapsed time between reaching larval maturity and emergence of the adults was 13-16 days for males (mean 14) and 13-17 days for females (mean 15). For a single male 6 days elapsed between larval maturity and pupation, and 10 days from pupation to adult emergence.

The cocoon is silken, modified fusiform in shape, delicate, white, and opaque. Nineteen male cocoons were 7 to 9 mm. long (mean 8 mm.), while 43 female cocoons were 7 to 13 mm. long (mean 10 mm.).

Apparently there are 2 generations a year in New York. My few nests from Derby and Rochester were stored from about June 10 to mid-July, and emergence of adults occurred from early in July until mid-August of the same year. Presumably in the field the progeny from these nests would store nests of their own, occupants of which would overwinter as diapausing larvae. It seems probable that there are 3 generations annually in the Washington area, or perhaps continual breeding during the warmer months. Adults emerged June 22 to August 25 from nests stored from about June 1 to early August. Occupants of nests stored from mid-August through the first half of September overwintered as resting larvae and emerged as adults the following spring. At Plummers Island females have been collected as early as May 19 and as late as September 23.

Emergence of progeny from an individual nest required periods ranging from 1 to 5 days during the summer broods, and from 1 to 7 days from overwintering nests. The two sexes usually emerged concurrently from nests which held both.

Parasites, mold, injury, and preservation of mature larvae for taxonomic study took some toll of the 157 stored cells. I reared 76 females and 31 males, which indicates a probable 2:1 sex ratio.

I was able to determine the arrangement of sexes in mixed nests by placing the cocoons in individual marked vials for rearing. Apparently the normal pattern is to have several sets of female cells separated by one or more male cells. The actual arrangement in 9 nests from Plummers Island containing 6 or more cells was as follows (x = stored cell in which a wasp failed to develop):

Nest	1	2	3	4	5	6	7	8	9	10	11
Y 54	♀	♀	♀	♀	♂	x	♀	♀	x		
Y 130	♀	♂	♀	♀	♀	♀	x	♂			
E 30	♂	♀	♀	♀	♂	♀	♀	x	♀	♀	♀
E 48	♀	♂	♀	x	♂	♀					
E 55	♂	♀	♂	x	♀	♀					
E 158	x	♀	♀	♀	♀	♂					
K 122	♀	♀	x	♂	x	x	♂				
M 79	x	♂	♀	♀	♂	♀	♀	♂			
M 99	♀	♂	♀	♀	♂	♀	x				

All the above nests were in 6.4-mm. borings, except E 30 which was in a 4.8-mm. boring. Because each cell contains but a single juvenile or adult spider, it is quite possible that the size of the spider prey may determine whether a female or male egg will be laid.

Parasites and predators. The eulophid *Tetrastichus johnsoni* Ashmead developed in the prepupae in 7 of 27 cells in 4 *sayi* nests from Plummers Island. I also found a live female of this parasite in a newly provisioned cell in a Plummers Island nest.

A secondary infestation by *Pyemotes* mites originated in the laboratory in 1 nest.

Previous observations. The Peckhams (1898, p. 144) reported *sayi* [as *Pompilus calipterus* Say] as nesting in a fence post in Wisconsin and storing females of *Xysticus ferox*. Townes (1957, p. 130) noted that *sayi* had been reared from dead wood of *Carya* in New York and of *Celtis* in Maryland. Krombein (1958b, p. 52) recorded it as preying on an adult female *Xysticus fraternus* in West Virginia.

Medler and Koerber (1957) in Wisconsin, Evans and Yoshimoto (1962, pp. 102-104) in New York, and Fye (1965a, pp. 735-736, fig. 8) in Ontario published detailed observations of *sayi* based on trap nest studies. In general their observations agreed with mine. Medler and Koerber used 6.4-mm. borings 153 mm. long in sumac and obtained over 200 nests; Evans and Yoshimoto used 6-mm. borings 130-150 mm. long and obtained 22 nests; and Fye got 25 nests in 6.4-mm. borings 140-152 mm. long.

Medler and Koerber stated that *sayi* superseded a vespid wasp in

4 nests and a megachilid bee in 6 nests. Conversely, *sayi* was superseded by a vespid in 2 nests and by a megachilid in 6 nests. Evans and Yoshimoto, and Fye did not note any supersedure.

Not one of these authors found any nests where the wasp had constructed a barrier at the inner end of the boring. They also noted the extreme variation in length of cells. Medler and Koerber found 1 to 13 cells with a mean of 4.3 provisioned cells in 148 completed nests; Evans and Yoshimoto recorded 1 to 10 cells with a mean of 3.6 cells for their completed nests; Fye reported 89 cells in 19 nests. None of these authors reported as great a range in thickness of partitions as I found. Medler and Koerber found that males were usually produced in smaller cells than females.

In the papers by Medler and Koerber, and by Evans and Yoshimoto the composition and size of the complex cell partitions and closing plugs were discussed in detail. In addition to the kinds of debris listed in the report on my nests, these authors found lichens, mosses, sand, seeds, and dead insects. Medler and Koerber found a vestibular cell in most of their completed nests, but Evans and Yoshimoto found this feature in only 6 nests.

Medler and Koerber listed as prey 14 species in the families Thomisidae, Salticidae, Gnaphosidae, and Amaurobiidae. They noted that all the spiders were adult or juvenile females and that most of them belonged to the genus *Xysticus*. Evans and Yoshimoto listed only thomisids as prey, mostly specimens of *Xysticus*. They recorded only 1 immature male as prey and several juveniles too immature for sex determination; the rest of the records were of female spiders. Fye's prey records were mostly females of several species of *Xysticus*, but he also found 2 other genera of Thomisidae being used, as well as 1 species of Agelenidae.

Evans and Yoshimoto observed one wasp transporting her prey by walking sideways on the ground and carrying the spider by the spinnerets. When she climbed up a tree trunk she walked backward. They found another female that had bitten off the legs of a spider and was feeding at the leg base and at the base of the abdomen. This spider was discarded and not used to provision a cell.

Medler and Koerber presented a series of photographs showing the gradual increase in size of the feeding larva. They described the egg as being creamy white and about 1 mm. in length. The egg hatched in about 2 days under field conditions, and the larva completed feeding in another 5 to 6 days. They stated that about 14 days elapsed in the summer generation between cocooning and emergence of the adult, so that the first generation required a minimum of about 24 days from provisioning of the cell to emergence of the adult. Fye reported 2 generations annually in northwestern Ontario.

Both Medler and Koerber, and Evans and Yoshimoto reported

that many nests were parasitized by *Melittobia chalybii,* most of these infestations having taken place in the laboratory. Evans and Yoshimoto also recorded rearing the mutillid wasp *Ephuta p. pauxilla* Bradley from a *sayi* nest, and 2 bombyliids, *Anthrax irrorata* Say, from another *sayi* nest.

Source material.

 Derby, N. Y. 1957 series: G 69. 1958 series: R 43, 44, 46.

 Rochester, N. Y. 1957 series: Bu 2.

 Cropley, Md. 1955 series: B 49.

 Plummers Island, Md. 1958 series: S 44, 45, 49. 1959 series: Y 54, 82, 96, 130, 135, 146. 1960 series: E 30, 48, 55, 158. 1961 series: K 100, 105, 116, 117, 122, 155, 157, 158, 217, 237, 238. 1952 series: M 3, 79, 99.

 Glencarlyn, Va. 1954 series: D 2.

 Dunn Loring, Va. 1954 series: C 2.

Identifications. Araneae by W. J. Gertsch, W. Ivie, and B. J. Kaston; Chalcidoidea by B. D. Burks; wasps and mites by the author.

DIPOGON (DEUTERAGENIA) PAPAGO ANOMALUS Dreisbach

I reared this wasp from 3 nests at 3 stations in open woods on Plummers Island, Md., in 1956 and 1961. One nest was in a 6.4-mm. boring suspended from the limb of a dead standing tree; 2 nests were in 4.8-mm. borings, 1 suspended from a dead limb, and 1 from the trunk of a dead standing tree.

Nest architecture. The 2 nests in 4.8-mm. borings were completed. There were 3 and 4 stored cells, respectively, 10-29 mm. long (mean 14.7 mm.), capped by plugs 3-20 mm. thick (mean 7.1 mm.). The plugs consisted mostly of rotten wood, occasionally with some debris from the ground including caterpillar frass. These two nests had empty vestibular cells 85 and 112 mm. long with closing plugs 9 and 32 mm. thick, respectively. The single nest in a 6.4-mm. boring was not completed. It had 3 cells 17-25 mm. long, capped by partitions 7-15 mm. long consisting of leaf fragments, particles of earth, insect frass, and a few spider webs. The space available for storage of prey in each cell was 8 to 10 mm. long.

Prey. The prey in the 6.4-mm. nest consisted of 2 genera of spiders. From one cell, I preserved the spider, which was identified subsequently as a penultimate instar female of a species of *Phidippus,* 9 mm. long. The 2 specimens of *Phidippus* in this nest had all the legs amputated at the coxae, but this was not done to the other spider of another genus in cell 3.

Life history. The 4-celled nest was probably stored between June 6 and 9, because there was a nearly full-grown larva in cell 1 and progressively smaller larvae in the other cells, when I opened the nest on June 12. One male and 3 females emerged from this nest June 28 to July 1.

A 3-celled nest was completed June 11-12, and the larvae hatched June 13-14, about 2 days after the eggs were laid. One of the larvae devoured its spider in 5 days. One male and 2 females emerged from the cocoons on July 6. Data from this nest indicate that individuals of the summer generation require only 25-26 days from oviposition to emergence of the adult.

The 3-celled nest in the 6.4-mm. boring was stored the first week of September. One of these larvae also spent 5 days in devouring its spider. One egg failed to hatch, and the other larva was preserved when full grown for taxonomic study. The occupant of the third cell overwintered as a resting larva and transformed to an adult the following spring.

The cocoons were fusiform and spun from opaque, dense, creamy silk. Six female cocoons were 7 to 10 mm. long (mean 8.2 mm.), and 2 male cocoons 7 mm. long.

The male was in the innermost cell in one nest, and in the outermost cell in the other.

Previous observations. Townes (1957, p. 122) reported that *anomalus* was reared from borings in dead wood of *Carya* in Massachusetts and of *Fagus grandifolia* in North Carolina. He also recorded a female preying on *Paraphidippus aurantius* (Lucas) in Kansas.

Evans and Yoshimoto (1962, pp. 104-105) recorded as prey in Connecticut and New York the gnaphosid spiders *Sergiolus variegatus* (Hentz) and *Haplodrassus hiemalis* (Emerton), the latter a female. They found a nest in an old beetle boring in a fallen poplar. The plug consisted primarily of wood chips. They also watched a female *anomalus* transporting her thoroughly paralyzed prey. She walked sideways over the ground grasping the spider by the spinnerets and holding it venter up. She carried it to a fallen tree, walked backward up a branch, and dragged the spider into an abandoned beetle (?) boring. Upon excavation later they found a single cell plugged by a partition of compacted earth and plant fibers. The egg was laid longitudinally on the side of the abdomen near the base and failed to hatch. The spider's legs were not amputated.

Source material.
   Plummers Island, Md. 1956 series: H 55. 1961 series: K 9, 10.

Identifications. Arnaeae by B. J. Kaston; wasps by the author.

DIPOGON (DEUTERAGENIA) IRACUNDUS Townes

I reared this wasp twice from nests in borings in Arizona. One was in a 6.4-mm. boring suspended from a branch of an oak sapling in full shade at about 6,000 feet elevation in Upper Bear Canyon

Camp in the Santa Catalina Mountains. The other was in a 4.8-mm. boring under a dead sycamore half a meter above the ground at an elevation of about 5,200 feet in Cave Creek Canyon in the Chiricahua Mountains.

Nest architecture. In the 6.4-mm. boring the cells including partitions were 17 and 15 mm. long. The partition closing cell 1, made of tightly packed wood fibers rasped from the boring walls, was 4 mm. thick. That closing cell 2 was 9 mm. thick and composed of 3 distinct layers, an inner one of bits of bark (?), other ground debris, and a few strands of silk; then a layer of rasped wood fibers; and finally a layer similar in composition to the inner one. There was an empty vestibular cell of 118 mm. The closing plug was 8 mm. thick and composed of tightly packed, intermixed bits of grass stem, rasped wood fibers, and ground debris but no silk.

The inner 45 mm. of the 4.8-mm. boring was empty, and then there was a narrow plug of debris. The cells with partitions were each 15 mm. long. The partitions 4 and 8 mm. thick, respectively, were composed of tightly packed and intermixed bits of mud, leaves, grass, and insect remains. There was an empty vestibular cell of 70 mm. The closing plug, 30 mm. thick, was composed of loosely packed debris similar in composition to the cell partitions.

Life history. When I examined the nest in October, occupants in the 6.4-mm. boring were diapausing larvae in cocoons. The cocoons in cells 1 and 2 were 12 and 8 mm. long respectively. A female and a male *iracundus* emerged the following May from cells 1 and 2, respectively.

The nest in the 4.8-mm. boring must have been completed about July 12, because the larvae in cells 1 and 2 were spinning their cocoons when I picked up the trap on the 20th. The cocoons were completed a day later; each was 8 mm. long. A female and a male of *iracundus* emerged on August 12, presumably from cells 1 and 2 respectively.

Source material.
 Upper Bear Canyon Camp, Santa Catalina Mountains, Ariz. 1957 series: Q 37.
 Cave Creek Canyon, Chiricahua Mountains, Ariz. 1959 series: X 110.

Identifications by the author.

DIPOGON (DIPOGON) GRAENICHERI ATRATUS Townes (?)

I obtained 1 nest of this wasp in a 3.2-mm. boring set out on a cowshed wall infested with old anobiid borings in Arlington, Va. I was unable to identify the single reared male which represents an undescribed form. Presumably it may be the opposite sex of *graenicheri atratus,* the only form of typical *Dipogon* known from this area in which the male is unknown.

Nest architecture. The boring was 60 mm. long. There was an empty space of 30 mm. at the inner end and then a plug composed of tiny wood chips 1-3 mm. long that had been rasped from the boring walls. The 2 cells with their closing partitions were 10 and 9 mm. long. The partitions closing the cells, 4 mm. long, were composed of tiny wood chips. There was an empty vestibular cell 6 mm. long containing a few wood chips mixed with caterpillar frass as a closing plug.

Life history. The nest must have been stored about August 31, because the larvae were spinning their cocoons when I examined the nest on September 6. The two cocoons were 5 and 6 mm. long, silken, creamy white, opaque, and modified fusiform in shape. The occupants of these cocoons overwintered as resting larvae. One died the following May shortly after pupation, and the other pupa developed normally and died during eclosion of the adult on May 21.

Source material.
    Arlington, Va. 1955 series: A 13.

Identification by the author.

AUPLOPUS CAERULESCENS SUBCORTICALIS (Walsh)

(Plate 9, Figures 42-44)

I obtained 2 nests of this species, one in a 6.4-mm. boring set in a tree crotch 2 meters above ground in a wooded area at Cropley, Md., the other in a 4.8-mm. boring attached to the trunk of a dead standing sycamore at Plummers Island, Md.

Supersedure and competition. In the former nest the *Auplopus* female was superseded by the sphecid wasp *Trypargilum clavatum* (Say), which stored several cells at the outer end of the boring.

Nest architecture. The nest from Cropley consisted of 3 barrel-shaped mud cells 40 mm. from the inner end of the boring. The cells, 6 to 7 mm. long and 4 mm. in diameter, were placed end to end in an uninterrupted row. The outer surface of the cell wall was rough and showed the shape of the individual mud pellets from which the cells were made, but the inner surface of the cell wall was smooth. The cell walls were 0.3 to 0.6 mm. thick. There was a mud partition sealing off the *Auplopus* cells. I was unable to determine whether this was made by the female *Auplopus* or by the female *Trypargilum,* which nested in the remainder of the boring. Most likely it was made by the latter wasp.

In the nest from Plummers Island there were 4 separated mud cells, each 8 mm. long (figs. 42, 44). The mother wasp may not have completed nesting in this boring, because the outermost cell had been recently completed and the outer 30 mm. of the boring was empty.

Prey. The spider in cell 4 of the nest from Plummers Island was an immature male of the clubionid *Clubiona obesa* Hentz, 7 mm. long (fig. 43). The spider in cell 2 appeared to be the same species. Both spiders had all of the legs amputated at the coxae.

Life history. The Cropley nest was stored during the latter half of July. On August 5 one of the cells contained a fully colored pupa in a white, silken, subopaque cocoon 5 mm. long. Two females of *subcorticalis* emerged from 2 of the cells before August 9. The occupant of the third cell was injured and died when the nest was opened earlier.

I picked up the Plummers Island nest on September 16, very shortly after the outermost cell was completed. There was a small larva on the spider's abdomen in cell 2, and an egg on the spider in cell 4; I did not inspect the other cells. The egg was sausage-shaped, 1.6 x 0.5 mm., and attached obliquely near the anterior part of the spider's venter. The cells were put in separate vials and the occupants overwintered outdoors as resting larvae. Three males of *subcorticalis* emerged the following spring.

Previous observations. Walsh (1869, pp. 131-132, fig. 105 c) mentioned that he always found clay cells of *subcorticalis* under loose bark of standing trees in Illinois. Townes (1957, p. 159) recorded it as having been reared from a cell found under bark in Texas and from mud cells taken from a pomegranate from Mexico. Evans and Yoshimoto (1962, p. 109) recorded the salticid spider *Phidippus audax* Hentz and the clubionid *Trachelas tranquillus* (Hentz) as prey in Kansas and the anyphaenid *Anyphaena pectorosa* Keyserling as prey in New York. The wasps had amputated some or all of the spiders' legs. Medler (1964b) reported finding a dozen nests of *subcorticalis* in borings in sumac twigs in Wisconsin. The nests contained 2-8 mud cells (mean 4.5), which sometimes were strung together like beads and sometimes separated by empty spaces of varying lengths. He found that the wasps amputated the spiders' legs. One spider was a species of *Clubiona*. He reported a random sequence of sexes in the nests. Hartman's observations (1905, pp. 48-51) on *subcorticalis* and *mellipes* are open to some question, because his descriptive remarks indicated that he reversed application of the names or perhaps that one or two other species of *Auplopus* were involved.

Source material.
Cropley, Md. 1955 series: B 3.
Plummers Island, Md. 1962 series: M 60.

Identifications. Araneae by W. Ivie; wasp by the author.

AUPLOPUS MELLIPES MELLIPES (Say)

(Plate 9, Figure 45)

This wasp nested in one 12.7-mm. boring and in two 6.4-mm. borings at Plummers Island. The first boring was attached to the side of a dead standing tree in moderately dense woods, and the other 2 were on the side of a dead standing sycamore trunk.

Supersedure and competition. The megachilid bee *Osmia pumila* Cresson nested in the inner 36 mm. of 1 nest. This was not a case of competition, because the pompilid nested at least a month later than the bee.

Nest architecture. The inner 60 mm. of the 12.7-mm. boring was empty. Then there was a clump of 3 mud cells in the next 25 mm. The remainder of the boring was empty.

There was a single mud cell 12 mm. long at the inner end of one 6.4-mm. boring. There were 2 mud partitions, 1 of them 2 mm. thick, at distances of 47 and 55 mm. from this cell.

The other nest in a 6.4-mm. boring had the bee nest in the inner 36 mm. There were 3 *mellipes* cells 8, 12, and 13 mm. long (fig. 45) in the outer section of this boring. Each was capped by a thin mud partition 20-30 mm. beyond each cell.

Life history. The 2 nests in 6.4-mm. borings were stored probably late in June 1962, possibly by the same female. They were not picked up until July 11. Pupation occurred July 12-20 in the 3-celled nest; 2 male *mellipes* emerged and died in the nest before August 1, and a female emerged from the outermost cell on that date. Pupation took place July 12-20 in the 1-celled nest also; I found a dead dry female *mellipes* in the nest on August 14.

The nest in the 12.7-mm. boring was probably stored about mid-August, 1959. On August 23 a wasp larva in 1 of the cells was feeding on a spider whose legs had been amputated by the mother wasp. By August 27 the occupants of at least 2 of the cells were in cocoons. The latter were silken, light tan, opaque, delicate, fusiform, and 7-9 mm. long. The occupants of the cells overwintered as resting larvae. On April 18, when I brought the nest into my office, the occupants were still prepupae. On the 22d there was a pupa in 1 cell, a prepupa in another. On May 4 a female of *mellipes* emerged from the nest. I found another female dead and dry inside the trap on May 10.

Previous observations. *A. m. mellipes* has been the subject of scattered notes and longer contributions by Walsh (1869, p. 132), the Raus (1916, pp. 42-43; 1918, pp. 86-89, figs. 18-20), Rau (1926, pp. 196-197; 1928, pp. 342-358), Krombein (1952, pp. 176-177; 1955a, p. 15), Evans (1953, p. 166), and Townes (1957, p. 153). It has been reported as constructing its clay or mud cells under loose bark of standing trees and fallen logs (Walsh, 1869; Raus, 1918), in abandoned clay cells of the mud-dauber wasps *Sceliphron caementarium* (Drury) and *Trypargilum politum* (Say) (Raus, 1916, 1918; Rau, 1928; Townes, 1957), on the exposed roots of standing trees (Hartman, 1905; Krombein, 1952), in abandoned borings of mining bees in a clay bank (Rau, 1926), in an oak-apple gall (Raus, 1918), in the crease of a wagon paulin (Hartman, 1905), and in an old *Polistes* nest (Evans, 1953; Townes, 1957). All observers who commented on the prey noted that the mother wasp amputated some or all of the legs of the spider prior to storing it in the cell. Only 1 spider was stored per cell. Rau (1928) noted that the paralyzed, amputated spider was transported venter to venter, the wasp clutching the spinnerets between her mandibles and using her front legs to help support the spider. Several families are represented among the spiders that have been recorded as prey, but all are errant spiders, as follows:

Pisauridae: *Pisaurina undata* Hentz (Rau, 1926)
Gnaphosidae: *Herpyllus vasifer* (Walckenaer) (Krombein, 1952)
Thomisidae: *Philodromus* sp. (Rau, 1928)
Salticidae: *Marpissa undata* (DeGeer) (Krombein, 1955); *Phidippus audax* (Hentz) [= *tripunctatus* Emerton] (Rau, 1928); *Phidippus* sp. (Rau, 1926).

Source material.
Plummers Island, Md. 1959 series: Y 110. 1962 series: M 29, 48.

Identifications by the author.

Superfamily SPHECOIDEA

Family AMPULICIDAE

Only one ampulicid species, *Ampulex canaliculata* Say, nested in these traps. It was unique among the sphecoid wasps nesting in wood borings in that it provided only 1 paralyzed cockroach per cell. (However, some ground-nesting Sphecidae also provide only 1 specimen of prey per cell.)

AMPULEX (RHINOPSIS) CANALICULATA Say

(Plate 11, Figures 49-51)

I obtained 6 nests of this species at Kill Devil Hills, 3 in 1955, 2 in 1956 and 1 in 1958. All were in traps suspended 1 to 2 meters above ground from dead limbs of loblolly pines at the edge of open woods. Four were at 1 station, 3 in 1955 and 1 in 1956, and 1 each at 2 other stations. Three nests were in 4.8-mm. and 3 in 6.4-mm. borings.

Nest architecture. *A. canaliculata* did not construct a barrier at the inner end of the boring in any nest. There were 3 cells in one nest, 2 in another, and 1 each in the other 4. The cells including the partitions capping each were 25 to 55 mm. long with a mean length of 42 mm. in 4.8-mm. borings, and 40 and 75 mm. long in the 6.4-mm. borings. The partitions capping the cells were 8 to 27 mm. long, with a mean length of 19 mm. The materials comprising the partitions were loosely compacted and consisted almost entirely of small bits of tough, leathery dry leaf with occasional intermixed leaf petioles and grass blades (fig. 49).

Prey. This wasp preys on cockroach nymphs which are stored 1 per cell. Apparently the nymph is just temporarily paralyzed, for in one nest it had recovered from the sting and bore a small feeding wasp larva. The prey in 2 cells was identified as *Parcoblatta* sp., in 4 cells as *Parcoblatta* (?) sp., and in another cell as probably *Parcoblatta* though possibly *Ischnoptera.* One nymph was 6 mm. long and probably about two-thirds grown.

Life history. Probably there are 2 generations or more a year in coastal North Carolina. Three of the nests were stored between July 22 and September 18, 1955. The single occupant in 1 nest had emerged before September 18, and the occupants of the other 2 nests overwintered as diapausing larvae and emerged next May in my office, 2 males on the 14th and 2 females on the 21st.

Another nest must have been provisioned about August 5 or 6, 1958. When I examined it on the 8th, there was a very small wasp larva feeding on the cockroach. Four days later it had cleaned out all the flesh and softer parts, leaving the integument of the thoracic dorsum, entire abdomen, and legs untouched. This larva was preserved for taxonomic study before it spun a cocoon.

The cocoon consists of an outer sheath of opaque white silk spun within the disjointed sclerotized parts of the cockroach (fig. 50). Inside of this is the inner cocoon, which is ovoidal, dark brown, hard but brittle, and with a sharp nipple at each end (fig. 51). Two inner cocoons of females were 11 mm. long and those of 2 males were 8 and 9 mm. long.

Previous observations. Williams (1929) published a lengthy contribution on his observations of a female *canaliculata* in captivity in Missouri. He provided hollowed-out elderberry twigs as a nesting site and specimens of *Parcoblatta virginica* (Brunner) as prey. He commented on the temporary paralysis induced by stinging. His wasp dragged the cockroach into a boring head first and deposited her egg along one of the mid coxae. She made the partition capping the cell from bits of pith, cork, and fragments of dry leaves. One egg hatched in 2 to 3 days. The larva fed externally at first and then with the anterior end of the body within the body of the cockroach. The period of feeding took 5 days. Williams's female was kept in confinement for 35 days and parasitized 50 or more cockroaches during that period. The progeny emerged from mid-July until early in September. About 5 weeks elapsed between storing of a nest and emergence of the resulting adult.

Source material.

Kill Devil Hills, N. C. 1955 series: C 494, 495, 496. 1956 series: C 227, 497. 1958 series: T 26.

Identifications. Orthoptera by A. B. Gurney; Hymenoptera by the author.

Family SPHECIDAE

Members of this family exhibited greater diversity in nest architecture, prey preferences, and cocoons than I found in any other family of wasps. Ten genera nested in these borings—*Solierella* of the Larrinae, *Trypoxylon* and *Trypargilum* of the Trypoxyloninae, *Diodontus* and *Passaloecus* of the Pemphredoninae, *Isodontia* and *Podium* of the Sphecinae, and *Euplilis, Crossocerus* (?), and *Tracheliodes* of the Crabroninae.

Nest architecture. Two species did not make any cells at all in the borings. *Solierella affinis blaisdelli* interspersed particles of soil and pebbles among its prey and laid eggs at intervals; the closing plug in 1 nest was a mixture of small bits of stone and soil and a few grass awns at the outer end. *Tracheliodes amu* did not bring any building materials into the nest but laid eggs at intervals among her prey; there was no closing plug in any of the nests, but perhaps none of the nests was completed.

Trypoxylon, Trypargilum (figs. 53, 54), *Diodontus, Passaloecus* (fig. 66) and *Euplilis* built the orthodox type of nest consisting of a linear series of stored cells each capped by a partition. *Diodontus* did not make an empty vestibular cell just before the nest entrance, but the other genera did construct such a cell, each one closed by a thicker entrance plug of the same substance used for the partitions capping the stored cells. In the *Diodontus* nests the mother coated the walls and ends of the cells with a delicate, subopaque membranous substance, presumably a glandular secretion; the nests of all other wasps lacked this feature. *Diodontus* and *Euplilis* used bits of rasped wood from the boring walls to make the partitions to seal the provisioned cells; *Euplilis* also formed the closing plug from this material. *Passaloecus* fashioned the cell partitions and closing plug from clear resin, whereas *Trypoxylon* and *Trypargilum* used mud or agglutinated sand for this purpose.

The nests of the two sphecine genera, *Isodontia* and *Podium,* were unusual in a number of respects. Almost always, *Podium rufipes* made a long cell in the boring for a single larva (fig. 62) and then constructed a thick, compact plug of various kinds of debris sealed by a coating of resin on the exterior surface. My single 2-celled nest of *Podium luctuosum* had the first cell sealed by a compound plug consisting of particles of rotten wood in the inner section and a mud partition on the outer section, and a compound plug sealing the second cell consisting of 2 sections of rotten wood particles on either side of a mud partition (figs. 64, 65). The nests of the 3 *Isodontia* species showed a transition from *elegans,* which built several individual cells each separated by a thick partition of grass stems and juniper fiber (fig. 57), through *mexicana* which made either much narrower, flimsier partitions of similar materials between stored cells (figs. 58, 59), or else had just a large brood cell in which several larvae developed without cannibalism, to *auripes* in which there was always just a single large brood chamber (figs. 60, 61). The closing plugs for the *Isodontia* nests were complex affairs consisting of compacted, soft vegetable fibers or grass stems at the inner end, then a section of coiled, wadded grass stems, and then some looser, longitudinally placed grass stems and blades which frequently protruded several centimeters beyond the boring entrance. None of the Sphecinae constructed an empty vestibular cell. Some of the *Isodontia,* and *Tracheliodes* and *Solierella* were the only wasps encountered in these traps which constructed brood chambers instead of separated cells; the only bee that did so was *Megachile (Sayapis) policaris.*

Prey. The larrine *Solierella* stored small hemipterous nymphs, a species of the lygaeid *Nysius.*

The several species of Trypoxyloninae stored spiders, principally immatures but occasionally adults. *Trypargilum* showed distinct prey preferences as follows: Both subspecies of *collinum* and both subspecies of *tridentatum* used entirely snare-building spiders; *striatum* (fig. 132) used about 90 per cent snare-building species and the remainder wandering spiders; and *clavatum* (fig. 133) and *johannis* (fig. 52) used 70-80 per cent wandering spiders and the remainder snare-building species. Prey preferences in *Trypoxylon* were not so diverse, most species preying on snare-builders of various kinds.

The pemphredonines *Diodontus* and *Passaloecus* (fig. 67) preyed on aphids, mostly immatures.

The sphecines used orthopterous prey. The 2 species of *Podium* preyed on woods cockroaches (fig. 62). The 3 species of *Isodontia* preyed mostly on nymphs of various species of snowy tree crickets (Gryllidae) (figs. 60, 61), but occasionally also on tettigoniid nymphs.

The crabronine wasps preyed on a variety of adult insects. *Tracheliodes* preyed on worker ants (fig. 68), *Liometopum occidentale luctuosum. Euplilis* preyed on various species of chironomids. An unidentified species, possibly belonging to the genus *Crossocerus,* stored a mixture of true flies and caddisflies.

Cocoons. The cocoons of the sphecid wasps showed diversity in shape and in texture. The cocoon in *Solierella* was unique in being ovoid with delicate walls made of masticated (?) mud and tiny pebbles and a thin network of silk.

In the Pemphredoninae the cocoons of *Diodontus* were cylindrical with rounded ends, delicate, white, and silky except for the anterior end which was tough and dark brown. In *Pas-*

saloecus the cocoon was vestigial and consisted of only a few strands of silk at just the anterior end or at both ends of the cell. The cocoons of *Trypargilum* were the most distinctive of all and the species could be identified specifically by the cocoon alone (text fig. 2) though not subspecifically. The cocoons were dark brown, varnished with rather tough though brittle walls. The wasp larvae incorporated some sand or mud from the cell partition in the anterior end of the cocoon wall. The cocoons of *Trypoxylon* were fusiform and spun of delicate, white subopaque silk except for *johnsoni*; its cocoon was cylindrical with rounded ends and incorporated grains of sand from the cell partition.

The cocoons of the Sphecinae were also fusiform. Those of *Podium* were silken, varnished, brown, quite delicate, and consisted of a single layer (figs. 63, 65); they were very similar in shape and texture to those of the mud-dauber wasp *Sceliphron*. *Isodontia* spun a double-walled silken cocoon, the outer one of loose silken fibers (figs. 57-59) and the inner a brown, varnished, brittle silken layer.

The cocoon of *Euplilis* was fusiform and made of delicate, subopaque silk. It had a small pore at the anterior end. *Tracheliodes* spun a peculiar cocoon consisting of a transverse septum of varnished silk with the rest of the cocoon forming a narrower cylinder with rounded posterior end of delicate, unvarnished silk (figs. 68, 69).

Nest storing. The single noteworthy feature is that *Trypargilum* males are the only male wasps known to participate, even though passively, in nest construction. The male remains in the nest boring while the female is out hunting spiders or gathering mud for the cell partitions. When she returns, he emerges from the boring to allow her to enter.

SOLIERELLA AFFINIS BLAISDELLI (Bridwell)

I received 2 nests of this small wasp from Portal, Ariz., both in borings having a diameter of 3.2 mm. Both stations were on the desert floor, one trap being fastened to the trunk of a yucca, and the other to a fence post.

Supersedure and competition. The *Solierella* superseded an unidentified vespid in the 1960 nest.

Nest architecture. The nests were not divided into individual cells. The mother wasp stored the 1960 nest with nymphs of a lygaeid *Nysius* sp., 2-3 mm. long. Small particles of soil and pebbles were interspersed among the specimens of prey. This nest contained a vespid cell 10 mm. long at the inner end, and then 10 *Nysius*, a cocoon, 7 *Nysius*, and another cocoon, and then 3 more cocoons, 1 of them a chrysidid, and about 8 more interspersed *Nysius*.

The closing plug of 8 mm. consisted of tiny pebbles intermixed with awns of a grass.

The 1961 nest had an empty space of 17 mm. at the inner end (possibly caused by shifting of the contents during mail transport (?)), and 4 *Solierella* cocoons with interspersed bits of mud and stone in the next 21 mm. The closing plug was 21 mm. thick and consisted of small bits of mud and stone with a few grass awns at the outer end.

Life history. There are 2 or more generations a year at Portal. I received the 1960 nest in December. Presumably it had been stored late the previous summer. The resting larvae in the cocoons hibernated and adults emerged late in April 1961.

The 1961 nest was stored early in April. The occupant of the second cocoon was ready to pupate when I opened the nest on April 24. A male *Solierella* emerged from the innermost cocoon on May 9, and 2 females on May 12 and 13 from the outermost cocoons. The prepupa in the second cocoon was preserved for taxonomic study.

The cocoons were 3 to 5 mm. long, ovoid, with delicate walls made of masticated (?) mud and tiny pebbles and a thin network of silk.

Parasites and predators. A specimen of the cuckoo wasp *Holopyga (?) taylori* Bodenstein was reared from the third of 5 cocoons in the 1960 nest.

Source material.

Portal, Arizona. 1960 series: X 12. 1961 series: G 10.

Identifications. Hemiptera by R. C. Froeschner; Hymenoptera by the author.

TRYPARGILUM Richards

Seven species and subspecies belonging to this genus nested in the artificial borings. These were *clavatum* (Say) and *johannis* (Richards) of Group Spinosum, *striatum* (Provancher) of Group Punctulatum, and *c. collinum* (Smith), *c. rubrocinctum* (Packard), *t. tridentatum* (Packard) and *t. archboldi* (Krombein) of Group Nitidum. Most of these species nested much more frequently in the artificial borings than did species of *Trypoxylon,* even though some of the latter were equally common in the field.

Probably one of the most profound biological differences between these two genera is the participation of *Trypargilum* males in nesting activities. These males remain in the nest while females hunt for prey or nesting materials. It has not been established that the males *regularly* help in actually storing spiders in the nest, though Rau (1928, pp. 410-415) has recorded that a male of *clavatum* "often assisted the mother by relieving her of the spider as she reached the doorway." Usually the male comes out of the nest when the female arrives with prey or nesting material and then climbs on her back while she enters. Frequently, according to Rau (*op. cit.*), mating takes place during this episode. I have found males of *clavatum, striatum,* and *c. rubrocinctum* on guard within nests at Plummers Island and those of *t. tridentatum* at Kill Devil Hills; but I have witnessed neither mating when the female returns with prey nor any assistance by the male in storing prey. However, I have never had an opportunity to keep these nests under constant, or even frequent, observation.

It has been conjectured that *Trypargilum* males prevent the entry of parasites. This may be true for parasites such as *Chrysis (Trichrysis) carinata* Say which have to penetrate to the stored cell for oviposition. However, males are very timid and retreat within the nest when frightened, so they may be of little assistance against such parasites as bombyliid and miltogrammine flies, which deposit eggs or newly hatched larvae at the boring entrance.

Probably the greatest assistance the males render is to prevent supersedure by other wasps or bees hunting for nesting sites. There is considerable competition, particularly among species of *Trypargilum,* for nesting sites, and the presence of a male in a boring may be sufficient to dissuade supersedure.

In my experience the species of *Trypargilum* exhibit very pronounced differences at the specific level in behavioral and ecological characters. Each species that I observed is treated in considerable detail on the following pages under the specific headings, but it may be useful to summarize here some of these differences.

Certainly the most striking are the differences in shape and texture of the cocoons. Although the larvae are extremely similar morphologically, and difficult to separate at the specific level, the cocoon that each species spins is clearly diagnostic. The cocoons of the 5 species that I observed are shown in text figure 2. The cocoon walls of these species except *johannis* are dark brown, heavily varnished and brittle; the cocoon wall of *johannis* is lighter brown, less heavily varnished and quite delicate in texture, almost like that of *Sceliphron caementarium* (Drury), the black and yellow mud-dauber. The cocoon of *collinum* (text fig. 2a) tapers slightly toward the anterior end; the anterior end is truncate and has a prominent nipple in the middle. The cocoons of *clavatum* (text fig. 2b) and *johannis* (text fig. 2c) also taper toward the anterior end and have a truncate anterior end with a less prominent nipple; in addition each of these species has a pale, silken flange (represented by the outlined part in the figures) that extends like a collar around the anterior end. The cocoon of *tridentatum* (text fig. 2d) has the sides parallel and the ends rounded, and is without a nipple or collar. In *striatum* (text fig. 2*e*) the cocoon flares outward toward the anterior end, and the anterior end is rounded and without a nipple or collar. There is variation in the size of the cocoons, but almost no variation in their shape The only exception to this seems to be *striatum*; when this species spins its cocoon in too large a boring (*e.g.*, 12.7 mm. diam.), the anterior end may be flared out disproportionately so that the greatest width of the cocoon is about three-fourths its length (fig. 56). The cocoons are not diagnostic at the subspecific level; those of *c. collinum*

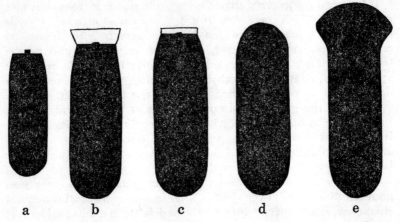

a   b   c   d   e

TEXT FIGURE 2.—Cocoons of *Trypargilum*, anterior end upward: *a, collinum* (Smith); *b, clavatum* (Say); *c, johannis* (Richards); *d, tridentatum* (Packard); *e, striatum* (Provancher). X 3.

and *c. rubrocinctum* (Packard) are identical, as are those of *t. tridentatum* and *t. archboldi* (Krombein).

These 5 species have varied habitat preferences. *T. collinum* and *clavatum* nest in wooded areas that are somewhat open to sunlight, and probably normally in borings in dead limbs; *striatum* also nests in wooded areas but prefers denser shade and apparently often nests in structural timber or in trunks of standing dead tees. Most of my nests of *johannis* came in traps set beneath a building, indicating, perhaps, that in the open it might prefer a rather shaded habitat . *T. tridentatum* nests in open areas where the vegetation is scrubby. These data indicate that *collinum, clavatum,* and *striatum* are in competition for nesting sites and perhaps also for spider prey, but that *tridentatum* normally does not have to compete with other species of the genus for either nesting sites or prey.

The choice of a nesting burrow of particular diameter is dictated to a considerable extent by the size of the wasp and perhaps to some degree by its aggressiveness. At each station I usually set out traps with boring diameters of 3.2, 4.8, 6.4, and 12.7 mm. Most individuals of *Trypargilum* are too large to use a 3.2-mm. boring, although I did find one nest of *c. rubrocinctum* in a 3.2-mm. boring.

Table 19 shows the nesting preferences for five species of *Trypargilum* at four different localities—Derby, N. Y., around Washington, D. C., Kill Devil Hills, N. C., and Lake Placid, Fla.; ratios for the first 4 species are for 4.8:6.4-mm. borings, and for

TABLE 19.—*Diameter of nesting burrow selected by species of*
Trypargilum *at several localities*

Species	N. Y.	D. C.	N. C.	Ariz.	Fla.
collinum 4.8:6.4 mm.	2:1	7:1	4:1	...	6:1
tridentatum 4.8:6.4 mm.	...	...	1:2	2:1	1:3
clavatum 4.8:6.4 mm.	1:1	1:1	1:4	...	...
johannis 4.8:6.4 mm.	...	...	...	...	3:2
striatum 6.4:12.7 mm.	1:1	1:1	...	...	...

the fifth species it is for 6.4:12.7-mm. borings; a dash indicates no data for a particular species at that locality.

The smallest species, *collinum*, clearly prefers the 4.8-mm. borings. In fact, it is likely that most of the 6.4-mm. borings used by this species were selected only because the 4.8-mm. borings at a particular station had been utilized already.

The next three species, *clavatum, johannis,* and *tridentatum,* are equal in size and intermediate between *collinum* and *striatum*. None of these competed with each other for nesting sites because each occurred in either a different habitat or a different locality. However, *clavatum* was in very definite competition for nesting sites with *striatum* at Derby and in the Washington area, and with *collinum rubrocinctum* at Derby, Washington, and Kill Devil Hills. The effects of this competition are very striking. At Derby and Plummers Island, where all 3 species were present, *clavatum* showed no preference for 4.8- or 6.4-mm. borings. However, at Kill Devil Hills, where there was competition with *collinum rubro-cinctum* only, *clavatum* chose the 6.4-mm. borings by a substantial ratio. This preference could have been due to the Kill Devil Hills population of *clavatum* being slightly larger than the *clavatum* population in the Washington area. However, at my home in Arlington, where neither *striatum* nor *collinum rubrocinctum* is present, *clavatum* prefers the 6.4-mm. borings by a 5:2 ratio.

The prey preferences exhibited by these species also require some comment. The spiders used by *Trypargilum* belong to two main groups having different habits. One group contains the wandering or vagabond spiders (running, jumping, crab, and hunting spiders) belonging to the families Clubionidae, Anyphaenidae, Thomisidae, Salticidae, Lyssomanidae, Oxyopidae, Pisauridae, and Lycosidae. These are spiders that do not build webs but that wander over the vegetation, tree trunks, or ground. The other large group comprises the snare builders and allies belonging to the families Theridiidae, Araneidae, Mimetidae, Linyphiidae, Tetragnathidae, and Dictynidae. These spiders, except the Mimetidae, construct silken webs or snares on vegetation, on tree trunks or near the ground. The Mimetidae are wandering spiders that prey on other spiders rather than on insects. They are sometimes found in webs of snare builders, which accounts for their being stored by *Trypargilum* wasps specializing on snare builders as prey.

None of the wasps is at all specific in its prey choices; it is not uncommon to find stored in 1 cell a number of species belonging to several families of one or sometimes both of the main groups listed above. However, each species of wasp does have decided preferences for spiders of one group or the other. There appear also to be some differences in the average number of spiders stored per cell, which indicates that some species use a larger number of smaller spiders per cell and others a smaller number of larger spiders.

Table 20 provides information on the spider prey used by the 7 species and subspecies observed. Columns 1-3 at the left show the percentages of snare builder and/or wandering spiders used and the number of spiders on which these percentages are based. Columns 4-6 at the right relate to the number of spiders stored per completed cell, the range, the mean number and the number of cells on which the mean number is based. Note that the mean (col. 5) is not always obtained by dividing col. 3 by col. 6; col. 3 includes spiders from incompletely stored cells in some cases. Also, sometimes the mean figure is based in part on counts of completely stored cells in which identifications were not made.

T. collinum and *tridentatum* apparently always provision their nests entirely with snare builder spiders, and *striatum* (fig. 132) prefers snare builders by a very substantial margin. In contrast, *clavatum* (fig. 133) and *johannis* (fig. 52), which are so closely related that with some justification they might be considered only subspecies, prefer wandering to snare builder spiders. This bias is a little more marked in *clavatum* than in *johannis*, but it is possible that the percentages found in the latter species are based on too limited data to reflect the actual prey preferences.

Earlier in this discussion I pointed out that *collinum*, *clavatum*,

TABLE 20.—*Preferred spider prey and number of spiders stored per cell by species and subspecies of* Trypargilum.

Species	Spider prey			Number of spiders per completed cells		
	(1) Percentage snare builder	(2) Percentage wandering	(3) Number spiders	(4) Range	(5) Mean	(6) Number cells
collinum rubrocinctum	100	0	334	5-27	16	19
collinum collinum	100	0	83	13-25	18	5
tridentatum tridentatum	100	0	535	11-42	23	14
tridentatum archboldi	100	0	160	9-36	16	10
clavatum	18	82	704	5-22	11	54
johannis	28	72	152	8-17	11	16
striatum	93	7	687	3-22	13	53

and *striatum* occur in the same type of habitat and that *clavatum* competes with both *collinum*, the smaller species, and *striatum*, the larger species, for nesting sites. The decided preference of *clavatum* for wandering spiders is a very effective mechanism for avoiding competition with *collinum* and *striatum* for prey.

Certainly, the preference for snare-builder spiders or wandering spiders implies profound behavioral differences in the way that *striatum*, or *collinum* and *tridentatum*, or *clavatum* and *johannis* hunt their prey. I have not observed prey hunting by these wasps in the field, but the percentages expressed in table 20 lead me to postulate the following types of hunting behavior. Species like *collinum* and *tridentatum*, that use snare-builder spiders entirely, probably snatch the spiders directly from the web. Species like *striatum,* that use snare builders almost entirely, probably dash at the spider in its web and frighten it into dropping off the web to the ground where the wasp picks it up. This method of hunting would explain why a small number of wandering spiders are picked up by a wasp that is actually hunting snare builders. With species like *clavatum* and *johannis* one gets the impression that they must hunt for wandering spiders crawling on grasses, low bushes, and foliage. Inevitably in this type of hunting the wasp would catch a certain number of snare builders, which are either looking for a place to construct a snare, or are involved in some activity away from the snare.

The mean number of spiders stored per completed cell also appears to be significant in some forms. The mean values listed in table 20 for *c. collinum, johannis,* and *tridentatum archboldi* probably should be disregarded as being based on too limited data for statistical significance. However, the mean values for *c. rubrocinctum, clavatum, t. tridentatum,* and *striatum* are based on a number of completed cells and appear to be significant. *T. clavatum* and *striatum* place an average of 11-13 spiders in a cell, indicating that on the whole *striatum,* as one would expect from its larger size, preys on a somewhat larger spider. However, *collinum rubrocinctum,* the smallest of the three, puts an average of 16 spiders in a cell, indicating that on the whole it preys on disproportionately smaller spiders than do *clavatum* and *striatum.*

The evidence afforded by the nests suggests that there are significant ethological differences among these species. It is to be hoped that eventually someone may be able to study in great detail the behavior of these species in the field. Such a study should also offer an opportunity to make valuable observations of competition among several closely related species in a circumscribed area and habitat.

In addition to the behavioral differences noted above, some phenological differences were apparent in the period of adult emergence and the median emergence date * from overwintering nests of *rubrocinctum, clavatum,* and *striatum.* The data in table 21 were obtained from nests of *striatum* taken at Derby and Plummers Island and from nests of *rubrocinctum* and *clavatum* taken at Kill Devil Hills as well as at the other two localities. Each year all the traps from these localities were placed in a carton and hung outside a window at my home about mid-October. In mid-April I brought the traps into my office and recorded the adult emergence for each date.

T. rubrocinctum and *clavatum* had relatively short spans of

---

* The date by which half the adults emerged.

emergence ranging from 5 to 11 days. The emergence span for the entire population of *clavatum* was 1 to 3 days less than that for the entire *rubrocinctum* population. On the other hand, *striatum* usually had a more protracted period of emergence from overwintering nests, sometimes lasting over a year, but never less than 11 days.

With regard to the median emergence date, that for *rubrocinctum* was 4 to 9 days earlier than for either of the other species. *T. clavatum* sometimes had an earlier median emergence date than *striatum* by 5 or 6 days, though in one year it was the same for both species and in another year *striatum* antedated *clavatum* by 3 or 4 days.

TABLE 21.—*Period of adult emergence and median emergence date for three species of* Trypargilum

Species	1957	1958	1959	1960
rubrocinctum	May 15-24 May 20	May 19-28 May 22	May 11-21 May 14	May 13-18 May 16
clavatum	May 23-29 May 26	May 26-June 2 May 28	May 19-28 May 22	May 23-27 May 24
striatum	May 19-29 May 23-24	May 25, 1958- May 20, 1959 May 28	May 18, 1959- May 24, 1960 May 27	May 20-June 13 May 28-29

An interesting collateral observation established that individuals of a single species from these three scattered localities emerged concurrently when the nests overwintered under identical conditions in Arlington, Va. (see table 21).

TRYPARGILUM COLLINUM COLLINUM (Smith)

Relatively few differences were noted between nests of typical *collinum* from Florida and of *c. rubrocinctum* (Packard) from New York, Maryland, and North Carolina. The mean cell length was somewhat longer in typical *collinum*, but there was a gradually increasing mean cell length in *rubrocinctum* from north to south. Cocoons of typical *collinum* had a greater mean length than those of *rubrocinctum* from New York and Maryland but were no longer than *rubrocinctum* cocoons from North Carolina. Both subspecies preyed entirely on snare-building spiders and preferred Araneidae to Theridiidae by a substantial percentage.

Typical *collinum* was reared from 14 nests from Lake Placid, Fla. These came from 11 different stations in the Highlands Ridge sand-scrub area of the Archbold Biological Station. Thirteen nests were suspended beneath limbs of living pines, oaks, and hickory or on the trunks of pines, and 1 was on a fallen tree trunk.

Supersedure and competition. This wasp superseded unidentified vespids in 2 nests. It was superseded by a species of *Stenodynerus* (*Parancistrocerus*) in 2 nests and by *Euodynerus foraminatus apopkensis* (Robertson) in another.

Nest architecture. This wasp used borings of both 4.8-mm. and 6.4-mm. in diameter but preferred the smaller by a ratio of 6:1. In all borings except one the wasp began nesting activities by placing some agglutinated sand at the inner end of the boring or by building a partition of this material a considerable distance from the inner end. The 66 provisioned cells in 4.8-mm. borings ranged in length from 12 to 43 mm. with a mean of 19.1 mm., and 7 provisioned cells in 6.4-mm. borings ranged from 10 to 23 mm. with a mean of 15.3 mm. There were 6-9 provisioned cells in the 7 4.8-mm. borings completely stored by *c. collinum*. Most of the completed nests had a vestibular cell, but 1 nest lacked such a cell. In 2 nests the vestibular cell was divided into 2 sections by a cross partition. There were no empty intercalary cells. The partitions between cells and the terminal plugs were made from firmly agglutinated sand. The partitions were 1-2 mm. thick, and 6 terminal plugs were 3-5 mm. thick (mean 4 mm.).

Prey. Consolidated determinations of the spider prey are as follows:

> Theridiidae (6): 2 *Theridion flavonotatum* Becker; 4 *T. glaucescens* Becker. Araneidae (77): 1 *Eustala anastera* (Walckenaer); 1 *E. triflex* (Walckenaer); 1 *Acacesia folifera* Marx; 1 *A. hamata* (Hentz); 9 *Neoscona minima* Cambridge; 4 *N.* sp.; 4 *Araneus juniperi* (Emerton); 1 *Conaranea floridensis* Banks; 22 *C.* sp.; 1 *Neosconella pegnia* (Walckenaer); 32 immature araneids.

Life history. Occupants of the nests were resting larvae or pupae when I received them. Judged from the dates when the nests were mailed, typical *collinum* nests from late March until at least mid-August in peninsular Florida. One 5-celled nest completed about April 1 produced no adults. Adults of *collinum* emerged May 13-16 from a nest picked up on April 8. Emergence continued through the summer until as late as September 19-20 from a nest stored about mid-August. However, in a 1-celled nest provisioned probably late in July the occupant remained as a resting larva from August 13 to October 2. The nest was placed out of doors in Arlington from October 12 to December 22. Pupation occurred on January 27, 5 weeks after the nest was brought indoors, and the pupa died in a couple of weeks after attaining some adult coloration.

Data from 2 nests suggest that females are produced in the inner and males in the outer cells. However, in one 5-celled nest females were produced in cells 2 and 5 and a male in cell 3. Thirty females and 6 males were reared from 66 stored cells. Forty-two cocoons were 8-13 mm. long (mean 10.5). The cocoon was identical in shape, color, and texture to that of *collinum rubrocinctum* (Packard).

Parasites and predators. One specimen of the bombyliid *Anthrax argyropyga* Wiedemann was reared from each of 2 nests and 2 specimens from a third nest. This bombyliid parasitized 40 per cent of the available cells in these 3 nests.

One specimen of *Chrysis (Trichrysis) carinata* Say was reared from *collinum*.

Crematogaster ants destroyed the contents of 1 or 2 of the innermost cells in 2 of the nests and the 2 outer cells in a third nest.

Phorids destroyed the prey in cells 1 and 2 of a 3-celled nest.

Previous observations. Ashmead's (1894, p. 45) record of *collinum* preying on aphids is certainly erroneous. He also recorded *T. striatum* as using aphids, but admitted in a letter to the Peckhams (1895, p. 306) that this was probably a case of mistaken identity. I reported (Krombein, 1964, p. 18) finding an old 3-celled nest of *collinum* in an abandoned boring 10 cm. long of another insect in the dead twig of a scrubby live oak in Florida.

Source material.
    Lake Placid, Fla. 1957 series: M 101, 162, 178, 243, 266. 1959 series: V 7, 78, 82. 1960 series: B 119, 148. 1961 series: F 146, 160, 204, 221.

Identifications. Araneae by B. J. Kaston and W. J. Gertsch; Diptera by W. W. Wirth; Hymenoptera by the author.

TRYPARGILUM COLLINUM RUBROCINCTUM (Packard)

(Plate 26, Figure 126; Plate 29, Figures 135-139; Text Figure 2a)

This was a frequent nester in traps at Plummers Island, Md., and Kill Devil Hills, N. C., and to a lesser extent at Derby, N. Y. It occurred most commonly in rather open wooded areas or at the edges of woods. It nested in 4 times as many 4.8-mm. borings as 6.4- and probably would have used only the smaller size had a sufficient number of borings been available. Only 1 nest was found in a 3.2-mm. boring. The nests at most stations were suspended from dead limbs of various trees or tied to dead tree trunks; the wasp nested less frequently in traps placed on window sills or tied to limbs of living trees. I had a total of 118 nests.

Supersedure and competition. T. *rubrocinctum* superseded unidentified species of *Megachile* in 2 nests at Derby, N. Y., and Arlington, Va.; a species of *Passaloecus* in 2 nests from Derby (based on finding aphids in cells capped by resin at inner end of boring); *Heriades carinata* Cresson in 1 nest at Derby; *Trypoxylon frigidum* Smith in 1 nest at Derby; and *Osmia lignaria* Say in 1 nest at Plummers Island. It was superseded by *Trypargilum clavatum* (Say) in 1 nest at Derby and in 1 nest from Plummers Island by *Ancistrocerus a. antilope* (Panzer).

Nest architecture. The wasp always began her nest by placing a little mud or agglutinated sand at the inner end of the boring or by building a plug of one of those materials some distance from the inner end. Table 22 presents measurements of the stored cells and cocoons in nests from Derby, N. Y., metropolitan area of

TABLE 22.—*Measurements (in mm.) of stored cells and cocoons in nests of* Trypargilum collinum rubrocinctum *(Packard)*

Locality	Boring diameter	STORED CELLS			COCOONS		
		No.	Range in length	Mean length	No.	Range in length	Mean length
N. Y.	4.8	30	6-39	12.4	17	7-10	9.0
	6.4	42	9-18	11.4	0	—	—
D. C.	3.2	4	12-18	14.0	2	8-9	8.5
	4.8	304	6-75	13.3	120	6-13	9.0
	6.4	68	6-50	11.0	41	7-10	8.7
N. C.	4.8	195	9-92	16.3	116	7-15	10.3
	6.4	34	9-80	15.8	26	8-14	11.2

Washington, D. C. (mostly Plummers Island, Md.), and Kill Devil Hills, N. C.

The differences in cell and cocoon lengths of the Washington and North Carolina populations are correlated with size differences in the wasps from the same areas, those from North Carolina being somewhat larger.

The number of provisioned cells in completely stored nests in 4.8-mm. borings from New York and Washington ranged from 4 to 13, and from 7 to 11 in those from North Carolina. In 6.4-mm. borings from New York and Washington there were 9 to 15 cells, and 11 cells in 1 nest from North Carolina. There were 4 cells in the 3.2-mm. nest and a vestibular cell of 8 mm. One nest from Cropley, Md., had an intercalary cell 15 mm. long, 1 from Kill Devil Hills had one 17 mm. long, and 1 from Plummers Island had 2 such cells 8 and 60 mm. long. Vestibular cells, present in 50 nests, were 3-92 mm. long (mean 33). Most vestibular cells were undivided, but 4 of them had one partition, and 1 each had 2, 4, and 6 such partitions. The partitions between the cells, made from agglutinated sand or mud, were 0.5-3 mm. thick (mean 1). The partitions in nests from Kill Devil Hills, made of agglutinated sand, were a little thicker than those from other localities, which were made of mud. The terminal plugs were made of the same materials and were 1-5 mm. thick.

Prey. Consolidated identifications of spiders from several areas are presented below. The number in parentheses following the family name indicates the number of specimens identified from the nests from that locality.

Metropolitan area of Washington, D. C.: 3 cells from 1 nest from Arlington, Va. (1954), and 13 cells from 7 nests from Plummers Island, Md. (1956, 1957).

Theridiidae (19): 1 *Conopistha* sp.; 1 *Theridula opulenta* (Walckenaer); 10 *Theridion lyricum* Walckenaer; 1 *T. murarium* Emerton (?); 5 *T. spirale* Emerton; 1 immature.

Araneidae (201): 2 *Eustala anastera* (Walckenaer); 1 *E. emertoni* Banks; 18 *E.* sp.; 12 *Neoscona* sp.; 1 *Araneus attestor* Petrunkevitch; 1 *A. juniperi* (Emerton) (?); 166 immatures.

Linyphiidae (3): 3 immatures.

Kill Devil Hills, N. C.: 4 cells from 4 nests (1956, 1958).

Theridiidae (26): 4 *Theridion flavonotatum* Becker; 1 *T. lyra* Hentz; 2 *T. lyricum* Walckenaer; 10 *T. murarium* Emerton; 2 *T.* sp.; 7 immatures.

Araneidae (77): 2 *Cyclosa conica* (Pallas); 20 *Eustala anastera* (Walckenaer); 4 *E.* sp.; 1 *Neoscona* sp.; 12 *Araneus miniatus* (Walckenaer); 1 *A. juniperi* (Emerton); 37 immatures.

Tetragnathidae (8): 8 *Leucauge venusta* (Walckenaer).

At Plummers Island *rubrocinctum* stored 1 to 5 species belonging to 1 to 3 families in each of the fully provisioned cells; at Kill Devil Hills it stored in each provisioned cell 3 to 6 species belonging to 1 to 3 families.

There were 5-22 paralyzed spiders (mean 15) in 16 completely stored cells in the Washington, D. C., area; in 3 cells from Kill Devil Hills there were 18-27 spiders (mean 22). Of the 351 spiders identified only 41 were adults; 1 or more adult spiders were found in almost every cell whose contents were preserved. Of the spiders that were mature enough for the sex to be determined, females outnumbered males 3:1. There was some variation in size of the spiders stored, but most of them were quite small. In 3 cells from Arlington, Va., 29 spiders were 1.8-3.1 mm. long.

H. E. Evans advised me that 1 cell in a nest from Ithaca, N. Y., contained 23 spiders as follows:

Theridiidae: 2 *Theridion albidum* (Banks); 3 *T. differens* (Emerton); 2 *T.* sp.

Araneidae: 3 *Araneus juniperi* (Emerton); 6 *A. trifolium* (Hentz); 7 *A.* spp.

Life history. There is only a single generation at Derby, N. Y.; nests are provisioned during July and August, and all adults emerge a year later. Around Washington there is a small second generation, characterized by the emergence from mid-July to mid-August of both sexes of some or all of the individuals from nests provisioned during the first 3 weeks of July. At Kill Devil Hills there are usually 2 complete generations and sometimes a small partial third.

Most, if not all, of the individuals in the small second generation in the Washington area apparently fail to leave progeny. There were 10 nests from Plummers Island in which some or all of the occupants transformed to adults of both sexes from July 16 to August 19. However, adults were able to emerge from only 2 of the nests; in the other 8 nests they died before emergence. In 4 nests, containing fom 8 to 16 cells, all the occupants transformed to adults during the summer; in 2 nests, containing 8 and 11 cells, only the occupant of the outermost cell transformed to an adult during the summer; in 2 nests of 12 and 13 cells all occupants transformed to adults during the summer except that in cell 1; and in 2 nests only the occupant of the innermost cell transformed during the summer and in attempting to escape killed the prepupae in 1 or more of the cells beyond it before finally succumbing itself. The conjecture that this partial second generation around Washington may largely fail to leave progeny is substantiated to some extent by the lack of nests provisioned later than July 24.

At Kill Devil Hills adults emerged August 2 to 12, 1955, from nests stored before July 21, and the following year from nests stored between July 22 and September 23, 1955. In 1956 two nests were provisioned before July 29—in one of these the occupants had emerged before July 29 and in the other they did not emerge till the following year; occupants of nests stored between August 8 and September 10 emerged the following year. The 1958 nests from this area showed the following emergence pattern: of 8 nests provisioned prior to July 28, adults emerged August 3 to 5 from 6 nests, the following year from 1 nest, and 1 nest had divided emergence with males and females in cells 7-10 emerging August 4 to 5, and occupants of cells 2-6 emerging the next year; of 3 nests provisioned between July 28 and August 8, occupants of 2 nests emerged August 31 to September 4, and the third nest had divided emergence, females and males in cells 2-7 emerging September 3 and the female in cell 1 the following year.

The egg hatches in 1 to 2 days and the larva devours the spiders stored for it in 2 or 3 days. The spinning of the cocoon requires another day or two. The wasp overwinters as a diapausing larva. The duration of the pupal stage is about 3 weeks for occupants of overwintering nests and about 2 weeks for members of the summer generation at Kill Devil Hills. From 4 to 5 weeks usually elapse between the spinning of the cocoon and emergence of the summer generation; so apparently about 2 to 3 weeks are spent in the pre-pupal state in this generation. However, a nest at Kill Devil Hills was completed about the end of July, and adults emerged from it on August 31. Inasmuch as this nest may have been stored over a period of several days, it cannot be assumed that the life cycle may be as short as 5 weeks.

The cocoon is dark brown except for a pale narrow strip around the anterior end and the anterior end itself. The posterior end is rounded, the pale strip tapers slightly toward the truncate anterior end, and the latter has a small nipple in the middle (figs. 126, 135-139, text fig. 2a). The pale strip and anterior closure with nipple are composed largely of sand or mud from the partition closing the cell. The cocoon walls are stiff and quite brittle. The cocoon is identical in shape and texture with that of typical *collinum*.

The range in length and mean length of cocoons irrespective of sex (because this was not determined for about half of the cocoons) are given in table 22. Cocoons of males average somewhat smaller than those of females: At Plummers Island 94 female cocoons averaged 9.0 mm., and 13 males averaged 7.7 mm.; at Kill Devil Hills 56 female cocoons averaged 10.5 mm., and 9 males averaged 8.7 mm.

Males usually emerge a day or two ahead of females, but there is frequently some overlap in emergence. For example, emergence from overwintering nests of the 1956 series was as follows: Derby—1 ♂, May 15 and 5 ♀♀, May 15-16; Plummers Island—3 ♂♂, May 16-18 and 20 ♀♀, May 17-24; and Kill Devil Hills—12 ♂♂, May 17-20 and 22 ♀♀, May 20-22. Emergence of all individuals in a single nest, except in nests where there was divided emergence, took place in from 1 to 7 days regardless of whether one or both sexes were present.

Apparently the males are almost always in the outermost cells of the nest. In the 14 nests containing females and males in which I noted the arrangement of sexes, males were in the outermost cell or cells in 9 and in the penultimate cell in 3. In one nest from Plummers Island there was a male in the innermost cell and females in the others, and in another nest from the same locality there were females in the inner cells and ♂-♀-♂ in the outermost.

Females are produced in greater numbers than males, the over-all sex ratio of reared material being about 6.6:1. However, there were year-to-year fluctuations in the ratios. For example, sex ratios at Plummers Island were 5:1 in 1956 and 7:1 in 1957, and at Kill Devil Hills they were 8:1 in 1955, 2:1 in 1956, and 13:1 in 1958.

Males are encountered much less frequently in field collecting, which substantiates the overall sex ratio obtained from rearing.

Parasites and predators. Three species of Chrysididae were bred from nests of *rubrocinctum. Chrysis (Trichrysis) carinata* Say was reared from or found in 16 nests from Plummers Island, 2 nests from Cropley, and 2 nests from Derby. *Chrysis (C) pellucidula* Aaron was reared from 1 nest from Derby. *Chrysogona verticalis* (Patton) was reared from 1 nest from Cropley.

The outermost cocoon in 1 nest from Plummers Island was parasitized by the mutillid *Sphaeropthalma (S.) pennsylvanica scaeva* (Blake) (Figs. 135-139). The outermost cocoon in a second nest was probably parasitized by this same mutillid; the parasite emerged before this nest was picked up.

The outermost cell in 1 nest at Plummers Island was parasitized by the ichneumonid *Messatoporus compressicornis* Cushman.

Twenty nests were infested with *Melittobia chalybii* Ashmead, 10 of the infestations originating in the laboratory. Nests infested in the field came from Derby, Cropley, Plummers Island, and Kill Devil Hills.

Phorid scavengers, a species of *Megaselia,* were found in 4 nests from Plummers Island. Wasps failed to develop in 8 of the 10 cells infested by these maggots.

Unidentified miltogrammine maggots, undoubtedly belonging to the genus *Amobia,* destroyed the outer 4 cells of an 11-celled nest and the outer 5 cells of a 9-celled nest from Derby, 2 cells of a 9-celled nest and the outer 7 cells of an 8-celled nest from Plummers Island, and the outer 4 cells of a 10-celled nest from Kill Devil Hills.

Bombyliids belonging to the genus *Anthrax* were reared from or found in 10 nests. Four specimens of *A. aterrima* (Bigot) were reared from 3 nests from Kill Devil Hills (figs. 126, 127) and 1 nest from Plummers Island; 5 specimens of *A. argyropyga* Wiedemann were reared from 2 nests from Plummers Island, 2 nests from Kill Devil Hills, and 1 nest from Cropley; and 4 specimens in 3 nests from Kill Devil Hills died as pupae. One of the nests from Kill Devil Hills that contained 9 cells had *A. aterrima* in cell 9 and *A. argyropyga* in cell 3.

One nest was infested in the laboratory by the dermestid *Trogoderma ornatum* (Say), which did not injure the prepupae in cocoons.

Three nests were infested in the laboratory by the mite *Pyemotes.*

Previous observations. The Peckhams (1895; 1898, pp. 77-84; 1905, pp. 178-190) recorded *rubrocinctum* in Wisconsin as nesting in holes in mortar between bricks, in borings in posts, and in straws in a strawstack. They gave no details of the nest architecture but noted that the nests were closed with mud. They found 7 to 14 spiders in each cell, most of them Araneidae but several other families represented; as many as 4 cells might be stored in 1 day. They stated that the egg hatched in 40 to 60 hours and that the larva fed for 7 or 8 days before spinning its cocoon. There was only a single generation in Wisconsin, nests being stored in late June, July, and early in August.

Rau (1922, p. 22) found a 2-celled nest in a boring 3.2 mm. in diameter in an elder twig at St. Louis, Mo. Cell 1 was 13 mm. long, and cell 2 44 mm. long. Cell 2 contained an empty cocoon of the cuckoo wasp *Chrysis* (*Trichrysis*) *parvula* Fabricius, which I suppose may have been a misidentification of the species called *carinata* Say in this paper. (There is a male of *carinata* in the U. S. National Museum bearing a Rau label indicating that it was collected at St. Louis in July 1918.)

Krombein (1954, p. 5) published some notes on a partially stored nest at Lost River State Park, W. Va. There were 3 theridiids and 7 araneids in a partially stored cell at this locality, consisting of 1 *Theridion murarium* Emerton, 1 *T. lyra* Hentz, 1 *T. alabamense* Gertsch and Archer, and 7 immature araneids.

Source material.

Derby, N. Y. 1954 series: VIII a. 1956 series: J 46, 72, 85, 89. 1957 series: G 13, 37. 1959 series: W 27, 45, 75, 77, 78, 81. 1960 series: D 85. 1961 series: L 43, 50.

Cropley, Md. 1955 series: B 25, 35, 42.

Plummers Island, Md. 1956 series: H 2, 19, 20, 24, 39, 66, 112, 116, 125. 1957 series: P 42, 43, 46, 52, 56, 71, 76, 77, 81, 83, 91, 96, 98, 105, 116, 126, 127, 179. 1958 series: S 35, 67. 1959 series: Y 31, 80, 132. 1960 series: E 11, 21, 22, 23, 24. 1961 series: K 16, 29, 32, 188. 1962 series: M 4, 17, 18, 43, 54, 56, 65. 1963 series: U 8.

Arlington, Va. 1954 series: A 2, 3. 1962 series: N 25.

Lost River State Park, W. Va. 1953 series: 7453 B.

Kill Devil Hills, N. C. 1955 series: C 67, 68, 72, 134, 168, 217, 241, 242, 249, 257, 269, 273, 282, 284, 332, 342, 396. 1956 series: C 172, 176, 192, 268, 378, 392, 394, 415, 420, 423, 619, 667, 677. 1958 series: T 19 43, 44, 49, 50, 51, 55, 56, 59, 61, 67, 68, 72, 74, 81, 173.

Identifications. Araneae by B. J. Kaston; Phoridae and Bombyliidae by W. W. Wirth; *Trogoderma ornatum* (Say) by R. S. Beal; Hymenoptera by the author.

TRYPARGILUM TRIDENTATUM TRIDENTATUM (Packard)

(Plate 24, Figures 115-118; Text Figure 2d)

The North Carolina population of typical *tridentatum* had a slightly larger body size than the population of that subspecies in Arizona, and a greater mean cell length in the nests. The Floridian race *t. archboldi* (Krombein) was about as large as the North Carolina population of typical *tridentatum*; the mean cell lengths were nearly identical in 4.8-mm. borings but somewhat longer in nests of *archboldi* in 6.4-mm. borings. Both subspecies preyed entirely on snare-building spiders and their allies, and preferred Araneidae to Theridiidae by a substantial margin. Typical *tridentatum* stored more spiders per cell (mean 23) than did *t. archboldi* (mean 16).

This wasp prefers to nest in open, unwooded areas as contrasted to *clavatum, collinum rubrocinctum,* and *striatum,* which prefer wooded areas open to the sun. The nests at Kill Devil Hills, N. C., were from barren sandy areas with scrubby vegetation, and those from several localities in Arizona were mostly from the desert floor. Most of the traps used in North Carolina were suspended from dead branches of pine and oak, but most in Arizona were suspended from branches of live or dead mesquite, desert willow, cottonwood, palo verde, and several from wooden fence posts.

Supersedure and competition. In Arizona typical *tridentatum* superseded the following bees and wasps in 1 or 2 nests each: *Stenodynerus toltecus* (Saussure), *S. rectangulis* (Viereck), an unidentified vespid, *Megachile gentilis* Cresson, *Chalicodoma* sp., *Dianthidium* sp., *Ashmeadiella* sp., and *A. meliloti* (Cockerell). At Cropley, Md., it superseded *Trypargilum clavatum* (Say) in the outermost cell of an 8-celled nest. In Arizona it was superseded in 1-3 nests each by the following wasps and bees: *Pachodynerus astraeus* (Cameron), *Euodynerus pratensis* (Saussure), an unidentified vespid, *Hylaeus asininus* (Cockerell and Casad), *Ashmeadiella* sp., *A. occipitalis* Michener, *Megachile (Sayapis)* sp., *M. inimica sayi* Cresson, and *Chalicodoma occidentalis* (Fox).

Nest architecture. The North Carolina population preferred 6.4- to 4.8-mm. borings by a ratio of 2:1, but the Arizona population reversed this preference by a ratio of 1:2. These preferences are correlated with relative size of the individuals in the two populations, those from North Carolina averaging somewhat larger than those from Arizona. It is probable that the North Carolina population would have nested exclusively in 6.4- and the Arizona population in 4.8-mm. borings had a sufficient number of each been available at all times. The wasp initiated nesting activities in almost every trap by placing a little sand or mud at the inner end of the boring, or by constructing a partition of one of these materials some distance from the inner end. I had a total of 137 nests.

Table 23 presents measurements of the stored cells by sex in 19 nests from Kill Devil Hills, N. C., and in 84 nests from several localities in Arizona. It will be noted that male cells have a greater mean length than female cells and that cells in 4.8-mm. borings are significantly longer than those in 6.4-mm. borings. There are also significant differences between the two populations in the mean lengths of the cells in borings of both diameters. The greater mean length of cells in North Carolina nests as compared with those in Arizona nests is correlated with the larger size of the individuals in the North Carolina population.

Completely stored nests in 6.4-mm. borings in North Carolina contained 7 to 11 provisioned cells (mean 9); there were 1 to 10 such cells in the Arizona nests (mean 6). In 4.8-mm. borings from Arizona there were 2 to 9 stored cells in completely provisioned nests (mean 6); the single completely stored nest in a 4.8-mm. boring in North Carolina contained 7 provisioned cells.

One of the North Carolina nests and 3 of the Arizona nests contained an empty intercalary cell between 2 stored cells. In at least 1 trap the emergence dates of the progeny suggested that

TABLE 23.—*Measurements (in mm.) of cells in nests of*
Trypargilum t. tridentatum *(Packard)*

Locality	Boring diameter	Sex	Number of cells	Range in length	Mean length
North Carolina	4.8	♀	5	19-22	20.6
		♂	8	15-30	24.0
	6.4	♀	39	8-21	13.9
		♂	11	13-17	14.6
Arizona	4.8	♀	86	12-40	16.8
		♂	88	12-120	20.9
	6.4	♀	57	9-25	14.7
		♂	37	10-85	16.9

this was actually a vestibular cell, and marked the division between nests made by 2 wasps.

There was an empty vestibular cell 10 mm. long in 1 of 5 completely stored nests in North Carolina. In Arizona there were 40 completed nests in 4.8-mm. borings and 20 in 6.4-mm. borings. Thirty-two 4.8-mm. nests had a vestibular cell 6-113 mm. long; in 5 nests this vestibular cell was divided by 1 or 2 cross partitions. In the 6.4-mm. nests 17 had a single vestibular cell 5-116 mm. long.

The partitions between the cells and the closing plugs were made from agglutinated sand in coastal North Carolina and from mud in Arizona. The partitions were about a millimeter in thickness (range 0.5-2 mm.). Closing plugs were 1-8 mm. thick (mean 2.7 mm.).

Prey. Typical *tridentatum* preyed entirely on snare-building spiders, or on mimetid spiders which may be found in webs of snare builders. Consolidated identifications for spiders from 11 cells in 9 nests in North Carolina and from 22 cells in 17 nests from several localities in Arizona are presented below. The number in parentheses following the family name indicates the number of specimens in that family.

Kill Devil Hills, N. C.: 11 cells from 9 nests, 1956, 1958.

Theridiidae (36): 3 *Latrodectus mactans* (Fabricius); 33 *Theridion murarium* Emerton.

Araneidae (131); 56 *Acanthepeira stellata* (Walckenaer); 1 *Cyclosa conica* (Pallas); 1 *Eustala* sp.; 13 *Neoscona* sp.; 60 immatures.

Arizona: 3 cells from 3 nests at Portal, 1959, 1961; 4 cells from 4 nests at Scottsdale, 1961; 15 cells from 10 nests at Granite Reef Dam, 1961, 1963.

Mimetidae (6): 6 *Mimetus hesperus* Chamberlain.

Araneidae (238): 17 *Metepeira arizonica* Chamberlain and Ivie; 24 *M.* sp.; 99 *Eustala rosae* Chamberlain and Ivie; 65 *Neoscona vertebrata* (McCook); 33 *Araneus* sp.

Theridiidae (121): 28 *Latrodectus mactans* (Fabricius); 66 *Theridion dilutum* Levi; 27 *T.* sp.

Dictynidae (3): 2 *Mallos* sp.

It is of interest that the black-widow spider, *Latrodectus mactans*, was preyed upon in both North Carolina and Arizona. Two nests from North Carolina were stored completely, or almost so, with specimens of *Acanthepeira stellata*. However, most of the cells in North Carolina nests contained 2 to 4 species belonging to 1 or both families preyed upon in that area. Completed cells in nests from Arizona localities contained from 2 to 4 species belonging to 2 or 3 families.

The number of paralyzed spiders in 4 completely stocked cells in North Carolina ranged from 12 to 42 (mean 23.0). In 10 completely stored cells from Arizona there were 11 to 41 spiders (mean 23.1). Although most of the spiders were immatures, there was considerable variation in their size. Most of them were quite small as is apparent when the mean number per cell and the mean cell length are compared with the same values for *clavatum*, a wasp of the same size.

Life history. Most of the nests contained mature larvae ready to spin cocoons or prepupae in cocoons when I obtained the traps. Five of the traps in North Carolina, which were still being stored when I picked them up, contained the father wasp on guard at the entrance. Several nests from Arizona were also collected while the father was inside.

In 1 cell of a North Carolina nest the egg was attached laterally on the abdomen of 1 of the last spiders placed in the cell. It was slightly curved with rounded ends, 2.2 mm. long and 0.6 mm. wide. The larva completed feeding and began to spin its cocoon 7 days after probable deposition of the egg. This larva died during the winter.

Some data were obtained from Arizona nests as to duration of the prepupal and pupal stages of wasps emerging during the summer from nests stored early in the season. The period between cessation of larval feeding and pupation was 13 days for a male larva and 12-14 days for 2 female larvae. The period between pupation and adult emergence was 19-22 days (mean 21) for 8 females and 21-30 days (mean 23) for 10 males. The period from completion of larval feeding to adult emergence was 41 days for a male and 34 days for 2 females.

The cocoon is dark brown and cylindrical with rounded ends (figs. 115-118, text fig. 2d). Grains of sand or particles of mud from the partition closing the cell are incorporated in the cocoon so that

TABLE 24.—*Length (in mm.) of cocoons of* Trypargilum t. tridentatum *(Packard)*

Locality	Boring diameter	Sex	Number of cocoons	Range in length	Mean length
North Carolina	4.8	♀	4	13	13.0
		♂	6	12-15	12.8
	6.4	♀	28	7-13	11.2
		♂	10	9-14	12.1
Arizona	4.8	♀	76	8-13	10.5
		♂	77	9-12	10.7
	6.4	♀	47	8-12	10.4
		♂	35	8-13	10.6

the very thin wall is extremely hard though brittle. The cocoon is identical in shape with that of *tridentatum archboldi.* Cocoon dimensions are presented in table 24.

The uniformity in range and mean lengths for Arizona cocoons in 4.8- and 6.4-mm. borings suggests that the variation in cocoons from North Carolina in borings of these sizes is due to inadequate sampling. It should be noted that the male cocoons are longer than those of the female in almost all categories. This difference is correlated with the greater mean length of male cells as compared with those of females and slightly larger size of the adult males.

There are 2 or more generations annually in both North Carolina and Arizona. In North Carolina adults emerged August 2 to 6 from traps set out on May 30 (dates of provisioning of nests not known) and in the spring from nests stored between August 10 and September 10 the preceding year. In Arizona *tridentatum* began to nest early in May. Adults emerged June 23-29 from a nest stored between May 4 and 20. Emergence took place continually during the summer until as late as September 11 from a nest stored between July 19 and 25. Occupants of nests completed later than July overwintered as resting larvae and emerged the following spring.

Males and females emerged concurrently in most nests in which both sexes developed. The period of emergence for all occupants of a single nest was 1-8 days (mean 3 days). In 3 traps from Arizona there was divided emergence, that is, some of the occupants emerged during the summer while others overwintered as diapausing larvae and emerged the following spring. In 1 trap this was quite clearly a case of 2 nests in a single boring with an empty space between the two; occupants of the inner nest emerged in September, and those of the outer nest the following spring. However, in the other 2 nests it was equally clear that each had been constructed by a single female, because there were no empty spaces separating series of cells. One 8-celled nest was stored during May; 2 males (cells 2-3) and 5 females (cells 4-8) emerged June 13-18, but the occupant of the innermost cell 1 overwintered as a resting larva and transformed to a male the following spring. The other 7-celled nest was stored during August; males emerged in cells 1 and 5 by September 21 and killed the resting larvae in cells 2, 3, 4, and 6 in their efforts to escape from the nest; the occupant of the outermost cell 7 overwintered as a resting larva and a female emerged the following spring.

In North Carolina only males were reared from 5 nests, only females from 6 nests, and males from the inner cells and females from the outer cells in 4 nests. In Arizona males only were found in 27 nests, females only in 17 nests, and males in the inner cells and females in the outer cells in 36 nests. In 4 of the Arizona nests there was an apparent random arrangement of sexes as follows (x = *Typargilum* mortality, b = bee in a superseded nest):

G 39: x x x ♀ x ♂ x
G 54: b ♂ ♂ ♀ x ♀ ♂
G 175: b b b ♂ ♀ ♀ ♂ ♀ ♀
T 14: ♀ ♀ ♂ ♂ ♀ ♀ x x x

Each of these nests appeared to have been constructed by a single female *tridentatum*, because there were no empty spaces between series of cells, and because emergence from the cocoons took place in glass vials within a span of just a few days in each nest.

I reared 44 females and 19 males from 100 stored cells at Kill Devil Hills, N. C., and 143 females and 125 males from 522 stored cells from the several localities in Arizona. It appears that there may be 2:1 sex ratio in North Carolina and a 1:1 ratio in Arizona. Females are collected more commonly than males in the field in the Eastern States, but I have no comparable experience with the Arizona population.

Parasites and predators. A male mutillid wasp, *Sphaeropthalma* (*Photopsioides*) *uro* (Blake), emerged from the outermost cocoon in 2 *tridentatum* nests containing 5 and 7 cells respectively from Portal in 1959 and 1961. A mutillid, perhaps of this same species, parasitized the single cell in another nest from Portal in 1961 but died as a resting larva.

The chrysidid *Chrysis* (*Trichrysis*) *mucronata* Brullé parasitized 16 of 50 cells in 11 nests at Portal in 1959 and 2 of 5 cells in 2 nests at Granite Reef Dam in 1963. A chrysidid, probably this same species, parasitized 3 of 9 cells in 3 more nests from Portal; these parasites died as prepupae.

A new species of the aphelinid *Tetrastichus* was reared from a mature *tridentatum* larva in a nest from Granite Reef Dam in 1961. The parasite infested cell 1 of a 7-celled nest.

Melittobia chalybii Ashmead infested 2 nests in the laboratory.

The only effective dipterous parasites belonged to the Miltogrammini, probably to species of the genus *Amobia*. Five of the North Carolina nests were infested by them in 1956 and 1958. The maggots destroyed 8 of 9 cells in 1 nest, but only 1 cell each in 2 other nests; altogether they destroyed 16 of 36 stored cells in these North Carolina nests. In Arizona they destroyed 1 of 2 cells in a nest from Portal in 1960, and 2 of 5 cells in a nest from Granite Reef Dam in 1961. In 1961 *Amobia floridensis* (Townsend) destroyed 8 of 18 cells in 2 nests from Portal and 15 of 16 cells in 3 nests from Scottsdale.

I noticed a tiny bombyliid larva on a *tridentatum* cocoon in a nest from Portal. However, the parasite must have died without penetrating the cocoon, because a male of *tridentatum* emerged from this cocoon a month later.

Pyemotes mites infested a 9-celled *tridentatum* nest in the field at Portal in 1961 and a 9-celled nest at Granite Reef Dam in 1963. All cells were infested in 1 nest, but only the outermost cell in the other. These mites also infested 9 of the Arizona nests in the laboratory.

Previous observations. Rau and Rau (1918, p. 134) found a nest of *tridentatum* in an abandoned boring in the pith of an elder twig at Lake View, Kans. The cells were about 20 mm. long. An adult of *tridentatum* emerged from 1 of the cells in mid-August. In 1934 (p. 259) Rau recorded a nest from Kirkwood, Mo., from which he reared 3 *tridentatum* and 3 *Chrysis* sp.

Hicks (1934, p. 267) found it nesting in a hollow stem of white sage near Pasadena, California. A specimen of *Chrysis* (*C*). *pellucidula* Aaron was also reared from this nest.

Blackman and Stage (1924, pp. 196-197) recorded *tridentatum* as nesting in limbs of a standing dead hickory that had been dead for at least 3 years.

Source material.

Cropley, Md. 1955 series: B 23, 43.

Oxford, N. C. 1957 series: O 11.

Kill Devil Hills, N. C. 1956 series: C 24, 650, 651, 683, 690, 692, 693, 696, 708, 710, 713, 714, 715, 716, 719, 723. 1958 series: T 159, 160, 185.

Arizona. 1957 series: Q 11.

Portal, Ariz. 1959 series: X 66, 69, 75, 80, 81, 82, 85, 181. 1960 series: X 89, no number, 126, 152, 207, 226. 1961 series: G 37, 39, 54, 56, 57, 68, 89, 102, 106, 107, 172, 175, 190, 191, 199, 245, 247, 253, 262, 263, 304, 306, 307, 308, 319, 322, 323, 335, 339, 343, 344, 349, 370, 374, 375, 376, 383, 385, 391, 395, 402, 410.

Molino Camp, Santa Catalina Mountains, Ariz. 1961 series: H 68, 284.

Scottsdale, Ariz. 1961 series: H 32, 33, 34, 36, 38, 46, 53, 69, 70, 82, 118, 120, 176, 178, 179, 183, 193, 244.

Granite Reef Dam, Ariz. 1961 series: H 48, 50, 54, 55, 62, 63, 64, 65, 104, 115, 166, 168, 169, 171, 174, 175, 186, 191, 196, 214, 257, 263, 279, 280. 1963 series: T 1, 2, 9, 10, 14, 15, 16, 19, 20, 27, 28, 34, 35, 36.

Identifications. Araneae by W. J. Gertsch and B. J. Kaston; Bombyliidae by W. W. Wirth; *Tetrastichus* by B. D. Burks, Mutillidae by W. E. Ferguson, other Hymenoptera by the author.

TRYPARGILUM TRIDENTATUM ARCHBOLDI (Krombein)

This wasp nested in a dozen traps at the Archbold Biological Station, Lake Placid, Fla., during 1957, 1961, and 1962. Seven of the nests were in 4.8-mm. borings and 5 in 6.4-mm. The nests came from 7 stations in the Highlands Ridge sand-scrub area. Eight nests at 3 stations were from the trunks of pine trees; the other nests were suspended from limbs of dead or live pine, oak, and hickory trees. The preponderance of nests associated with pine suggests that the wasp may ordinarily nest in old borings of other insects in pine bark or wood.

Supersedure and competition. T. tridentatum archboldi was superseded in 1 nest by an unidentified vespid and in another nest by a species of *Chalicodoma.*

Nest architecture. The wasps commenced nesting activities in all nests by placing some agglutinated sand at the inner end of the boring, or by constructing a partition of this material some distance from the inner end. Table 25 presents measurements of stored cells by sex and boring diameter. The somewhat larger male cells are correlated with larger male cocoons and the fact that males average a bit larger than female wasps.

An empty vestibular cell 96 mm. in length was present in one nest. The other nests lacked vestibular cells, but in these nests the partition closing the terminal cell was always thicker than those closing earlier cells. There were no empty intercalary cells. The partitions capping all stored cells except the terminal one were 1-3 mm. thick and made of agglutinated sand. The terminal plugs, made from the same material, were 2-6 mm. thick (mean 4.1 mm.).

TABLE 25.—*Cell dimensions (in mm.) in nests of* Trypargilum tridentatum archboldi *(Krombein)*

Boring diameter	Sex	Number of cells	Range in length	Mean length
4.8	♀	3	19-21	19.7
	♂	8	20-29	24.0
6.4	♀	11	13-28	17.5
	♂	4	18-21	19.0

Completed nests in 4.8-mm. borings had 4-7 stored cells per nest except for the single nest with an empty vestibular cell, which contained only 1 stored cell. The nests in 6.4-mm. borings had 3-9 stored cells. Both sexes were reared from 4.8- and 6.4-mm. borings.

Prey. Consolidated determinations for spiders from 17 cells in 6 nests are as follows:

Mimetidae (1): 1 *Mimetus* sp.
Araneidae (132): 28 *Gea heptagon* (Hentz); 1 *Drexelia directa* (Hentz); 1 *Eustala anastera* (Walckenaer); 13 *Larinia directa* (Hentz); 39 *Singa* sp.; 1 *Neoscona arabesca* (Walckenaer); 8 *N.* sp.; 12 *Conaranea floridensis* Banks; 6 *C.* sp.; 23 immatures.
Theridiidae (27): 3 *Theridula quadripunctata* Keyserling; 1 *Theridion flavonotatum* Becker; 1 *Chrysso clementinae* (Petrunkevitch); 22 immatures.

This wasp preys entirely on snare-building spiders just as does typical *tridentatum.* Immature spiders were preferred by a ratio of 3:2. Ten stored cells contained 9 to 36 spiders per cell (mean 16.4). Those wasps storing larger numbers of spiders per cell used smaller individuals only 1.8-4.2 mm. long. There was no correlation between the number of spiders in a cell and the cell length. Cells in 4.8-mm. borings containing 23 and 36 spiders were 17 and 20 mm. long, respectively; 4 cells in 1 nest containing 9, 17, 12, and 12 spiders were 28, 21, 18, and 18 mm. long, respectively. One wasp stored almost entirely *Gea heptagon* (Hentz) in each of 2 cells, and another individual stored mostly *Singa* sp. However, some of the wasps used quite a variety of species in each cell. One wasp stored 5 species belonging to 3 families in 1 cell.

Life history. I have no data on the egg or larva because occupants of all the nests were mature larvae, prepupae, or pupae when I received the nests. One larva reached maturity on July 28 and a female emerged from this cell on September 1. In overwintering nests 6 males required 24-28 days between pupation and emergence of the adults, and 3 females took 24-25 days. Most of the nests were apparently stored between July 1 and mid-September.

The cocoons were indistinguishable from those of the typical subspecies, being cylindrical with rounded ends and with sand grains incorporated in the anterior end. Fourteen female cocoons were 10-13 mm. long (mean 11.8), and a dozen male cocoons 11-15 mm. (mean 13.2).

Females usually emerged first from nests containing both sexes, but in 1 nest there was concurrent emergence. This peculiarity of prior emergence of females is undoubtedly correlated with the arrangement of sexes in mixed nests where females were always in the outer cells.

Two nests showed the phenomenon of divided emergence. In 1 nest females emerged from cells 5, 6, and 8 on September 1, from cells 3 and 4 on February 27, and a male emerged from cell 2 on February 28. In the other nest females emerged from cells 6 and 7 August 23 and 24, and males from cells 1 and 3 on February 26 and March 5. In both nests the resting larvae in the innermost cells had to be subjected to 2 months of chilling before they pupated.

I obtained males only from 3 nests and females only from 2 nests. In the 5 nests from which I reared both sexes, females were in the outer cells and males in the inner just as in most mixed nests of typical *tridentatum*.

I reared 14 females and 12 males from 64 stored cells.

Parasites and predators. A male bombyliid *Anthrax argyropyga* Wiedemann emerged from one of the nests of *t. archboldi* on February 10. No wasps were reared from this nest, but the host cocoon was unmistakably that of *t. archboldi*.

A bombyliid larva, probably *Lepidophora lepidocera* (Wiedemann), fed on the spiders in 3 cells of a 7-celled nest; it died before pupating.

Melittobia chalybii Ashmead infested several cells of 2 nests in the laboratory.

Pyemotes mites infested 4 cells in 3 nests. One of these infestations orignated in the field, the others in the laboratory.

Previous observations. In my original description of this subspecies I published biological notes based on the 4 nests obtained during 1957 (Krombein, 1959a, pp. 151-152).

Source material.
     Lake Placid, Fla. 1957 series: M 107, 124, 164, 249. 1961 series: F 270, 282, 283, 303. 1962 series: P 18, 42, 144, 146.

Identifications. Araneae by W. J. Gertsch, W. Ivie and B. J. Kaston; Diptera by W. W. Wirth; Hymenoptera by the author.

TRYPARGILUM CLAVATUM (Say)

(Plate 3, Figure 11; Plate 28, Figure 133; Text Figure 2*b*)

T. clavatum, like *T. collinum rubrocinctum* and *T. striatum,* prefers rather open wooded areas or the edges of denser woods as nesting sites. There was local variation in abundance of these 3 species: At Derby *clavatum* and *striatum* were less common than *rubrocinctum;* in the Washington area *clavatum* nested in traps twice as frequently as *rubrocinctum* but only two-thirds as frequently as *striatum;* and at Kill Devil Hills, where *striatum* is not known to occur, *rubrocinctum* used a few more traps than *clavatum.* *T. clavatum* nested most commonly in traps suspended from dead branches or tied to dead tree trunks, and in traps placed on structural timber containing deserted borings of other insects; occasionally it nested in traps hanging from limbs of living trees or in traps placed in rock crevices. Altogether I had 139 nests.

At Derby and at Plummers Island *clavatum* nested in both 4.8- and 6.4-mm. borings without decided preference for either, but at Kill Devil Hills it selected 6.4-mm. borings by a ratio of 7:2. There may be two factors operating toward the selection of larger borings at Kill Devil Hills: One is the somewhat larger size of the *clavatum* individuals there; the other is the absence of *striatum,* apparently a more aggressive species, with which *clavatum* competes for the larger borings at Plummers Island. That the latter factor may be the actual determinant is suggested by limited nesting data taken at my home in Arlington; there, where *striatum* was not present, *clavatum* preferred 6.4- to 4.8-mm. borings by a ratio of 3:1 in the 8 nests stored.

Supersedure and competition. At Derby, N. Y., *clavatum* superseded the vespid *Ancistrocerus c. catskill* (Saussure) in 1 nest; at Cropley, Md., it superseded the pompilid *Auplopus caerulescens subcorticalis* (Walsh) in 1 nest; at Plummers Island it superseded the pompilid *Dipogon s. sayi* Banks in 1 nest and the megachilids *Osmia l. lignaria* Say and *O. b. bucephala* Cresson in 1 nest each; and at Kill Devil Hills it superseded an unknown vespid in 1 nest. At Derby it was superseded by *Trypoxlon frigidum* Smith in 1 nest (fig. 11) and by *Trypargilum collinum rubrocinctum* (Packard) in 1 nest; at Plummers Island it was superseded in 2 nests by *Trypargilum striatum* (Provancher), in 1 nest by a species of *Auplopus,* and in another nest by an unidentified vespid; at Cropley it was superseded by *Trypargilum tridentatum* (Packard) in 1 nest; and at Kill Devil Hills 1 nest was invaded by the ant *Crematogaster* which destroyed the 1 prepupa in that nest.

Nest architecture. *T. clavatum* began all except 3 nests by placing a little mud or agglutinated sand at the inner end of the boring or by building a partition of one of these materials some distance from the inner end. Table 26 presents measurements of the stored cells irrespective of sex in 4.8- and 6.4-mm borings from Derby, N. Y., metropolitan area of Washington, D. C., and Kill Devil Hills, N. C.

The mean length of cells at the 3 localities is correlated with a gradual increase in size of the wasps as one goes from north to south except for the mean length of cells in 4.8-mm. borings from Derby where there were several abnormally long cells among the few available for measurement. In 1 nest in a 12.7-mm. boring at Plummers Island the 4 cells averaged 17 mm. in length.

Completely stored nests in 4.8-mm. borings contained 3 to 10 cells (mean 8) and in 6.4-mm. borings there were 8 to 13 cells

TABLE 26.—*Cell measurements (in mm.) in nests of* Trypargilum clavatum *(Say)*

Locality	Boring diameter	No. cells	Range in length	Mean length
N. Y.	4.8	16	14-34	20.1
	6.4	27	10-37	14.2
D. C.	4.8	232	9-50	17.1
	6.4	242	9-52	14.5
N. C.	4.8	34	10-40	19.4
	6.4	173	9-53	16.0

(mean 10). A vestibular cell was found in 48 of the 74 completed nests; these cells were 8-93 mm. long (mean 26). In 3 nests the vestibular cell was divided by a cross partition. There was 1 empty intercalary cell in each of 7 nests; these cells were 19 to 34 mm. long. The partitions between the cells were 0.5-3 mm. thick (mean 1.3). The closing plugs were made of the same material as the partitions and were 1-11 mm. thick (mean 4.6).

Prey. Consolidated determinations from 3 different areas are detailed below. The number in parentheses following the family name indicates the number of specimens in that family identified from the nests from that locality.

Derby, N. Y.: 9 cells from 3 nests, 1954, 1955, 1957.
Dictynidae (1): 1 *Dictyna sublata* (Hentz).
Thomisidae (49): 23 *Misumenops* sp.; 5 *Misumenoides aleatorius* (Hentz); 1 *Xysticus* sp.; 1 *Philodromus marxii* Keyserling; 2 *P. pernix* Blackwall; 10 *P. rufus* Walckenaer; 5 *P.* spp.; 1 *Thanatus formicinus* (Olivier); 1 *T. striatus* Koch.
Salticidae (38): 7 *Salticus scenicus* (Linnaeus); 5 *Evarcha hoyi* (Peckham); 1 *Habronattus* sp.; 2 *Phidippus audax* (Hentz); 6 *Phidippus* sp.; 2 *Hentzia mitrata* (Hentz); 1 *Icius elegans* (Hentz); 3 *I. hartii* Emerton; 5 *Metaphidippus insignis* (Banks); 3 *M. protervus* (Walckenaer); 3 immature salticids.
Pisauridae (3): 3 *Dapanus mira* (Walckenaer).

Araneidae (9): 5 *Argiope trifasciata* (Forskål); 1 *Mangora gibberosa* (Hentz); 1 *Araniella displicata* (Hentz); 2 immature araneids.
Tetragnathidae (1): 1 *Tetragnatha* sp.
Metropolitan area of Washington, D. C.: 48 cells from 31 nests from Plummers Island, Md., 1956, 1957; 1 cell from 1 nest from Cropley, Md., 1955; 6 cells from 2 nests from Arlington, Va., 1955, 1956.
Clubionidae (8): 3 *Clubiona* sp.; 5 immature clubionids.
Anyphaenidae (23): 14 *Anyphaena pectorosa* Koch; 1 *Anyphaena* sp.; 8 *Anyphaenella saltabunda* (Hentz).
Thomisidae (76): 1 *Misumenops asperatus* (Hentz); 37 *M. oblongus* (Keyserling); 3 *M.* sp.; 7 *Misumenoides aleatorius* (Hentz); 7 *Synema parvula* (Hentz); 1 *Xysticus triguttatus* Keyserling; 5 *X.* sp.; 2 *Philodromus rufus* Walckenaer; 2 *P. satullus* Keyserling; 8 *P. washita* Banks; 3 *P.* sp.
Salticidae (347): 1 *Onondaga lineata* (Koch); 1 *Evarcha hoyi* Peckham; 25 *Phidippus clarus* Keyserling; 20 *P.* sp.; 7 *Paraphidippus marginatus* (Walckenaer); 2 *P.* sp.; 1 *Zygoballus bettini* Peckham; 1 *Z. nervosus* (Peckham); 2 *Thiodina iniquies* (Hentz); 18 *Hentzia mitrata* (Hentz); 2 *Maevia vittata* (Hentz); 5 *Icius elegans* (Hentz); 6 *Metaphidippus galathea* (Walckenaer); 86 *M. protervus* (Walckenaer); 167 immature salticids.
Pisauridae (1): 1 *Dapanus mira* (Walckenaer).
Lycosidae (1): 1 *Pardosa* sp.
Oxyopidae (11): 11 *Oxyopes salticus* Hentz.
Araneidae (117): 2 *Argiope aurantia* Lucas; 5 *A. trifasciata* (Forskål); 1 *Mangora gibberosa* (Hentz); 1 *M. maculata* (Keyserling); 7 *Eustala anastera* (Walckenaer); 1 *E.* sp.; 1 *Neoscona minima* Cambridge; 1 *N. domiciliorum* (Hentz); 43 *N.* sp.; 4 *Araneus juniperi* (Emerton); 1 *Araniella displicata* (Hentz); 50 immature araneids.
Kill Devil Hills, N. C.: 2 cells from 2 nests, 1956.
Salticidae (19): 11 *Paraphidippus marginatus* (Walckenaer); 6 *P.* sp.; 1 *Hentzia mitrata* (Hentz); 1 immature salticid.

There were 5-22 spiders per cell (mean 11) in 55 fully provisioned cells from 31 nests. Most of the spiders stored were immatures. There was considerable variation in the size of the spiders, which accounted for the variable number per cell. In 1 cell they were 1.8-7.2 mm. long.

Usually the cells contained spiders belonging to 5 or 6 species representing 3 families. However, there was considerable variation in the number of species stored. One cell was stored entirely with 1 species, while 3 others contained 10 species each. The number of families represented ranged from 1 to 5.

I preserved the spiders in 2 or more cells in several nests. The identifications of these indicate that in a single nest a mother wasp may store as many as 16 species belonging to 5 families.

I also preserved prey from nests stored during 6 different periods from late June to late August in both 1956 and 1957 at Plummers Island, Md. Analysis of the identifications from these nests shows that salticids were stored more commonly than representatives of any other family during each of the 6 periods in each season.

Araneids were stored next most commonly during all these periods except one. Thomisids were next in order of frequency and out-numbered the remaining families except during 2 periods when there were several more anyphaenids than thomisids. Individual wasps showed a definite preference for running, jumping, and hunting spiders, the so-called vagabond or wandering spiders, over the snare-builder spiders. In 58 completely stored cells from the 3 areas listed above, 19 of the cells contained vagabond spiders only (fig. 133), and 39 cells both vagabond and snare-building spiders; no cells contained snare-builders only; and in the cells containing both vagabonds and snare-builders, the former were predominant in all but 2 cells.

Comparisons of the prey lists from the three areas tabulated above may not be valid because the samples from Derby, N. Y., and Kill Devil Hills, N. C., are so limited. The predominance of thomisids, low number of araneids, and absence of anyphaenids appear note-worthy in the New York samples. The presence of salticids only in the North Carolina samples is of interest, as is also the presence of only a single species of the salticid *Paraphidippus marginatus* in 1 of the 2 cells.

H. E. Evans advised me that he found 10 brown salticids and 3 green thomisids in a cell of *clavatum* at Ithaca, N. Y. A specimen of each was identified as *Metaphidippus galathea* (Walckenaer) and *Misumenops asperatus* (Hentz) respectively.

Life history. Data from a limited number of nests suggest that at Derby there is only a single generation a year, nests being built from the last of June to the end of July, and the occupants over-wintering as diapausing larvae and emerging the following year. In the Washington area there is a very small second generation, and at Kill Devil Hills there are 2 generations. There may be 2 genera-tions at Oak Ridge, Tenn.

At Plummers Island nests of *clavatum* were stored from about June 25 to as late as September 5 in 1956; corresponding nesting dates in 1957 were about June 25 to August 22. All but 2 of the occupants in these 55 nests overwintered as diapausing larvae and emerged as adults the following season; the exceptions were males of *clavatum* in the outermost cell of each nest; 1 pupated in mid-July and died when fully colored; the other was found dead and dry outside of its cocoon but still in the nest on May 21, a week or more before the other occupants of the nest transformed to adults —very clearly it had emerged sometime the preceding year. Emer-gence data from these nests do not indicate definitely that there is a small, partial summer generation. However, when nests were examined in the laboratory the relative development of the occu-pants indicated that adults from the overwintering larvae stored nests at Plummers Island from about June 25 to July 25. In the field there must be a summer emergence of a limited number of *clavatum* from some of the nests stored early in July, because adults were actively nesting again from about August 7 until early in September. There was no nesting activity between July 25 and August 7.

At Kill Devil Hills occupants of almost all nests stored between May 30 and July 21 emerged August 2 to 21; occupants of one nest stored during that period emerged the following year. Occupants of all nests stored after July 24 emerged the following year.

In the 2 nests from Oak Ridge, Tenn., adults emerged from 1 early in August and from the other in the year following that in which the nest was stored.

I obtained no precise information on the length of time required to store and cap an individual cell. Developmental data from some of the nests suggest that 7 or 8 cells may be stored within a 3-day period.

The egg is sausage shaped, 2.1 mm. long, and laid obliquely on the abdomen of one of the last spiders placed in the cell; it hatches in 1-2 days. The larva feeds voraciously and devours all the spiders stored for it in 3-4 days. Spinning of the cocoon requires about 2 days. In the overwintering generation the pupal stage lasts about 26 days, and the newly eclosed adult remains in the cocoon for 2 days before leaving the nest. I did not obtain exact information on the length of time between oviposition and emergence of the summer generation, but I suspect that it requires 5-6 weeks.

The cocoon is dark brown except for much of the anterior part, which is pale brown because of the mud or sand incorporated in it from the closing plug. The cocoon is more or less cylindrical with a rounded posterior end; the cocoon walls converge slightly about two-thirds the distance toward the anterior end; at the anterior end there is a light tan, silken flange that flares outward and extends beyond the anterior end; the anterior end itself is truncate, has a dark brown area in the middle and a small, low central nipple (fig. 11; text fig. 2*b*). The cocoon walls are stiff and brittle.

There was no significant difference in length between cocoons in the 4.8- and 6.4-mm. borings, but there was a gradually increasing mean length in cocoons from north to south correlated with increasing size of the adults. At Derby 18 cocoons had a mean length of 10.4 mm. (range 8-13 mm.); 309 cocoons from the area around Washington had a mean length of 11.1 mm. (range 8-14 mm.); and at Kill Devil Hills 111 cocoons had a mean length of 12.4 mm. (range 8-15 mm.). The above measurements are irrespective of sex. In the Washington area 73 cocoons from which females were reared had a mean length of 11.4 mm., and 69 male cocoons averaged 10.7 mm.; however, at Kill Devil Hills 22 female cocoons averaged 12.6 mm., and 6 male cocoons averaged 12.7 mm.

In the laboratory spring emergence from nests that overwintered outdoors took periods of 5-10 days. The two sexes emerged concurrently from nests of both the overwintering and summer generations. Occupants of individual nests in the overwintering generation usually emerged in a period of 1 to 3 days (51 nests), but in 5 nests from 4 to 7 days elapsed between emergence of the earliest and latest individuals; occupants of individual nests of the summer brood emerged in 1 to 2 days.

Arrangement of the sexes was variable in the 20 nests where the sex of the occupant of each cell was determined definitely. Males were at the inner end and females at the outer end in 5 of the nests, and females at the inner end and males at the outer end in 6 nests; in 4 nests females were at each end with a male in the middle, and in 1 nest males were at each end with a female in the middle. In 4 nests, 2 each from Plummers Island and Kill Devil Hills, the arrangement by cells was as follows (x indicates an individual that died before maturity):

1	2	3	4	5	6	7	8	9	10
♂	♀	♀	♂	♀	♂	x			
♂	♀	♂	♀	♂	♂	♀	♀	♀	
♂	♀	♂	♂	♀	♀	♂	♀		
♂	♀	x	♀	♂	♀	x	x	♀	♂

There was considerable mortality in nests due to enemies or injury. I reared 148 males and 166 females from 1185 stored cells, and so the sex ratio may normally be 1:1.

Parasites and predators. Chrysis (*Trichrysis*) *carinata* Say was reared from 4 Plummers Island nests and 1 Derby nest. An unidentified chrysidid, probably this same species, was found in 3 additional nests from Plummers Island and 1 from Cropley, Md. (fig. 133).

A mutillid cocoon, probably that of *Sphaeropthalma* (*S.*) *pennsylvanica scaeva* (Blake), was found in the outermost cocoon of *clavatum* in a 13-celled nest from Plummers Island; the mutillid prepupa was attacked and killed subsequently by *Melittobia chalybii* Ashmead.

Twenty-two nests were infested with *Melittobia chalybii*. Eleven of these from Cropley, Plummers Island, and Kill Devil Hills were infested in the field; the rest were infested in the laboratory.

Phorid scavengers, probably *Megaselia* sp., were found in 2 nests from Plummers Island and 1 from Kill Devil Hills. Wasps failed to develop in the 8 cells infested by these maggots.

The bombyliid *Anthrax aterrima* (Bigot) was reared from 11 cells of 7 nests from Kill Devil Hills. An unidentified species of *Anthrax*, possibly this same species, was found in 2 cells of another nest from Kill Devil Hills; these individuals died in the pupal stage. An unidentified bombyliid destroyed the resting larva of a chrysidid which parasitized a cell in a Plummers Island nest.

The miltogrammine *Amobia distorta* (Allen) was reared from 2 cells of a 4-celled nest from Derby. Unidentified species of Miltogrammini, possibly the same or another species of *Amobia*, destroyed 6 of 17 cells in 3 nests from Plummers Island and 2 of 9 cells in a nest from Kill Devil Hills.

Larvae of the dermestid *Trogoderma ornatum* Say infested 5 of 19 cells in 3 nests from Plummers Island. Three of 13 cells in 2 other nests from the same locality were infested by dermestid larvae, probably belonging to the same species.

A clerid larva, possibly a species of *Cymatoderes,* infested 1 cell in an 11-celled nest at Plummers Island. It was injured and failed to mature.

Twelve nests were infested by the mite *Pyemotes ventricosus* (Newport); 7 of these were field infestations of nests at Kill Devil Hills, Arlington, and Plummers Island, and 5 originated in the laboratory.

In one nest at Plummers Island the wasp stored a spider bearing an attached parasitic larva from which I reared a polysphinctine ichneumonid.

Previous observations. T. clavatum frequently nests in old mud-dauber nests built by *Sceliphron caementarium* (Drury), *Chalybion californicum* (Saussure) and *Trypargilum politum* (Say). The larger cells in these nests are usually divided by a clay partition to form 2 *clavatum* cells. This behavior was noted first by Ashmead (1894, p. 45) and was confirmed by Rau and Rau (1916, pp. 41-42) and Muma and Jeffers (1945, p. 246).

Rau and Rau (1918, p. 136) reported this wasp as tunneling into wood and making her own burrow; I feel certain that the evidence was misinterpreted and that they observed a female cleaning out the frass from an abandoned beetle boring. Blackman and Stage (1924, p. 196) bred this species from hickory trees that had been dead 4 years and on the ground for 1 or 2 years.

Two additional unusual nesting sites were reported by Rau (1922, p. 22; 1926, p. 198). One was an old *Polistes* nest; the female *clavatum* used the brood cells and capped each with a mud plug. The other site consisted of abandoned burrows of mining bees in a clay bank; the wasps constructed from two to eight provisioned cells in a linear series with one or two empty vestibular cells.

Rau (1928, pp. 418-420) and Muma and Jeffers (1945, p. 255)

presented some detailed data on the spiders used as prey in Missouri and Maryland. The specimens of prey listed by these authors belonged to the following families:

	MARYLAND	MISSOURI
Dictynidae	—	1
Anyphaenidae	1	17
Thomisidae	61	15
Salticidae	202	46
Pisauridae	—	1
Lycosidae	4	—
Oxyopidae	6	2
Theridiidae	7	—
Araneidae	30	10
Linyphyiidae	—	1

The cells reported individually by Rau contained from 2 to 6 species and from 7 to 11 individuals. Rau recorded 2 generations a year in Missouri.

Rau (1931a, p. 200), reporting on a series of homing experiments, stated that 1 of 3 marked females returned to her nest the following morning after being liberated a mile away late the preceding afternoon.

Source material.

Derby, N. Y. 1954 series: I b, VIII a. 1955 series: D 11 b, D 11 c, D 18 c. 1956 series: J 25. 1957 series: G 34.

Rochester, N. Y. 1954 series: R 3, 4.

Cropley, Md. 1955 series: B 3, 4, 5, 13, 20, 22, 23.

Plummers Island, Md. 1956 series: H 6, 7, 21, 33, 34, 45, 46, 48, 49, 54, 56, 65, 70, 72, 78, 104, 117, 120, 121, 136, 140, 141, 142, 143, 145, 150, 153, 155, 163, 165, 168, 173, 178. 1957 series: P 21, 22, 24, 26, 27, 29, 32, 34, 37, 106, 107, 109, 110, 112, 113, 115, 130, 133, 168, 207, 213, 239. 1959 series: S 44, 76. 1959 series: Y 13, 14, 23, 47, 90, 120, 128. 1960 series: E 44, 57. 1961 series: K 6, 15, 20, 56, 151, 156, 160, 161, 221, 266.

Arlington, Va. 1955 series: A 3, 8. 1956 series: K 2, 3. 1958 series: U 7, 8, 9, 12.

Kill Devil Hills, N. C. 1955 series: C 147, 148, 149, 153, 154, 169, 170, 175, 177, 178, 265, 267, 376, 377, 401, 405, 409, 417, 418, 419, 421, 422, 425, 426, 1956 series: C 410, 620, 725, 726. 1958 series: T 27, 89, 128, 155, 156, 161, 164, 189, 190.

Oak Ridge, Tenn. 1954 series: OR 1. 1955 series: OR 6.

Identifications. Araneae by B. J. Kaston; *Amobia* by W. L. Downes, Jr.; *Anthrax* spp. and *Megaselia* sp. by W. W. Wirth; *Trogoderma* by R. S. Beal; *Cymatoderes* (?) by G. B. Vogt; Ichnemonidae by L. M. Walkley; other Hymenoptera by the author.

TRYPARGILUM JOHANNIS (Richards)

(Plate 12, Figure 52; Text Figure 2c)

This species is very close to *clavatum* but differs in certain details of color, male genitalia, and shape and texture of the cocoon

(Krombein, 1959). It was reared from or its cocoons identified in 41 nests from Lake Placid, Fla. Thirty-one of the nests came from a station in an open area beneath the laboratory building at the Archbold Biological Station in 1957 and 1961. The other traps were suspended from live and dead branches of oak and scrub hickory at 4 stations in the Highlands Ridge sand-scrub area on the Station grounds in 1957, 1960, and 1961.

Supersedure and competition. T. johannis was superseded by the vespid *Stenodynerus fulvipes rufovestis* Bohart in 1 nest, and it superseded the vespid *Euodynerus foraminatus apopkensis* (Robertson) in another nest.

Nest architecture. This wasp nested in half again as many 6.4- as 4.8-mm. borings. In almost all the nests the wasps began nesting activities by placing some agglutinated sand or sand and mud at the inner end of the boring, or by constructing a partition of this ma-

TABLE 27.—*Cell dimensions in mm. in nests of* Trypargilum johannis *(Richards)*

Boring diameter	Sex	Number of cells	Range in length	Mean length
4.8	♂	20	22-65	30.5
6.4	♂	19	16-26	21.5
	♀	33	17-50	26.5

terial some distance from the inner end. Table 27 presents measurements of stored cells by sex in 4.8- and 6.4-mm. nests. It is noteworthy that only males were reared from the smaller diameter borings.

An empty vestibular cell was present in only half of the completed nests in 4.8-mm. borings, but there was such a cell in three-fourths of the nests in 6.4-mm. borings. The vestibular cells were 6 to 47 mm. long (mean 21.4 mm.). There was one empty intercalary cell in each of 2 nests.

The partitions between cells and the closing plugs were made from agglutinated sand or a mixture of sand and mud or cement. The partitions between cells were 1-5 mm. thick (mean 2). The closing plugs were thicker in nests that lacked a vestibular cell; in these nests the plugs were 5-11 mm. thick (mean 7). In nests with a vestibular cell the plugs were 2-7 mm. thick (mean 4.5).

There were 1-7 provisioned cells (mean 4.6) per nest in completely stored borings. There was no significant difference between the number of cells in 4.8-mm. borings as compared with that in 6.4-mm. borings, perhaps because the 4.8-mm. borings apparently contained only the shorter male cells.

Prey. Consolidated determinations of spiders from 16 cells from 11 nests are as follows:

Lyssomanidae (43): 42 *Lyssomanes viridans* (Hentz); 1 *L. viridis* (Walckenaer).
Thomisidae (24): 7 *Misumenops bellulus* (Banks); 9 *M. celer* (Hentz); 3 *M.* sp.; 2 *Tmarus* sp.; 1 *Tibellus* sp.; 2 immatures.
Salticidae (36): 1 *Pellenes* sp.; 3 *Paraphidippus marginatus* (Walckenaer); 3 *Phidippus audax* (Hentz); 1 *P. variegatus* Lucas; 8 *P.* sp.; 1 *Icius* sp.; 3 *Hentzia ambigua* (Walckenaer); 9 *H. palmarum* Hentz; 1 *H.* sp.; 4 *Maevia hobbsi* Barnes; 1 *M. michelsoni* Barnes; 1 *Thiodina sylvana* Hentz.
Mimetidae (1); 1 *Mimetus notius* Chamberlain.
Lycosidae (1): 1 *Pardosa* sp.
Oxyopidae (6): 4 *Oxyopes salticus* Hentz; 2 *Peucetia abboti* (Walckenaer).
Araneidae (35): 11 *Gea heptagon* (Hentz); 1 *Drexelia directa* (Hentz); 9 *Eustala anastera* (Walckenaer); 1 *Mangora placida* (Hentz); 3 *Wagneriana tauricornis* Chamberlain; 7 *Neoscona arabesca* (Walckenaer); 1 *N. minima* (Keyserling); 1 *N.* sp.; 1 immature.
Tetragnathidae (6): 6 *Leucauge venusta* (Walckenaer).

There were 8-17 spiders (mean 11) in 16 cells from 11 nests. The individual wasps stored both immature and adult spiders. Furthermore, some wasps preyed exclusively on errant spiders (fig. 52) while other individuals preyed on both errant and snare-building spiders; none of them preyed on snare-building spiders alone. At least one wasp preyed almost entirely on the pale green *Lyssomanes viridans* (Hentz). Another wasp stored in a single cell as many as 8 different species belonging to 6 families.

H. E. Evans wrote me that 3 cells from 2 nests of *johannis* from Welaka, Fla., 160 miles north of the Archbold Biological Station, contained 19, 12, and 10 spiders, respectively. Representatives of the following species were found in 2 of the cells:

Lyssomanidae: *Lyssomanes viridis* (Walckenaer).
Drassidae: *Sergiolus trilobus* Chamberlain.
Salticidae: *Phidippus clarus* Keyserling; *Thiodina pseustes* Chamberlain and Ivie.
Oxyopidae: *Oxyopes* sp.; *Peucetia abboti* (Walckenaer).
Araneidae: *Argiope aurantia* Lucas; *A. trifasciata* (Forskål); *Gea heptagon* (Hentz).

Life history. The egg is deposited on one of the last spiders placed in the cell (fig. 52). It is slightly curved, sausage shaped, 2.5 × 0.7 mm.

Limited data suggest that the larva may hatch 4 days after oviposition, because in a nest probably completed June 30 the egg in the outermost cell hatched on July 3. The only figure available for the length of the larval feeding period is based on this same cell; feeding lasted for a week. This larva pupated 9-10 days later, and an adult female emerged 20-21 days after pupation. The total elapsed time between egg hatch and emergence of this female was 37 days. In contrast, 2 males from another nest also stored during the summer required 42-43 days from egg hatch to adult emergence. They pupated 20-22 days after egg hatch, as compared with a similar period of 16-17 days for the female mentioned above. A female in another nest required 13-14 days after completion of the larval feeding until pupation occurred.

Data from other nests showed that during the midsummer 5 males required 20-27 days (mean 25) between pupation and adult emergence, and 7 females required 27-30 days (mean 28). In nests stored in mid or late August comparable periods were 33-36 days for 2 males and 35-36 for 1 female. The period between the completion of larval feeding and adult emergence in midsummer was 31 to 39 days (mean 35) for 3 females and 34 days for 1 male; so the prepupal period is usually about 7-9 days.

Thirty-three male cocoons ranged in length from 10 to 15 mm. (mean 12.6); 18 female cocoons were 12-16 mm. long (mean 14.0). The cocoon is similar in general appearance to that of *clavatum*. The inner end is rounded. The main body of the cocoon is cylindrical, is narrowed just before the outer end, and has a collar which is narrower than in *clavatum* and does not flare outwardly (text fig. 2c). The cocoon is a lighter brown than in *clavatum* and the walls are more delicate.

In nests containing both sexes, the males emerged first in 4, females first in 1, and both sexes concurrently in 5 nests. Males in individual nests emerged over a period of 1 to 4 days and females over a period of 1 to 7 days. However, males emerged from cells 5 and 6 in one nest 24 days after males emerged from cells 2-4. It is probable that cells 5 and 6 were stored by a different female several weeks after cells 1-4.

The sequence of sexes was variable in the 10 nests containing both sexes. In 5 nests females were in the inner cells and males in the outer, and the converse was true in 2 nests. In the other 3 nests the arrangement was as follows (x indicates an individual that died before maturity):

Nest	1	2	3	4	5	6
P 174	♀	♂	♂	♀	♀	x
F 266	♀	♀	x	♂	♀	
F 274	x	x	♂	♀	♂	

I reared 33 *johannis* females and 39 males from 177 stored cells. Apparently the sex ratio is 1:1 as in the very closely related *clavatum*.

There is more or less continual nesting activity from late April until late October, for I received nests from April 30 until October 28. Emergence from most nests stored from April 30 through late August took place from June 4 to October 12. In nests stored during September and later the resting larvae were subjected to 2 months of chilling before pupation took place; this also happened with 2 nests stored during the latter half of June. There appear to be several generations a year, probably with considerable overlapping of broods.

Parasites and predators. The miltogrammine *Amobia floridensis* (Townsend) was present in 1 nest. Six maggots destroyed the contents of 4 out of 7 cells, pupated on June 4 and emerged 2 weeks later. In another *johannis* nest, miltogrammine maggots, probably of this same species, destroyed cells 1-5 of a 6-celled nest. Two other 6- and 7-celled *Trypargilum* nests were totally destroyed by miltogrammine maggots; I believe that these were nests of *johannis* because they came from the station beneath the laboratory building and no other species of *Trypargilum* was reared from that station. The maggots left one nest before I received it. All 6 cells in the other nest were destroyed by 8 maggots; 4 pairs of *A. floridensis* emerged a week after I received this nest.

Prepupae in 3 cocoons in 2 nests of *johannis* were heavily infested with the chalcidoid *Melittobia chalybii* Ashmead; probably these infestations originated in the laboratory.

Source material.
Lake Placid, Fla. 1957 series: M 253, 291, 292, 294, 295, 296, 299, 300, 303, 304, 305, 306, 308, 312, 314. 1960 series: B 121, 203. 1961 series: F 225, 226, 260, 266, 274, 275, 286. 1962 series: P 79, 81, 82, 85, 105, 112, 113, 115, 116, 117, 118, 174, 176, 187, 191, 196, 204.

Identifications. Araneae by W. J. Gertsch, B. J. Kaston and H. K. Wallace; Diptera by W. L. Downes; Hymenoptera by the author.

TRYPARGILUM STRIATUM (Provancher)

(Plate 12, Figures 53-56; Plate 28, Figures 132, 134; Plate 29, Figure 135; Text Figure 2e)

This species is common at Plummers Island, Md., and most of my nests came from that locality. In addition I obtained a few nests from Derby, N. Y., Cropley, Md., and Lost River State Park, W. Va. The wasp occurs most commonly in rather open wooded areas or at the edges of woods. There were 136 nests in 6.4-mm. borings, 113 in 12.7-mm. borings, and 3 in 9.6-mm. borings. I used very few 9.6-mm. borings, and so the limited usage here implies no preference for the other borings. Also, I used only half as many borings of 12.7-mm. diameter as of 6.4; so probably *striatum* accepts any boring from 6.4 to 12.7 mm. with equal facility. *T. striatum* nested most commonly in traps suspended from dead limbs or tied to dead trunks, and about half as commonly in traps placed on structural timber riddled by borings of other insects; a few nests were made in traps suspended from limbs of live trees.

Supersedure and competition. At Plummers Island *T. striatum* superseded *T. clavatum* (Say) in 2 nests, and *Monobia quadridens* (Linnaeus), a species of *Dipogon* (probably *sayi* Banks) and *Osmia lignaria* Say in 1 nest each. It superseded a vespid in 1 nest at Derby. It was superseded by *Monobia quadridens* (Linnaeus) in 2 nests at Plummers Island.

Nest architecture (figs. 53, 54). Except in 8 nests *striatum* began by placing a little mud at the inner end of the boring (fig. 55) or by building a mud plug some distance from the inner end (fig. 53). There were no significant differences in range and mean length of the stored cells in nests from various localities. In nests from Plummers Island 462 provisioned cells in 6.4-mm. borings were 13-60 mm. (mean 25), and 498 provisioned cells in 12.7-mm. borings were 11-41 mm. long (mean 17). Completed nests in 6.4-mm. borings from Plummers Island usually contained 5 cells stored with spiders and an empty vestibular cell; similar nests in 12.7-mm. borings usually contained 7 provisioned cells and an empty vestibular cell. Vestibular cells were present in 130 of the 157 completed nests; the vestibular cells were divided into 2 sections by a cross partition (fig. 54) in 7 nests. Eighty-one vestibular cells in 6.4-mm. borings were 5-125 mm. long (mean 30), and 49 vestibular cells in 12.7-mm. borings were 3-70 mm. long (mean 17). There was an empty intercalary cell between 2 stored cells in 1 nest. The partitions between the cells, made from mud, were 0.5-4 mm. thick (mean 1.7); each partition was thinner at the center, noticeably so in the 12.7-mm. borings where the thickness was usually not over 0.5 mm. The closing plugs, made of the same material as the partitions, were 1.5 to 7 mm. thick (mean 3.4).

Prey. There were 3-21 spiders per cell (mean 11) in 30 fully provisioned cells from 21 Plummers Island nests. Most of the spiders stored were juvenile snare builders (fig. 132). There was considerable variation in the size of the spiders stored, which accounted for the variable number per cell. Consolidated identifications for 41 completely or partially provisioned cells from 29 nests from Plummers Island, 1956, 1957, and 1960, are given below. The number in parentheses following the family name indicates the number of spiders taken as prey in that family.

Clubionidae (2): 1 *Clubiona obesa* Hentz; 1 *C. pallens* Hentz.
Anyphaenidae (16): 1 *Aysha gracilis* (Hentz); 1 *Anyphaena celer* (Hentz); 2 *A. fraterna* (Banks); 12 *A. pectorosa* Koch.
Thomisidae (4): 3 *Philodromus washita* Banks; 1 *P.* sp.
Salticidae (1): 1 immature.
Pisauridae (1): 1 *Pisaurina mira* (Walckenaer).
Mimetidae (3): 3 *Mimetus puritanus* Chamberlain.
Araneidae (330): 7 *Wixia ectypa* (Walckenaer); 27 *Eustala anastera* (Walckenaer); 1 *E. emertoni* Banks; 1 *Acacesia hamata* (Hentz); 2 *Mangora ma-*

culata (Keyserling); 15 *Neoscona arabesca* (Walckenaer); 7 *N. domiciliorum* (Hentz); 135 *N.* sp.; 1 *Araneus juniperi* (Emerton); 4 *A. marmoreus* Clerck; 4 *A.* sp.; 1 *Araniella displicata* (Hentz); 125 immatures.

At Plummers Island *striatum* stored 1-5 species in each of the fully provisioned cells. I preserved the spiders from 2 cells in each of 4 nests. Four to 6 species representing 2 to 3 families were present in each pair of cells. Individual wasps showed a definite preference for snare-building spiders over running and jumping spiders. In 33 completed cells 21 contained only snare builders, and 12 contained both snare builders and running and jumping spiders; the snare builders predominated in all mixed cells.

Twenty-two completely provisioned cells from 6 nests from Derby in 1960 contained from 9 to 22 spiders each (mean 15). Consolidated prey records for these cells are as follows:

Thomisidae (16): 1 *Philodromus pernix* Blackwall; 15 *P.* sp.
Pisauridae (2): 2 *Dapanus mira* (Walckenaer).
Araneidae (302): 165 *Eustala anastera* Walckenaer; 45 *Neoscona arabesca* Walckenaer; 1 *N.* sp.; 33 *Araneus patagiatus* Clerck; 51 *A.* sp.; 1 *Araniella displicata* Hentz; 1 *Neosconella pegnia* (Walckenaer); 5 immatures.

At Derby *striatum* stored 1-4 species in each of the fully provisioned cells, and each cell contained a predominance of snare-building spiders. Ten of 14 cells contained snare-builders only, and the other 4 contained both snare-building and errant spiders.

A comparison of the prey preferences of *striatum* and *clavatum*, which nested at the same stations at Plummers Island, shows striking differences. Both species stored the same mean number of spiders per cell, but *striatum* preyed on fewer species. Also, *striatum* stored predominantly snare-building spiders (Araneidae) and an insignificant number of spiders belonging to other families. *T. clavatum* preferred errant spiders (Salticidae, Thomisidae, Anyphaenidae, Clubionidae) over snare-builders by a ratio of 4:1. It is quite likely that these prey biases may have originated because of competition between the two wasps. There is occasional competition between *striatum* and *clavatum* for 6.4-mm. borings. *T. striatum* is larger and apparently more aggressive, for it superseded *clavatum* in two 6.4-mm. nests but was never superseded by *clavatum*. When I picked up one of these nests, it contained an adult female *striatum* and 2 provisioned cells, each with an egg; a female *clavatum* was reared from cell 1, and cell 2, undoubtedly stored by *clavatum*, contained 10 saliticids, 1 thomisid, 1 anyphaenid, and 3 araneids. The other nest was completely stored when I picked it up; it contained a mature larva in cell 1, successively smaller larvae in cells 2 to 7 and an egg in cell 8; cells 1 to 4 were smaller than 5 to 8; the contents of this nest were infested by *Melittobia*, but the cocoons in cells 1 to 4 were definitely those of *clavatum* and those in 5 to 8 were definitely those of *striatum*.

Life history. Although many of the nests from Derby were infested by *Melittobia*, the few from which *striatum* was reared indicate that there is only a single generation in that area; the wasps emerged the following year from 8 nests provisioned during late July, August, and early September. A single nest was stored at Lost River State Park early in July. The occupants overwintered as resting larvae, and so there may be only a single brood in the mountains of West Virginia.

In the Washington area there is occasionally a small second generation. Field emergence from overwintering nests occurred during June at Plummers Island. In 1956 adult wasps emerged July 16 from 1 nest stored June 14 to 29, and on August 14 from 3 of 6 nests stored between June 29 and July 11; the occupants of the other 3 nests stored June 29-July 11, and of nests stored later that summer, overwintered as resting larvae. In 6 of 9 nests stored June 11 to July 2, 1957, adults eclosed during that summer but were unable to emerge from the nests; occupants emerged the next year from the other 3 nests stored June 11-July 2. In 1958 1 nest was stored between July 4 and 13, and an adult emerged August 12; occupants of nests stored later that summer emerged the following year.

At Plummers Island in 1956 nests were provisioned by *striatum* as late as the period July 25-August 15. Female *striatum* were nesting as late as the last week in September in both 1957 and 1958, and in early September in 1960 and 1961. However, in 1962 the latest nests were stored early in August.

T. striatum is not characterized, as is *collinum rubrocinctum,* by the partial emergence of the progeny in 1 nest a month or so after the nest is completed and the emergence of the other occupants of the same nest early the following summer. However, in a few nests there was delayed emergence of 1 or more wasps a long time after most individuals of that generation emerged. This phenomenon was noted in only 2 other species: The wasp *Podium luctuosum* Smith and the bee *Prochelostoma philadelphi* (Robertson). This delayed emergence occurred in both 6.4- and 12.7-mm. nests. Nine of these nests were from Plummers Island. One was a 2-celled nest provisioned July 17-24, 1957; the small larva in cell 2 died by July 26; the occupant of cell 1 overwintered as a diapausing larva, remained in that state during the following summer, went through the winter of 1958-59 still as a larva, transformed to a pupa April 22, 1959, and died 5 weeks later as a fully colored male almost ready to eclose. The second was a 3-celled nest also provisioned July 17-24, 1957; *striatum* males emerged May 28-June 2, 1958, from cells 1 and 2; an adult male eclosed in cell 3 on October 6, 1958, and emerged on the 9th. A 4-celled nest was provisioned

July 20-August 17, 1958; occupants of cells 2 and 3 died as immatures; an adult male emerged from cell 1 May 27, 1959; the occupant of cell 4 pupated about October 1 and an adult male emerged about a month later. The fourth was a 5-celled nest provisioned August 17-31, 1958; the occupant of cell 4 died as an immature; males emerged from cells 2 and 3 on June 25 and July 6, 1959, 4 to 6 weeks after most other individuals in that overwintering generation had emerged; occupants of cells 1 and 5 remained in the larval stage throughout the 1959 season, that in cell 1 dying during the winter of 1959-60 and that in cell 5 transforming to a pupa by April 28 and emerging from the cocoon as an adult female on May 24, 1960. The next 4 nests with delayed emergence at Plummers Island were from the 1962 series. One was stored before July 11; a male and a female emerged from cells 3 and 5, respectively, before May 17, 1963, and males from cells 1, 4, and 2, respectively, on June 2, 7, and July 2, 1963. The next nest was stored between July 12 and 21, 1962; females emerged from cells 4 and 2 on May 17 and 25, 1963, a male eclosed but died in cell 1 on June 14, a female emerged from cell 3 on July 6, a female pupa died in cell 5 on September 12, and the occupants of cells 6 and 7 died as larvae. In another nest stored between July 12 and 21, 1962, females emerged from cells 6, 4, and 3 on May 19, September 30, and October 22, 1963, and the occupants of the other 4 cells died before maturity. The next Plummers Island nest was stored August 1-7, 1962; females emerged from cells 1, 2, and 3 on May 16, 17, and August 27, 1963; the occupants of the other 4 cells died before maturing although 1 diapausing larva lived through the winter of 1963-64. The ninth nest with delayed emergence at the Island was one stored the first week in August 1962. There were 7 cells in this nest; the eggs in cells 6 and 7 died shortly after the nest was stored, and the resting larva in cell 5 died during the winter; females of *striatum* emerged May 16-17 from cells 1 and 2 and from cell 3 on August 27, 1963; the occupant of cell 4 remained in the larval stage through the winter of 1963-64, transformed to a female pupa on March 7, 1964, and died several weeks later before eclosion of the adult. The tenth such nest was a 4-celled nest from Derby; the occupants of cells 1 and 4 died as immatures; a male emerged from cell 3 on June 15; a female eclosed in cell 2 during the last week of July and died in the nest.

I obtained no exact data on the length of time required to store and cap an individual cell. During the summer as many as 8 cells might be stored in a single nest in a week, but that number undoubtedly does not represent the total nesting activity of a single individual. In September, when cooler weather is normal, the provisioning rate of an individual female decreases. At Plummers

Island in September 1958 there was only 1 female nesting at a station located beneath the porch roof of the cabin. I picked up the traps in which she nested at weekly intervals; she stored 4 cells during the first week of September, 2 cells during the second, 5 cells during the third, and 1 cell during the fourth.

The egg is 2.5 mm. long and hatches in 1+ days. The larva devours all the spiders stored for it in 4-5 days. Spinning the cocoon requires 1-2 days. The wasp overwinters as a diapausing larva. The duration of the pupal stage is 15-20 days for occupants of overwintering nests, and probably somewhat less for the summer generation at Plummers Island. The adult remains in the cocoon about 4 days after eclosion. Members of the summer generation go from egg to emerged adult in 36-40 days.

The cocoon is dark brown except for the anterior end, which is lighter because of the mud incorporated in it from the closing plug. The cocoon is cylindrical with a rounded posterior end; the cocoon wall flares outward at the anterior end which is convex but without a median nipple (figs. 53, 55, 134; text fig. 2e). In some cocoons built in 12.7-mm. borings the flared-out section is much wider and the anterior end less convex than in the cocoons constructed in 6.4-mm. borings (figs. 54, 56). The cocoon walls are stiff and brittle.

At Plummers Island 225 cocoons in 6.4-mm. borings were 11-18 mm. long (mean 15.4); 183 cocoons in 12.7-mm. borings were 10-18 mm. long (mean 14.7). The greater mean length of the cocoons in smaller borings is believed to be due to the greater convexity of the anterior end. The above measurements are irrespective of sex; there appears to be no significant difference in mean length between male and female cocoons.

Emergence in the laboratory each spring from nests that overwintered outdoors took periods ranging from 9 to 11 days except where there was delayed emergence. Males began to emerge 2-3 days before females but there was considerable overlap of emergence of the 2 sexes. Occupants of a single nest emerged usually within a period of 1-3 days, although occasionally 9 days would elapse before all occupants emerged.

Mostly males were reared from 6.4-mm. nests, and approximately twice as many females as males from 12.7-mm. nests. At Plummers Island from 1956 to 1962 a total of 477 provisioned cells in 6.4-mm. borings yielded 11 females and 162 males, whereas 500 provisioned cells in 12.7-mm. borings yielded 123 females and 53 males. As is apparent from the above figures there was considerable mortality; this was due to parasites, mold, injury, and preservation of prey or wasp larvae. The over-all sex ratio ($\female$:$\male$) was almost 2:3.

Most nests from which only males were reared were in 6.4-mm. borings, and most nests from which only females were reared were in 12.7-mm. borings. Cocoons were placed in individual glass vials from 21 nests in 12.7-mm. borings and from 8 nests in 6.4-mm. borings. In all the 12.7-mm. nests, and in 6 of the 8 6.4-mm. nests, 1 or more *striatum* males were in the innermost cell or cells, and females in the outermost cells. In 1 of the 6.4-mm. nests containing a different arrangement, there was a female in cell 1 and males in cells 2 and 3; in the other nest there were 3 cells with males, the next with a female, and the outermost with another male. The low ♀:♂ ratio was a direct effect of the arrangement of sexes in many nests, because the outer cells were more subject to infestation by chrysidid and miltogrammine parasites.

Parasites and predators. Chrysis (*Trichrysis*) *carinata* Say was reared from 25 nests from Plummers Island (figs. 132, 134) and probably in 1 nest from Cropley. An unidentified chrysidid, possibly this same species, was found in 2 nests from Derby and 1 nest from Plummers Island; adult parasites were not reared.

The outermost *striatum* cocoon in each of 3 nests from Plummers Island was parasitized by the mutillid *Sphaeropthalma* (*S.*) *pennsylvanica scaeva* (Blake). Probably this same mutillid parasitized the outermost cell in another nest, but it died as a prepupa (fig. 135).

A total of 112 nests was infested with *Melittobia chalybii* Ashmead; 32 of the infestations originated in the laboratory. The 80 nests infested in the field came from both Plummers Island and Derby.

Phorid scavengers belonging to the genus *Megaselia* were found in 2 nests from Derby and 10 nests from Plummers Island. Wasps failed to develop in the 19 cells infested by these maggots. The braconid *Snyaldis* sp. was reared from some of the phorid puparia in the nest from Derby.

The bombyliid *Anthrax aterrima* (Bigot) was reared from 1 cell in each of 2 nests from Plummers Island. *A. argyropyga* Wiedemann was reared from 1 cell in a third nest from Plummers Island. Two slender first-instar bombyliid larvae were found trying to penetrate the anterior end of a cocoon in another nest from Plummers Island; I preserved one on a slide, and the other died without injuring the wasp prepupa.

The miltogrammine *Amobia distorta* (Allen) was reared from 9 of 14 cells in 2 nests from Plummers Island and from all 6 cells in a nest from Derby. Unidentified species of Miltogrammini, possibly the same species, destroyed 23 of 31 cells in 6 nests from Derby and 31 of 55 cells in 13 nests from the area around Washington.

Dermestid larvae, probably *Trogoderma ornatum* Say, were found in 9 nests from Plummers Island.

All stages of an acarid mite, *Tyrophagus* sp., were found on a dead, mature larva in a nest from Plummers Island. Unidentified mites, possibly of the same species, were found in 2 other nests. In 1 nest from Plummers Island the mites were found with the dead spider prey and dermestid larvae. In the other nest from Lost River State Park several larval mites were clustered on the shriveled wasp egg in one of the cells containing fresh paralyzed spiders.

Five nests from Plummers Island became infested in the laboratory by the mite *Pyemotes ventricosus* (Newport).

In several of the nests from Plummers Island the wasps had stored spiders each bearing a small parasitic larva attached to the abdomen. I was able to rear adults from 2 of these larvae. One was the acroceratid *Ogcodes dispar* Macquart, and the other was the ichneumonid *Hymenoepimecis wiltii* Cresson.

Previous observations. Ashmead (1894, p. 45) certainly is in error in stating that *striatum* [recorded as *albopilosum*] preys on aphids in Florida; the Peckhams (1895, p. 306) quoted Ashmead as writing that this was "probably a case of mistaken identity on his part." Krombein and Evans (1954, p. 233) recorded a female *striatum* preying on a small, immature orb weaver spider, *Neoscona minima* Cambridge, near Arcadia, Fla.

The Peckhams (1895; 1898, pp. 85-86; 1905, pp. 190-193) recorded this species [as *albopilosum*] as nesting in wooden posts. They stated that it bores in wood, the female entering an empty hole in the post, gnawing at the wood, and carrying out loads of wood dust. In my experience *striatum* never bores in wood; I think that what the Peckhams interpreted as wood dust was actually frass of the beetle(?) larva that made the original boring. They recorded *striatum* as using larger orb weaver spiders than *rubrocinctum*, and went on to say that it stored 25-30 per cell; this figure does not agree with my findings on this species. I infer that there is only a single generation in Wisconsin from their statements that "the hard working little creatures enjoy a well earned holiday on the blossoms of the aster and the golden rod" after August 15, and that they obtained no emergence by August 31 from nests stored as early as June 30.

Rau (1926, p. 199; 1928, pp. 423-428) recorded *striatum* as *albopilosum* as nesting in deserted galleries of mining bees in a clay bank in Missouri and preying on orb weaver spiders. Later (1931a, p. 200), in reporting on a series of homing experiments, he stated that 3 of 4 marked females were able to return to their nests 15 to 75 minutes after being liberated a mile away.

Krombein (1956b, pp. 155-156) published on a nest in a wooden trap from Lost River State Park, W. Va. The spiders in 1 cell consisted of 3 *Neoscona minima* Cambridge, 5 juvenile *N. minima* (?), 1 immature araneid, and 1 *Anyphaena pectorosa* Koch.

Balduf (1961) recorded *striatum* as nesting in abandoned carpenter bee borings in structural lumber.

Source material.

Derby, N. Y. 1954 series: XIV a, XV a. 1955: D 5 c (new), D 14 c. 1958 series:
R 56, 59, 60. 1959 series: W 61, 79. 1960 series: D 61, 63, 64, 65, 66, 68,
71, 72, 86, 87, 88. 1961 series: L 73, 74, 75, 81, 82, 83, 84.

Cropley, Md. 1955 series: B 14, 21, 26, 39.

Plummers Island, Md. 1956 series: H 4, 8, 22, 31, 32, 41, 42, 50, 60, 80, 85,
91, 95, 98, 105, 110, 113, 114, 115, 118, 121, 122, 148, 154, 169, 179. 1957
series: P 5, 20, 35, 39, 44, 48, 53, 55, 59, 60, 65, 68, 73, 74, 75, 84, 88, 90,
94, 95, 107, 118, 121, 128, 131, 137, 138, 139, 145, 147, 151, 162, 164, 165,
183, 185, 188, 196, 197, 200, 208, 217, 221, 222, 223, 224, 237, 242, 248, 255,
257, 267, 269, 277, 281. 1958 series: S 30, 39, 52, 69, 81, 88, 94, 99, 103,
105, 106, 109, 112, 114, 116, 117. 1959 series: Y 40, 50, 55, 57, 61, 62, 66,
68, 125, 126, 131, 147. 1960 series: E 37, 42, 46, 49, 51, 58, 59, 61, 63, 64,
66, 67, 68, 69, 72, 86, 87, 88, 89, 91, 92, 93, 94, 95, 96, 109, 111, 112, 113,
114, 115, 116, 117, 118, 119, 128, 130, 131, 132, 139, 161, 166, 167, 172, 181,
183, 187, 190. 1961 series: K 43, 61, 68, 109, 130, 132, 133, 134, 135, 138,
139, 141, 142, 143, 144, 164, 167, 173, 193, 194, 195, 196, 197, 199, 200, 202,
203, 204, 205, 206, 207, 208, 209, 210, 211, 212, 213, 214, 215, 216, 224, 227,
228, 241, 246, 248, 251. 1962 series: M 37, 42, 70, 72, 76, 80, 81, 83, 84, 85,
86, 93, 94, 97, 102, 103, 104, 119.

Lost River State Park, W. Va. 1955 series: E 14.

Identifications. Acarina by E. W. Baker; Araneae by B. J. Kaston;
Megaselia sp. and *Anthrax* by W. W. Wirth and P. H. Arnaud;
Amobia by W. L. Downes; *Ogcodes* by C. W. Sabrosky; *Synaldis*
sp. by C. F. W. Muesebeck; *Hymenoepimecis* by L. M. Walkley;
other Hymenoptera by the author.

TRYPOXYLON Latreille

I obtained biological data on 5 species of this genus, *backi* Sandhouse and *frigidum* Smith belonging to Group Figulus, *carinatum*
Say a representative of Group Scutatum, and *johnsoni* Fox and
clarkei Krombein of Group Fabricator. While some of these species are quite common, e.g., *frigidum* and *backi,* none of them nests
nearly so frequently in trap nests as species of *Trypargilum.* Furthermore, the differences in shape and texture of the cocoon and prey
preferences are not so marked as in the species of *Trypargilum.*
The species of *Trypoxylon* also differ from those of *Trypargilum*
in one other very significant biological detail—the males are not
known to help in the nesting operation by standing guard inside
the boring while the females hunt for prey or gather nesting
materials.

These 5 species are all small. They preferred to nest in 3.2-mm.
borings, though occasionally *frigidum, johnsoni,* and *clarkei* used
larger borings, perhaps when none of the smaller size was available.
All species nested in the same habitat, that is, wooded areas rather
open to sun during part of the day. They have also adapted them-

selves to nesting in structural timber containing abandoned borings
of anobiid beetles. About half of my nests came from traps set out
on porch rafters or wooden walls containing such borings.

I did not obtain numerous prey records for any of the species,
but perhaps enough have accumulated to indicate the possibility
that there are some differences between the species in prey selection.
T. frigidum preyed on a variety of snare builders though occasionally it took jumping spiders or micryphantids which are presumed to occur in leaf litter. *T. carinatum* of Group Scutatum
stored *Theridion lyricum* Walckenaer of the Theridiidae. *T. johnsoni* of Group Fabricator preyed only on narrow elongate snare
builders belonging to several species of Tetragnathidae and
Araneidae. *T. clarkei*, also of Group Fabricator, preyed on a snare-
builder of ordinary shape, *Mangora gibberosa* Hentz.

The 3 species belonging to Groups Figulus and Scutatum and
clarkei of Group Fabricator spin delicate cocoons of opaque silk
that do not incorporate anal secretions of the larva to form a
brittle varnished cocoon wall. The shape is modified fusiform with
the cocoon walls tapering gradually outward from the narrowed
posterior end to the rounded anterior end (fig. 11). The cocoon of
johnsoni of Group Fabricator is very different in shape and texture.
It is cylindrical with rounded ends and has brittle walls with incorporated sand grains taken from the partition at the posterior end
of the cell.

TRYPOXYLON FRIGIDUM Smith
(Plate 3, Figure 11)

I reared this species from 17 nests from Derby and 20 nests from
the area around Washington. Twenty-seven of the nests were in
3.2-mm. borings, 8 in 4.8-mm. borings, and 2 in 6.4-mm. borings.
There was a decided preference for the smallest borings; probably
the two larger sizes were utilized only when no small ones were
available. More than half of the nests were at stations located on
structural timber, *e.g.*, wooden window sills, porch rafters, or building walls containing abandoned borings of anobiid beetles. Four
nests came from settings on stone walls and the rest from settings
on branches of living or dead trees and on dead tree trunks.

Supersedure and competition. *T. frigidum* superseded *Trypargilum clavatum* (Say) in two nests at Derby (fig. 11) and was
superseded by *Trypargilum collinum rubrocinctum* (Packard) in 1
nest at Derby.

Nest architecture. In all but 2 nests the wasp began nesting at
the inner end of the boring without making an initial mud plug
or partition. In 2 nests the wasps left an empty space capped by a

mud plug at the inner end. Table 28 summarizes measurements of the stored cells irrespective of sex in nests from these two areas.

Completed nests in 3.2-mm. borings contained 2 to 7 stored cells (mean 3.2), and in 4.8-mm. borings there were 2 to 8 cells (mean 5.3). An empty vestibular cell was found in only 7 of the nests from Derby but occurred in 14 of the nests from around Washington. These cells were 4 to 127 mm. in length; one such cell was divided by 3 cross partitions. Three of the Derby nests contained 1 or 2 empty intercalary cells, and 6 of the Washington nests contained 1 or 2 such cells. These cells were 4 to 11 mm. in length. The parti-

TABLE 28.—*Cell dimensions (in mm.) in nests of* Trypoxylon frigidum *Smith*

Locality	Boring diameter	No. of cells	Range in length	Mean length
N. Y.	3.2	37	10-40	14.7
	4.8	3	10-12	11.0
	6.4	2	9-11	10.0
D. C.	3.2	53	6-43	14.0
	4.8	17	9-48	14.8
	6.4	1	14	14.0

tions between cells and the closing plugs were made of mud. The partitions were 0.2-2.0 mm. thick, and the plugs were 1-4 mm. thick.

Prey. The number of spiders per cell in 20 completely provisioned cells ranged from 4 to 16 with a mean of 8.3. Juvenile and adult spiders were stored in equal numbers. They were 2 to 2.6 mm. long in 1 cell and 1-1.5 mm. in a cell in another nest. Consolidated determinations from Derby and the Washington area are detailed below. The number in parentheses following the family name indicates the number of specimens in that family identified in the nests from that locality.

Derby, N. Y.: 1 cell from a 1955 nest.
   Theridiidae (8): 8 *Theridion*(?) sp. in *murarium* group.
Metropolitan area of Washington, D. C.: 6 cells from 4 nests from Arlington, Va., 1958 and 1959; 2 cells from 2 nests, and partial sample from several cells in a third nest from Plummers Island, Md., 1959, 1960, 1961.
Salticidae (2): 2 immatures.
Theridiidae (17): 2 *Theridion albidum* Banks; 2 *T. differens* Emerton; 1 *T. frondeum* Hentz(?); 1 *T. lyra* Hentz; 9 *T. murarium* Emerton; 2 *T. unimaculatum* Emerton.
Araneidae (14): 1 *Eustala* sp.; 13 immatures.
Linyphiidae (2): 1 *Tennesseelum formicum* (Emerton); 1 immature.
Tetragnathidae (2): 1 *Leucauge venusta* (Walckenaer); 1 *Tetragnatha* sp.
Micryphantidae (9): 1 *Ceratinopsis interpres* Cambridge; 5 *C. purpurescens* Keyserling; 3 micryphantids.

At my home in Arlington, Va., *frigidum* stored 1-5 species of spiders per cell in 4 completely provisioned cells. As many as 3 families were present in 1 cell. It is clear from the records listed above that *frigidum* prefers snare-building spiders by a very substantial percentage.

H. E. Evans advises me that samples of spider prey from 2 nests of *frigidum* at Ithaca, N. Y., were identified as *Theridion albidum* Banks, *T. globosum* Hentz, *T. unimaculatum* Emerton, and *Eustala anastera* (Walckenaer). One cell contained 14 spiders.

Life history. There are 2 or more generations a year at both Derby and Washington. Nests at Derby were provisioned more or less continually during the period June 6 to August 5, and adults emerged from July 1 to August 11. Nests in the Washington area were stored from May 16 until at least late in August, and emergence occurred from June 1 to August 24 except for 1 nest stored late in June, the occupants of which emerged the following spring. In 1963 at Plummers Island I collected adults almost every week from May 19 to September 28.

No data are available to indicate the maximum number of cells that may be stored in 1 day. One trap at Arlington was set out late one evening and was capped by the following evening. This nest contained 2 provisioned cells separated by 2 intercalary cells and a vestibular cell; so that mother stored at least 2 cells with spiders and constructed 5 mud partitions during 1 working day. Developmental data in 2 nests from Arlington and Plummers Island suggest that as many as 4 cells may be stored within a day.

The egg is sausage shaped, 1.3-1.5 mm. long, 0.3-0.4 mm. wide, and deposited on the abdomen of one of the last spiders brought into the cell; it hatches in 1-2 days. The larva devours all the stored spiders in 4 to 6 days, and spinning of the cocoon requires 1 to 2 days. About 4 days are spent as a prepupa and 6 days as a pupa. The newly eclosed adult remains in the cocoon about 4 days before leaving the nest. The total elapsed time between oviposition and emergence of adults from the nest ranged from 19 to 27 days (mean 20.8) for 13 individuals from different nests in the Washington area.

The fusiform cocoon increases gradually in diameter from the posterior end to the rounded anterior end. It is silken, opaque, delicate, and off-white to cream in color (fig. 11). Thirty-two female cocoons were 6.5 to 10 mm. long (mean 8.4), and 20 male cocoons were 5.5 to 8 mm. long (mean 7.0).

Females only were reared from 14 nests; males only from 12 nests. In the 9 nests from which both sexes were reared, females were always in the inner and males in the outer cells. From 117 provisioned cells I obtained 48 females and 34 males; the remaining cells were parasitized or the wasp larvae were preserved for taxonomic study.

Parasites and predators. *Chrysogona verticalis* (Patton) was reared from 1 cell of a 5-celled nest at Arlington, and from 2 cells in a 4-celled nest from Derby. A newly hatched chrysidid larva, probably of this same species, was found in 1 cell each in 2 other nests from Arlington; these first instar larvae were preserved for taxonomic study.

Two nests from Derby contained an infestation of the chalcidoid *Melittobia chalybii* Ashmead.

A pupa of a species of *Anthrax*, probably *argyropyga* Wiedemann, was found in a *frigidum* cocoon from Glencarlyn, Arlington County, Va.

Two cells in a 4-celled nest at Plummers Island were destroyed by a miltogrammine maggot, *Amobia distorta* (Allen).

One cell of a 3-celled nest at Derby was destroyed by phorid scavengers probably belonging to the genus *Megaselia*.

One egg in an Arlington nest was destroyed by the mite *Pyemotes ventricosus* (Newport).

An ichneumonid spider parasite, probably *Zatypota luteipes* Townes, was reared from 2 spiders in a nest at Plummers Island.

Previous observations. Packard (1867, p. 415) recorded *frigidum* as having been reared from stems of *Syringa*. Blackman and Stage (1924, p. 197) bred it from burrows in hickory twigs and limbs that had been killed 2 years earlier. Rau (1926, p. 197) recorded this wasp [as *plesium* Rohwer] as nesting in a burrow in a fallen log, and later (1928, pp. 439-441) he described 3 nests in borings in sumac twigs. Taylor (1928, p. 225) found *frigidum* nesting in white pine leaders containing burrows of *Pissodes strobi* (Peck). Pate (1937, p. 5) recorded some material as having been bred from borings in a dead cherry.

The only detailed biological notes are in Rau's later contribution and in Thomas (1962). Rau found that the cells were 6.5-10.3 mm. long; there were 5, 6, and 8 cells in the 3 nests. In 2 nests at the bottom of the burrow there was an empty space covered by a mud plug, and in 2 nests there was an empty vestibular cell about 25 mm. long. He reared 2 specimens of *Chrysis (Chrysis)* sp. and 4 specimens of a metallic green chalcidoid belonging to the Cleonymidae [possibly *Ptinobius magnificus* (Ashmead)] from these nests. Thomas (1962) reported that *frigidum* eggs hatched in 3 days, that the larvae fed for 4 days, and that spinning of the cocoon required a day. Pupation occurred 6 days after the completion of feeding, the adults eclosed 10-12 days later and left the nest in another 2-3 days. Thomas (1962, 1963) reared *Chrysogona verticalis* (Patton) from nests of *frigidum* in wooden borings.

Source material.

Derby, N. Y. 1955 series: D 3 a, 11 d, 13 a, 14 a, 18 a, 18 c. 1956 series: J 85, 103, 131. 1957 series: G 106, 119, 126. 1958 series: R 19. 1959 series: W 6. 1961 series: L 3, 15, 17.

Plummers Island, Md. 1959 series: Y 2, 10. 1962 series: E 84, 97, 99, 124. 1961 series: K 73, 76, 85.

Arlington, Va. 1954 series: D 19, 20, 21. 1958 series: U 4, 5, 6. 1959 series: A 6, 7, 19, 23. 1962 series: N 20.

Identifications. Araneae by B. J. Kaston and W. J. Gertsch; *Anthrax* by W. W. Wirth; Hymenoptera by the author, except *Zatypota* by L. M. Walkley.

TRYPOXYLON BACKI Sandhouse

This species nested in five 3.2-mm. borings placed on rafters on the cabin porch at Plummers Island, Md., in 1959 and 1961.

Supersedure and competition. It was superseded by *T. johnsoni* Fox in one of these nests, and it superseded *Diodontus atratus parenosas* Pate in another nest.

Nest architecture. The wasp made the first cell at the inner end of the boring without an initial mud plug. The 3 borings that were completely stored by *backi*, contained 1, 3, and 4 stored cells, respectively, and a vestibular cell of variable length; the fourth nest contained 3 cells of *backi* at the inner end and 2 cells of *johnsoni* and a vestibular cell at the outer end. The fifth nest contained 2 cells of *atratus parenosas* at the inner end and 1 cell of *backi*; there was no vestibular cell. The provisioned cells were 8-14 mm. long (mean 10); the 3 vestibular cells were 25, 28, and 55 mm. long. The partitions separating the cells were made of mud and were ¼ mm. thick in 3 nests and 1 mm. thick in the fourth. The closing plugs were 0.5-2 mm. thick.

Prey. Each cell in the three 1959 nests contained 5-7 spiders about 2.8 mm. long of the same species of Micryphantidae. All but 1 of the spiders were females.

Life history. The nests were completed on May 29, and about June 1, 8, 23, and July 22. The egg in 1 cell hatched in 2 days. The larvae fed on the stored spiders for 6-7 days. The cocoons were spun of delicate opaque creamy silk, were 6-7 mm. long, and were very similar in appearance to those of *T. frigidum* Smith. From 19 to 24 days elapsed between the spinning of the cocoon and emergence of the adult from the nest. In 1 cell the larva pupated 7 days after devouring the spiders, spent 12 days as a pupa, and the adult remained in the cocoon 2 days before leaving the nest. All the reared specimens were females.

There are at least 2 generations a year, judged from the data reported above and from collection dates at my home in Arlington.

There I have gotten adults during each of the warm months; actual dates ranged from May 27 to October 1.

Previous observations. Apparently *backi* usually nests in abandoned borings in structural timber. Sandhouse (1940, p. 165) recorded it as nesting in burrows of powder post beetles and Krombein (1956a, p. 42; 1958a, pp. 21-22) found it nesting in a wooden wall filled with anobiid borings. Krombein recorded it as preying on the linyphiid spider *Tennesseelum formicum* (Emerton), which occurs in leaf litter as do many micryphantids. Thomas (1962) reported the chrysidid, *Chrysogona verticalis* (Patton), as a parasite of *backi*.

Source material.
Plummers Island, Md. 1959 series: Y 3, 4, 6. 1961 series: K 74, 176.

Identifications. Araneae by B. J. Kaston; wasps by the author.

TRYPOXYLON CARINATUM Say

I obtained 2 nests in 3.2-mm. borings, 1 from Plummers Island, Md., from a station beneath a dead branch in open woods, and 1 in a trap attached to a cowshed wall at my home in Arlington, Va.

Nest architecture. There was a single stored cell in each nest, 18 and 50 mm. long, respectively. The former nest had a vestibular cell 42 mm. long divided by a cross partition, and the latter nest contained a vestibular cell of 13 mm. The partitions capping the stored cells were of mud, 1-2 mm. thick. The closing plugs were 2 mm. thick.

Prey. Several spiders stored as prey in the Plummers Island nest were preserved and identified subsequently as males of the theridiid *Theridion lyricum* Walckenaer. The spiders in the Arlington nest were also snare builders.

Life history. The Arlington nest was capped on June 12. The wasp egg was laid obliquely on the right side of the anterior part of the globular abdomen. It was sausage-shaped, 1.4 mm. long and 0.4 mm. wide. It hatched on the 13th, and the larva had nearly finished its cocoon on the 21st; a female wasp emerged on July 13. The Plummers Island nest was picked up on June 21, apparently a day or two after its completion. The cocoon was completed by June 27; a male wasp emerged on July 13.

The cocoons were 6 and 8 mm. long, white and light tan, respectively, and indistinguishable from those of *frigidum* in shape and texture.

There are 2 or more generations a year in the Washington area, where I have netted adults from June 2 to September 4. *T. carinatum* nests in deserted anobiid borings in cowshed walls at my home in Arlington. In 1954 I watched females sealing two nests on

June 13; the progeny from these nests emerged on July 11. At Plummers Island it also nests in abandoned beetle borings in cedar posts on the cabin porch.

Previous observations. Sandhouse (1940) reported that a series of 4 males was reared from a tunnel in the partially decayed trunk of a tulip poplar.

Source material.
     Plummers Island, Md. 1960 series: E 78.
     Arlington, Va. 1961 series: J 8.

Identifications. Araneae by B. J. Kaston; wasp by author.

TRYPOXYLON CLARKEI Krombein

T. clarkei nested in 3 traps at Plummers Island, Md. Two of the nests were in 3.2-mm. borings fastened to the side of a dead standing tree trunk in open woods in 1961. The other was in a 4.8-mm. boring set on a fallen dead tree trunk in open woods in 1962; this trunk was standing in 1961.

Supersedure and competition. The *clarkei* nest in the 4.8-mm. boring was superseded by the vespid *Ancistrocerus campestris* (Saussure).

Nest architecture. In the 4.8-mm. boring the wasp placed a little mud at the inner end and then constructed a single cell 14 mm. long in which a female wasp developed. In one of the nests in a 3.2-mm. boring the wasp left an empty space of 32 mm. and then built a thin mud partition; the 2 stored cells were 9 and 10 mm. long, and the vestibular cell was 7.5 mm. A male was reared from 1 of the cells; the occupant of the other died as a larva. In the other nest in a 3.2-mm. boring the wasp stored 2 cells 35 and 22 mm. long, and there was no vestibular cell. A female emerged from 1 of these cells; the occupant of the other cell died as a larva. The partitions and closing plugs were of mud; in the 3.2-mm. nests the former were 0.5-1.0 mm. thick, and the latter 1.5-4.0 mm.

Prey. The spiders in the 3.2-mm. nests were all of the same species, the araneid *Mangora gibberosa* Hentz, about 3 mm. long. There were 5 and 6 spiders, respectively, in the 2 cells in which 1 female eventually developed, and 4 spiders in each of the 2 cells in which 1 male developed. This spider has the normal shape for a snare builder, not the slender elongate form of the snare builders on which its close relative *johnsoni* preys.

Life history. The 2 nests in 3.2-mm. borings were completed between June 28 and July 4, 1961. Both may have been stored by the same mother wasp, because the larvae in the nest in which a female wasp developed were slightly larger than the newly hatched larvae in the other nest. A male emerged from this latter nest on

July 24; a female in the earlier nest was ready to eclose on that same date but died before doing so.

The third nest was completed between July 12 and 21, 1962. The cocoon in the single *clarkei* cell in this nest contained a pupa when the nest was examined on July 24. A female *clarkei* emerged from the cocoon but died in the nest between July 25 and August 8.

Two of the cocoons were 9 mm. long, dirty white to light tan in color, delicate, and with a shape and texture similar to those of *frigidum* rather than to those of *johnsoni*. No mud was incorporated in the cocoon walls.

There are at least 2 generations annually in the Washington area. Male wasps have been taken from May 26 to August 24.

Source material.
   Plummers Island, Md. 1961 series: K 145, 146. 1961 series: M 22.

Identifications. Araneae by W. J. Gertsch; Hymenoptera by the author.

TRYPOXYLON JOHNSONI Fox

This uncommon species was reared from 9 nests, 2 in 3.2-mm. borings at Derby and 7 from Plummers Island, 5 of these in 3.2-mm. borings and 2 in 4.8-mm. borings. Half of the nests were from settings on structural timber containing old anobiid beetle borings and half from traps tied to dead branches or dead tree trunks.

Supersedure and competition. *T. johnsoni* superseded the sphecid wasp *T. backi* Sandhouse and the vespid *Symmorphus canadensis* (Saussure) in 2 nests at Plummers Island. *T. johnsoni* was superseded by *Symmorphus canadensis* in 1 nest at Plummers Island.

Nest architecture. This wasp used soil with a high sand content for partitions and closing plugs. In 6 traps the wasps began their nests by placing some mud at the inner end of the boring or constructing a partition of this material some distance (40-56 mm.) from the inner end; in the other 3 nests there was either supersedure of another species of wasp or the inner end of the boring was not visible when measurements were made.

There was not much difference in the length of stored cells in the 3.2-mm. borings as compared with those in 4.8-mm. borings. In 3.2-mm. borings the cells were 10-32 mm. long (mean 16.3), and in 4.8-mm. borings they were 7-23 mm. long (mean 13.6). There were no empty intercalary cells. A vestibular cell 4 to 23 mm. long was present in 5 nests; in 4 nests there was an empty, uncapped space 6-24 mm. long at the outer end of the boring. The partitions between cells were 0.5-3 mm. thick, and the closing plugs 0.5-4 mm. thick.

The number of stored cells was variable in borings used entirely by *johnsoni*. Three of the 3.2-mm. borings contained only a single stored cell with an empty space at the inner end and an uncapped space or a vestibular cell at the outer end. There were 6 and 8 stored cells in the 2 4.8-mm. borings in addition to an empty space of 56 mm. at the inner end of one nest and an empty space of 25 mm. at the outer end of both nests.

Prey. This wasp has a predilection for narrow, elongate snare-building spiders, judged from Plummers Island nests. The 1 nest stored in 1956 contained 12 half-grown tetragnathids in 1 cell belonging to 3 species of *Tetragnatha*. One spider preserved from the 1957 nest was a young *Tetragnatha*; the other spiders in this cell appeared to be the same species. In the three 1959 nests (all from different stations) the mother wasps stored the araneid *Micrathena gracilis* (Walckenaer). A penultimate male and penultimate female were preserved from 1 of the cells; the other spiders in these nests were the same species, most of them males.

Life history. There are apparently only 2 generations a year in the Washington area, judged from nesting data and field collection of adults. I have collected adults here from June 6 to August 2. At Plummers Island adults emerged early in July from nests stored early in June, while occupants of nests stored from mid-June to mid-August overwintered as diapausing larvae and emerged as adults the following spring. The 2 Derby nests were stored probably late in August, the occupants overwintered as diapausing larvae and emerged as adults the next spring.

Storing of the nest is apparently a rather protracted affair, perhaps because *johnsoni* is more restricted in its prey preferences than *frigidum*. Developmental data from one of the multicelled nests suggest that about 4 days may be required to store 5 cells.

I obtained only fragmentary data based on a few observations on duration of the various stages. The egg hatches in about 2 days, and the larva feeds for about 4 days. Spinning the cocoon requires about 2 days. Emergence of the summer generation adults occurs 20 to 25 days after oviposition. Duration of the pupal stage is much longer in the overwintering generation, about 14 days. Emergence of occupants of multicelled overwintering nests took periods ranging from 5 to 26 days.

The cocoon is very different from those of the other species of *Trypoxylon*. This difference is not a character of group significance, because the cocoon of the closely related species *clarkei* Krombein is quite similar to that of *frigidum*. The cocoon of *johnsoni* is cylindrical with rounded ends. The walls are quite brittle because sand grains from the partition at the inner end of the cell are incorporated with the silk. Female cocoons are a bit longer (range

6-9 mm., mean 8.0 mm.) than male cocoons (range 6-8 mm., mean 7.0 mm.).

Most nests produced only females or only males. In the 1 nest from which both sexes were reared a male was in cell 6 and females in 7 and 8; occupants of the other cells died or were preserved as immatures.

Previous observations. Rau and Rau (1918, pp. 137-139) described a nest of this species in a boring made by another insect in a stem of soft wood. They found 2 cocoons separated by mud partitions from which they reared *johnsoni.* They also found 1 female that entered 3 holes in a clay bank. Later, Rau (1922, p. 22) recorded another female in a hole an inch deep in some soil clinging to the roots of an upturned tree. The reason for this habit is not known. Rau and Rau speculated that the wasp might have been searching for a domicile or hunting for prey. It is also possible that the wasps might have been gathering soil for construction of a partition in the nest.

Source material.
    Derby, N. Y. 1956 series: J 112, 116.
    Plummers Island, Md. 1956 series: H 5. 1957 series: P 163. 1959 series: Y 3, 5, 7. 1960 series: E 104, 106.

Identifications. Araneae by B. J. Kaston; wasps by the author.

DIODONTUS ATRATUS PARENOSAS Pate

I obtained 15 nests of this species, 13 from Arlington and 1 each from Plummers Island and Derby. All were in 3.2-mm. borings. Those from Arlington were in traps that had been placed on an old cowshed wall containing many abandoned borings of anobiid beetles. The Plummers Island nest was on a porch rafter, and the Derby nest was suspended from the limb of a pine tree.

Supersedure and competition. There was supersedure in 1 Arlington nest by a species of *Trypoxylon,* and in the Plummers Island nest by *Trypoxylon backi* Sandhouse.

Nest architecture. The mother wasp stored aphids right at the inner end of the boring in all nests. The 101 stored cells were 5-41 mm. long (mean 7). Thirty-seven of these cells that produced male wasps had a mean length of 6.2 mm.; 4 female cells had a mean length of 7.4 mm. Only 1 of the nests contained an empty vestibular cell, 12 mm. long. There were no empty intercalary cells. The wasp covered the wall and ends of each cell with a delicate sub-opaque membranous coating, similar to that made by the bee *Hylaeus* except for its opacity. The partitions between the cells and the closing plug were made of tiny bits of wood fiber cemented together, and were from $1/4$ to 2 mm. in thickness. Eleven completely stored nests contained 7 to 10 cells each (mean 8.5).

Prey. All nests were stored with wingless aphid nymphs. The three 1958 Arlington nests contained a species of *Macrosiphum.* One completed cell held 27 paralyzed aphids 1.3-2.1 mm. long. In 1959 a sample from 1 cell contained nymphs of *Drepanaphis* and *Therioaphis* (?); a sample from another nest contained only *Drepanaphis* nymphs.

Life history. There are 2 or more generations a year at both Derby and in the Washington area. The single nest from Derby was stored the first week in July and adults from it had emerged and died in the shipping container when I first examined the nest on August 21. In Arlington wasps from overwintering nests are on the wing earlier. Adults emerged June 22 to July 6 from nests stored during the first half of June. Another nest at Arlington was stored during the latter half of August. The single dispausing larva in it died during the winter.

I did not determine how long it took a mother wasp to store and cap an individual cell. However, developmental data in 2 nests suggest that normally a female may store 2 to 3 cells a day.

After the cell is completely stored the egg is laid on 1 of the aphids near the outer end of the cell. In the single case observed it was laid lengthwise on the aphid just to the right of the middorsal line, and extended from the neck of the aphid nearly to the tip of the abdomen. The egg was sausage shaped, 1.41 mm. long by 0.38 mm. wide. The egg hatched in 2 days or so, and the larva devoured all the aphids stored for it in somewhat over 3 days. Spinning of the cocoon took about a day. The feces were voided as a black, spiral ribbon, 3-4 mm. long, about a day or so after completion of the cocoon. In the first generation pupation occurred a day or so after voiding of the feces. Adults eclosed about 10 days later and left the nest 2 to 3 days after eclosion. In all, about 20-21 days elapsed in the first generation between storing of the cell and departure of the resultant adult from the nest.

The cocoon walls were subopaque, white, thin, and delicate, but the cap was tough and dark brown. Seventeen cocoons were 4 to 6.5 mm. long, with a mean length of 4.9 mm. There was no apparent difference in length of male and female cocoons.

Emergence of occupants from an individual nest took periods ranging from 1 to 6 days. Both sexes emerged concurrently.

Several nests contained both sexes and others contained only males or only females. In one 10-celled nest I reared 7 males and 1 female. The latter was in the first or second cell at the inner end of the boring.

There was some mortality from parasites, injury or because mature larvae were preserved for taxonomic study. I reared

44 males and 7 females from 102 stored cells, so apparently a preponderance of males is produced.

Parasites and predators. One cell of a 2-celled nest from Plummers
Island was parasitized by a chrysidid probably belonging to the
genus *Omalus.* This parasite died as a resting larva.

Two of the Arlington nests were infested in the field with mites
belonging to the genus *Pyemotes,* the straw itch mite.

Five of the Arlington nests were infested by *Lackerbaueria krombeini* Baker, an acarid mite whose biology was reported recently
(Krombein, 1961).

Previous observations. Malloch (1933, p. 5) reported this species
[as *trisulcus* Fox] as flying around a wooden outbuilding in Washington, the males far outnumbering the females. He did not find
the nesting site. Krombein (1955a, pp. 15-16; 1958, p. 22) reported
it at Arlington, Va., as preying on alate viviparous females of
Drepanaphis acerifoliae (Thomas) and nymphal aphids probably
belonging to the same species. These prey records were made late
in July and late in September, thus suggesting the probability of 3
or more generations annually in Arlington.

Source material.
   Derby, N. Y. 1959 series: W 9.
   Plummers Island, Md. 1961 series: K 74.
   Arlington, Va. 1955 series: A 14. 1958 series: U 1, 2, 3. 1959 series: A 1,
   2, 5. 1961 series: J 1, 4, 5, 6, 11. 1962 series: N 2.

Identifications. Acarina by E. W. Baker; Aphidae by L. M.
Russell; wasp by the author.

PASSALOECUS ITHACAE Krombein

This species made 6 nests at Derby, 4 in 3.2-, and 2 in 4.8-mm.
borings. The traps were suspended from limbs of pine, balsam, oak,
and elm, and 1 was on a pile of cut firewood.

Supersedure and competition. In 1 nest there was supersedure
by the vespid *Symmorphus canadensis* (Saussure).

Nest architecture. The mother stored aphids right at the inner
end of the boring in 5 nests; in the sixth nest there was an empty
space 6 mm. long at the inner end and then a thin resin partition.
Twenty stored cells in 3.2-mm. borings were 6 to 12 mm. long
(mean 8.6). Most (12) cells in 4.8-mm. borings were 6 to 10 mm.
long (mean 8.6), but there were also 3 exceptionally long cells 19, 25,
and 90 mm. long. Limited data indicate that in 3.2-mm. borings
the female cells have a mean length of 9.6 mm. and the male cells
of 6.7 mm. There were no empty intercalary cells. There was an
empty vestibular cell 10 to 20 mm. long in 4 of the completed nests;
1 of these cells was divided into 2 sections by a cross partition.
The cell partitions, made of resin, were ¼ to ½ mm. thick. The
closing plugs, made of the same substance, were ½ to 1 mm. thick.

Three of the nests in 3.2-mm. borings were completely filled and each contained 6 stored cells and an empty vestibular cell. The 1 completed nest in a 4.8-mm. boring contained 12 stored cells and an empty vestibular cell.

Prey. One completely stored cell contained 14 nymphs and adults of a species of *Cinara*. A sample from several cells in another nest contained many *Anuraphis rosea* Baker and 1 *Rhopalosiphum fitchii* (Sanders).

Life history. Apparently there are at least 2 generations annually in Derby. Four nests were stored during late May and June and adults emerged from June 23 to July 18. In a fifth nest stored in mid-July an adult emerged on August 17.

I have very little information on the development because occupants were nearly mature larvae, prepupae, or pupae when I received the nests. Adults emerged from several cells in 2 nests 24 days after the nests were completed. Apparently about 16 days elapse between completion of feeding by the larva and emergence of the adult, and about 12 days between pupation and emergence of the adult. My notes have no information on the cocoon. If one is present at all, it presumably consists of just a few strands of silk at the anterior and posterior ends of the cell as in *Passaloecus cuspidatus* Smith.

Both sexes were present in at least 2 of the nests and emerged concurrently. Emergence of the occupants in a single nest took place in 1 to 2 days. I noted the actual arrangement of sexes in only 1 nest. In this 6-celled nest there were females in the inner 3 cells, males in cells 4 and 5, and the egg in 6 died. I reared 12 females and 4 males from the 35 stored cells.

Previous observations. Fye (1965a, pp. 737-740, tables IV, IX, fig. 9) published on 37 nests he obtained in 6.4-mm. and 8.0-mm. borings in elderberry and chinaberry twigs in northwestern Ontario. I examined material from all these nests in 1965 and found that specimens from 2 nests (205, 206) were actually *cuspidatus* Smith (=*mandibularis* Cresson) not *ithacae* Krombein; consequently the data recorded for nest 205 in his table IX should be transferred from *ithacae*. In 6.4-mm. borings he found that female cells had an average length of 8.6 ± 0.5 mm. and males 7.8 ± 0.3 mm.; in 8.0-mm. borings these figures were 10.0 mm. for females and 14.4 mm. for a single male. He reported that vestibular cells were 26-77 mm. long and that they might be divided into as many as 5 sections by transverse partitions. The cell partitions and closing plugs were of resin, occasionally with intermixed chips from the boring wall. The closing plugs were 1.6-3.2 mm. thick. He obtained 5-10 cells (mean 7) in five 6.4-mm. borings and 5 cells in one 8.0-mm. boring.

Fye found that the prey consisted mainly of *Cinara* spp., but he also recovered specimens of *Euceraphis, Neosymdobius, Ptero-comma,* and *Amphorophora.* He found 7-63 aphids per cell and 50-200 aphids per nest.

He concluded that in northwestern Ontario there was a univoltine strain of *ithacae* with a high population and a bivoltine strain with a very low population level. Larval feeding periods were 1-3 weeks for the bivoltine strain and 2-6 weeks for the univoltine strain. He reported a case of divided emergence in 1 nest which he thought was due to facultative voltinism or to disruption of the cycle by handling. He found that *ithacae* spun a tough, whitish cocoon which varied in density.

Fye reared 2 ichneumonids, *Poemenia albipes* (Cresson) and *P.* sp. near *americana* (Cresson), and two chrysidids, *Omalus aeneus* (Fabricius) [reported as *laeviventris* Cresson] and *O.* sp. near *irides-cens* (Norton), from nests of *ithacae.*

Source material.
    Derby, N. Y. 1959 series: W 2, 7, 22, 24. 1960 series: D 80, 84.

Identifications. Aphidae by L. M. Russell; wasps by the author.

PASSALOECUS CUSPIDATUS Smith
(Plate 15, Figures 66, 67)

This species nested in seven 3.2-mm., two 4.8-mm. and one 6.4-mm. borings at Derby, and in thirteen 3.2-mm. borings in Arlington. Six of the Derby traps had been set out on piles of cut firewood, 2 on the trunk of an elm, and 2 on sills or sides of a wooden house. All the traps at Arlington had been placed on a wooden cowshed wall containing many abandoned borings of anobiid beetles.

Nest architecture. There was no empty space at the inner end of the boring in any of the nests. Fifty-eight provisioned cells in 3.2-mm. borings were 8 to 52 mm. long (mean 16.3). The 4 provisioned cells in 4.8-mm. borings were 7, 8, 13, and 126 mm. in length. The 4 provisioned cells in the 6.4-mm. boring were 7, 6, 7, and 9 mm. long. In the 3.2-mm. borings 18 female cells were 12 to 47 mm. long (mean 16.1), and 14 male cells were 10 to 31 mm. long (mean 14.8). None of the nests contained an empty intercalary cell. All completed nests except 1 had an empty vestibular cell 5 to 145 mm. long; 1 of these cells was divided into 2 sections by a cross partition. The partitions between the cells and the closing plug were made of resin. The partitions were usually very thin, about 1/4 mm. thick; but an occasional partition would be as much as 4 mm. thick. The closing plugs varied from 1/4 to 4 mm. in thickness but were usually about 1 mm. thick. Completed nests in 3.2-mm. borings contained 1 to 5 provisioned cells (mean 3) and an empty vestibular cell (fig. 66).

I was able to make a few observations on a female bringing in resin to her nest about 1830 hours on May 26, 1959. The drop of resin was held beneath her head, not in her mandibles, but apparently between the labrum and mandibles. Each load of resin was about a third the size of her head. One such droplet left on the wall of a boring was 0.8 mm. in diameter. It took this female periods of 2½, 3¼, and 4 minutes to gather 3 droplets. She spent intervals of ½ and 3 minutes inside her nest between these resin-gathering flights, presumably working on the partition capping a cell. At night she rested inside near the boring entrance with her head toward the outside.

Prey. The aphids were packed rather tightly into the cell head first (fig. 67). Eight nymphs left in 1 cell of a Derby nest were of a species of *Macrosiphum.* One fully stored cell in an Arlington nest contained 22 *Macrosiphum* nymphs. A fully stored cell in another nest contained 18 *Macrosiphum pisi* (Harris) nymphs and 1 *Myzus porosus* (Sanders), 1.2-3.0 mm. long. A sample from a cell in another Arlington nest consisted of 6 nymphs, 1.2-2.6 mm. long, 1 of *Myzus porosus* (Sanders) and 5 *Macrosiphum rosae* (Linnaeus) (?). A cell in still another Arlington nest contained mostly nymphs, but also 3 alate specimens; the latter were *Masonaphis* sp.

Life history. There is only a single generation a year. Arlington nests were provisioned from about May 17 to 30 in 1959, from about June 1 to 7 in 1960, and from about May 22 to June 1 in 1962. At Derby nests were stored from about June 7 to July 4 in 1959, and from about June 16 to July 9 in 1960. Occupants of all nests overwintered as diapausing larvae and adults emerged the following spring.

The following information is based on Arlington nests. Developmental data from 3 nests indicate that 1-2 cells may be stored per day. One trap was set out the evening of May 27; a nest, consisting of 4 provisioned cells and an empty vestibular cell, was completed in it sometime on May 30.

The egg is sausage shaped, 1.3-1.4 mm. long and 0.4-0.5 mm. wide (fig. 67). In 1 cell it was attached obliquely across the thoracic venter of 1 of the last aphids placed in the cell with the anterior end toward the abdomen of the aphid. In 2 other cells it was attached lengthwise on the thoracic sternum of an aphid at the outer end of the cell. In a fourth cell it was laid loosely on the side of an aphid about one-third from the outer end of the cell, and on the top layer of aphids in the cell. The eggs hatched in about 2 days, and the larvae fed for 7 to 9 days. Spinning of the very vestigial cocoon took less than a day. The feces were voided 2 to 3 days later as small black pellets, about 20 per larva.

The cocoon in 1 nest consisted of just a few strands of silk at the anterior end. In another nest there were a few strands of silk at each end of the cell. Emergence of occupants of an individual nest took periods ranging from 2 to 4 days. Both sexes emerged concurrently. I reared 14 males and 22 females from the 66 provisioned cells. In 2 of the nests that contained both sexes, the arrangement of sexes by cell was as follows, x standing for mortality:

1	2	3	4
♂	♀	♂	
♀	x	♂	x

Parasites and predators. The chrysidid *Omalus aeneus* (Linnaeus) was found in 2 cells of a 4-celled nest from Derby and in 1 cell of a 3-celled nest from Arlington.

The ichneumonid *Poemenia americana americana* (Cresson) was reared from a 1-celled Derby nest that was unquestionably stored by *P. cuspidatus.* A larva of this ichneumonid was also found in 1 cell of a 3-celled nest and in 1 cell of a 2-celled nest both from Derby, but 1 larva was preserved for taxonomic study, and the other died before maturity.

Previous observations. Packard (1874, p. 161) reported *cuspidatus* (as *mandibularis* (Cresson)) as nesting in stems of elder and syringa. He stated that the cells were lined with silk [I presume that his *Passaloecus* was using the old nest of some other insect], that the female stored aphids, and that the nests were parasitized by "Chalcids" [I suppose probably *Melittobia*]. Krombein (1956a, pp. 42-43; 1958a, pp. 24-25) recorded *cuspidatus* (as *mandibularis*) in Arlington as preying on nymphs and adults of *Macrosiphum rosae* (Linnaeus) and nymphs of *Macrosiphum* sp., and nesting in abandoned anobiid borings. He stated that it was univoltine and that adults emerged in mid-May.

Fye (1965a, pp. 740, 742, tables IV, IX) reported on 2 nests in 6.4-mm. borings in elderberry and/or chinaberry twigs in northwestern Ontario. He used the synonymous name *mandibularis* for this species. In 1 nest 3 female cells were 10-21 mm. long (mean 15) and 1 male cell was 11.2 mm. long. This nest had a vestibular cell 102 mm. long capped by a resin plug 3.2 mm. thick. Nest 205, reported as *ithacae* Krombein in table IX, is actually a nest of *cuspidatus,* as I discovered when I examined Fye's material in 1965. This nest in a 6.4-mm. boring had 5 stored cells 6.4-14.4 mm. long; females were reared from cells 3 and 5, 6.4 and 8.0 mm. long, respectively. This nest had a vestibular cell 30 mm. long, divided into 2 sections by a cross partition, and capped by a plug 1.6 mm. thick.

Fye recorded as prey 2 species of *Cinara*, and 1 species each of a psyllid, and of *Euceraphis*, *Rhopalosiphum* and *Macrosiphum*. There were 11-52 aphids per cell.

He found a single generation a year. Pupation occurred during the first week in June and adults emerged June 21-30. The egg was attached to the abdomen of 1 of the aphids.

One cell was parasitized by the chrysidid wasp *Omalus aeneus* (Fabricius) [reported as *laeviventris* Cresson].

Source material.

Derby, N. Y. 1956 series: J 113. 1957 series: G 110. 1959 series: W 3, 4, 11, 16, 19. 1960 series: D 4, 19, 38.

Arlington, Va. 1959 series: A 3, 4, 8, 13, 15, 20. 1960 series: C 1, 2, 5, 6. 1962 series: N 4, 5, 6.

Identifications. Aphidae by L. M. Russell; *Omalus* by R. M. Bohart; Ichneumonidae by L. M. Walkley; *Passaloecus* by the author.

ISODONTIA, subgenus MURRAYELLA Bohart and Menke

The North American species of *Isodontia* may be divided into 2 subgenera on the basis of whether the females have 2 or 3 mandibular teeth. The latter subgenus (*Murrayella*) contains 3 species, *elegans* (Smith), *mexicana* (Saussure), and *auripes* (Fernald), all of which nested in my traps. The typical subgenus also contains 3 species, but none of them occupied a single trap. So, it may be that the propensity to nest in borings in sound wood is a characteristic of those species with 3 mandibular teeth. There are no published biological notes on nesting preferences of species with 2 mandibular teeth, but 1 of these species, *philadelphica* (Lepeletier), was reared by J. C. Bridwell from a boring in the rotten stub of a tree limb 30 feet above the ground; the partitions between the cells in this nest were made of firmly packed bits of rotten wood. The species belonging to the subgenus *Murrayella* constructed the partitions and closing plugs from various kinds of vegetable fibers like grass stems and blades and inner bark fiber. So, perhaps the nature of the material used in the plugs and partitions may also separate these 2 groups of species.

One of the most remarkable attributes of *Isodontia (Murrayella)* is that some species construct in the boring a single large brood chamber in which a number of larvae develop amicably. Occasionally, there is some mortality of younger larvae in these brood chambers. Most likely this is due to lack of food rather than to actual predation by the larger larvae.

A most fascinating result of my study was the demonstration that *elegans*, *mexicana*, and *auripes* illustrate the evolution of nest structure from a species that makes individual cells, through one that usually makes a brood chamber but occasionally makes individual cells, to a species that always makes a single large brood chamber. In nests of *elegans* there was always a fairly substantial partition 7-20 mm. thick between each larva (fig. 57). In *mexicana* these partitions were present in a minority of the nests (figs. 58, 59), were very flimsy and from 2 to 4 mm. thick. The nests of *auripes* (figs. 60, 61) always consisted of a single large brood chamber in which usually 2 to 5 wasps developed to maturity. Tsuneki (1964) reported a similar situation in 3 of the Japanese species, in which *nigella* (Smith) and *maidli* (Yasumatsu) ordinarily made unicellular nests, but occasionally placed 2 eggs in a brood cell, whereas *harmandi* (Perez) customarily made a large brood chamber in which 2 to 12 larvae developed. Tsuneki found that cannibalism occurred only in those nests in which the mother stored an insufficiency of prey for the number of eggs placed in the brood chamber.

J. van der Vecht has called to my attention a curious structure on the labrum of members of the subgenus *Murrayella*. It consists of a pair of short, apposed, slightly separated parallel flanges or tubercles near the apex of the labrum; this structure is not found in typical *Isodontia*. Presumably this feature helps to steady the lengthy grass stem during its transport to the nest.

ISODONTIA (MURRAYELLA) ELEGANS (Smith)
(Plate 13, Figure 57)

I obtained 12 nests of this species from 8 stations at Portal, Ariz., in 1959, 1960, and 1961, all in 12.7-mm. borings. Five nests came from Cave Creek Canyon and were attached to structural timber or placed in the crown of a sotol plant. The others came from stations on the desert floor on mesquite or on live or partly dead sycamore trees along dried stream beds.

Nest architecture (fig. 57). The inner end of the boring was empty except for 1 trap where the wasp had packed 15 mm. of vegetable fibers into it. The completed nests contained from 2 to 4 cells, each with a single occupant, and with each of the inner cells capped by a partition of fine, loosely packed, dry vegetable fibers consisting of grass stems and blades or rasped fibers of the soft inner bark of juniper. Twenty-four cells were 18 to 90 mm. long (mean 38). The partitions closing all cells except the outer one in each nest were 2 to 20 mm. thick (mean 8). Seven closing plugs were 14 to 45 mm. thick (mean 25). The closing plug was complex and consisted of 10 to 15 mm. of fine, soft, firmly compacted fibers including inner bark of juniper and 5 to 17 mm. of long, coiled, wadded grass stems packed in transversely. One nest contained these 2 sections and then another 12 mm. of coarser, looser stems. One 2-celled nest contained an empty vestibular cell 45 mm. long capped by a compound closing plug of 15 mm.

This species, as is normal in the genus, apparently makes a temporary plug to cap the cell while the wasp is provisioning it. Two borings contained just a loose plug of fine grass fibers about halfway to the inner end when the nests were picked up.

Prey. Notes were made on the prey in 6 of the nests. Apparently snowy tree crickets (Gryllidae) are the preferred prey when they can be obtained. A cell in 1 nest contained 5 nymphs of a single species; one of these was identified as *Oecanthus quadripunctatus* Beutenmüller, 11 mm. long. Fragments of 4 specimens from another nest were *O. c. californicus* Saussure. In a third nest all the specimens were typical *californicus* about 10 mm. long, except for a tettigoniid nymph, *Dichopetala* sp., 7 mm. long. The remains in 2 other nests were noted as being snowy tree crickets. From the last nest I recovered fragments of 3 nymphal tettigoniids, probably belonging to a species of *Eremopedes.*

Life history. Very limited data are available on the immature stages. One cell contained a newly hatched larva and 5 snowy tree crickets when I picked up the nest on July 19. Five days later the larva had completely eaten all the prey stored for it; this larva died subsequently. The duration of the pupal stage is variable. In an overwintering nest 1 occupant pupated between April 28 and May 2, and an adult male left the cocoon on May 22. Development was more rapid in summer generation nests; the occupant of 1 cocoon was in the prepupal stage when I examined it on June 26 and a female wasp emerged from this cocoon on July 11.

There are at least 2 generations a year in Arizona. In 1961 one nest which contained only a plug of fibers in the middle was begun early in May. Occupants emerged June 23 through 30 from a 3-celled nest picked up on May 21. Occupants of a 4-celled nest picked up on June 21 emerged from July 7 through 11. A female emerged as late as August 15 from a nest stored early in July. Occupants of 2 nests stored at an unknown period, but picked up in December, emerged the following spring.

Rather meagre evidence indicates that the rate of provisioning is variable. On July 19 I picked up an incompleted nest (fig. 57) with the mother inside. There were 3 completely stored cells which held respectively a resting larva in a cocoon, a full-grown larva, and a newly hatched larva. The wasp must have begun storing this nest at least a week before I gathered it. However, 2 females and a male emerged during a 3-day period from 1 nest, and 3 females and a male during a 5-day period from another. It seems likely that the storing of these nests probably would have required 3 to 7 days.

Males and females usually emerged concurrently from mixed nests.

The arrangement of sexes in mixed nests was apparently a random one. Three of the 7 completed nests contained females only. In the other 4 nests the arrangement of sexes was as follows: ♀ ♂ ♀; ♀ ♂ ♂; ♀ ♂ ♂; and ♂ ♀ ♀ ♀. I reared 13 females and 6 males from 22 completely stored cells.

Previous observations. Ashmead (1894, p. 64) cited Coquillett as observing *elegans* preying on *Oecanthus niveus* DeGeer in California. Davidson (1899), working in Arizona, found *elegans* biting holes in vertical stems of white sage and nesting in the hollow stems; he reported that partitions were made of fine strips of loose fibrous bark of *Audibertia polystacha*, and that 7 or 8 tree crickets were stored per cell for 1 egg; he found most individuals overwintering as adults with about 20 per cent of the population overwintering as diapausing larvae in cocoons; he also found that *elegans* was parasitized by the miltogrammine fly *Amobia floridensis* (Townsend) [reported as *P. trypoxylonis* Townsend], by the chalcidoid *Epistenia coeruleata* Westwood, and by the mutillids *Photopsis unicolor* (Cresson) and *P. ferruginea* (Blake). Both Fernald (1906, p. 364), quoting a letter from S. A. Johnson in Colorado, and Ainslie (1924) in North Dakota reported *elegans* nesting in borings in vertical adobe or sand banks. Johnson discovered that *elegans* was nesting in abandoned borings of the bee *Anthophora occidentalis* Cresson; it stored *Oecanthus* sp. and occasionally grasshopper nymphs; usually there were 2 cocoons in a tunnel; Johnson mentioned that the nests were composed of finely chewed fibers of dead weeds and grass with tightly packed, coarser grass stems forming the closing plug, from which I infer that the cocoons in the tunnels were probably separated by partitions of fine grass. Ainslie stated that the single *elegans* he observed was making a compact closing plug of dried grass roots; beyond this was a brood cell holding 14 tree crickets, *Oecanthus quadripunctatus*; he was unable to find a wasp egg.

Source material.
   Portal, Ariz. 1959 series: X 275, 282(?), 288(?). 1960 series: X 297, 322. 1961 series: G 129(?), 143(?), 149, 229, 271, 274, 362.

Identifications. Orthoptera by A. B. Gurney; wasp by the author.

ISODONTIA (MURRAYELLA) MEXICANA (Saussure)
(Plate 13, Figures 58, 59)

This species nested in three 12.7-mm. traps at Kill Devil Hills, N. C., and in five 12.7-mm. traps at Lake Placid, Fla. Each trap came from a different station and undoubtedly each had been stored by a different individual. The Kill Devil Hills nests were in traps suspended from dead limbs of pine and sassafras trees at the edge of wooded areas; the Florida nests were in open wooded areas suspended from living limbs of oak and hickory.

Supersedure and competition. I. mexicana superseded a species of *Megachile* which had begun to nest in 1 of the Florida traps. One nest at Kill Devil Hills was invaded by *Crematogaster* ants.

Nest architecture (figs. 58, 59). The inner end of the boring in 1 nest contained several mm. of packed grass; there was no grass at the inner end of the other nests. Six of the nests contained a single large brood chamber 95 to 120 mm. long. In the other 2 nests the 5 cells in each were separated by flimsy partitions of loose dried grass 2 to 4 mm. in thickness.

The plugs that closed the nests were complicated affairs. Immediately adjacent to the brood cell was a section of firmly compacted material 10 to 23 mm. thick. This part of the plug consisted of soft vegetable fibers, or long grass blades or stems that were coiled inside the boring and firmly compacted to form a transverse plug. In 4 of the nests the outer 15 to 25 mm. of the boring adjacent to the firmly compacted section of the plug contained loose grass blades or stems placed parallel to the long axis of the boring. These pieces of grass sometimes protruded as much as 50 mm. beyond the trap. One nest contained an even more complicated closing plug which consisted of 10 mm. of soft compacted fibers adjacent to the brood chamber, then 10 mm. of tightly coiled grass stems, and finally 15 mm. of looser straight grass stems.

Prey. This wasp preyed principally on crickets (Gryllidae), though occasional specimens of long-horned grasshoppers (Tettigoniidae) were stored also. One nest at Kill Devil Hills contained prey remains of a species of *Oecanthus*. Another nest from the same locality contained a number of tree crickets; 10 of these that were preserved were identified as *Oecanthus angustipennis* Fitch, 1 adult 17 mm. long and 9 nymphs 7-11 mm. long. Of the Florida nests 1 contained remains of a species of *Oecanthus,* another contained mostly *Orocharis saltator* Uhler, a gryllid, in addition to 1 specimen of the tettigoniid *Conocephalus* sp., and a third contained the conocephaline *Odontoxiphidium apterum* Morse, both nymphs and adult males.

Life history. As the occupants of all nests were in the prepupal, pupal, or adult stages when I opened the nests for study, I have no data on duration of the egg and larval stages. Apparently there are at least 2 generations a year in North Carolina and Florida. In North Carolina adults emerged from the last of July until the last of August from nests stored between May 30 and some time prior to July 29 when they were picked up. Presumably adults that emerged in the wild during this period would have provisioned new nests whose occupants would have overwintered as diapausing larvae. In

Florida adults emerged May 11 to 27 from nests stored during April, and in August from nests stored during July. In this area there would presumably have been more or less continual breeding throughout September.

Both sexes were present in several of the nests. Usually there was no prior emergence of males, both males and females emerging on the same dates. Occupants of a single nest emerged within a period of 1 to 4 days. Five of the nests with a single large brood chamber contained 2, 5, 6, 7, and 8 cocoons respectively; the sixth such nest contained 6 cocoons and 3 dead half grown larvae. The 2 nests with smaller individual cells contained 5 cells each.

Parasites and predators. One nest at Kill Devil Hills was invaded by *Crematogaster* ants which destroyed 2 larvae and 1 of the prepupae in its cocoon.

Previous observations. Several observers have recorded some diverse nesting sites for this species (mostly under the name *harrisi* Fernald). Jones (1904, p. 17) and Rau (1935a) reported it as nesting in pitcher plants, *Sarracenia* spp., in North Carolina and Georgia, respectively. Rau also reported it in Missouri as using hollow stems, abandoned carpenter bee burrows, and artificial nesting sites made from glass tubes in rolls of paper. Engelhardt (1929) found that in Texas the species nested in the narrow tubes formed by the folding of dead yucca leaves. Also in Texas, Lin (1962) reported it nesting in cavities in wood and in bamboo. In Mexico Rau (1943a, p. 648) noticed nests of *harrisi* in the bamboo canes which formed supports for a thatched roof. In Hawaii Suehiro (1937) noted that it nested in the hollow midribs of *Pandanus,* and Swezey (1947) reported it as nesting in abandoned carpenter bee burrows in *Vitex.* Medler (1965c) obtained nests from borings in sumac twigs in Wisconsin.

Only Engelhardt, Rau (1935a), and Medler commented in detail on the nest architecture. The first two authors reported that the larvae occurred in individual cells separated by thin partitions of grass blades; Medler found partitions between most cells, but also reported several cells each of which contained 2 larvae or cocoons. Most of the authors cited above commented on the closing plug of long grass blades and stems that protruded from the nest entrance.

Medler's notes on nest architecture agree in most details with my own observations. He reported an occasional plug of grass at the inner end of the boring. He gave the mean thickness of partitions closing the cells as 6.2 ± 2.4 mm. in 6.4-mm. borings, and as 4.7 ± 2.1 mm. in 7.9-mm. borings. His closing plugs averaged 17.8 mm. in length. He also mentioned that nesting females made a temporary, flimsier grass plug to close a cell while the cell was being stored with prey. Cells occupied by a single larva had a mean length of

28.8 ± 8.4 mm. (range 17-50 mm.); cells occupied by several individuals were 52-100 mm. long.

Ashmead (1894-95, p. 241) recorded *mexicana* [as *philadelphicus*] as preying on *Oecanthus fasciatus* Fitch, while Jones cited just *Oecanthus* as prey. Engelhardt stated that it was preying on nymphs of the tettigoniid *Rehnia spinosa* Caudell. Later in his paper he quoted H. B. Parks as writing him that later in the season it preyed on spiders, and later still on nymphs of a green cricket. I am certain that there must have been 2 or more species of wasps involved in Park's observations because most likely the spiders were stored by a species of *Trypargilum*. Rau (1935a) reported 2 cells that contained a total of 65 first instar nymphs of a tettigoniid, either *Orchelimum* or *Conocephalus,* and 5 specimens of *Conocephalus* and *Scudderia.* Rau also recorded as prey of *mexicana* 1 specimen of *Oecanthus quadripunctatus* Beutenmüller in Missouri and 4 small nymphs of *Conocephalus fasciatus* DeGeer in Georgia. Lin in Texas found it storing about 10 *Oecanthus argentinus* Saussure per cell, or a mixture of that species and *Gryllus assimilis* Fabricius. Medler reported that in Wisconsin *mexicanus* stored juvenile Tettigoniidae (*Orchelimum* sp., *Conocephalus* sp., and *Neoconocephalus* sp.) and mostly juvenile, but some adult, Gryllidae (*Oecanthus fultoni* T. J. Walker, *O. nigricornis* F. Walker, *O. niveus* (DeGeer), *O. quadripunctatus* Beutenmüller, and *Neoxabea bipunctata* (DeGeer)). He found a positive correlation between the number of prey and the total weight of food available to the wasp larva. He also reported that 14-20 juveniles of *Oecanthus* were stored per cell and only 7-9 adults.

Rau (1935a) stated that there were probably 2 generations a year at St. Louis, and Engelhardt quoted Parks to the effect that there were 3 generations annually in Texas. The latter observation is open to some question because of the erroneous prey records noted by Parks. Lin reported only a single generation in Texas. Suehiro reported that *mexicana* remained in the cocoons in Hawaii for 18 months before emergence of the adults, perhaps an indication that this adventive wasp is imperfectly adapted to tropical areas. Medler found 2 generations in Wisconsin.

Medler found that young larvae fed for 4-6 days at 22°C. Cocoon spinning required another day. This was followed by a prepupal period of 1 day in members of the summer generation. There was a period of 2-3 weeks between pupation and adult emergence. He described the cocoon as being fusiform and composed of several layers; first, a loose webbing of silk thread on the outside lined by a layer of thin, parchmentlike material; then another silk layer forming a closely interwoven mat; and finally a thicker, brown opaque inner layer. The larval feces formed a conelike, brownish black coil at the posterior end of the innermost cocoon layer.

Medler reared 64 males and 79 females from a total of 340 cells in 117 nests. He stated that both sexes were reared from some nests, and that only females or only males were reared from others. Females were always in the inner and males in the outer cells in nests containing both sexes.

Medler found that 15 per cent of the nests were infested by Diptera, and that these flies were present in 23 of 45 recognizable cells. They caused the death of any wasp eggs or larvae in infested cells. He was not able to determine the exact role played by the Diptera in infested nests, but he thought it was likely that they acted as parasitoids rather than as scavengers. He reared the following adult flies from infested nests: *Amobia distorta* (Allen), *Senotainia* sp. in the *trilineata* Wulp complex, and *Sarcophaga* sp. of the Sarcophagidae; *Megaselia aletiae* (Comstock) of the Phoridae; and *Eustalomyia vittipes* (Zetterstedt) of the Anthomyiidae.

Source material.
Kill Devil Hills, N. C. 1958 series: T 233, 237, 238.
Lake Placid, Fla. 1959 series: V 50, 53, 57. 1962 series: P 68, 69.

Identifications. Orthoptera by A. B. Gurney; Hymenoptera by the author.

ISODONTIA (MURRAYELLA) AURIPES (Fernald)
(Plate 13, Figures 60(?), 61(?))

I reared this species from 12 traps containing 12.7-mm. borings. Six of the nests were from Plummers Island, Md., where 5 had been set on or suspended from rafters on the cabin porch, and 1 had been hung on the trunk of a dead red cedar, *Juniperus virginiana.* Presumably *auripes* normally nests in abandoned carpenter-bee borings in the cabin porch at Plummers Island. Three nests came from 2 stations at Kill Devil Hills, N. C., where 2 had been suspended from a dead limb of a pecan tree, and 1 had been tied to the exposed roots of a dying oak on the edge of a bank. The other 3 nests were from 2 stations at Lake Placid, Fla., where 2 had been suspended from a dead limb on a turkey oak and 1 from a hickory limb.

In addition there were 8 nests stored by *Isodontia* from which I did not rear adults. Six of them almost undoubtedly were stored by *auripes* because they were from identical stations and provisioned at the same time as nests from which *auripes* was reared. Four of these nests were in 12.7-mm. borings that had been placed on porch rafters at Plummers Island. The other 4 nests were from Kill Devil Hills. Two of these were in glass tubes, having an inside diameter of

10 mm., that were placed inside 12.7-mm. wooden borings and tied to the exposed tree roots mentioned in the preceding paragraph, and the other 2 were in 12.7-mm. borings suspended one each from dead limbs of pecan and pine. In the discussion which follows I am including some information from these 8 questionable nests qualified so as to indicate its source.

Nest architecture (figs. 60, 61). In 4 of the nests constructed by *auripes* the females placed 2 to 5 mm. of compacted plant fibers at the inner end; in another nest there was an empty chamber 55 mm. long at the inner end and then a partition of fibers 2 mm. thick. In the other 7 nests the mothers began to store prey at the inner end without placing fibers first.

Judged from my data *auripes* always constructs a common brood chamber when she deposits more than 1 egg in a nest, rather than making individual cells for each egg separated by partitions of compacted fibers. Nine of the nests contained 2 to 5 eggs, larvae, or cocoons; the brood chambers for these nests were 80 to 105 mm. long (mean 94). Two of the nests contained a single cocoon each in cells 75 and 34 mm. long. In 4 of the nests probably constructed by *auripes* there were 2 to 4 eggs, larvae, or cocoons in brood chambers 38 to 102 mm. in length (mean 80).

The closing plug sealing the brood chamber was of complex construction much as in *harrisi*. Immediately adjacent to the brood chamber was a section of tightly packed grass stems, red cedar bark fibers, or other plant fibers. This inner part of the plug was 10 to 60 mm. thick with a mean of 25 mm. In the Plummers Island nests *auripes* almost always used fine soft fibers of the inner bark of red cedar for this part of the plug. In 5 of the nests the outer part of the boring (25-50 mm.) was filled with loose grass stems and blades placed parallel to the long axis of the borings. Usually these stems and blades protruded for some distance beyond the boring entrance.

On 1 Plummers Island nest I made a few observations indicating that a female constructs a temporary plug while she is away seeking prey. This nest was under construction on July 2. I watched the female carry in several blades of grass or fibers of cedar bark between noon and 1300 hours. At 1339 she left the nest and returned 3 minutes later with a piece of grass 60 mm. long. She left the nest a minute and a half later and returned again in 3 minutes with a piece about 40 mm. long. Ten minutes later she was back with another piece of grass and left in 4 minutes. I took up the nest at 1420 and set out an empty 12.7-mm. trap in its place. The wasp returned in half an hour and tried to find her nest. She entered the empty trap several times and then continued to hunt around the immediate vicinity. Fifteen minutes later she had dropped a paralyzed tree cricket on the porch floor beneath the replacement trap.

When I opened the earlier nest on the next day, I found 3 mm. of compacted grass and wood fibers at the inner end, a brood chamber 102 mm. long containing 2 paralyzed nymphs of the gryllid *Neoxabea bipunctata* (DeGeer), *neither of them with a wasp egg,* and a plug of loose grass and wood fibers 16 mm. thick near the outer end. Presumably the wasp would have stored more crickets before laying any eggs.

Incidentally, this same mother probably went ahead during the succeeding week and stored the substitute trap. On July 10 I frightened her away while she was constructing the closing plug in the replacement trap. There were 3 cocoons in the brood chamber when I examined this substitute trap the next day, only 9 days after it had been set out.

I set out a second replacement trap at this same station on July 10. By now this mother wasp may have been thoroughly confused by the disappearance of her nests. During the succeeding week she was probably the individual that filled the entire boring of this second replacement trap with compacted red-cedar fibers with a few long grass stems at the entrance, but no brood cell or prey.

, *Prey.* Samples from 3 Plummers Island nests were identified as nymphs of *Neoxabea bipunctata* (DeGeer), 1 of the tree crickets. One of these nests contained 18 paralyzed nymphs and 1 small wasp larva and an egg packed into the outer 30 mm. of a brood chamber 100 mm. long. The inner end of this chamber contained 2 nearly mature larvae and at least 1 smaller larva. A nest from Kill Devil Hills contained fragments of several nymphs of the tettigoniid *Scudderia* sp. The 3 Florida nests contained mostly nymphs of the gryllid *Orocharis saltator* Uhler, another tree cricket; but in addition 1 had at least 2 specimens of the gryllid *Oecanthus exclamationis* Davis, another had 1 specimen of *Oecanthus* sp., and the third contained a specimen of *Conocephalus* sp., a tettigoniid.

Two of 3 nests at Plummers Island probably stored by *auripes* contained nymphs of *Neoxabea bipunctata,* 9 nymphs for 3 wasp larvae in 1 nest and 12 nymphs for 4 larvae in the other. The third Plummers Island nest held 1 nymph of *Neoxabea bipunctata* and 15 nymphs of *Oecanthus angustipennis* Fitch (?) for 4 wasp larvae (figs. 60, 61). One nest at Kill Devil Hills probably stored by *auripes* contained a nymph of the tettigoniid *Orchelimum* (?) for each of 2 larvae.

Life history. I obtained some limited information on the early stages from nests undoubtedly stored by *auripes* at Plummers Island and Kill Devil Hills. The egg was deposited only after several specimens of prey were stored if the nymphs were small. The egg was sausage shaped, 3.6 mm. long and 0.77 mm. wide. In the 1 nest in which egg placement was noted, it was laid transversely across the sternum of *Neoxabea bipunctata* between the fore- and midlegs. The posterior end was glued to the left side of the sternum, and the anterior end projected beyond the right side of the thorax. The eggs hatched in 1 to 2 days. In the initial stages of feeding the small larva sucked fluid from the body. As the larva grew larger it fed with its head inside the thorax or abdomen of the cricket. Eventually the larvae devoured all the prey stored in the brood chamber except for such parts as the antennae and terminal leg segments. The larvae completed feeding about 2½ to 3 days after the eggs hatched. Spinning of the double-walled cocoon required about 2 days. Cocoons were fusiform in shape and 20-27 mm. long (mean 24).

These data indicate that the time required from oviposition to completion of the cocoon is about 6 to 7 days. This figure is substantiated by the evidence presented under the section on nest architecture, where I reported that a nest was completely stored by the mother and the occupants were in cocoons 9 days after the trap was set out.

There are apparently at least 2 generations a year in coastal North Carolina and Florida. The 3 Florida nests were provisioned April 10-17 and May 7-14, and the occupants emerged May 19-21 and June 9, respectively. At Kill Devil Hills occupants emerged July 29 to August 2 from 3 nests stored during June or July. Presumably adults that emerged in nature during these periods in Florida and North Carolina would have provisioned new nests whose occupants would have emerged as adults that same season or overwintered as diapausing larvae. The situation at Plummers Island is somewhat confused, but it appears that there may be only a partial second generation. The 5 Plummers Island nests from which I obtained adult *auripes* were provisioned during the first 2 or 3 weeks in July. Adults emerged August 3 to 15 from 3 of the nests, but occupants of the other 2 overwintered as diapausing larvae and emerged as adults the following year.

The nests contained 1 to 5 cocoons, with a mean of a little over 3 per brood chamber. None of the nests produced both males and females. Emergence of all occupants from a single nest took place in 1 to 3 days.

Larvae of the same size apparently live amicably within the brood chamber. However, I did note in 3 nests that there was mortality of 1 or more smaller larvae that apparently originated from eggs laid 1 or 2 days later than the rest. These smaller larvae just disappeared and must have been eaten by their larger siblings. However, there was no evidence as to whether this was actual predation or whether the younger larvae just succumbed from lack of food and had then been eaten.

Parasites and predators. A male of the bombyliid *Anthrax aterrimus* (Bigot) was reared from the outermost of 2 cocoons in a nest from Plummers Island.

Maggots of an unknown species of Miltogrammini, probably belonging to the genus *Amobia,* destroyed the contents of a nest probably constructed by *auripes* at Kill Devil Hills.

The contents of another Kill Devil Hills nest possibly stored by *auripes* were destroyed by phorid scavengers probably belonging to the genus *Megaselia.*

One Kill Devil Hills nest probably stored by *auripes* contained a female of the chalcidoid *Melittobia chalybii* Ashmead when it was brought in from the field. This same parasite infested in the laboratory a nest from Plummers Island probably stored by *auripes.*

Previous observations. Packard (1874, p. 168) in New York, Rau and Rau (1918, pp. 203-205), and Rau (1928, pp. 362-368) in Missouri reported *auripes* as nesting in abandoned carpenter bee borings. Rau (1926, pp. 200-201) also found it utilizing abandoned borings of mining bees in a clay bank in Missouri. Rau's (1928) record of this species nesting in sumac stems is open to question because he found only old *Isodontia* nests in these stems. These nests could have been provisioned by any one of several species of *Isodontia.*

Rau did not present details of the nest architecture, but he did state that grass stems protruded from the burrow entrances in characteristic fashion as I have described for some of my nests. Packard mentioned that his nest was in a boring 6 inches long, that the oval cylindrical cocoons were packed loosely side by side or consecutively in a space about 4 inches long, and that the outer 2 inches were filled with "coarse sedge arranged in layers as if rammed in like gun wadding." Packard stated that the interstices between the cocoons were filled with bits of rope that he thought probably had been bitten into pieces by the wasp. I do not infer from his description of this material that it was arranged to form actual partitions between the cocoons such as I have described for nests of *elegans* and some nests of *mexicana.*

Packard's notes suggested that there are 2 generations a year around New York City. Presumably there are 2 or more generations annually in Missouri because Rau and Rau mentioned that adults were active in July and early in October.

Rau (1928) mentioned finding 15 *Oecanthus latipennis* Riley and 1 *Conocephalus memorale* Scudder in 1 nest. He also took 2 specimens of *Orchelimum vulgare* Harris from a female wasp.

Rau (1928) recorded an unidentified chrysidid as a parasite of *auripes.* He also thought that the bombyliid *Anthrax tigrina* (DeGeer) [reported under the generic name *Argyramoeba*] was parasitic on *auripes,* because it hovered in front of borings in which the wasp was nesting. However, it is clear from Hurd's paper (1959, pp. 56-57) that this bombyliid is parasitic on the carpenter bee itself.

Rau (1931a, p. 200), reporting on a series of homing experiments, stated that a marked female of *auripes* returned to her nest several days after having been liberated 2 miles away. On a second trial this same individual returned in 2 hours.

Source material.

    Plummers Island, Md. 1956 series: H 88(?). 1957 series: P 30, 50, 134(?).
        1958 series: S 36, 78, 82(?), 89(?), 93, 95.
    Kill Devil Hills, N. C. 1955 series: C 289, 291(?), 292(?). 1958 series: T 226(?),
        228, 229, 231(?).
    Lake Placid, Fla. 1959 series: V 59, 65, 66. 3 nests.

Identifications. Orthoptera by A. B. Gurney; *Anthrax* by W. W. Wirth; Hymenoptera by the author.

PODIUM RUFIPES (Fabricius)
(Plate 13, Figure 62; Plate 14, Figure 63)

This wasp is uncommon in collections, probably not so much because of its rarity but more likely because it is difficult to capture. It prefers an open wooded habitat and runs swiftly over tree limbs and trunks instead of taking flight. However, it will accept borings in wooden traps as a nesting site and used 88 such borings for nests. At Kill Devil Hills, N. C., it nested in fourteen 4.8-mm. borings and in sixteen 6.4-mm. borings at 14 different stations. At Lake Placid, Fla., it used twenty-five 4.8-mm. borings and thirty-three 6.4-mm. borings at 27 different stations. Four of the Kill Devil Hills nests were suspended from live limbs of oak, dogwood, and sweet gum and 26 from dead limbs of loblolly pine, oak, and pecan. At Lake Placid 48 of the nests were suspended from live limbs of oak, hickory, and pine and 7 from dead limbs of oak and pine. All the traps were set at the edges of wooded areas or in woods open to the sun.

Supersedure and competition. *P. rufipes* superseded the vespid *Euodynerus foraminatus apopkensis* (Robertson) in 3 nests at Lake Placid. It occupied the outer end of a fourth boring containing a nest of this same vespid at the inner end. The vespid apparently had completed this latter nest, for there was an empty vestibular cell capped by agglutinated sand between the stored vespid cells and the *rufipes* nest. In addition it superseded an unidentified vespid in 2 other borings in Florida. At Kill Devil Hills *rufipes* used a boring that contained at the inner end 2 cells of the bee

Megachile mendica Cresson and the dead mother bee facing inward. This was evidently not a case of competition, for the bee had been killed by a conopid fly developing in the abdomen.

In 2 of the Lake Placid nests an unidentified vespid constructed 1 cell in the outer end of a boring used by *rufipes*. However, in each of these the *rufipes* had already completed its nest and had left some empty space at the outer end of the boring. *P. rufipes* almost always made only 1 cell in each boring and usually utilized the whole boring for its nest, though occasionally some empty space was left at the outer end.

Nest architecture. Usually the mother wasp did not construct a plug at the inner end of the boring but brought in paralyzed cockroaches as soon as she had selected the nesting site. However, in 1 Kill Devil Hills nest the wasp constructed a plug of debris with a resin capping 75 mm. from the inner end and then began to store prey. Usually *rufipes* used almost the entire boring for the 1 cell that was placed in each trap. The cells in 4.8-mm. borings were somewhat longer than those in 6.4-mm. borings. The cells in 4.8-mm. borings were 106 to 153 mm. long (mean 147); those in 6.4-mm. borings 65 to 153 mm. long (mean 132). One Lake Placid trap contained 2 *rufipes* nests 120 and 30 mm. long, respectively. It is quite likely that these were made by different *rufipes* females, or at least that they were not constructed consecutively, because the occupant of cell 1 was in its cocoon before April 2, while the occupant of cell 2 did not spin its cocoon until April 8.

The plugs closing the nests in 4.8-mm. borings were not as thick as those closing nests in 6.4-mm. borings. In the former the plugs were 2 to 11 mm. thick (mean 5.8), while in the latter they were 3 to 23 mm. thick (mean 9.2). The plug itself was of complex construction and consisted of a long inner section composed of compacted bits of debris, etc., with a coating of resin on the outer surface; usually the resin was about 1 mm. thick, but sometimes it was as much as 3 mm. in thickness. The inner section of the plug was composed of a variety of substances. At Kill Devil Hills more than half of the nests had fragments of wood pulp from dead trees or raspings of wood fibers from the boring walls in this part of the plug. Sometimes the fragments of wood pulp were intermixed with sheet spider webs. In some nests there was a mixture of ground debris and/or bits of wood pulp along with sand. At Lake Placid most of the nests also had fragments of wood pulp or rasped wood fibers in this part of the plug. In other nests the wasps used cockroach feces to form this part of the plug, occasionally intermixed with bits of spider webbing or of wood or sand. In 1 nest the plug was made of sand with a resin coating outside.

Prey. *P. rufipes* preyed on either adult or nymphal cockroaches which it presumably found under loose bark of dead trees and in similar situations. Usually it stored about 6 specimens in a cell, though occasionally there might be only 3 or 4 or as many as 14. At Kill Devil Hills *Chorisoneura texensis* Saussure and Zehntner only was stored in 14 nests (fig. 62). One nest contained a specimen of *Cariblatta lutea* (Saussure and Zehntner) among the *Chorisoneura*. Three additional nests had remains of *Parcoblatta* species.

In Florida *Latiblatella rehni* Hebard was the preferred prey in 24 nests. Most of these contained only *Latiblatella rehni,* but 1 nest held a nymph of another species, a second a *Parcoblatta* (?) nymph, and a third an adult *Chorisoneura texensis.* Another Florida nest contained about 14 nymphs and adults of *Cariblatta minima* Hebard, a very small species. In 1961, 1 nest contained 4 second or third instar nymphs of *Eurycotis floridana* (Walker), 1 adult and a last instar nymph of *Latiblatella rehni,* and 6 adults of *Chorisoneura texensis;* another nest contained 1 adult each of the *Latiblatella* and *Chorisoneura* and 11 nymphs of *Eurycotis floridana* (?); and a third nest held 13 nymphs and 2 adults of the *Chorisoneura* and 1 nymph of the *Eurycotis floridana* (?).

The cockroaches were thoroughly paralyzed but were able to void feces and wave their palpi feebly. The wasp placed them in the boring head first and venter up (fig. 62). Sometimes they would be shingled, the anterior end of the second specimen lying on the abdomen of the first cockroach and so forth, or they might be placed end to end with the head of the second just touching the apex of the abdomen to the first and so on. Sometimes the cockroaches were placed at the inner end of the boring, and sometimes they were placed about in the middle of the cell.

Life history. The egg was sausage shaped, about 1.5 mm. long and 0.35 mm. wide. In the 1 Kill Devil Hills nest which I obtained early enough, I found that the egg was placed on the first cockroach brought into the nest (fig. 62). It was fastened obliquely on the sternum between the fore- and mid-coxae on the left side. This larva began to feed through a slit on the sternum between the coxae. It took 2 days to empty this first cockroach. In another 5 days it had devoured the other 5 cockroaches stored for it. Spinning the cocoon required 2 days. A male *rufipes* emerged from this nest 29 days later. So for this particular nest probably about 39 days elapsed between storing of the nest and emergence of the resultant adult. In another Kill Devil Hills nest obtained about the same time a male emerged 35 days after hatching of the egg. In 1 of the Florida nests stored in mid-April a female *rufipes* emerged 33 days after hatching of the egg. However, in 4 other Florida nests stored during March and April the adults emerged 31 to 59 days after the larva reached maturity. Probably these differences in development were due to variation in the temperatures in my office during the pupal period. In 3 nests where the duration of the pupal period was observed exactly it lasted 19 to 21 days. In another nest stored in June a male wasp emerged 29 days after the larva reached maturity. The adult wasp spent 2 to 4 days in the cocoon after eclosion before leaving the nest.

The cocoon was oriented with the head end toward the boring entrance in all nests but one. The cocoon was chestnut-brown and modified fusiform, the sides tapering toward the bluntly rounded anterior end (fig. 63). It was composed of a single layer of silk impregnated with a varnish, so that it had a delicate, brittle texture. In shape and texture it was very similar to the cocoon of the black-and-yellow mud-dauber, *Sceliphron caementarium* (Drury). The cocoons were 18 to 23 mm. long (mean 21). There was no apparent difference in length between male and female cocoons.

There were 2 or more generations annually at Kill Devil Hills. Occupants of nests stored from mid-June until the first week in August emerged during August and September. Occupants of nests stored later in August and September overwintered as resting larvae and adults emerged the following year. In Florida there was apparently more or less continual breeding during warmer weather from about mid-March to mid-December, with adults emerging from April to September. Occupants of nests stored from October to December required exposure to cold to break the laval diapause before emerging as adults early the next year.

About 40 per cent of the *rufipes* nests were parasitized, and there were also losses from mold, injury, and preservation of mature larvae for taxonomic study. Under these circumstances it is difficult to determine the true sex ratio. It may be about 1:1; I reared 9 females and 4 males from Kill Devil Hills nests, and 10 females and 10 males from Florida nests. There is some evidence that a preponderance of females is produced in 6.4-mm. borings and of males in 4.8-mm. borings. Seven females and 10 males were reared from the smaller borings, and 11 females and 5 males from the larger borings.

Parasites and predators. The chrysidid *Neochrysis panamensis* (Cameron) was reared from 6 nests at Kill Devil Hills and 13 nests at Lake Placid. Probably this same species parasitized 2 other nests at Kill Devil Hills and 8 nests at Lake Placid.

The chalcidoid *Melittobia chalybii* Ashmead infested 2 Kill Devil Hills nests in the field.

The pupa of a clerid beetle, *Cymatodera undulata* Say, was found in a *rufipes* nest at Kill Devil Hills. The beetle larva may have injured (or fed on) the *Podium* larva which failed to spin a cocoon.

The scavenger phorid *Megaselia* sp. was found in 1 Kill Devil Hills nest.

The bombyliid *Lepidophora appendiculata* (Macquart) was reared from a Lake Placid nest. It fed on the cockroaches stored for the wasp larva.

A number of anoetid mites, identified tentatively as the European *Histiostoma myrmicarum* Scheucher, were found in a Lake Placid nest in which the *rufipes* larva failed to develop. The hypopi of this particular mite are found on worker ants belonging to the genera *Myrmica, Lasius, Camponotus,* and *Formica.* It is presumed to be a scavenger in the ants' nests. The presence of an infestation in this *Podium* nest can probably be attributed to the mite having been brought in with some of the ground debris used by the wasp to form the closing plug.

Previous observations. Rau (1937b) recorded *rufipes* [as *carolina*] in Missouri as nesting in abandoned clay nests of the black-and-yellow mud-dauber wasp. He reported that the closing plugs were made of mud with a coating of resin on the outside. Three cells in which the wasp failed to develop contained 1 to 3 nymphs of *Parcoblatta pennsylvanica* (DeGeer) about one-third grown. The nests were gathered in June and an adult *rufipes* emerged a year later. This suggested that there is only a single generation a year in Missouri.

Krombein (1958c, pp. 147-149) summarized data on some nests of *rufipes* [as *carolina*] in traps from Kill Devil Hills. Data from these nests have been incorporated in the foregoing discussion.

Source material.
Kill Devil Hills, N. C. 1955 series: C 135, 136, 218, 246, 248, 368, 381, 382, 385, 431, 508. 1956 series: C 99, 100, 137, 208, 239, 252, 253, 256, 384, 386, 387, 388, 389, 390, 391, 626, 627, 629. 1958 series: T 40.
Lake Placid, Fla. 1957 series: M 17, 18, 19, 33, 56, 77, 78, 89, 92, 93, 94, 117, 118, 119, 120, 128, 129, 144, 148, 152, 154, 226, 229, 271, 273, 274, 276. 1959 series: V 108, 124, 144. 1960 series: B 28, 93, 127, 130, 141, 202, 212, 214, 215, 221, 227, 232. 1961 series: F 210, 214, 215, 219, 223, 231, 241, 242, 246, 254, 273, 278, 279, 293, 298.

Identifications. Acarina by C. G. Jackson; Orthoptera by A. B. Gurney; Diptera by W. W. Wirth; Coleoptera by G. B. Vogt; Hymenoptera by the author.

PODIUM LUCTUOSUM Smith

(Plate 14, Figures 64, 65)

P. luctuosum nested in a 12.7-mm. trap fastened to the trunk of a dead, standing barked tree in a rather densely shaded area on Plummers Island. The tree contained many abandoned borings of other insects in which a number of species of wasps nested.

Nest architecture (fig. 64). I picked up the nest on the morning of July 4, 1961, probably a day or two after it had been stored. There were 2 cells 55 and 86 mm. long. Cell 1 was capped by a plug 11 mm. thick, which consisted of an inner section 9 mm. long of loosely compacted particles of rotten wood and an outer partition 2 mm. thick of plastered mud. The plug of cell 2 was 25 mm. thick; it had an inner section 15 mm. thick of rotten wood particles, a middle partition 4 mm. thick of plastered mud, and an outer section 6 mm. thick of rotten wood particles. The remaining 10 mm. of the boring was empty. There was a female *luctuosum*, probably the mother, flying around this tree trunk when I picked up the nest, and it may be that she had not completed the final closing plug on July 4.

Prey. Cell 1 contained 4 adult females and 1 adult male of a woods cockroach, *Parcoblatta uhleriana* (Saussure), and cell 2 contained 6 adult females and an adult male of the same species. The cockroaches were placed in the nest head inwards, but on their backs, sides, or bellies. They were thoroughly paralyzed, but able to void feces.

Life history. On the evening of July 4 there was a newly hatched *luctuosum* larva on the innermost cockroach in each cell, just beginning to feed beneath a forecoxa. Judged from the orientation of these larvae, the egg must have been laid longitudinally beneath or at the apex of the right forecoxa with the anterior end nearest the coxa. The larvae continued to hollow out this first cockroach for 2 days. On July 7 each began to feed on another cockroach, and both completed feeding on all the prey on the 10th and began to spin cocoons on the 11th. Both larvae pulled bits of rotten wood out of the partitions capping the cells and spun them loosely around the cocoon. The cocoons were 22 and 24 mm. long. They were similar in shape and texture to those of *rufipes,* but of a darker brown (fig. 65).

Both wasps overwintered outdoors as resting larvae. That in cell 2 finally pupated September 22-25, 1962, but died as a fully colored female pupa some days later. The occupant of cell 1 overwintered outdoors for a second winter (1962-63) as a resting larva and finally pupated March 16, 1963, after it had been indoors for a short time. It also died as a fully colored female pupa some days later. Both females had developed enough to be identified with certainty as *luctuosum.*

Parasites and predators. There was a female of *Melittobia chalybii* Ashmead in the nest on July 4, which I removed and killed. I suspect that *Neochrysis panamensis* (Cameron) may be a parasite of *luctuosum.* I captured a female of it on the trunk of the same tree from which this *luctuosum* nest came, and I have reared it from *Podium rufipes* (Fabricius) in nests from North Carolina and Florida. *P. rufipes* does not occur on Plummers Island.

Previous observations. I published a few miscellaneous notes on *luctuosum* (Krombein, 1964b) as follows: I saw a female sealing a nest with mud on July 17, 1961, in the same dead tree trunk on which I obtained the nest described above; perhaps the same female built both nests. I recovered a full-grown *luctuosum* larva from this boring several weeks later. I also found another female gathering mud for her nest in the dusk as late as 2020 hours.

Source material.
    Plummers Island, Md. 1961 series: K 136.

Identifications. Orthoptera by A. B. Gurney; *Podium* by A. Menke.

TRACHELIODES AMU Pate
(Plate 15, Figures 68, 69)

There is a possibility that the nests described below are those of a new species rather than of *amu*. I reared only females, 7.5-8.5 mm. long, from these nests from Arizona, and *amu* was described from a male from Pecos, N. Mex. The only lack of concordance between my females and *amu* males is that the former have a large white spot on the scutellum which is lacking in the latter.

I received 4 nests from a single station at Soldier Camp, Santa Catalina Mountains, Ariz., 8,000 feet elevation. Two were in 4.8-mm. and 2 in 6.4-mm. borings. The traps were suspended from a maple branch about 2 meters above the ground in a small clearing in a ponderosa pine forest. The traps were tipped at an angle of 35° so that the borings opened toward the ground. Three of the nests were stored between July 11 and August 10, 1961, and the fourth between August 10 and October 21, 1961.

The occupants of all nests were resting larvae in cocoons when I opened 3 nests on September 1 and 1 nest on November 6. Occupants of the outer 3 or 4 cocoons in one of the earlier nests and of the outer 6 cocoons in the later nest had been lost to predation or had emerged before I received the nests; most likely they suffered predation by some other insect.

Nest architecture. When I opened these nests, my initial impression was that there was a series of linear cells 5 to 14 mm. long (mean 8.8) in each. However, closer inspection showed that the partitions separating the boring into "cells" were not constructed by the mother, but that they were very thin, transverse septa of varnished silk constructed by the mature larvae (figs. 68, 69). In the 4.8-mm. nests there was usually only a single cocoon in each of these "cells," but in the 6.4-mm. nests there were 1 to 3 cocoons in each "cell" (mean 1.5). There were 20 cocoons in 18 "cells" in the 4.8-mm. nests and 22 cocoons in 15 "cells" in the 6.4-mm. nests. The outer 55-100 mm. was empty in each boring. There was no indication of a vestibular cell or of a closing plug of any kind in the nests, and it is possible that none of the nests was actually completed. It was impossible to determine from comparative developmental data whether the 3 earlier nests had been made by the same mother, or whether each was the work of a different female.

Prey. The hollowed-out remains of the prey, worker ants of the dolichoderine *Liometopum occidentale luctuosum* Wheeler, 3.5-4.5 mm. long, covered the cocoon walls. I recovered 42 heads, 37 thoraces, and 29 abdomens from the single cocoon in one "cell." Probably a few parts were lost during my extraction of the cocoon from the nest, thus accounting for the discrepancy in number of parts found.

Life history. It is apparent from the foregoing data on nest architecture that the *amu* female must pack a great many paralyzed ants into the boring, laying an egg at appropriate intervals on 1 of the ants. The *amu* larvae are probably not cannibalistic so long as there is a sufficient store of ants for each to reach maturity. Obviously, they cannot normally be antagonistic because of my finding several cocoons in a single "cell."

The occupants of my nests overwintered as resting larvae outdoors in Arlington, being brought into the house only when the temperature threatened to go below 32° F. Most of the larvae were attacked by *Pyemotes* mites the following spring, but 3 females pupated early in the spring and emerged a couple of weeks later.

The cocoons from which these *amu* females emerged were 6-10 mm. long (mean 8). The anterior end was a very thin, transverse septum of dark brown, varnished silk across the entire lumen of the boring. The cocoon walls were of opaque, soft, tan silk. Immediately posterior to the transverse septum the cocoon reduced abruptly to a diameter of about 4 mm. The remainder of the cocoon was cylindrical with a rounded posterior end. There was no pore at the anterior end, such as is present in cocoons of the crabronine genera *Ectemnius* and *Euplilis*.

Previous observations. Pate (1942) summarized biological observations on the European species, *quinquenotatus* (Jurine) and *curvitarsus* (Herrich-Schaeffer), made by Ferton and Grandi. The former nests in the soil, frequently in pre-existing burrows, and the latter nests in abandoned borings of other insects in wood. They prey on workers of the dolichoderine ants, *Tapinoma* and *Liometopum* respectively. Neither of the European observers noted more than 1 cell in a nest, and neither one specified the character of the closing partition. Grandi reported a number of cells containing

17 to 94 ants, but he did not find an egg in any of these cells. He speculated that perhaps the 1 cell containing 94 ants was intended to furnish sustenance for 2 or more contiguous cells, because the other cells held an average of 26 ants. He did find a wasp egg in 1 cell with only 9 ants. Hicks (1936) reported *hicksi* Sandhouse preying on an undetermined species of *Liometopum*, which Pate presumed to be *occidentale luctuosum* (recorded as *apiculatum luctuosum*), because the ants were found on pine. Pate's theory that each species of *Tracheliodes* preys on a different species (or subspecies) of dolichoderine ant is not substantiated by the prey preference reported above for *amu*.

Source material.
    Soldier Camp, Santa Catalina Mountains, Ariz. 8,000 feet elev. 1961 series: H 116, 177, 185, 200.

Identifications. Liometopum by M. R. Smith, wasp by the author.

EUPLILIS (CORYNOPUS) COARCTATUS MODESTUS (Rohwer)

I reared this species from 2 nests in 3.2-mm. borings, 1 from Derby and 1 from Plummers Island. Probably it nested in 2 other 3.2-mm. borings in the latter locality; the nest architecture in these was identical with that of *modestus*, but I failed to rear adults. The Plummers Island nests came from 3 stations attached to standing, dead tree trunks.

Supersedure and competition. A species of *Trypoxylon*, undoubtedly *johnsoni* Fox, superseded *modestus* in the nest from Derby.

Nest architecture. The crabronine stored paralyzed flies right at the inner end of the boring. Eight stored cells ranged from 8 to 29 mm. in length (mean 13.9 mm.). The partitions capping the cells, usually 1-2 mm. thick, were made of tiny bits of cemented wood fiber probably rasped from the boring walls. One cell was capped by a section 7 mm. thick of debris brought in from outside, and then the usual thin section of tiny wood fibers. Apparently none of these nests was completely stored; at least none had an empty vestibular cell. There were 2 or 3 *modestus* cells in each nest.

Prey. The dipterous fragments adhering to one cocoon from the Derby nest were identified as probably belonging to species of Chironomidae.

Life history. It is not known when any of the nests were actually stored. Occupants of all cells were resting larvae in cocoons when I opened the nests in September and October. Three *modestus* males emerged from the Derby nest and 1 female from 1 of the Plummers Island nests, all after overwintering as resting larvae. There are several generations annually in the Washington area, for I have collected adults at Plummers Island from mid-May to mid-October.

Parasites and predators. Phorid maggots, probably a species of *Megaselia,* were found in 3 cells of 2 nests from Plummers Island. A third 2-celled nest from Plummers Island was infested in the field by *Melittobia chalybii* Ashmead.

Previous observations. Recently I published an extended account of the life history of *modestus* (Krombein, 1964a) based on 6 nests found in dead hibiscus stems at Plummers Island. *E. modestus* nested in the pith of these stems, and the nests were always begun in the cut or broken ends. Female cells had a mean length of 11.2 mm. and male cells of 9.6 mm. The partitions between cells were made of small particles of pith loosely compacted and had a mean thickness of 8.5 mm. Most nests had an empty vestibular cell at the upper (outer) end of the boring. The cocoons were 6-8 mm. long, light tan, fusiform, had a small pore at the anterior end, and were covered with prey remains. Prey stored in these nests included 3 species of *Chironomus* and the ceratopogonid *Palpomyia subasper* (Coquillett). The wasp was parasitized by the platygasterid *Tetrabaeus americanus* (Brues) and by the eurytomid *Eurytoma inornata* Bugbee.

Source material.
Derby, N. Y. 1956 series: J 120.
Plummers Island, Md. 1960 series: E 101. 1961 series: K 177(?), 179(?).

Identifications. Diptera by P. H. Arnaud; Hymenopera by the author.

UNIDENTIFIED SPECIES OF CRABRONINAE

I obtained only 1 nest of this species, and I was not successful in rearing adults from it. It was in a 4.8-mm. boring that had been set in a pile of firewood at Plummers Island. I describe this nest because it is the first record of a North American crabronine including Trichoptera among its prey. The European *Crossocerus (Hoplocrabro) quadrimaculatus* (Fabricius) has been recorded as nesting in sandy soil and including Diptera and Trichoptera as prey. The identity of the wasp constructing this nest at Plummers Island is a puzzle, for we have no *Hoplocrabro* in this area. However, it is probably a fair-sized species, judged from the diameter of the boring, size of cells, and number of prey stored; and so I suspect that the nest might have been stored by *Crossocerus (Nothocrabro) nitidiventris* (Fox), the only large species of *Crossocerus* in this area.

Nest architecture. The nest was stored between July 18 and 25. There was 4 mm. of moderately firmly packed wood fibers at the inner end of the boring. The 2 provisioned cells were 16 and 12 mm. long. The partitions capping the cells were made of moderately firmly packed wood fibers that had been rasped from the sides of the boring. There was an empty vestibular cell 57 mm. long and the outer 65 mm. of the boring was empty. The closing plug of loose wood fibers was 7 mm. thick.

Prey. The egg in cell 1 was laid on the first fly placed in the cell. The prey in that cell consisted of a couple of dolichopodid flies, 1 chironomid fly, 1 muscoid fly, several caddisflies, and others which could not be seen. The second cell contained at least 3 dolichopodids and 1 other dipteron, but I could not see an egg. The larva in cell 1 hatched on July 26 but was lost subsequently.

Source material.
    Plummers Island, Md. 1956 series: H 76.

Identifications by the author.

Superfamily APOIDEA

Family COLLETIDAE

Females of this family have the unique habit of lining the cell ends and walls with a delicate transparent membrane secreted by the salivary glands. This membrane is impermeable to the very liquid nectar-pollen mixture which the bees regurgitate into the cells as food for the young. Only 2 species of *Hylaeus* used these borings as nesting sites, although the twig-nesting habit has been reported for a number of species in the genus.

HYLAEUS (PARAPROSOPIS) ASININUS (Cockerell and Casad)

I received 4 nests of this bee from 4 stations on the desert floor at Portal, Ariz., in 1960 and 1961. Three were in 3.2-mm. borings, and 1 was in a 4.8-mm. boring. Station data were not available for 1 nest; of the others 2 were from settings on a wire fence or wooden fence post and 1 was from beneath the branch of a desert willow.

Supersedure and competition. There was a single cell of *Trypargilum t. tridentatum* (Packard) in the inner end of the 4.8-mm. boring. Considering the diminutive size of the bee this supersedure could not have been the result of competition.

Nest architecture. The cell ends and walls were lined with a very delicate, transparent membrane formed from salivary secretion. Twenty-five cells in 3.2-mm. borings were 4-7 mm. long (mean 5.2). It is possible that female cells were a little longer because 6 of them were 6-7 mm. long (mean 6.2) whereas 4 male cells were 4-6 mm. long (mean 5.0). In the 4.8-mm. boring there were about a dozen cells in a space of 24 mm.; 2 or 3 individual cells occurred side by side, and measurements were not made of individual cells.

In 1 of the 3.2-mm. nests the partitions between the membranous cells were 1-1.5 mm. thick and made of wood fibers about ¼ mm. long.

There were 10 cells each in the 2 completed nests in 3.2-mm. borings. Each had an empty vestibular cell 5 and 8 mm. long respectively, plugged by a thin membranous cap. There was a vestibular cell 100 mm. long in the 4.8-mm. boring with a cross partition 10 mm. from the outer end.

In one nest there were a few fine wood fibers at the inner end of the boring.

Life history. Only 1 nest was sent to me shortly after it was completed. Presumably, it was provisioned between April 27 and May 3. When I opened it on May 12, I found a small larva in each cell lying partially submerged on the outer end of the very fluid pollen-nectar mass. These food stores were about 2 mm. long. A larva in cell 2, mature on May 19, was preserved for taxonomic study. The rest of the larvae overwintered in diapause.

The other 3 nests were sent to me in October or December, and all of their occupants were already diapausing larvae when I opened the nests. Presumably these nests had been stored the previous spring, because the data from the nest reported above suggests that this is an univoltine species. Published records indicate that the species is active April to June.

Tiny brown to black fecal pellets were voided at the inner end of each cell.

Four males pupated March 13-16 and emerged April 2-3; 2 females pupated during the same period and emerged April 3 and 4. Most of the other bees died as resting larvae during the winter or as fully colored pupae in the spring.

In one nest in which both sexes occurred there were males in cells 4 and 8-10 and a female in cell 5; bee occupants did not mature in the other cells.

Parasites and predators. I reared a male *Anthrax irroratus* Say from 1 *asininus* cell. Another bombyliid larva, presumably the same species, fed on a pale *asininus* pupa in another nest; it died before pupation.

Source material.

Portal, Ariz. 1960 series: 1 nest, not numbered. 1961 series: G 5, 238, 374.

Identifications. Bombyliidae by W. W. Wirth; bees by P. H. Timberlake and the author.

HYLAEUS (PROSOPIS) MODESTUS MODESTUS Say

I reared this bee from 4 nests in 3.2-mm. borings from Derby, N. Y., 1 each in 1955, 1957, 1958, and 1960. Two nests were from settings on a woodpile and 1 each in a crevice in a rock wall and suspended from the branch of a walnut tree.

Supersedure and competition. A species of the vespid *Symmorphus* superseded the bee in 1 nest.

Nest architecture. The cell walls and ends were coated with a very delicate, transparent membrane. In 3 nests the first cell was placed at the inner end of the boring, and in the fourth nest there was an empty space of 28 mm. between the inner end and the first cell.

Eleven cells were 6-11 mm. long (mean 7.3); 3 female cells were 6-9 mm. long (mean 7.3) and 5 male cells 6-11 mm. long (mean 7.6).

The first nest contained 4 stored cells end to end, then an empty space of 22 mm., and then an empty membranous vestibular cell 10 mm. long.

The second nest was incomplete and had just the 28-mm. empty space at the inner end and 2 stored cells end to end.

The third nest varied from the first two in having empty spaces and partitions of fine cemented wood fibers 2 mm. thick between the stored cells. There was a stored cell at the inner end, an empty space about 15 mm. long, a partition of wood fibers, stored cell 2, another partition of wood fibers, stored cell 3, an empty space of 5 mm., a partition of wood fibers, stored cell 4, another partition of wood fibers, and an empty space of 10 mm.

The last nest had 2 stored cells each capped by a partition of wood fibers 0.5 mm. thick, and then the nest was superseded by *Symmorphus.*

Life history. There was apparently only 1 generation a year at Derby because occupants of all nests overwintered as diapausing larvae.

One partially completed 2-celled nest was being stored on June 23. The larva in cell 2 completed feeding on July 8.

The small fecal pellets were voided at the inner end of the cell.

The period between pupation and adult emergence was 12 or 13 days for 2 males and 2 females. The adults remained in the cells about 3 days after eclosion. Males emerged 3-9 days earlier than females in the 2 nests in which both sexes developed; males were in the outermost cells in these nests.

Parasites and predators. I did not rear any parasites from the *modestus* nests from Derby. However, I did rear the type series of *Coelopencyrtus hylaei* Burks from the 1-celled nest of a species of *Hylaeus* from Plummers Island; the host bee might have been *modestus,* which does occur there.

Previous observations. Rau (1930) reported finding nests of *modestus* in hollows in sumac twigs, mostly constructed originally by other insects. He thought that the transparent cell walls constructed by the mother bee were cocoons made by the larvae. He also found disclike dividing walls between these "cocoons" which he thought were made by the mother bee or the larva; I did not find such partitions in my nest. He reported 11 bee "cocoons" in a boring 7.6 cm. long. In one nest he found a vestibule 13 mm. long and then a closing plug 9.5 mm. thick. Earlier (Rau, 1922, p. 36) he recorded males [as *sayi*] spending the night in a tunnel in a sumac twig.

Source material.
   Derby, N. Y. 1955 series: D 19a. 1957 series: G 125. 1958 series: R 69. 1960 series: D 76.

Identifications by the author.

Family MEGACHILIDAE

Most of the bees which nested in these traps belonged to this family. They exhibited great diversity in the nesting materials used and in details of the nest construction. In most species female cells were in the inner and males in the outer cells in the boring, but the reverse was true in at least 1 species. A few species were univoltine, but most species were multivoltine. In the univoltine vernal species of *Osmia* the bees transformed to adults in midsummer but remained in their cocoons throughout the ensuing winter. Occupants of other overwintering nests spent the winter as larvae in prolonged diapause.

Nest architecture. A few bees, *Prochelostoma philadelphi* (Robertson) (fig. 86) and *Osmia (Osmia) l. lignaria* Say (figs. 82, 84, 87), built relatively simple nests, using only mud to cap the cells and to plug the boring entrance.

A number of species built similarly simple nests, but they made very thin cell partitions from masticated leaf pulp which dried into tough, flexible or stiff septa. The closing plugs were made of the same substance but were much thicker. The bees which made nests like this included all but 2 species of *Ashmeadiella* (fig. 78), *Osmia (Osmia) ribifloris* Cockerell, and all species of the other subgenera of *Osmia* except *Centrosmia*.

Still other species built simple nests but used resin or gum to construct the cell partitions and closing plugs. These bees were *Heriades, Ashmeadiella cactorum* (Cockerell) and *A. opuntiae* (Cockerell), and all species of *Chalicodoma (Chelostomoides)*. Closing plugs in *Chelostomoides* bees were occasionally more complex because debris was sometimes incorporated with the resin. *Chelostomoides* also differed from the other resin-using species in usually having the cell walls opposite the pollen-nectar masses more or less coated with resin.

Normally there was a vestibular cell at the boring entrance in the simple nests of all the species mentioned above. However, this cell was occasionally lacking in 1 or more nests of almost all the species. This was especially noticeable in *Ashmeadiella occipitalis* Michener where only about half of the nests had such a cell. In those nests where a vestibular cell was lacking there was customarily a much thicker plug capping the terminal stored cell.

The remaining megachilids had much more complex nests with the cell partitions and/or closing plugs consisting of several materials or with the cells themselves being made from several kinds of plant products.

Osmia (Centrosmia) b. bucephala Cresson had thick compound cell partitions usually consisting of a thin layer of leaf pulp on either side of a thick section of bits of compacted wood fiber (fig. 90). Sometimes the wood fibers were just mixed with the leaf pulp. The wood fibers were obtained from the boring walls of the section that was to form the next stored cell. In longitudinal section the nests had a distinctive appearance unlike those of any other bee or wasp because the stored cells were barrel-shaped and wider than the compound plugs separating them (fig. 89).

The species of *Dianthidium* used resin in building their nests but incorporated other materials to form compound partitions and plugs. *D. floridiense* Schwarz lined the walls of its provisioned cells with a thin coating of resin and *D. p. platyurum* Cockerell lined these cells with resin mixed with tiny pebbles; the other 2 *Dianthidium, heterulkei fraternum* Timberlake and *ulkei perterritum* Cockerell, lined only the cell walls opposite the pollen-nectar mass with a thin coating of resin. The partitions capping the stored cells in *heterulkei fraternum* were only 2-3 mm. thick and consisted of a mixture of resin and tiny pebbles; the closing plug was 5 mm. thick and composed of the same materials. In the other 3 *Dianthidium* species there were much thicker compound partitions consisting of a thin layer of resin, then a section of various kinds of debris such as leaf bits, pebbles, bark, and then another thin layer of resin (fig. 81). In the nests of *floridiense* and *ulkei perterritum* there was an empty space beyond the last provisioned cell and then a terminal plug of resin alone or of some debris and then resin.

Anthidium maculosum Cresson was the only species of that genus which used these traps (figs. 79, 80). It is a carder bee and it used cottony plant fibers, presumably obtained from cottonwood or desert willow, to construct its nests. The bee coated the inner end of the boring and cell walls with a thick layer of this material, stored a rather liquid mix of pollen and nectar in a cell in the cotton, laid an egg on the food store, and then sealed the cell with a partition of the matted fibers. Then it lined another cell, provisioned it, and so forth. Many nests were plugged only with a thick wad of this cotton, but in other nests there was a compound plug consisting of a cotton wad, then a section of pebbles, leaf bits or other debris, and then another wad of cotton.

The species of *Megachile* belonging to the subgenera *Litomega-chile* (figs. 99, 100), *Megachile sensu str., Eutricharaea,* and *Melano-sarus* (fig. 98) are leaf cutters which make their nests from pieces of green leaf or petals which the females cut from a number of plants and shrubs. Michener (1953) discussed leafcutting and cell con-struction by *M. brevis* Say in great detail. In all the species which I observed the cell construction appeared to be uniform. The inner end of the cell and the cell walls were made from more or less rectangular, overlapping leaf cuttings. These leaf cuttings were bent inward at the inner end to form the base of the cup-shaped cell. Michener stated that *brevis* mouthed the edges of the leaf cutting after it had been positioned in the nest, presumably to make the sections stick together. This processing must have been accom-plished by the species I observed also because the cuttings forming the cell walls did adhere more or less tightly to one another. After the cup was formed from as many as 15 rectangular pieces the bee stored a mixture of pollen and nectar, laid an egg, and then sealed the cup with several circular leaf cuttings. Then more rectangular sections were brought in to form the base and walls of the next cell. When one of these nests was exposed by splitting the trap, the whole series of stored cells could be lifted out as a long cylinder. Usually the stored cells occupied the inner half or two-thirds of the boring. In some species, *e.g.,* those belonging to the subgenera *Litomega-chile* (figs. 99, 100) and *Eutricharaea,* the bees left most of this space empty or placed in it only a few scattered, oval to circular leaf cuttings, and then sealed the end of the boring with several circular leaf cuttings which adhered together. However, in *Megachile (Melanosarus) xylocopoides* Smith the bees filled this space with loosely shingled, rectangular to oval leaf cuttings and placed a few tightly packed, circular leaf cuttings at the entrance (fig. 98).

The most unusual nests were made by species of the subgenus *Sayapis.* In Florida typical *inimica* Cresson made individual, unlined cells capped by compound partitions consisting of 1 or 2 circular leaf cuttings at the inner surface and then a section 3-4 mm. thick of firmly agglutinated sand; the closing plug in 1 nest consisted of a number of loosely arranged, more or less circular leaf cuttings and in another it was a thick plug of agglutinated sand. In nests of *inimica sayi* Cresson from Arizona there were individual, unlined cells also; but the partitions had several circular leaf cuttings on the inner surface and then a layer 2-12 mm. thick of tiny pebbles mixed with leaf pulp; the closing plugs were made from similar materials.

The nests of *Megachile (Sayapis) policaris* Say were unique among all bees in these traps (figs. 92, 97). The females made 1-4 brood cells per boring each with a single large store of pollen and nectar on which several to many larvae developed without cannibalism. The partitions capping the brood cells were compound plugs usually 0.5-5 mm. thick, consisting of 2 or more layers of small, compressed, *entire* leaflets separated by thin septa of hardened, gummy leaf pulp. The closing plugs were thicker and composed of more alternating layers of these same materials. In the Arizona nests the female *policaris* used only entire leaflets, but in the single Florida nest the female included a few circular leaf cuttings also as well as entire leaflets.

Sex sequence and ratio. Females were in the inner cells and males in the outer cells of mixed nests of most species. The reverse was true in *Anthidium maculosum.* Occasionally this sequence was upset by the interpolation of a male cell in a series of female cells. It was conjectured that this anomalous situation might be due to failure of the sperm to fertilize the egg, temporary "fatigue" of the spermathecal gland thus inhibiting release of sperm, or possibly to supersedure by another nesting female of the same species.

An unusual situation was discovered in *Megachile policaris* which made brood cells. In several nests it was found that both sexes were produced in each of several brood cells in a sequence.

In most species of which I obtained more than a few nests, I found that only males were produced in some nests, only females in others, and both sexes in still others. This condition was very evident in *Osmia lignaria;* in this species I found that only males were produced in almost all the nests in 4.8-mm. borings and both sexes in nests in 6.4-mm. borings.

Among the few species having a 1:1 sex ratio were *Ashmeadiella bigeloviae, A. bucconis denticulata, Chalicodoma georgica,* and *C. occidentalis.* In other species more females were produced than males. Among these were *Anthidium maculosum* (3:1), *Prochelostoma philadelphi* (4:1), *Ashmeadiella meliloti* (3:2), *A. occipitalis* (3:1), and *Osmia pumila* (3:1). And in a few species it appeared that fewer females were produced than males. Among these were *Osmia lignaria* (1:2), *Megachile gentilis* (1:5), *M. mendica* (1:3), and *M. policaris* (1:2).

Number of generations. Many of the bees which nested in these traps were multivoltine and had at least 2 generations a year. Occupants of nests of these species stored late in the nesting season overwintered as diapausing larvae. However, there were a number of species which were definitely univoltine.

All members of the genus *Osmia* were univoltine. Their nests were stored in the spring and the occupants transformed to adults during midsummer. These adults remained in the cocoons through the ensuing winter and emerged early the next spring. This type of development is an obvious adaptation to insure that adults will be on the wing during the spring blooming period.

Developmental data suggested that *Ashmeadiella occipitalis* usually had only a single generation a year, that adults emerged from numerous nests over an extended period during August and probably overwintered in that stage. Only 1 nest was stored late in the season, indicating the possibility of a small, partial second generation; occupants of this nest overwintered as diapausing larvae.

In nests of other univoltine species the occupants overwintered as diapausing larvae. *Dianthidium floridiense* was univoltine, but the other species of the genus were multivoltine. *Prochelostoma philadelphi* was univoltine, and it was also the only bee exhibiting the phenomenon of delayed emergence. In some *Prochelostoma* nests the overwintering larvae in a few cells transformed to adults the first spring and others in the same nest did not transform to adults until the second spring after the nests were stored.

Both species of *Heriades* were univoltine, but *carinata,* which I reared from nests from New York and North Carolina, was found to be multivoltine in Missouri by Rau (1922). Matthews (1965) reported *carinata* as being univoltine in Michigan and in Oregon.

Megachile (Sayapis) i. inimica was univoltine in Florida nests. However, *inimica sayi* was multivoltine in Arizona nests. The other species of *Sayapis, policaris,* was multivoltine in both Florida and Arizona nests. The other species of *Megachile (gentilis, mendica, centuncularis, concinna, rotundata,* and *xylocopoides*) were also multivoltine with the possible exception of *M. (Eutricharaea) rotundata* of which I obtained only a single late season nest from Virginia; Stephen and Torchio (1961) found it to be univoltine in Oregon and Idaho.

Most species of *Chalicodoma (Chelostomoides)* were multivoltine, but typical *campanulae* and *c. wilmingtoni* appeared to have only a single generation with nests being stored in midsummer or later.

Adult activities. I watched several species provisioning cells. When the female returned to her nest after a provisioning flight, she entered the boring head first, remained inside for a few seconds, presumably to regurgitate the nectar from her crop, and then she backed out of the boring (figs. 70-73). Then she turned around, backed into the boring (figs. 74, 75), remained inside for half a minute to remove pollen from the abdominal scopa, and then flew off on another provisioning flight.

At night the females slept in their nests with the abdomen toward the entrance. In the narrow borings, bees such as *Prochelostoma philadelphi* had to rest with the abdomen straightened out. The species of *Osmia* which used larger borings curled the tip of the abdomen under so that the middle of the abdominal dorsum faced the entrance.

Social parasites. Parasitic megachilid bees belonging to the genera *Coelioxys* and *Stelis* were reared from a few nests of their megachilid hosts. I did not obtain any of the parasitized nests soon enough to observe the early activities of the parasites. Graenicher (1927) mentioned that the female *Coelioxys* discovered a nest of the host bee and continued to visit it, laying eggs in the pollen-nectar mass. The eggs hatched into larvae with a large, heavily sclerotized head bearing elongate mandibles. The *Coelioxys* larva migrated through the pollen-nectar mass, opening and closing its mandibles until it found the host egg or young larva. It killed and fed on the liquid contents of the host, molted to a normal second instar larva, and developed on the food stored for the host larva.

Enough host records have accumulated in *Coelioxys* to enable one to speculate as to the correlation of certain groups of parasites with groups of their hosts. The shiny black *Coelioxys,* with the scutellum mostly impunctate and with an angulate posterior margin, of which *dolichos* Fox is our sole representative, apparently have as their hosts the large black leaf-cutter bees belonging to *Megachile* subgenus *Melanosarus*. *C. dolichos* has been reared only from *xylocopoides* Smith, but we should anticipate that it probably parasitizes *bahamensis* Mitchell also, the only other member of *Melanosarus* in the United States. There is another species group of *Coelioxys* which is characterized by having the acute tip of the last abdominal tergum turned upward into a small spicule. I have reared one member of this group, *modesta* Smith, from nests of the resin-using bees *Chalicodoma* (*Chelostomoides*) *campanulae wilmingtoni* (Mitchell) and *georgica* (Cresson), and Hicks (1927, p. 20) reared another member, *gilensis* Cockerell, from *Chal. (Chel.) subexilis* (Cockerell). I suppose that the upturned apex of the last tergum may have some function in enabling these parasites to penetrate resin partitions for oviposition. If this correlation is valid, we should anticipate that the other known members of this species group, *deani* Cockerell, *obtusiventris* Crawford and *scitula* Cresson, will eventually be found to have as their hosts various species of *Chelostomoides*.

ANTHIDIUM (ANTHIDIUM) MACULOSUM Cresson

(Plate 17, Figures 79, 80(?))

I reared this carder bee from a dozen nests from 10 stations on the desert floor at Portal, Ariz., in 1959 and 1961. There were 6 nests each in 6.4- and 12.7-mm. borings. In addition, there were 2 nests in 12.7-mm. borings from another 2 stations in 1959 from which adults had emerged before the nests were gathered, and apparently *maculosum* plugged the entrance of an otherwise empty 4.8-mm. boring at one of the stations where it stored a 6.4-mm. nest. Three stations were on dead branches of mesquite, 2 each on desert willow and fence posts, and 1 each on a yucca trunk, a dead sycamore branch, and a pine log.

Supersedure and competition. Megachile (*Sayapis*) *policaris* Say superseded *maculosum* in a 6.4-mm. boring.

Nest architecture (figs. 79, 80). *A. maculosum* lined the cell walls and ends with cottony fibers which it obtained from plants. A positive identification of this susbtance could not be made, but it resembled such fibers from desert willow or cottonwood.

In the 6.4-mm. nests, where the cells were arranged in a linear series (fig. 79), 40 of them were 12-17 mm. long (mean 13.5). There was no difference in length between male and female cells. In those 12.7-mm. nests where they were arranged in a linear series, but crosswise in the boring (fig. 80), 23 cells were 8-12 mm. long (mean 10). In some 12.7-mm. nests the cells were arranged more or less side by side or in a shingled manner; there were 5 cells in 35 mm. in 1 nest, 5 cells in 52 mm. in another, 6 cells in 50 mm. in a third, and 13 cells in 82 mm. in the fourth.

Partitions capping the cells were of cotton about 1 mm. thick.

There was no vestibular cell. The closing plugs were somewhat variable. In 6 nests there was just a thick wad of cotton 5-45 mm. thick beyond the last stored cell. In 3 nests there was a compound plug consisting of a cotton wad 13-35 mm. thick, then a section of pebbles, leaf bits, and other debris 15-25 mm. thick, and then another cotton wad 5-7 mm. thick; one of the plugs had one more section of debris 14 mm. thick and a final cotton plug 9 mm. thick. In another nest there was a layer 60 mm. long of wood, pebbles and other debris in the lower part of the boring, and above this wadded cotton. In 2 nests the plugs beyond the last capped cell were 40-70 mm. long and consisted of small pebbles (fig. 79), bits of twigs or wood, and even a few pellets of lizard dung.

Life history. The bees stored a rather liquid mix of pollen and nectar, which frequently stained the cotton lining the cell walls. In one 12.7-mm. nest these masses were more or less hemispherical in shape with the outer end truncate, about 5 mm. thick and 7 mm. across. One mass in a 6.4-mm. boring was 12 mm. long.

Because of the opaque nature of the cell walls, I obtained very little data on the immature stages. In one overwintering nest 28-30 days elapsed between pupation and emergence of an adult female; this period was 27 days for a male in a summer generation nest.

The cocoons, about 11 mm. long, had rounded ends and were made of delicate, dark-brown, varnished silk; there was a narrow nipple of creamy silk 2 mm. long projecting from the anterior end in the middle.

It was apparent in summer-generation nests that occupants of the outermost cells usually pupated earlier and emerged earlier than bees in the inner cells and that this development was progressively slower from outer to inner cells. In one of these nests there was an eclosed adult in the outermost cell 6 on July 20 and a newly pupated individual in cell 1. The sex sequence and emergence from the summer generation nests were as follows (x = larval mortality):

Nest	1	2	3	4	5	6
X 162	♂, 8/16	♂, 8/15	♂, 8/14	♀, 8/7	♀, 8/5	♀, 7/28
X 183	♀, 8/16	♀, 8/16	♀, 8/14	♀, 8/14	lost	♀, 8/13
X 186	x	♀, 8/27	♀, 8/17	♀, 8/17	♀ 8/16	♀, 8/14
G 133	x	♂, 8/6	♂, 7/30	♀, 8/4	♀, 8/4	♀, 8/9
G 150	♂, 8/1	♂, 8/3	♂, 8/3	x	x	x
G 204	♀, 8/15	♀, 8/8	♀, 8/6	♀, 7/28		
G 211	x	♀, 8/11	♀, 8/18	♀, 8/18	x	♀, 7/28

	7	8	9	10	11	12
X 162						
X 183	♀, 8/7					
X 186	♀, 7/31	♀, 7/31				
G 133	♀, 8/3	♀, 8/4	♀, 7/20	♀, 7/8	♀, 7/8	♂, 7/13
G 150						
G 204						
G 211	♀, 7/26	♀, 7/11				

The cocoons from the last 4 nests (G series in table above) were put in individual glass vials which may account for the anomalous, premature (?) emergence of certain individuals.

This differing rate of development was noted to a lesser extent in overwintering nests also. The sequence of sexes and emergence dates for these nests were as follows, all cocoons having been placed in individual glass vials:

Nest	1	2	3	4	5	6	7	8
G 137	♂, 4/23	♂, 4/15	♂, 4/5	♀, 4/5	♀, 4/4	♀, 4/12	♀, 4/4	x
G 140	♂, 4/18	♀, 4/15	♀, 4/21	♀, 4/18	♀, 4/15	♀, 4/16		
G 228	♂, 4/22	♀, 4/23	♀, 4/21	♀, 4/16	♀, 4/18			
G 332	♀, 5/6	x	♀, 5/3	♀, 4/23	♀, 4/18	♀, 4/22	♀, 4/16	
G 354	♂, 5/10	♀, 5/14	♂, 5/4	♀, 5/6	♀, 4/30			

It will be noted that *maculosum* is one of the very few species in which male eggs are placed in the inner cells in mixed nests and female eggs in the outer cells. There was an anomalous sequence in only the one 12-celled nest (G 133) where there were 2 male cells, then 9 female cells, and then 1 more male cell. It is possible, as has been suggested below in *Osmia lignaria* Say, that the occurrence of a male out of normal sequence may be due to failure of the sperm to fertilize the egg or to temporary fatigue of the muscle controlling egress of sperm from the spermatheca.

Nests of the summer generation were stored the latter half of May in 1961. Emergence of adults from these nests occurred from July 11 to August 18. Occupants of 5 nests probably stored during September 1961, overwintered as diapausing larvae, transformed to pupae the following spring, and adults emerged April 4 to May 10.

I reared 32 females and 3 males from 40 stored cells in 6.4-mm. nests; females probably would have developed in at least 3 of the cells from which I did not rear adults. In 12.7-mm. nests I obtained 24 females and 14 males from 42 stored cells; probably at least 1 female and 1 male would have developed in the 4 cells from which I failed to rear adults.

Source material.
    Portal, Ariz. 1959 series: X 83(?), 162, 183, 186, 251(?), 253(?). 1961 series:
    G 133, 137, 140, 150, 204, 211, 228, 332, 354.

Identifications by the author.

DIANTHIDIUM FLORIDIENSE Schwarz

This pretty megachilid bee nested in only one 6.4-mm. trap at Lake Placid, Fla., during 1957. The trap was one of several fastened to the trunk of a dead tree a meter above the ground in the Highlands Ridge sand-scrub area.

Nest architecture. The bee smeared resin over the inner end of the boring and then stored a cell adjacent to this. The provisioned part of the cells were 16, 16, 15, and 14 mm. long, and their walls had a thin coating of resin. There were compound plugs capping cells 1-3 consisting of a resin partition 1.5-2 mm. thick; then a space 14-16 mm. long loosely filled with irregular bits of dried leaf, a few scales of pine bark and occasional bits of grass stem; and finally another resin partition 1.5-2 mm. thick. The boring walls opposite the debris were not coated with resin. Beyond cell 4 was an empty space 38 mm. long with a few dribbles of resin on the walls, and then a terminal plug of resin 5 mm. thick at the outer end of the boring. Resin was smeared on the outer end of the trap over a circular area about 13 mm. in diameter.

Life history. I received this nest on April 30. Presumably it had been stored between April 15 and 25. Cell 1 contained a mature bee larva that I preserved for taxonomic study. Cells 2 to 4 contained progressively smaller bee larvae that had not begun to defecate. The pollen stored by the bee was orange, quite moist, and apparently filled all of the space in each cell except for the outer 2 to 3 mm. The larva in cell 4 died in several days, but those in cells 2 and 3 reached maturity and spun cocoons between May 3 and 5. The occupants remained in larval diapause in the cocoons until the end of January. The nest was stored outside from October 12 to December 22 except during periods of freezing weather. The occupant of cell 2 transformed to a pupa between January 28 and 31, about 5 to 6 weeks after the nest was brought back into a warm room. The adult eclosed between February 15 and 17 and left the cocoon on February 20. It was a female *floridiense,* and I extracted another live female of the same species from cell 3 on that date.

In spinning its cocoon the larva coated the walls of the cell with white silk. The inner cocoon was of tough brown varnished silk. It was 8 mm. long, the inner end was rounded and the outer end flattened with a prominent median nipple protruding 1 to 1.5 mm.

Apparently the bee is univoltine.

Previous observations. D. *floridiense* was described as a discrete species and was later reduced to a subspecies of *curvatum* (Say), and Mitchell has now raised it back to specific rank. Its nesting habits are different from those of *curvatum sayi* Cockerell. Custer and Hicks (1927) found that *sayi* excavates its nest in the ground and uses resin in the construction of the cells. The tunnel entrance is closed by bits of chaff and mud covered with a resin plug.

Source material.
   Lake Placid, Fla. 1957 series: M 233.

Identifications by T. B. Mitchell.

DIANTHIDIUM HETERULKEI FRATERNUM Timberlake

I received 1 nest of this anthidiine bee from the vicinity of the Southwestern Research Station above Portal, Ariz., in 1960. The nest was in a boring of 6.4-mm. diameter.

Nest architecture. The inner part of each cell, undoubtedly the area where the pollen-nectar mass was stored, was coated with a thin layer of dark resin and tiny pebbles. The 6 stored cells were 12-15 mm. long (mean 13); 3 male cells were 12-15 mm. long and a single female cell was 12 mm. The partitions capping cells 1-5, 2-3 mm. thick, were composed of dark resin with some intermixed tiny pebbles; the partition capping cell 6, presumably the closing plug, was 5 mm. thick and composed of the same materials.

Life history. Occupants of the cells were diapausing larvae when I received the nest and opened it for study in mid-December.

The cocoons had a small nipple 1 mm. long at the anterior end. Six of them were 6-8 mm. long; 3 male cocoons were 7-8 mm. long and the single female cocoon 8 mm.

The nest was kept outdoors in Arlington until April 16. Occupants of cells 3 and 4 pupated April 19-27, adult males eclosed May 19 and left the nest on the 31st. Occupants of cells 1 and 2 pupated June 1-7; the occupant of cell 1 eclosed on June 21 and that in cell 2 on the 25th; both individuals, a female and a male, left the nest on July 2. It is assumed that the female was in cell 1. The prepupa in cell 5 was preserved for taxonomic study.

Parasites and predators. The prepupa in cell 6 was attacked by a bombyliid larva the previous fall; it pupated April 19-27 and an adult female *Anthrax irroratus* Say emerged on May 15.

Source material.

    Portal, Ariz. 1960 series: X 315.

Identifications. Dianthidium by P. H. Timberlake; *Anthrax* by W. W. Wirth.

DIANTHIDIUM PLATYURUM PLATYURUM Cockerell

I reared this bee from 2 nests stored on the desert floor at Portal, Ariz., in 1961. One was in a 4-8-mm. boring from a setting beneath the live branch of a desert willow (*Chilopsis* sp.). The other was in a 6.4-mm. boring in a similar setting but at a different station.

Supersedure and competition. In the 6.4-mm. boring the *platyurum* female superseded *Ashmeadiella occipitalis* Michener.

Nest architecture. There were 3 *platyurum* cells in the 6.4-mm. nest, 27, 39, and 57 mm. long, lined with resin intermixed with small pebbles and other debris. The plug closing cell 3 made up 45 mm. of the entire cell length; it consisted of loose debris with a 3-mm. cap of resin at the outer end. There was no vestibular cell.

In the 4.8-mm. nest the inner 4 mm. was empty and capped by a clear resin partition 1 mm. thick. Three stored cells were 22, 22, and 13 mm. long; the plugs closing cells 1 and 2 were 10 mm. thick and consisted of 1 mm. of clear resin, 8 mm. of debris, and 1 mm. of clear resin; the plug closing cell 3 was just of clear resin 1 mm. thick. Consequently, the spaces available in these cells for the pollen-nectar mass and egg were 12-13 mm. long. The vestibular cell was 88 mm. in length and had a closing plug composed of 7 mm. of debris, 3 mm. of clear resin, and a final cap of resin and mud mixed together.

Life history. The 6.4-mm. nest, presumably stored the latter part of May by *platyurum,* was picked up June 6. When I opened it on the 15th, the occupants of the 2 inner *platyurum* cells were in cocoons; but the larva in the outer cell was still feeding. Adult females emerged from cells 3, 2, and 1 on July 18, 22, and August 6 respectively.

The nest in the 4.8-mm. boring was presumably stored about the same period as the other nest. The occupants were prepupae in cocoons when I opened the nest on June 26. Two females emerged from cells 2 and 3 on July 28 and a female from cell 1 on August 12.

The cocoons were similar in shape to those described for *Dianthidium floridiense* Schwarz. Five of them were 6-8 mm. long.

Source material.
    Portal, Ariz. 1961 series: G 261, 310.

Identifications. Dianthidium by P. H. Timberlake; *Ashmeadiella* by the author.

DIANTHIDIUM ULKEI PERTERRITUM Cockerell

(Plate 17, Figure 81)

I received 2 nests of *perterritum* from a single station on a mesquite trunk on the desert floor near Portal, Ariz., in 1961. Both were stored between September 9 and October 18 and presumably by the same female. One was in a 4.8-mm. boring and the other in a 6.4-mm. boring.

Supersedure and competition. D. perterritum superseded an unknown vespid in the 6.4-mm. boring.

Nest architecture. In the 4.8-mm. boring an old abandoned *Trypargilum tridentatum* nest in the inner end was sealed off by a resin partition 2 mm. thick. Then there were 3 stored cells 21-22 mm. long and a vestibular cell of 12 mm. The partitions and closing plug were of resin; the latter was 9 mm. thick.

In the 6.4-mm. boring there was a 2-celled vespid nest in the inner 38 mm. There were 3 *platyurum* cells 22, 31, and 16 mm. long and a vestibular cell of 31 mm. The cell partitions and closing plug were composed of a little resin and then some debris such as small pebbles and bits of leaf or stem (fig. 81). The closing plug was 10 mm. thick. The part of the cell containing the pollen-nectar mass was lined with resin.

Life history. Occupants of the cells overwintered outdoors as diapausing larvae. Two males in the 6.4-mm. nests pupated April 28-May 4 and emerged May 23; 1 larva was preserved for taxonomic study. Two females in the 4.8-mm. nest pupated at the same time and emerged May 24 and 29; the occupant of the innermost cell had been parasitized the previous fall by the meloid beetle *Nemognatha nigripennis* LeConte.

Four cocoons of both sexes were 9-10 mm. long. They were

light tan, varnished, with a posterior rounded end, and the anterior end truncate and bearing in the middle a nipple of creamy silk 1 mm. long (fig. 81).

Source material.
    Portal, Ariz. 1961 series: G 315, 347.

Identifications. Dianthidium by P. H. Timberlake; *Nemognatha* by W. R. Enns.

PROCHELOSTOMA PHILADELPHI (Robertson)
(Plate 17, Figure 86)

I reared this small slender megachilid bee from 14 nests in 3.2-mm. borings from Arlington, Va., in 1959, 1961, and 1962. All the nests were from stations on the wall of an old wooden cowshed. The bee normally nested in deserted anobiid borings in the walls of this shed.

Supersedure and competition. P. philadelphi superseded a species of *Trypoxylon* in 1 nest, apparently as a result of competition, because there were a few paralyzed spiders walled off at the inner end of 1 of the borings. One *philadelphi* female superseded another in each of 2 nests following the death of the first bee in the boring after she completed 1 or 2 cells.

Nest architecture (fig. 86). The bees began to store pollen and nectar at the inner end of the boring in all nests except the one where *philadelphi* walled off the spiders with a mud partition.

There was no significant difference in length between male and female cells. The 90 stored cells were 7-10 mm. long (mean 8.2).

The partitions capping the cells and the closing plug at the nest entrance were made of mud. The former were 0.2-0.5 mm. thick and the latter 0.75-7 mm. thick (mean 2.3). I noted that it took 1 female about 50 seconds to fly off and return with a pellet of mud to use in the plug.

All but one of the completed nests had a vestibular cell 3-17 mm. long (mean 8.8).

There were 5-8 stored cells per completed nest (mean 6.4).

Life history. The pollen-nectar masses were occasionally quite moist so that the cell partitions were also saturated with the nectar. These masses filled the inner half or two-thirds of the cell; they were cylindrical with a slightly sloping anterior end. The masses provided for female bees were a little larger than those provided for males; 16 of the former were 4-7 mm. long (mean 5.0) and 4 of the latter 4-6 mm. long (mean 4.6).

The egg was sausage shaped, slightly curved, and 1.5-1.6 mm. long by 0.4-0.5 mm. wide. The tail end was inserted slightly into the pollen-nectar mass and about half of the egg was in contact with the food. Egg hatch required 4 days in nests stored between May 26 and June 7.

The larvae began to void small fecal pellets 5-7 days after hatching. About 14 days after hatching they began to spin the fecal pellets together into a loose net at the anterior end of the cell. The larvae completed feeding 27-37 days after egg hatch.

The cocoons were white, opaque, and delicate. They averaged just a little less than the inside length of the cells, or 7-8 mm. long.

The larvae went into extended diapause and overwintered in that stage. Pupation occurred in the spring and 16-26 days elapsed between pupation and emergence of the adults.

This species was the only bee that exhibited delayed emergence with some or all of the larval occupants of certain nests remaining in diapause over 2 winters before finally transforming to pupae and adults 2 years after the nests were stored. There was no delayed emergence in the 3 nests stored during 1959. Of the 4 nests stored in 1961 there was no delayed emergence in 1 nest which contained both sexes; all the occupants (both sexes) in a second nest emerged the second spring after the nests were stored; and in 2 nests the occupants of the outer cells (all females in 1 nest, both sexes in the other) emerged the first spring and the female occupant of the innermost cell in each nest transformed and emerged the second spring. In the 7 nests in 1962 there was no holdover in 3 nests, 2 of which contained both sexes and 1 which contained females only; the occupants of 2 nests remained in larval diapause over 2 winters and females emerged from 1 nest and both sexes from the other; and in 2 nests both sexes emerged from the outermost cells after the first winter, the occupant of cell 1 in each nest remained in larval diapause over the second winter, and a female developed in 1 nest and the occupant of the other died as a prepupa.

Males developed only in the outermost cells in the 10 nests in which both sexes developed, but only females developed in 4 nests. Usually there was only 1 male per nest, as is indicated by my rearing 47 females and 13 males from the 90 stored cells. In the 30 cells from which I failed to rear adults, females probably would have developed in at least 21 cells and males in at least 4, judged from the sex of the bees reared from adjacent cells.

Data from egg hatch suggest that 2-3 cells were stored per day during periods of good weather. Eggs in two 6-celled nests hatched over a 2-day period, and over a 3-day period in one 6-celled and two 7-celled nests.

Parasites and predators. Two nests were infested in the laboratory by the grain itch mite, *Pyemotes ventricosus* (Newport), and 1 nest each by *Melittobia chalybii* Ashmead and a dermestid larva, presumably *Trogoderma ornatum* Say.

Previous observations. Several years ago (Krombein, 1959b) I published a few biological notes on the population nesting in the anobiid borings in the cowshed wall in 1954. I noted that males were active May 15-16, that mating took place a few days later, and that females began to provision nests May 22-23. Six nests were marked and their progeny trapped the next spring. These nests yielded 7 males May 19-21 and 18 females May 19-26. The peak of male emergence was May 19 and of females on May 23. Only males were obtained from 1 nest, only females from 3 nests, and both sexes from 2 nests. Males emerged before females from the 2 nests containing both sexes.

Source material.
    Arlington, Va. 1959 series: A 14, 17, 18. 1961 series: J 7, 9, 10, 12. 1962 series: N 1, 9, 13, 14, 15, 16, 17.

Identifications by the author.

HERIADES (NEOTRYPETES) LEAVITTI Crawford

I reared *leavitti* from 2 nests from 2 stations at Lake Placid, Fla., in 1960. The nests were in 3.2-mm. borings beneath branches of live scrub hickory and oak in the sand-scrub area of the Archbold Biological Station.

In addition, I received 3 other nests in 3.2-mm. borings which probably were stored by this same bee. These were from 3 stations at Lake Placid in 1957 and 1960. One of them almost certainly was a nest of *leavitti* because it came from the same station and was stored during the same week as one of the *leavitti* nests.

Nest architecture. The bees began to store pollen and nectar at the inner end of all 5 borings.

A single male cell in 1 nest and a single female cell in the other were each 11 mm. long. Five other cells in these 2 *leavitti* nests were 12-16 mm. long. The cells in the 3 nests presumed to have been stored by *leavitti* were 9-15 mm. long.

The partitions capping the cells and the closing plugs at the nest entrances were made from resin. The former were 0.2-0.3 mm. thick and the latter 2 mm. thick.

There was an empty intercalary cell 8 mm. long between 2 stored cells in 1 *leavitti* nest. Vestibular cells in the 2 *leavitti* nests were 15 and 21 mm. long; in the supposed *leavitti* nests 2 of them were 11 and 46 mm. long, and the third nest lacked such a cell.

There were 3 and 4 stored cells, respectively, in the 2 *leavitti* nests and 2 to 4 cells in the other nests presumed to have been made by this bee.

Life history. The bees placed pollen-nectar masses 6-9 mm. long (mean 8.2) in each of the stored cells. I did not obtain precise data on the duration of the combined egg and larval feeding stages, but 1 larva finished feeding May 27 in a nest stored during the week beginning April 27. The female cocoon was 5 mm. long.

These 5 nests were stored from the latter part of March until the first week in May. Apparently there is only a single generation because the occupants of 2 nests entered an extended period of larval diapause and required exposure to chilly weather for a couple of months before they transformed to pupae and then to adults the following spring.

A female was reared from the innermost cell in 1 nest and a male from the outermost in another. Consequently, no conclusions can be drawn as to the sequence of sexes in nests containing both sexes, although it is presumed that this would follow the usual pattern of males in the outermost cells.

Source material.
Lake Placid, Fla. 1957 series: M 100 (?), 1960 series: B 2 (?), 11 (?), 12, 186.

Identifications by the author.

HERIADES (PHYSOSTETHA) CARINATA Cresson

I reared this small bee from 3 nests from 3 stations at Derby, N. Y., in 1957 and 1961, and it probably built a fourth nest at Derby in 1957 from which I failed to rear adults. I also reared it from a single nest at Kill Devil Hills, N. C., in 1955. Two nests were in 3.2-mm. borings and 3 in 4.8-mm. borings. At Derby 2 of the nests were from settings on wooden window sills, and 1 each was from a setting beneath oak and pine branches. The Kill Devil Hills nest was from a setting beneath a branch of *Myrica* at the edge of a wooded area.

Supersedure and competition. H. carinata superseded a vespid wasp in 1 nest at Derby, and in another nest from the same locality it was superseded by *Trypargilum collinum rubrocinctum* (Packard). This latter supersedure took place after the bee had made an empty cell 6 mm. long, which probably represented the vestibular cell, in its nest.

Nest architecture. In the nests begun by *carinata* the bee began to store pollen and nectar at the inner end of 1 boring. In 2 borings it left an empty space 33-87 mm. long and made a thin partition of resin before storing the first cell. In 1 boring a wasp (?) had made a partition of mud 27 mm. from the inner end and the *carinata* female coated this with resin before storing the first cell; this was the nest which was superseded eventually by the *Trypargilum;* so that wasp may have made the initial partition.

In 3.2-mm. nests 3 male cells were 9-11 mm. long; 5 stored

cells from which I failed to rear adults were 7.5-9 mm. long. Six female cells in 4.8-mm. nests were 5-9 mm. long (mean 7); 3 cells from which I failed to rear adults were 6-7 mm. long.

Vestibular cells in the 3.2-mm. nests were 13 and 22 mm. long. In one 4.8-mm. nest an empty cell 6 mm. long beyond the last cell stored by *carinata* probably represented a vestibular cell. There was no vestibular cell in a second 4.8-mm. nest; that nest probably was incomplete because there was no thicker closing plug either. In the 4.8-mm. nest from Kill Devil Hills there was an empty space of 57 mm. between the single stored cell and the boring entrance; the bee coated the edge of the entrance with resin but abandoned the nest before completing the closing plug.

Resin was used to construct the cell partitions and closing plugs. The partitions were 0.2-0.5 mm. thick and the closing plugs were 1-3 mm. thick in the 3.2-mm. nests.

Life history. I did not obtain data on the length of the egg stage. The larval feeding period was apparently rather protracted because in a 6-celled nest completed on June 22 a larva in cell 2 did not finish feeding until July 22. In a 6-celled nest completed July 22 a larva in cell 3 did not complete feeding until August 18. These data suggest a combined egg and larval feeding period of about 29-32 days.

The pollen-nectar masses stored in several female cells in a 4.8-mm. boring were 2-3 mm. long.

Nests of *carinata* were completed at Derby from June 22 to August 1; the 1 nest presumed to have been stored by *carinata* was completed June 11. The Kill Devil Hills nest was probably stored no later than mid-June. The occupants of all these nests overwintered as diapausing larvae.

The cocoons were ovoid, delicate, white, subopaque, and lacked a nipple. Those of males in 3.2-mm. borings were 5-6 mm. long. One female cocoon was 8 mm. long.

The period between pupation and adult emergence was 19-21 days for 2 males and 17-23 days for 5 females. One adult female remained in the cocoon 4 days after eclosion from the pupal exuvia.

Only females were reared from 3 nests and only males from the fourth nest. I reared 5 females and 3 males from 15 stored cells at Derby. At least 1 female and 3 males probably would have been obtained from the 7 stored cells from which I failed to rear adults. I reared a female from the single cell in the Kill Devil Hills nest.

Previous observations. Rau (1922, pp. 39-40) reported nests of *carinata* in borings in sumac twigs. He obtained emergence early in August from nests collected a month earlier. He did not include information on the cell length but mentioned that one boring was 4.8 mm. in diameter and about 100 mm. long.

Matthews (1965) contributed a detailed study on the bionomics of *carinata* in borings in white-pine sticks in Michigan and Oregon. In Michigan he used borings of variable length and 3.2, 4.0, 5.6, and 6.4 mm. in diameter; he obtained 77 nests of which 86 per cent were in 3.2-mm. borings 101 mm. long. In Oregon he used 3.6-mm. instead of 3.2-mm. borings in his settings and obtained 55 nests, 62 per cent of them in 3.6-mm. borings 71 mm. long. One *carinata* nest was superseded by *Trypoxylon; carinata* superseded *Hylaeus* spp. in 4 nests, and *Osmia* (*Chalcosmia*) *coerulescens* (Linnaeus), *Osmia* (*Nothosmia*) sp., and *Chelostomoides angelarum* (Cockerell) in 1 nest each. A wasp, *Solierella* sp., was a successful competitor of *carinata* for nesting sites in Michigan, but it did not supersede the bee in any borings.

Matthews noted that some bees began to store pollen at the inner end of the boring, while others made a preliminary resin plug before provisioning the first cell. He found that 243 provisioned cells in 3.2-mm. borings in Michigan had a mean volume of 0.1067 cu. mm. and that 48 closing plugs of clear resin had a mean volume of 0.0337 cu. mm.; comparable figures for nests in 3.6-mm. borings in Oregon were 0.1252 cu. mm. for 175 provisioned cells and 0.0900 cu. mm. for 24 closing plugs. Michigan nests in 3.2-mm. borings 101 mm. long had an average of 4.6 provisioned cells (range 1-10) per nest, whereas Oregon nests in 3.6-mm. borings 71 mm. long had an average of 6.4 cells (range 2-13). Empty vestibular cells in Michigan nests had a mean length of 48 mm. (range 10-89), whereas Oregon nests had a mean length of 13 mm. (range 5-55). Vestibular cells were occasionally lacking; in these nests the resin partition closing the last provisioned cell was thicker than usual.

Matthews found that the construction and storing of a single cell averaged 2.7 days in Oregon nests and 1.1 days in Michigan nests; he correlated this with the larger size of cells in Oregon nests. He mentioned that a single cell might be completed in a little less than 4 hours under optimum conditions but that over 6 days were needed to store 1 cell during periods of inclement weather. Eggs hatched in 5½ days. There were at least 4 larval instars and about 25 days (range 15-33) elapsed between egg hatch and cocoon construction. The larvae began to void feces after the second molt, about 6 days (range 4-11) after egg hatch. About 7½ days after defecation commenced the larva spun a very delicate, transparent cap, the operimentum, at the anterior end of the cell; Matthews theorized that this structure probably served to orient the larva so that it spun its cocoon with the anterior end toward the boring entrance. Cocoons were completed 7 days (range 3-11) after cessation of feeding. There was only a single generation, and the winter was spent in larval diapause. Matthews reported that in nests over-wintering under natural conditions a period of about 35 days elapsed between pupation and adult emergence. After refrigeration for 115 days pupation occurred 12-18 days after the nests were placed in 72° F. chambers, and adult emergence took place 21-25 days after pupation. Males averaged 5 days earlier in emergence than females.

In most mixed nests Matthews found that males were in the outer and females in the inner cells. He reported 1 nest containing only females, but none in which only males developed. He found 4 nests in which female cells were interspersed among male cells and 1 nest in which males were in the inner and females in the outer cells. In Oregon nests in 1962 he obtained a ratio of 2♀:1♂; in Michigan nests the ratios were 1♀:3♂ in 1963 and 2♀:1♂ in 1964.

Matthews reared the sapygid wasp *Sapyga louisi* Krombein and the megachilid bee *Stelis vernalis* Mitchell from *carinata* nests in Michigan. The sapygid parasitized at least 9 cells and the bee 10 cells during the 2 years that traps were used in Michigan. He also observed attempted parasitism by the chalcidoid wasp *Leucospis affinis* Say in Michigan. He experienced no field parasitism in Oregon, but in the laboratory many cells were infested by *Melittobia chalybii* Ashmead. He also noted the loss of many cells from mold during 1963 in Michigan.

Source material.
   Derby, N. Y. 1957 series: G 128, 152(?). 1961 series: L 41, 43.
   Kill Devil Hills, N. C. 1955 series: C 191.

Identifications by the author.

ASHMEADIELLA (ASHMEADIELLA) BIGELOVIAE (Cockerell)

I reared this bee from 10 nests at 7 stations on the desert floor at Portal, Ariz., in 1959 and 1961; from 3 nests at 2 stations at Granite Reef Dam, Ariz., in 1961; and from a single nest from Scottsdale, Ariz., in 1961. A dozen nests were in 3.2-mm. borings and 2 were in 4.8-mm. borings. At Portal 4 traps were beneath branches of desert willow, 3 beneath dead or live limbs of mesquite, and 3 on wooden fence posts. The traps at the other localities were beneath branches of palo verde.

Supersedure and competition. A species of *Osmia,* possibly *gaudiosa* Cockerell, superseded *bigeloviae* in 1 nest in a 4.8-mm. boring.

Nest architecture. In 10 nests the bees began to store pollen and nectar at the inner end. In 1 nest the bee spread a thin layer of leaf pulp at the inner end, and in another nest the bee walled off an abandoned *Trypargilum tridentatum* nest by a thin partition of leaf pulp.

In 3.2-mm. borings 18 female cells were 5-14 mm. long (mean 7.1) and 20 male cells were 5-6 mm. long (mean 5.0). Eight female cells in 4.8-mm. borings were 5-6 mm. long.

There were 10 completed nests in 3.2-mm. borings. Eight of them had vestibular cells 19-45 mm. long. The single nest sealed by *bigeloviae* in a 4.8-mm. boring had a vestibular cell 45 mm. long. This latter nest also had an empty intercalary cell 6 mm. long between 2 stored cells.

The partitions capping the stored cells and the closing plugs were made from gummy, masticated leaf pulp which dried into a tough hard layer. The partitions were usually 0.2-0.5 mm. thick, but in two 3.2-mm. nests they were 1.5 mm. thick. The closing plugs were 1-4 mm. thick (mean 2.1) in 3.2-mm. nests and 8 mm. thick in the single 4.8-mm. boring sealed by *bigeloviae*.

There were 2-6 stored cells (mean 4) in the eight 3.2-mm. nests which had an empty vestibular cell. In the two 3.2-mm. nests which lacked such a cell there were 10 and 12 stored cells, respectively. There were 5 and 7 stored cells respectively in the 4.8-mm. nests, but *bigeloviae* did not use the entire boring in either nest.

Life history. The pollen-nectar masses in 7 cells were quite moist and 3-8 mm. long (mean 5); 2 of them from which females were reared subsequently were 5 and 5.5 mm. long. The eggs were more than half submerged in the rather liquid masses in 1 nest.

I did not obtain any data on the duration of the egg or larval feeding stages. However, this combined period is apparently rather short, probably no more than 20 days. Pupation in the summer generation occurred about 8-10 days after completion of larval feeding. The period between pupation and adult emergence was 21-25 days for 3 males in the summer generation and 23-30 days for 2 females; in 1 female in an overwintering nest it was 18-20 days.

The cocoon was silken, subopaque, and delicate; 1 female cocoon in a 3.2-mm. nest was 5 mm. long.

Emergence of adults occurred 42-60 days after completion of nests stored from about April 20 to May 20. This period was 37-46 days in a nest stored during the last week in July. Emergence of adults from an individual multicelled nest took 3-11 days in nests containing both sexes and 1-10 days in nests containing only a single sex. The protracted 11-day emergence period in the 12-celled nests suggests that the rate of storing may be quite slow. However, I know that 1 adult female remained in the cell at least 10 days after eclosion; so protracted emergence may actually be due to certain individuals remaining in the cell a longer time after eclosion.

Adults emerged during mid-June, July, August, and early September from nests stored from mid-April to early July. However, *bigeloviae* must provision nests until at least mid-October. In one nest picked up on October 18 there were still feeding larvae when I opened it on November 3. This was the only nest in which the occupants overwintered as diapausing larvae.

In 4 nests from which I reared both sexes, males were in the outer and females in the inner cells. I reared 18 females and 20 males from 56 stored cells in 3.2-mm. nests. Females would probably have developed in at least 7 and males in at least 3 of the cells from which I failed to rear adults. I reared 8 females from a dozen stored cells in 4.8-mm. nests; the sex of occupants in 4 of the cells could not be forecast.

Parasites and predators. One nest was infested in the laboratory by the grain itch mite *Pyemotes ventricosus* (Newport).

Source material.
 Portal, Ariz. 1959 series: X 4, 20, 21. 1961 series: G 23, 25, 59, 71, 152, 153, 165.
 Granite Reef Dam, Ariz. 1961 series: H 12, 18, 157.
 Scottsdale, Ariz. 1961 series: H 22.

Identifications by C. D. Michener and the author.

ASHMEADIELLA (ASHMEADIELLA) BISCOPULA Michener

I obtained only 2 nests of this bee. Both were from the desert floor at Portal, Ariz., in 4.8-mm. borings, 1 in 1959 and 1 in 1961. One was from a setting on a sycamore tree along a stream and the other was from a desert willow.

Supersedure and competition. A. *biscopula* superseded *A. occipitalis* Michener in 1 nest.

Nest architecture. In the boring stored entirely by *biscopula* the mother bee began to store pollen and nectar at the inner end. The 26 stored cells in the 2 nests were 5-13 mm. long (mean 6.3). Only 1 cell was 13 mm. long and the others were 5-10 mm.; this unduly long cell was the terminal one in a nest lacking a vestibular cell and half of its length consisted of the closing plug. Eight female cells were 7-10 mm. long (mean 8). Two terminal cells in which males probably developed were 5 mm. long.

Although both nests were completed, only one of them had a vestibular cell 41 mm. long.

The cell partitions were ¼ mm. thick and made from stiff, gummy leaf pulp. The closing plugs, made of the same material, were 2 and 6 mm. thick.

Life history. The occupants of cells 5-17 of the 1959 nest had already emerged when I picked up the nest on July 19. The 4 females in the innermost cells emerged July 19-28. The occupant of cell 1 was misoriented and lay with its head toward the inner end of the boring.

The later nest was completed the week of June 1, and I examined it on the 15th. At that time the *biscopula* larvae in cells 4-12 had already completed feeding, whereas the larger *occipitalis* larvae in cells 1-3 were still feeding. Two males of *biscopula* emerged from the nest on July 28 and 6 females emerged July 28-August 2.

The cocoons were delicate, opaque, and white and completely filled the space between the partitions, so that their mean length was just a little less than 6 mm.

Data from these nests indicate that there are at least 2 generations a year. Development in the later nest suggests that 8-9 weeks are required for the entire life cycle.

Source material.
  Portal, Ariz. 1960 series: X 60. 1961 series: G 169.

Identifications by C. D. Michener and the author.

ASHMEADIELLA (ASHMEADIELLA) BUCCONIS DENTICULATA (Cresson)

This bee nested in 6 traps on the desert floor at Portal, Ariz., in 1961. Three nests were from a station on a partially dead desert willow. The others were from 3 stations, 2 from settings on dead mesquite and 1 from an old yucca stem. Three nests were in 3.2-mm. and 3 in 4.8-mm. borings.

Nest architecture. The bees began 3 nests by placing a thin coating of leaf pulp at the inner end of the boring; in the other nests the bees began to store pollen and nectar at once.

Nine stored cells in 3.2-mm. nests were 6-9 mm. long (mean 7); 1 female cell was 8 mm. long and 4 male cells were 7 mm. long. In 4.8-mm. borings 41 stored cells were 5-10 mm. long (mean 6); 7 female cells were 5-7 mm. and 3 male cells were 5-6 mm. long. The abnormally long (10 mm.) cell in 1 nest was the terminal cell with a closing plug 6 mm. thick.

The 2 completed nests in 3.2-mm. borings had vestibular cells 9 and 52 mm. long. Of 3 completed nests in 4.8-mm. borings, 2 had vestibular cells 77 and 125 mm. long, and 1 lacked such a cell.

The partitions capping the stored cells, 0.2-0.5 mm. thick, were made from stiff, gummy leaf pulp. The closing plugs, made from the same substance, were 2-11 mm. thick (mean 5).

There were 1 and 5 stored cells, respectively, in the 2 completed nests in 3.2-mm. borings. In the 3 completed nests in 4.8-mm. borings there were 4 and 12 cells in the 2 nests provided with vestibular cells, and 25 cells in the nest which lacked such a cell.

Life history. This bee stored a rather dry mixture of pollen and nectar. These masses were 4-5 mm. long in the 3.2-mm. nests and 3-4 mm. long in a 4.8-mm. nest.

Three nests were stored May 9-29. In a nest completed May 23-29 a male larva finished feeding on June 19, and the adult bee emerged July 22 or 23. A female bee emerged July 30 or 31 from a nest stored May 9-15; this larva completed feeding about June 10.

Precise data were not obtained for the period between pupation and adult emergence in nests of the summer generation, although it was at least 19-20 days for 1 male. In overwintering nests this period was 18-20 days for 1 male and 19-26 days for 7 females (mean 24).

The cocoons were delicate, white, and subopaque. Two of them were 6-7 mm. long.

There are quite possibly 3 generations a year. I received 2 nests stored between September 9 and October 18. Larvae had not finished feeding in one of these nests on November 3, and so it probably was not stored before early October.

I reared only 8 females and 7 males from 50 stored cells. The occupants of many cells were destroyed in laboratory infestations by *Pyemotes* mites. However, judging from cell lengths and assuming that males would have developed in the outermost cells of mixed nests, I estimate that there would have been a 1:1 sex ratio in the nests had bees developed in all cells.

Parasites and predators. I reared a female of the cuckoo wasp *Chrysura sonorensis* (Cameron) from the outermost cell of 1 nest. The bombyliid *Anthrax irroratus* Say parasitized 2 cells in another nest. In still a third nest a first instar meloid larva of a species of *Nemognatha* close to *nigripennis* LeConte destroyed the bee egg in the innermost cell. The grain itch mite *Pyemotes ventricosus* (Newport) invaded a number of cells in 2 nests after they had been in the laboratory for several weeks.

Source material.
    Portal, Ariz. 1961 series: G 15, 19, 55, 67, 189, 296.

Identifications. Nemognatha by R. B. Selander; *Anthrax* by W. W. Wirth; *Chrysura* by R. M. Bohart; bees by the author.

ASHMEADIELLA (ASHMEADIELLA) CACTORUM CACTORUM (Cockerell)

I received 5 nests of this bee, 2 in 3.2-mm. borings from Portal, Ariz., in 1959, and 3 from Granite Reef Dam in 1961, 2 of the latter in 3.2-mm. and 1 in a 4.8-mm. boring. The nests from Portal were from stations on the desert floor, 1 on a wire fence and the other on a dead fallen pine log in a dry wash. The stations at Granite Reef Dam were on a desert mountainside, 2 beneath limbs of palo verde and 1 on the stem of an ocotillo.

Nest architecture. The bees began to store pollen and nectar at the inner end of the boring in all nests. Sixteen stored cells in 3.2-mm. borings were 6-9 mm. long (mean 6.4); 5 female cells were 7-9 mm., and 2 male cells 6-7 mm. The only stored cells in the 4.8-mm. nest were 2 female cells 11 and 6 mm. long.

All the nests were completed, and all but 1 of the 3.2-mm. nests had a vestibular cell. These were 22-40 mm. long (mean 32) in the 3.2-mm. nests, and 133 mm. long in the 4.8-mm. nest.

The partitions capping the cells, made from gum or resin, were 0.2-0.5 mm. thick. The closing plugs were made of the same material; they were 0.5-4 mm. thick.

There were 3-6 stored cells (mean 4) in 3.2-mm. nests and only 2 stored cells in the 4.8-mm. nest.

Larval food. The pollen masses in 2 cells in a nest from Portal contained 96 per cent *Prosopis* (= mesquite in Leguminosae), 2.6 per cent *Anisacanthus* (Acanthaceae), 0.4 per cent Compositae divided equally between anemophilous and entomophilous species, and 1 per cent unknown.

Life history. The 2 nests from Portal were stored between April 1 and sometime in June. There were pupae in some cells and prepupae in others when I picked up and opened the nests on July 19. A male and a female in 1 nest emerged August 10 and 21, respectively. Only a male bee developed in cell 3 of the other nest; it was misoriented and lay with its head inward; it died as an adult during August at the inner end of the boring.

The Granite Reef Dam nests were not sent to me until late in the year. Occupants of the cells were diapausing larvae in cocoons when I examined the nests on January 8. They had been stored between July 19 and November 25, a definite indication that there are at least 2 generations a year. These larvae overwintered in that state and transformed to pupae and adults in the spring. The period between pupation and adult emergence was 17-21 days for 4 females.

The cocoons were delicate, white, and semitransparent to subopaque. In 3.2-mm. nests 3 female cocoons were 5-6 mm. long and 2 male cocoons 4-5 mm.

I reared 7 females and 2 males from 18 provisioned cells. It appeared likely that at least 4 females and 1 male would have developed in cells from which I failed to rear adults. In the only nest in which both sexes developed, there was a male in cell 4 and a female in cell 2.

Source material.
  Portal, Ariz. 1959 series: X 14, 17.
  Granite Reef Dam, Ariz. 1961 series: H 29, 160, 235.

Identifications. Pollen by P. S. Martin; bees by C. D. Michener and the author.

ASHMEADIELLA (ASHMEADIELLA) MELILOTI MELILOTI (Cockerell)

I received 27 nests of *meliloti* from 13 stations on the desert floor at Portal, Ariz., in 1959 and 1961. There were 15 nests in 3.2-mm. borings, 11 nests in 4.8-mm. borings, and a single nest in a 6.4-mm. boring. A dozen nests were from settings on wooden fences or posts, 6 from branches of desert willow, 3 each from a partially dead sycamore and from mesquite branches, 2 from the stem of a yucca, and 1 from the stem of an agave.

Supersedure and competition. There were several cases of supersedure in 4.8-mm. nests. *A. meliloti* superseded *Osmia gaudiosa* Cockerell in 2 nests, *A. occipitalis* Michener in 1 nest, and an unidentified resin-using megachilid in another nest. It was superseded in 2 nests by *Trypargilum tridentatum* (Packard). There apparently was no competition in 1 nest because the *meliloti* made an empty vestibular (?) cell before the wasp took over the boring. However, in the other nest there may have been competition because the *meliloti* stored a sixth cell and did not lay an egg; this cell was capped with mud by the wasp.

Nest architecture. In 6 borings used initially by *meliloti* the bees coated the extreme inner end of the boring with a thin layer of leaf pulp or (1 nest) made a partition of this substance 17 mm. from the inner end. In the other nests the *meliloti* bees began to store pollen and nectar right at the inner end of the boring.

There was just a single stored female cell at the inner end of the 6.4-mm. boring. The walls and ends of this cell were of leaf pulp, and the cell was 6 mm. long and about 3.5 mm. wide. The vestibular cell was 135 mm. long with a closing plug 1 mm. thick.

In 3.2-mm nests 25 female cells were 5-11 mm. (mean 7.7) and 33 male cells were 5-14 mm. (mean 7.5). Ten of the 15 completed nests had a vestibular cell 3-48 mm. long (mean 14); the others had just a thick plug capping the last stored cell instead of the usual thin partition. Two vestibular cells were divided into 2 sections by a transverse partition.

Thirty-three female cells in 4.8-mm. borings were 5-8 mm. long (mean 6.4) and 1 male cell was 6 mm. Only 8 nests were completed by *meliloti;* each had a vestibular cell 10-129 mm. long (mean 61).

The partitions capping the stored cells and the closing plugs were made from gummy leaf pulp which hardened into a stiff septum or plug. The partitions were usually about 0.2 mm. thick, but in 1 nest 1 of them was 2.5 mm. The closing plugs were 1-8 mm. thick (mean 3).

There were 2-8 stored cells (mean 6.2) in completed nests in 3.2-mm. borings. In six 4.8-mm. nests completely stored by *meliloti* there were 3-24 provisioned cells (mean 11.2).

Larval food. The pollen-nectar masses stored in several of the nests varied from somewhat moist to very sticky in consistency. Two masses in female cells in 3.2-mm. borings were 5-7 mm. long and a mass in a male cell was 4 mm. long. In a 4.8-mm. nest these masses in several female cells were 3-4 mm. long.

Pollen masses were analyzed from 2 of the 1959 nests. One nest sample contained 100 per cent *Prosopis* (= mesquite in Leguminosae). The other had a mixture of 74 per cent Scrophulariaceae (*cf. Stemodia*) and 26 per cent Chenopodiaceae; also seen on slide preparations were pollen grains of *Acacia*-4, *Prosopis*-10, *Krameria*-1, entomophilous Compositae-2, *Pinus*-1, and unknowns-5.

Life history. Four nests were completed May 5-8. Males emerged from them June 16-21 and females from June 21-July 1. These data suggest that the life cycle may be as short as 6-7 weeks for males and 8-9 weeks for females.

The period between pupation and adult emergence from nests of the summer generation was 24-28 days for 1 male and 29 days for another male.

The cocoons were delicate, white, and semitransparent and consisted of a single layer of silk. In 3.2-mm. borings 14 male cocoons were 5-9 mm. long (mean 6.4) and a single female cocoon was 6 mm. In 4.8-mm. borings 2 female cocoons were 5-5.5 mm. and a single male cocoon was 5 mm. long. A male larva in the outermost cell of one 3.2-mm. nest misoriented, so that it pupated with its head toward the blind inner end.

Almost all the nests were stored between the last week of April and the first week in June, and adults emerged from them June 14-August 4. Two nests were stored between September 6 and October 18. Their occupants overwintered as diapausing larvae and emerged the following spring. Obviously there must be at least 2 generations a year.

Emergence from single multicelled nests occurred during a period of 1-9 days. In 1 nest 8 males and 15 females emerged on a single day, but in another nest 3 males emerged over a 9-day period. In nests containing both sexes the males usually emerged 2-5 days before the females.

Males were always in the outer cells and females in the inner cells in nests containing both sexes. I reared 72 females and 45 males from 184 stored cells. Probably at least 11 females and 8 males would have developed in cells from which I failed to rear adult bees.

Parasites and predators. A larva of the predaceous clerid beetle

Trichodes horni Wolcott and Chapin destroyed the occupants of a 17-celled nest. Most of these were larvae or pupae, but 1 adult male bee had eclosed and was identified as *meliloti* from the remaining fragments. The grain itch mite *Pyemotes ventricosus* (Newport) infested several cells in 1 nest while in the laboratory.

Source material.
    Portal, Ariz. 1959 series: X 1, 7, 10, 52, 53. 1961 series: G 2, 4, 11, 12, 13, 32, 38, 44, 45, 95, 156, 159, 160, 163, 164, 172, 173, 175, 180, 231, 237, 252.

Identifications. Pollen by P. S. Martin; *Trichodes* by G. B. Vogt; bees by C. D. Michener and the author; wasps by the author.

ASHMEADIELLA (ASHMEADIELLA) OCCIPITALIS Michener

(Plate 17, Figure 78)

Of any member of the genus this species of *Ashmeadiella* was the most common user of traps at Portal, Ariz. I reared it from 81 traps from 20 stations on the desert floor at that locality in 1959 and 1961 and from 3 traps from 2 stations at Granite Reef Dam, Ariz., in 1961. Six nests were in 3.2-mm. borings, 45 in 4.8-mm., 31 in 6.4-mm., and a couple in 12.7-mm. borings. It was obvious that the 3.2-mm. and 12.7-mm. borings were used only when none of the intermediate series was available. Only abnormally small *occipitalis* females were able to utilize the 3.2-mm. borings. The stations at Portal included dead or live branches of mesquite (26 nests), desert willow (22) and sycamore (14), dead yucca stems (3), wooden fences or posts (14), and a wire fence (2). Two of the Granite Reef Dam nests were from a setting on a palo verde and 1 on a mesquite.

Supersedure and competition. At Portal *occipitalis* superseded a species of *Megachile (Sayapis)*, probably *policaris* Say, and *Trypargilum tridentatum* (Packard) in 1 nest each; it was superseded by an unidentified gum-using megachilid bee in 5 nests, and in 1 nest each by *Ashmeadiella biscopula* Michener, *A. m. meliloti* (Cockerell) and *Dianthidium p. platyurum* Cockerell; and a species of leaf-cutting *Megachile*, probably *gentilis* Cresson, plugged the entrance of a boring with leaf cuttings in which *occipitalis* had stored only 4 cells. At Granite Reef Dam *occipitalis* superseded *Trypargilum tridentatum* in 1 nest and was superseded by a species of *Chalicodoma (Chelostomoides)* in another; there was no competition with the *Trypargilum* because the wasp made an empty vestibular cell before the bee took over the remainder of the boring.

Nest architecture (fig. 78). In about half of the nests *occipitalis* placed pollen and nectar at the inner end of the boring, and in half of the nests it placed a thin layer of leaf pulp at the inner end or (3 nests) made a partition of that material 8-27 mm. from the inner end.

Only males were produced in the nests in 3.2-mm. borings. The 14 stored male cells were 7-20 mm. long (mean 10). The single abnormally long cell was the terminal one in a nest which lacked a vestibular plug; the partition capping this cell was 9 mm. thick. Thirteen stored cells from which I failed to rear adults were 7-21 mm. long (mean 10); males should have developed in all of them considering their length and position in the nests. All the nests in 3.2-mm. borings were completed, but only 4 of them had vestibular cells 11-45 mm. long (mean 25).

There were 449 stored cells in 4.8-mm. borings. Females were reared from 243 of them and males from 80; occupants of the other cells were parasitized or died as immatures. The female cells were 6-18 mm. long (mean 11); the 2 abnormally long cells, 14 and 18 mm. long, respectively, were terminal cells capped by partitions 4 and 7 mm. thick. Male cells were 5-21 mm. long (mean 8.4); the usual range for nonterminal male cells was 5-11 mm. (mean 7.6); but there were 10 terminal cells 11-21 mm. long capped by thick partitions 6-12 mm. thick. Thirty-six of the 45 nests in 4.8-mm. borings were completed, but only 18 of them had an empty vestibular cell 5-109 mm. long (mean 29). The terminal cells in nests which lacked a vestibular cell were capped by much thicker partitions than usual (fig. 78).

There were 421 stored cells in 6.4-mm. borings from which I reared 283 females and 68 males. Female cells were 5-17 mm. long (mean 8); 2 abnormally long cells, 14 and 17 mm. long, were terminal cells in nests lacking a vestibular cell; they were capped by partitions 5 and 9 mm. thick. Thirty-nine of the male cells were 3-16 mm. long (mean 7.2); the usual range for nonterminal male cells was 3-9 mm. (mean 5.9), but there were 8 terminal cells 9-16 mm. long capped by thick partitions 4-12 mm. thick. There were 29 male cells and an empty cell arranged in pairs, side by side, in the 6.4-mm. borings; these cells were 6-8 mm. long. Twenty-eight of the 31 nests in 6.4-mm. borings were completed, but only 13 of them had an empty vestibular cell 6-125 mm. long (mean 38). The terminal cells in nests which lacked a vestibular cell were capped by a much thicker partition than usual.

In the 2 nests in 12.7-mm. borings the cells were more or less irregularly arranged, side by side and crosswise. The cell walls and ends were made of a thin layer of leaf pulp. There were 9 cells in the inner 16 mm. in 1 boring and 40 cells in the other. The vestibular cells were 86 and 18 mm. long, respectively.

It is noteworthy that vestibular cells were present in only half of the completely stored borings. Six of these cells were divided into two sections by a thin transverse septum of gummy leaf pulp.

The cell partitions and closing plugs were made of gummy leaf pulp which hardened into a very stiff material. The partitions were usually 0.2-0.5 mm. thick. The closing plugs were 1.5-21 mm. thick (mean 6.7).

There were 2-6 stored cells (mean 4.5) in completed nests in 3.2-mm. borings. In 4.8-mm. borings there were 3-17 stored cells (mean 11.6) per completed nest. There were 3-24 stored cells (mean 15.2) per completed nest in 6.4-mm. borings. The 2 nests in 12.7-mm. borings had 9-40 stored cells (mean 24.5).

Larval food. The pollen-nectar masses in 3.2-mm. borings were quite dry and 4-7 mm. long (mean 5) in the male cells. In 4.8-mm. borings the consistency varied from rather dry to quite moist and sticky; the pollen-nectar masses in female cells were 5-7 mm. long and in male cells 3-4 mm. long. In 6.4-mm. borings the masses were quite sticky and 2-4 mm. long.

Life history. There is strong circumstantial evidence that only a single generation of *occipitalis* develops each year, but that adults emerge over an extended period during the midsummer and then must hibernate in that stage. All nests with definite completion dates were stored from late in April until early in June, with the peak of the nesting season occurring about mid-May. Only 1 nest could have been stored late in the season; there were still a few feeding larvae in some of the cells when I opened this nest for examination on November 1. Inasmuch as over 500 females emerged in midsummer from my nests, more than a single nest should have been stored the latter part of the season if there was a substantial second generation. This theory is substantiated in part by the fact that none of the 8 females I collected in the field in late July and early August at Rustlers Park, Portal, and Continental was gathering pollen. However, the prolonged emergence period (1 month) of females from nests in these borings would appear to be an adaptation to insure that some females will be on the wing during the period of maximum summer bloom on the desert. This situation implies the occurrence of a second generation.

The cocoons were made of delicate, subopaque white silk except that the outer ends were made of dense, tough opaque silk. Nineteen female cocoons in 4.8-mm. borings were 7-10 mm. long (mean 8.2); male cocoons were shorter. Only 6 pupae and prepupae were misoriented and lay with their heads toward the inner, blind end of the boring.

The period between egg hatch and adult emergence was 70 days for a male in the outermost cell of 1 nest completed early in May. The egg stage must last at least 10 days because this nest was picked up in the field on May 4, and the egg in the outermost cell was about to hatch when I examined the nest on the 13th. Ten weeks is probably about the minimum period between egg hatch and adult emergence. In some specimens, especially females, it must be nearly 14 weeks. A 14-celled nest was completed May 4, but the female in cell 1 did not emerge until August 13.

The larval feeding period apparently was about 17-30 days depending upon the sex of the larva and the prevailing temperatures during this period of the development. The period between completion of feeding and pupation averaged about 10 days for males and 16 days for females. These data were based on a period of 37 days between completion of feeding and emergence of an adult male and 45-49 days (mean 46) for 5 females. The period between pupation and emergence was 27 days for 3 males and 29-36 days (mean 30) for 26 females.

However, developmental data in some nests indicated that the prepupal period for occupants of outer cells was usually considerably shorter than for those in inner cells even though both were of the same sex. For example, in 1959 I examined the nests on July 19. In 5 of them the female pupae in the outer cells were further advanced in development than the female pupae or prepupae in the inner cells (fig. 78). However, in one 21-celled nest there were pale pupae in all cells, males in 16-21 and females in 1-15. In another nest there were pale female pupae with black eyes in cells 11-12, all pale female pupae in cells 1, 8 and 10, and female prepupae in cells 2-7 and 9; these prepupae transformed to pupae about 3 days later.

Emergence of adults occurred over a lengthy period. In 1959 20 males emerged from July 28 to August 20 with a peak emergence of 9 on August 13-14; 110 females emerged from August 2 to September 3 with a peak emergence of 79 during August 16-25. In 1961 males emerged July 19 to August 3 and females July 21 to August 17. Emergence from a single nest containing both sexes and more than 10 occupants extended over as long a period as 5 weeks (2♂, 10♀), or it might take place on a single day (15♀, 2♂).

Thirty-five nests produced only females, 9 produced only males, and 40 produced both sexes. Males were in the outer and females in the inner cells in all but 3 of the mixed nests. In 1 of the 3 nests with a random arrangement there were females in cells 1-5 and 12, a male in cell 13, a female and a male in cells 6 and 7 or vice versa, and 2 females and a male in cells 9-11 or vice versa; the larva in cell 8 was preserved. In a second nest there was a male in cell 11, a female in cell 8, and a male and 4 females in cells 1, 3, 5-7, the exact arrangement not known; occupants of the other cells died as larvae. In the third nest there were females in cells 1-3, 6,

7, and 11, males in cells 12 and 13, and a male and female in cells 9 and 10 or vice versa; the larvae died in cells 4, 5, and 8.

I reared 564 females and 173 males from a total of 946 stored cells. In the cells from which I failed to rear adults females would probably have developed in at least 88 cells and males in 20, indicating a probable sex ratio of about 3:1.

Parasites and predators. I reared the cuckoo wasp *Chrysura sonorensis* (Cameron) from 4 cells in 3 nests. The meloid beetle *Nemognatha nigripennis* LeConte fed on the larvae in 6 cells of a 13-celled nest. A clerid beetle larva, *Trichodes horni* Wolcott and Chapin, destroyed the prepupae in 11 cells of an 18-celled nest. The grain itch mite *Pyemotes ventricosus* (Newport) infested 1 nest in the laboratory.

Source material.
> Portal, Ariz. 1959 series: X 57, 58, 59, 61, 62, 63, 64, 70, 158, 159, 160, 161, 163. 1961 series: G 14, 29, 33, 34, 35, 42, 46, 47, 48, 49, 53, 61, 62, 63, 70, 72, 73, 74, 75, 77, 82, 83, 84, 85, 93, 94, 96, 98, 99, 103, 104, 110, 111, 112, 113, 120, 121, 139, 144, 154, 155, 158, 166, 167, 168, 169, 170, 171, 174, 175, 177, 178, 182, 183, 184, 186, 188, 193, 194, 200, 201, 207, 215, 233, 235, 244, 261, 266.
> Granite Reef Dam, Ariz. 1961 series: H 59, 171, 180.

Identifications. Pollen by P. S. Martin; *Nemognatha* by W. R. Enns; *Trichodes* by G. B. Vogt; *Chrysura* by R. M. Bohart and the author; other wasps and bees by the author.

ASHMEADIELLA (ASHMEADIELLA) OPUNTIAE (Cockerell)

I obtained a nest of this bee in a 4.8-mm. boring from Portal, Ariz., in 1961. The nest was from a setting on the dead stem of a yucca on the desert floor.

Nest architecture. The inner 30 mm. of the boring was empty; it was capped by a gum plug 1 mm. thick. There were 10 stored cells 7-8 mm. long and a vestibular cell of 35 mm. The partitions capping the cells were 1/4 mm. thick and the closing plug was 2 mm. thick. Both the partitions and closing plug were made of gum.

Larval food. The 4 pollen-nectar masses in cells 6-9 were 4-4.5 mm. long. The pollen was all from cactus. It was identified as being that of *Opuntia*, 95.2 per cent of subgenus *Cylindropuntia* and 4.8 per cent of subgenus *Platyopuntia*.

Life history. I picked up the nest on July 19. At that time there were prepupae in cocoons in cells 1-5, the eggs in cells 6-9 died, and there was a feeding larva in cell 10 which was infested subsequently by *Melittobia chalybii* Ashmead.

The larvae in cells 1-5 went into extended larval diapause after spinning their cocoons and overwintered in that stage. Pupation occurred early the next spring. Males developed in cells 2 and 3 and a female in cell 1; the prepupae in cells 4 and 5, one of which was parasitized by *Melittobia*, were preserved for taxonomic study. The period between pupation and adult emergence was 22-23 days.

Parasites and predators. This nest was infested in the laboratory by the eulophid *Melittobia chalybii* Ashmead.

Source material.
   Portal, Ariz. 1959 series: X 67.

Identifications. Pollen by P. S. Martin; bees by the author.

ASHMEADIELLA (AROGOCHILA) CLYPEODENTATA Michener

I received only 1 nest of this rare bee. It was in a 3.2-mm. boring from a setting on a partially dead mesquite on the desert floor at Portal, Ariz., in 1961.

Nest architecture. The nest was not picked up until the last week in December and I examined it on January 13. There were only 2 completed cells at the inner end of the boring and then a partially stored cell. The mother bee stored pollen and nectar right at the inner end of the boring. The cell partitions were the usual thin, transverse tough septa made from masticated leaf pulp.

Life history. The date of storing of the nest could not be calculated; it could have been anytime during the previous spring, summer, or early fall. The female occupants of cells 1 and 2 were pale pupae on January 13, so undoubtedly they would have overwintered as diapausing larvae if the nest had not been brought indoors late in December. An eclosed adult died in cell 2 on February 3.

Source material.
   Portal, Ariz. 1961 series: G 161.

Identification by C. D. Michener.

Genus OSMIA Panzer

During this study I had an opportunity to examine nests of 8 species of *Osmia* belonging to 6 subgenera. All but one of these species used masticated leaf pulp to form the partitions capping the cells and for the plug for the entire nest. The exception to this general rule was *lignaria* Say, which used mud for these partitions and plugs (figs. 82-85, 87, 88). This character is not of subgeneric importance, because *ribifloris* Cockerell, which also belongs to the typical subgenus, uses leaf pulp in its nests.

The only other distinctive nest was that made by *bucephala* Cresson (figs. 89-91). Most of the partitions capping the *bucephala* cells were compound, consisting of a thin layer of leaf pulp on either side of a thicker section of compacted bits of wood fiber. These wood chips were rasped from the boring walls adjacent to the completely stored cell. Consequently, most of the cells in a linear series were barrel-shaped in longitudinal section. Another distinctive feature of the *bucephala* nest was the lining of the inner two-thirds of each cell with a thin layer of leaf pulp. This was the section of the cell which contained the pollen-nectar mixture. Inasmuch as *bucephala* was the only species of the subgenus *Centrosmia* studied, it is impossible to state whether these distinctions in nest construction are of subgeneric or specific value.

No notes were made on the cocoons of *coerulescens* (Linnaeus) and *georgica* Cresson. Some variation was noted among the cocoons of the other 6 species. The outermost layer was of soft white silk, either forming a solid lining for the cell walls, as in *pumila* Cresson, *subfasciata* Cresson, and *gaudiosa* Cockerell, or a layer which could be separated only with difficulty from the inner varnished layer as in *bucephala,* or forming merely a loose network of threads attaching the ovoid, varnished inner cocoon to the cell walls as in *lignaria* and *ribifloris.* The inner cocoon of all species was ovoid, varnished, light to dark brown, and brittle or leathery in texture. The walls of these ovoid inner cocoons consisted of a single layer except in those of *lignaria* and *ribifloris,* which construct the inner cocoon in several layers. There was a median nipple on the anterior end in all species except *bucephala.* The nipple consisted of dense, tough white silk, except in *lignaria;* in this species the silk was reddish.

OSMIA (OSMIA) LIGNARIA LIGNARIA Say
(Plate 16, Figures 70-77; Plate 17, Figures 82-85, 87; Plate 18, Figure 88; Plate 23, Figures 111-114; Plate 27, Figures 128-130)

This is the most common vernal wood-nesting bee at Plummers Island. Altogether, I obtained 141 nests from that locality (20 in 1958, 60 in 1959, 7 in 1960, 32 in 1961, 21 in 1962, 1 in 1964) and none from any other locality. One hundred nests were obtained from settings on structural timber containing abandoned borings of other insects and 41 from stations on standing dead tree trunks. Forty-five nests were in 4.8-mm., 84 in 6.4-mm, and 12 in 12.7-mm. borings. The 12.7-mm. borings were available to *lignaria* during 3 seasons only. The preference for 6.4-mm. over 4.8-mm. borings by a ratio of nearly 2:1 expresses a real predilection for the larger of these 2 borings. *O. lignaria* nests at the same time as *O. pumila* Cresson, and probably competes with that species for 4.8-mm. borings.

Supersedure and competition. This bee was superseded in 1 nest each by the pompilid, *Dipogon s. sayi* Banks, by an unknown vespid wasp, and by 3 sphecids, *Trypargilum clavatum* (Say), *T. collinum rubrocinctum* (Packard), and *T. striatum* (Say). It is possible that none of this supersedure was a result of competition. *O. lignaria* superseded the carpenter bee, *Xylocopa v. virginica* (Linnaeus) in 1 nest. This supersedure probably was not a result of competition either, even though the *Osmia* finished a partially completed cell partition of the third cell in the *Xylocopa* nest, and constructed 1 cell of her own. I may have discouraged the *Xylocopa* by probing the boring with a grass stem.

Nest architecture (figs. 82-85, 87, 88). In 78 of the nests provisioned initially by *lignaria*, the bees began to store pollen and nectar at the inner end of the boring; in the other 62 nests the mother bee placed some mud at the inner end, or constructed a mud partition 2 to 105 mm. from the inner end, before storing any pollen and nectar. Table 29 summarizes measurements of stored

TABLE 29.—*Measurements (in mm.) of cells, partitions, and plugs in nests of Osmia lignaria Say*

Boring diameter	Sex	Length stored cells			Length vestibular cells			Cell partitions		Closing plug	
		No.	Range	Mean	No.	Range	Mean	Range	Mean	Range	Mean
4.8	♀	3	16-20	17.7	40	6-94	22.6	0.5-5.0	1.9	2-8	4.0
	♂	240	10-30	14.6							
6.4	♀	235	10-22	14.3	60	5-114	25.5	0.5-3.0	1.7	2-8	4.2
	♂	255	8-17	10.8							

and vestibular cells and of the thickness of cell partitions and closing plugs in 4.8- and 6.4-mm borings. Similar measurements are not presented for nests in 12.7-mm. borings because most of the cells did not extend across the entire boring (fig. 84). A vestibular cell was present in all but 3 of the nests completely stored by *lignaria*. There were no empty intercalary cells. The partitions between cells and the closing plugs were made of mud.

An analysis of 75 completely stored nests in which there was no empty space at the inner end of the boring showed that 27 in 4.8-mm. borings contained a median of 9 male cells (range 4-12). In 48 nests in 6.4-mm. borings the median lay between 10 and 11 stored cells (range 2-14) (figs. 82, 83), and usually each nest contained bees of both sexes. Two completed nests in 12.7-mm. borings had 22 and 23 stored cells, respectively, and yielded both sexes (figs. 84, 85).

Life history. There is a single generation a year. Adult bees may be active in the Washington area from April 7 until June 8. How-

ever, most nests are built during a 3-week period beginning about
the last week in April. In years in which there is an early spring,
the first nests may be completed by April 17. During a late or cool
spring eggs may be laid as late as the first week of June. The occupants overwinter in their cocoons as adult bees and leave the nest
for the first time the following spring.

In 1959 I made a few field observations at Plummers Island on
provisioning flights and nest construction in 4.8- and 6.4-mm. borings. That year I set out traps on April 5; no bees were active on
this or the following day. On April 9 *lignaria* bees were storing
pollen and nectar in at least 4 of the traps on the cabin porch.
On April 17, a sunny day with an air temperature of 77° at
1100 hours, I watched the nesting activities of a few of the bees.
When the bee returned from a provisioning flight, she flew directly
to the boring entrance, entered head first, and remained inside for
a few seconds to regurgitate the nectar from her crop onto the
pollen mass. Then she backed out of the boring, turned around on
the end of the trap, backed into the boring, and then scraped off
the load of pollen from her abdominal scopa. Then she crawled
out head first and took flight at once to gather more pollen and
nectar. Usually the bees took 30-60 seconds to discharge a load
of nectar, and about 30 seconds to remove a load of pollen. The
provisioning flights usually lasted 7 to 9 minutes, but occasionally
a bee returned to the nest in about a minute or two, presumably
without a full load. About 1530 hours the sky became overcast and
the temperature dropped to about 70°. Under these conditions the
bees spent 8 to 15 minutes gathering a load of pollen and nectar,
and 2 to 3 minutes in the nest discharging the load. Twice during
the morning I saw 2 bees trying to provision 1 trap, so the
competition for nesting sites may have been quite keen.

A 12.7-mm. boring is large enough for the bee to turn around
inside it to scrape off the pollen mass after regurgitating nectar.
Consequently, after returning from flower visits the bee does not
come out of the 12.7-mm. boring until she is ready to make another
provisioning flight.

I watched 1 bee fly in with large pellets of damp mud in her
mandibles to construct a clay partition capping a cell near the boring entrance. She made 5 flights during a period of 11½ minutes.
She required 1½ to 3 minutes to gather a load of mud and spent
25 to 40 seconds in the nest working each pellet of material into
the partition. She fashioned the partition with her head, rotating
around in the boring while she did so.

I made the accompanying photographs (figs. 70-77) of nest
provisioning and partition construction on April 28 and May 5,
1962.

I did not obtain any field information on the flower visiting habits of this bee. It has been recorded as visiting flowers of a number of genera of diverse families. Specimens from Plummers Island collected by earlier workers are labeled as having been collected on *Erythronium albidum* Nuttall, *E. americanum* Ker., *Dentaria laciniata* Muhlenberg, *Cercis canadensis* Linnaeus, and *Glechoma hederacea* Linnaeus.

During the night the female rests head inward in the boring near the entrance with the abdomen curled downward so that its dorsum blocks the boring.

I did not observe the nesting activities for a long enough period to determine how many loads of pollen and nectar are required to store a single cell. However, I did measure the average length of a number of the pollen masses; these data are presented in table 30

TABLE 30.—*Size of pollen masses in cells of* Osmia lignaria *Say*

Boring diameter	Sex	Number of masses	Range in length (in mm.)	Mean length (in mm.)	Mean volume (mm³)
4.8 mm.	♀	3	8-12	10.0	178
	♂	157	4-11	7.1	126
6.4 mm.	♀	154	5-13	8.2	260
	♂	169	4-10	5.5	174

(see also figs. 82, 84, 87, 88, 128, 129). These data showed considerable variation in the quantity of food stored per cell. Although there was overlap in the volume range of provisions stored for males and females, it was evident that larvae destined to produce females were usually provided with a substantially larger store of food. The data also demonstrated that bees in the 4.8-mm. borings are provided with less food than their brothers or sisters in the 6.4-mm. borings. We would expect larger bees to be produced in the larger borings, and this actually happens. However, almost all the cells destined to produce females were constructed in the larger borings, so it is evidently not simply a matter of larger bees preferring to nest in larger borings. Presumably, when a mother bee is ready to lay fertilized eggs which will develop into females, she selects a larger diameter boring and constructs a series of longer female cells at the inner end, followed by a series of shorter cells in which unfertilized eggs will be laid.

Observations were not made in the field on the length of time required to complete a nest. However, data obtained from observation of egg hatch in a series of 14 nests in 1959 probably give a reasonably accurate estimate as to the duration of construction of single nests. Seven of the nests were in 4.8-mm. borings and contained an average of 8.3 stored cells and 1 vestibular cell; the other 7 nests were in 6.4-mm. borings and had an average of 10.9 stored cells and 1 vestibular cell. Eggs in the 4.8-mm. nests hatched over a period of 2 to 5 days per nest, while those in the 6.4-mm. nests hatched over a period of 4 to 6 days. In the 4.8-mm. nests about 2.5 cells were provisioned per day, and in the 6.4-mm. nests about 2.4.

The consistency of the pollen-nectar masses was variable even within a single cell. Sometimes the mixture was quite dry and not all of the pollen was saturated with nectar; sometimes there was a larger proportion of nectar so that the mass, or parts of it, was quite moist. However, there was never such an admixture of nectar that the mass was semifluid. Occasionally, an excess of nectar might be regurgitated at the inner end of a cell so that the mud partition closing the adjoining cell would be well saturated with it.

The pollen-nectar masses were usually quite uniform in shape (fig. 128). They were rounded at the inner end of the cell where they were in contact with the concave surface of the partition closing the preceding cell. The main part of the mass was cylindrical since it completely filled the boring. The outer end was oblique, sloping downward and outward, and probably was shaped by pressing the abdomen against the mass.

The egg is white and slightly curved and ranges from 2.9 to 3.6 mm. long by 1.1 to 1.3 mm. wide. The posterior end is deposited in the soft pollen-nectar mass at an angle of about 45°, so that most of the egg is free from the oblique end of the mass (fig. 128).

Body segmentation and tracheation were visible a day before hatching (fig. 87, cell 11). The newly hatched larva kept its posterior end anchored in the pollen-nectar mass during the first week of feeding. In 5 to 7 days after hatching the larva began to excrete fecal pellets. Usually it spun these together against the cell walls about 5 to 8 days after the first pellets were voided. The larva continued feeding for 17 to 27 days before spinning a cocoon. The developmental time varied according to the prevailing temperatures. Usually the entire pollen mass was consumed, but occasionally a larva left a small bit of the mass at the inner end of the cell. Pupation took place 10 to 11 weeks after egg hatch, in 3 specimens during July 15-21 from eggs hatching May 7-8. These adults eclosed August 12-18, but remained inside the cocoons without breaching the wall until the following spring.

The cocoon is ovoid in shape and only slightly less than the diameter of the boring in width (figs. 83, 85, 114). It is composed of several layers of silk. The outermost layer is a loose network of fine white fibers attaching the inner cocoon to the cell wall. At the anterior end there is a small cap of dense white fibers which covers the nipple of the inner cocoon. Inside the loose network of silk is the outer layer of the inner cocoon, which is varnished, light brown, very thin and pliable. It can be readily peeled off from the next layer, which also is varnished, but is somewhat darker, thicker and tougher. Finally, inside this middle layer is a very thin, delicate, and almost colorless layer which can be separated only with difficulty. The nipple at the anterior end consists of a conical protuberance about 1.5 mm. wide and 0.5 mm. thick in the center. It is composed of about half a dozen layers of coarse, dense, unvarnished reddish silk.

There was considerable variation in length of inner cocoons, and also in overlap of the 2 sexes. However, male cocoons were definitely smaller than those of females on the average. In the 4.8-mm. borings, 2 female cocoons were 10 and 11 mm. long; 118 male cocoons had a mean length of 8.9 mm. (range 8-11 mm.). In the 6.4-mm. borings 125 female cocoons had a mean length of 10.6 mm. (range 8-12 mm.) and 140 male cocoons had a mean length of 8.6 mm. (range 7-11 mm.).

In the laboratory emergence from nests containing both sexes took an average of 3.3 days per nest (range 1 to 8 days). Emergence from individual nests containing only males or only females averaged 2.7 days per nest (range 1 to 5 days). The peak of male emergence was 1-3 days earlier than the peak of female emergence, but there was some overlap. In 1959, when the largest number of nests was obtained, 208 males emerged March 24 to 30, 1960, with a median emergence date of the 27th; 101 females emerged March 26 to April 4 with a median emergence date of the 28th.

A total of 239 males and 3 females were reared from 308 stored cells in 4.8-mm. borings. In 6.4-mm. borings the sexes were reared in almost equal numbers, 235 females and 255 males from 688 stored cells. Fifty-four females and 34 males were reared from 124 stored cells in 12.7-mm. nests. Bees did not develop in many cells because of parasitism or mortality due to mold or other factors. It appears that the sex ratio is probably about 1♀:2♂♂.

It is apparent from the data presented in the paragraph above that female eggs are deposited almost entirely in larger diameter borings. The situation is somewhat analagous to that discovered by Brunson (1938) for *Tiphia vernalis* Rohwer in which female eggs were deposited mostly on third-instar Japanese beetle larvae and mostly male eggs on the smaller second-instar larvae. The physiological basis for this phenomenon in *Osmia lignaria* is not known. One may speculate that the smaller (4.8-mm.) diameter boring may so restrict the positioning of the mother's abdomen that sperm cannot be released from the spermatheca. In the larger borings (6.4-12.7-mm. diameter) the abdomen of the mother bee is capable of greater freedom of movement while the bee is in the boring, so that egress of sperm from the spermatheca can take place. In this connection it is of interest to note that Flanders (1962) described 2 different oviposition postures for *Coccophagus ochraceus* Howard, which forecast the sex of the egg to be laid.

An accurate determination was made of the arrangement of sexes in 51 mixed nests in 6.4-mm. borings during 1958, 1959, 1961 and 1962, either by placing the cocoons in individual vials for rearing, or by opening the cocoons and recording the sex of the occupants. There were 3 mixed nests in 1958, 25 in 1959, 9 in 1961, and 14 in 1962. In 39 of these the females were always in the innermost cells and males in the outermost. The number of each sex was variable, but the arrangement of sexes in these 39 nests was constant. Sometimes there would be only 1 female followed by as many as 10 males in 1 nest, and occasionally there might be 8 females and then 2 males. In the remaining 12 nests the arrangement of sexes was a random one as shown in table 31, where X represents a cell in which no bee developed.

The random arrangement of sexes in these few nests could be due to several factors. One might be the failure of the sperm to fertilize an egg, resulting in the development of a male rather than a female bee. This hypothesis can be tested, but not confirmed, by analyzing the length of the cells and pollen masses to determine whether a male might have developed in a longer cell or from a larger pollen mass than is normal for that sex. This could have explained why males developed in the "wrong" cells in the first 4 nests, Y 37, Y 42, Y 45 and Y 94. Given only the data on length of cells and pollen masses, one would predict that females should have developed in cells 1-7 of Y 37 and Y 42, in cells 1-5 of Y 45, and in cells 1-3 of Y 94.

Another factor might be competition or supersedure, whereby all the eggs in a nest would not be laid by the same female. On an earlier page I mentioned observing 2 bees trying to provision the same boring, so that this possibility is a very definite one. It could explain the random sequence of sexes recorded for some of the other 8 nests. The same number of traps was available at any one time in each year. However, more than twice as many nests of *lignaria* were obtained in 1959 as in any other year, so the competition for nesting sites must have been much fiercer in that year. Significantly perhaps, 1959 was the year in which I obtained the largest number of nests with random arrangement of sexes and the highest ratio of random sex arrangement.

A third factor might be temporary "fatigue" of the muscles

controlling egress of sperm from the spermatheca, whereby release of sperm is inhibited and deposition of unfertilized eggs results. This phenomenon has been demonstrated in some of the parasitic

TABLE 31.—*Sequence of sexes and lengths (in mm.) of stored cells and pollen-nectar masses in selected nests of* Osmia lignaria *Say in 6.4-mm. nests*

Year	Nest		1	2	3	4	5	6	7	8	9	10	11	12	13
1959	Y37	sex	♀	♀	♂	♀	♀	♀	♀	♂	♂	♂			
		cell	13	15	13	14	14	13	13	10	10	10			
1959	Y42	sex	♂	♀	♀	♂	♀	♀	♀	♂	♂	♂	♂	♂	
		cell	14	12	13	14	13	15	14	10	11	11	10	14	
		pollen	10	8	7	8	9	10	8	6	5	6	5	5	
1959	Y45	sex	♀	♂	X	♀	♀	X	♂	♂	♂	♂	♂		
		cell	19	15	15	15	13	11	11	10	9	11	10		
		pollen	10	9	8	9	7	5	5	5	4	4	4		
1959	Y94	sex	♀	♂	♀	♂	♂	X	♂	♂	♂	♂	♂	♂	♂
		cell	12	14	11	12	11	11	10	10	9	9	10	10	11
		pollen	9	.8	6	4	5	6	5	5	5	5	5	4	5
1958	S16	sex	♂	X	♀	♂	X	♂	♂	X	X	X	♂		
		cell	12	11	14	11	10	11	10	14	11	12	13.		
		pollen	6	6	10	7	6	6	7	8	7	8	7		
1958	S29	sex	♀	X	X	♂	X	♀	♂	♂					
		cell	13	12	10	12	14	12	10	12					
1959	Y51	sex	♀	♀	♀	♀	♂	♂	♀	♂	♂	♂			
		cell	15	16	15	13	11	11	11	10	11	8			
		pollen	8	9	8	8	6	6	5	4	4	4			
1959	Y91	sex	♀	♂	♀	X	X	X	X	X	♂	X			
		cell	12	12	11	17	13	14	12	11	10	10			
1959	Y105	sex	X	♀	♂	♀	♂	♂							
		cell	12	11	10	12	12	19							
1959	Y92	sex	X	X	♂	♂	♂	♂	X	♀	♀	♂	X		
		cell	20	13	14	12	11	12	12	12	11	9	9		
		pollen	8	5	.6	5	5	4	8	7	5	5	4		
1959	Y93	sex	♀	♂	♂	♂	♂	♂	♀	♀	♀	♀	X		
		cell	14	11	11	13	10	11	16	14	14	14	9		
		pollen	7	6	5	5	4	5	9	8	9	8	5		
1962	M73	sex	♂	♂	♂	X	X	♀	X	♀	X	♂	♂	♂	
		cell	15	12	11	13	15	15	15	12	10	10	9	10	
		pollen	5	5	5	9	11	12	?	10	5	6	7	5	

Hymenoptera (Flanders, 1962). It may cause such sequences as occurred in the last 3 nests listed in Table 31, Y 92, Y 93 and M 73. In these nests males developed at the inner end of the nest or in the middle.

Parasites and predators. Chrysura kyrae Krombein was reared from 22 nests (figs. 87, 88, 128-130). Chrysidid larvae, undoubtedly of this same species, were found but not reared in an additional 12 nests. These chrysidids were found in 78 of 313 cells in the 34 parasitized nests. This is *lignaria's* most important parasite at Plummers Island, for it parasitized 25 percent of the available nests, and 25 percent of the available cells in the nests which it infested.

A pair of the torymid *Monodontomerus obscurus* Westwood was reared from 1 cell of a *lignaria* nest.

This bee is such an early nester that it is rarely attacked by *Melittobia chalybii* Ashmead. I found a primary infestation by this chalcid in only 1 cell each in 3 nests. I destroyed these 3 females before the infestation spread to adjoining cells.

The chaetodactylid mite *Chaetodactylus krombeini* Baker infested 12 nests (figs. 111-114). Usually only 1 or 2 cells were infested initially, but frequently the infestation spread to 1 or 2 of the adjacent cells before the bee larvae were protected in their cocoons.

Dermestid larvae invaded 1 cell each in 3 nests, but caused no mortality.

Previous observations. Say (1837, p. 399), in his original description of *lignaria,* noted that it "nidificates in old wood." Rau (1926, p. 203) found it nesting in Missouri in abandoned borings of mining bees in a clay bank, in abandoned mud nests of the mud-dauber *Sceliphron caementarium* (Drury) and later (1937a) in the cells of old *Polistes* nests. Chandler (1958) in Indiana also found *lignaria* utilizing old mud-dauber nests and later (1962) obtained nesting in wooden trap nests. Bohart (1955) and Levin (1957) also utilized wooden trap-nests to obtain *lignaria* nests, and recently (Krombein, 1962a) I summarized very briefly some of my earlier trap-nest studies at Plummers Island. Balduf (1961) found *lignaria* nesting in old carpenter bee borings in structural lumber.

Packard (1874, p. 140) quoted Harris's manuscript notes to the effect that *lignaria* constructed earthen cells under stones. I think this probably was a misidentification and that Harris actually observed a species of *Osmia* (*Nothosmia*), possibly *inspergens* Lovell and Cockerell, which I found some years ago at Ithaca, N. Y., building cells under stones similar to the way Harris described it.

Several authors have commented on competition and supersedure. Bohart (1955) noted that supersedure of *lignaria* by *Osmia* (*Cephalosmia*) *californica* Cresson could be either abrupt or gradual. He did not determine whether the abrupt supersedure was a result of aggressive behavior by *californica* or the disappearance of the *lignaria* from other causes. In the gradual supersedure both species continued to work in the same nest simultaneously for several days before complete supersedure occurred by *californica*. Chandler (1962) observed that *lignaria,* because of its earlier emergence, preempted the larger diameter burrows, so that *Osmia (Nothosmia) cordata* Robertson was forced to nest in smaller and more dispersed burrows.

Rau (1937a) presented a table of measurements of cells in 48 *lignaria* nests in artificial borings in clay blocks. Unfortunately his data are not precise enough for detailed analysis. The nests were in 4.8- and 9.6-mm. borings with no indication as to which size boring an individual nest came from; the borings ranged from 40 to 190 mm. in length. Further, almost all of the bees had emerged prior to measurement of the cells. However, most of his nests showed the same pattern I found in most of my 6.4-mm. nests, that is, a series of larger cells at the inner end and a series of smaller cells at the outer end. In almost half of the nests there was an empty cell 13 to 83 mm. long at the inner end of the boring. Rau did not mention the occurrence of vestibular cells in these nests, but presumably they were present because the sum of the lengths of cells and the empty inner space in an individual nest do not equal the total length of the burrow. In 5 nests in which he found a few bees, the females occurred in the larger innermost cells, and males in the smaller outermost cells, except in 1 nest which contained only male bees.

Rau (1937a) recorded adult *lignaria* as being active in Missouri for 5 to 6 weeks. In Missouri it emerged about 2 weeks earlier than populations around Washington; Rau noted first emergence from March 21 to April 5 over a period of 9 years. He did not find adults active later than May 17. He noted that 3 flights to obtain pollen and nectar required 7 to 12 minutes. Balduf timed several provisioning flights at 4½ to 5½ minutes, and stated that the bee spent 1 to 1½ minutes in the nest depositing her load. Rau found that 2 eggs had an incubation period of 10 days, which is considerably longer than I observed for 6 eggs; perhaps Rau held his nests at outdoor temperatures whereas mine were held indoors at 65°-70°. He recorded a feeding period of 30 days for 1 larva. Balduf found that 12 cocoons were 10-13 mm. long and 5-7 mm. wide at the middle, but did not correlate these with sex. Rau obtained a sex ratio of 7♀:11♂ in laboratory rearing of 18 bees, and calculated a 1:1 sex ratio based on analysis of the length of cells in his clay blocks. Chandler recorded about a 1:1 sex ratio.

Rau (1937a) recorded only 1 parasite of *lignaria*. He found a number of mites on 2 males which were identified as nymphs of a species of *Trichotarsus.* Undoubtedly this was the same species which was described recently as *Chaetodactylus krombeini* Baker.

Source material.

   Plummers Island, Md. 1958 series: S 2, 4, 5, 6, 14, 15, 16, 17, 18, 20, 21, 22, 23, 24, 29, 34, 54, 74, 75, 89. 1959 series: Y 17, 18, 19, 20, 21, 22, 25, 26, 27, 28, 32, 37, 38, 41, 42, 43, 44, 45, 46, 49, 51, 52, 53, 56, 59, 60, 63, 64, 65, 69, 70, 73, 74, 75, 76, 77, 78, 79, 84, 85, 86, 87, 88, 89, 90, 91, 92, 93, 94, 95, 97, 99, 100, 101, 102, 103, 104, 105, 107, 109. 1960 series: E 3, 38, 39, 40, 41, 54, 62. 1961 series: K 1, 2, 3, 4, 17, 18, 26, 27, 28, 37, 38, 39, 40, 41, 42, 48, 51, 52, 53, 54, 57, 58, 62, 63, 65, 66, 69, 70, 72, 93, 94, 128. 1962 series: M 5, 6, 9, 20, 25, 26, 27, 28, 30, 31, 32, 33, 34, 44, 45, 50, 56, 68, 69, 73, 78. 1964 series: Z 23.

   Identifications. Acarina by E. W. Baker; Hymenoptera by the author.

OSMIA (OSMIA) RIBIFLORIS Cockerell

   I received 2 nests of this species in 4.8-mm. borings from Portal, Ariz. Both had been set out at the same station, the side of a mesquite trunk about ⅔ meter above the ground on the desert floor.

   Nest architecture. A 1-celled nest was stored between April 26 and May 3, and a 7-celled nest (probably started by the same mother bee when she completed the previous one) was provisioned between May 4 and 8. The cells in these two nests were respectively 20, and 24, 25, 13, 16, 13, 13, and 15 mm. long. In the earlier nest the inner 25 mm. was empty, then there was a leaf pulp partition 2 mm. thick, then the single stored cell capped by a 0.5-mm. partition, and finally a 95-mm. vestibular cell capped by a 2-mm. plug. In the other nest there was 2 mm. of leaf pulp at the inner end, then the 7 provisioned cells separated by leaf pulp partitions 1-2 mm. thick, and finally a vestibular cell of 24 mm. with a 4-mm. leaf pulp cap. All the partitions and plugs were made from gummy leaf pulp, so that the nests provided quite a contrast when compared with those of the only other species of the subgenus *Osmia* which I studied.

   Life history. Cells 1-4 of the larger nest were destroyed by a lepidopterous larva. There were small bee larvae in the other cells of both nests when I examined them May 13 and 16. Three larvae reached maturity and spun cocoons 9-10 mm. long between June 10 and 30. The cocoons were dark brown, tough, varnished, and had a small nipple of dense, tough, white silk at the anterior end; they differed from those of *lignaria* only in the type of silk in the nipple. The occupants of 2 of the 3 cocoons died as prepupae. A male *ribifloris* emerged from the third cocoon early the next spring after overwintering outside in the Washington, D. C., area. This male must have transformed to an adult the previous summer, although it was a prepupa as late as July 29.

Source material.

   Arizona. 1961 series: G 26, 27.

   Identifications by author.

OSMIA (CENTROSMIA) BUCEPHALA BUCEPHALA Cresson

(Plate 18, Figures 89-91)

I obtained 9 nests of this vernal bee at Plummers Island, all of them in 6.4-mm. borings; only 6 of the borings were completely stored by *bucephala*. Judged from certain architectural peculiarities as noted below 2 additional nests in 6.4-mm. borings were undoubtedly made by this bee. Six of the nests were from 4 different stations on dead tree trunks, 4 were from a rafter on the cabin porch roof, and 1 was from a woodpile.

Supersedure and competition. The sphecid wasp *Trypargilum clavatum* (Say) nested in the outer end of 1 boring. This was probably not a case of competition, but merely the use by the wasp of the part of the boring that had been abandonded earlier by the bee.

Nest architecture (figs. 89, 90). *Osmia bucephala* is the only megachilid bee that I have found in these traps which uses wood fibers rasped from the boring walls to construct the partitions between its cells. The cells are actually barrel-shaped in longitudinal section because the fibers used to plug a completed cell are obtained from the walls of the area which will form the next cell (fig. 89). The partitions are usually composed of a thin layer of masticated leaf pulp on both sides of a thick section of bits of compacted wood fiber (fig. 90), thus resulting in a compound partition that is different from that recorded for any other trap-nesting bee or wasp. However, in several nests the partitions between the cells were much thinner, and consisted of wood fibers interspersed among the masticated leaf pulp.

In most nests the mother bee lined the inner end of the boring with a thin layer of masticated leaf pulp. However, in 2 nests the female placed a plug of rasped wood fibers 6-7 mm. thick at the inner end of the boring, and then spread a thin layer of leaf pulp over these fibers and the adjacent cell wall. About the inner two-thirds of each cell, the part destined to hold the pollen-nectar mixture, was lined with a thin layer of masticated leaf pulp. This prevented absorption of nectar by the wooden cell walls.

Eight female cells had a mean length of 17.5 mm. (range 14-24 mm.); 17 male cells had a mean length of 14.8 mm. (range 12-18 mm.). The cell partitions composed of just a few wood fibers mixed with leaf pulp were 1-1.5 mm. thick; the compound partitions composed of a large section of compacted wood fibers between thin layers of leaf pulp were 2-7 mm. thick (mean 4.1 mm.).

Only 6 of 11 nests were completely stored. A vestibular cell 45 to 115 mm. long was present in each of 4 nests; and in 2 nests there was no vestibular cell, the stored cells extending to the entrance with the final one being capped by a thicker plug than usual. In 1 nest the vestibular cell was divided by 2 cross partitions. Perhaps this unusual construction was caused by my having destroyed the stored cells by probing the nest with a grass stem during the nesting process. The plugs capping these 6 nests were 2 to 21 mm. thick (mean 10.8 mm.). The terminal plug in 5 of the nests was composed of leaf pulp, but in the sixth nest it was 13 mm. thick and composed of 4 layers of leaf pulp 1-2 mm. thick separated by 3 layers of corky material and/or wood fibers of the same thickness.

There was 60 per cent mortality in the 32 provisioned cells in the 6 completed nests. Consequently, there are insufficient data to predict the usual number of male and/or female cells per completed nest. There were 8 and 9 stored cells respectively in the 2 nests lacking empty vestibular cells, 1, 3, 5, and 6 cells in the 4 nests containing a vestibular cell.

Life history. O. *bucephala* has a single generation a year. It is active in the Washington area somewhat later than O. *lignaria.* The earliest capture at Plummers Island was April 25. In 1963 females began to occupy the traps for nesting between May 6 and 12, and the latest nest was completed between June 10 and 15. This probably is the latest date for actual nesting, because during the period June 16-28, 1963, one or two of these bees on the cabin porch merely capped two 6.4-mm. borings with leaf pulp and did not store any pollen at the inner end. Developmental data from 2 nests suggest that the mother bee usually completes no more than a single cell a day. However, the average daily production is certainly substantially less than this.

The pollen-nectar masses were 5 to 7 mm. long with the anterior end squarely to somewhat obliquely truncate. Presumably a larger amount is stored in a cell in which a female bee is destined to develop. The only pollen-nectar mass measured for a female was 7 mm. long. Five masses on which males developed were 5 to 7 mm. long (mean 6.0). The egg is placed obliquely with the lower half of its posterior fourth pressed into a slight depression in the truncated outer surface of the mass (fig. 91). In a more liquid mass the egg may come to lie half submerged lengthwise on the truncate surface. The egg is sausage-shaped, and about 4.2×1.2 mm.

Egg hatch occurred 5 days after oviposition in 2 cells. Two larvae, which developed into male bees, required 27 days to completely consume the pollen-nectar mass stored for them. Presumably female larvae would require a few days longer to reach maturity, if they received a larger store of food. The period between the attainment of larval maturity and pupation was 17-19 days for 2 male larvae, and 22 days for a female larva; probably the first 2 or 3 days of this period were occupied in spinning the cocoon. The pupal period lasted 22-26 days for male bees, and 24-30 for females. Consequently, the elapsed time between oviposition and eclosion of the adult bee would be about 10 weeks for the male and 11 for the female. The adults remained in the cocoons over the winter.

Female cocoons were somewhat larger than those of the males. Eight female cocoons were 12-14 mm. long (mean 13 mm.), whereas 17 male cocoons were 8-13 mm. (mean 11 mm.). The cocoon is cylindrical with rounded ends and only slightly less than the diameter of the boring in width. The outermost layer is composed of thin, delicate, soft, subopaque white silk. It can be separated only with difficulty from the rather brittle, varnished, thin, light tan inner layer. The thick cap at the anterior end is composed of the outer, soft white layer; then a thick, varnished brittle layer; then a tough, dense, thick white layer of soft, unvarnished silk; and finally a varnished layer which is coextensive with the inner layer of the sides of the cocoon. This latter varnished layer has a small central area made up of several layers of coarse strands of light tan silk which lie immediately beneath the tough, dense, thick layer of soft white silk. There is no nipple at the anterior end as in *lignaria* cocoons.

I reared 8 females and 17 males from a total of 53 provisioned cells in completed and incomplete nests. Both sexes were present in only 4 nests, and the arrangement of sexes was as follows (x = mortality):

Nest	1	2	3	4	5	6	7	8
Y 47	♀	♂	♀	♂	♂	♂		
K 64	♀	♀	♀	♂	♂	x		
U 20	♂	x	♀	x	x	x	x	x
U 21	♀	♀	x	x	♂	♂		

Parasites and predators. The parasitic sapygid wasp *Sapyga centrata* Say parasitized the only cell in 1 nest. A sapygid larva, probably of this same species, destroyed the bee egg in cell 5 of a 9-celled nest.

One cell of a 6-celled nest was infested in the laboratory by *Melittobia chalybii* Ashmead.

An infestation by a chaetodactylid mite, probably *Chaetodactylus krombeini* Baker, was found later in 5 cells of an 8-celled nest. The bee eggs or newly hatched larvae in these cells died, perhaps as a result of attack by the mites.

Immature acarid mites were found in all of the cocoons in a 6-celled nest. Probably they belonged to a scavenger species, because they did not attack the bees.

Previous observations. Packard (1874, p. 139) reported a nest of this species (as *lignivora,* a synonym) in a tunnel in a maple tree. He assumed that this boring had been made by the bee. The burrow was 7.5 cm. long and about 7.5 mm. in diameter. He described the cells as being jug-shaped. He also mentioned that the partitions between the cells were made by the bee of coarse chippings.

Source material.
    Plummers Island, Md. 1958 series: S 40, 55(?). 1959 series: Y 47, 122, 123.
        1961 series: K 64(?), 71(?). 1963 series: U 19, 20, 21, 22, 23(?), 24(?).

Identifications. Hymenoptera by R. M. Bohart and the author; Acarina by E. W. Baker.

OSMIA (CHALCOSMIA) COERULESCENS (Linnaeus)

Of 4 nests from Rochester, N. Y., available for study, 2 were in 6.4-mm. borings and 2 in 4.8-mm. borings. Two were from the edges of wooded areas and 2 from a station placed on the wall of a wooden garage.

Nest architecture. Very limited data are available. One nest contained 4 stored cells and a vestibular cell 110 mm. long divided by a cross partition. The other nests contained 5, 8, and 10 cells, respectively, and unmeasured vestibular cells. Five female cells were 7 to 11 mm. long (mean 8.4 mm.), and 1 male cell was 9 mm. long. The cell partitions, constructed of masticated leaf pulp, were 0.5 mm. thick. The closing plugs were made of the same material; one of them was 13 mm. thick.

Life history. The nests were stored during the first 3 weeks in June. The pollen-nectar masses in the 1 nest observed were pale, quite moist, and 5 mm. long. The larvae reached maturity during July. Pupation occurred from mid-July into August. The larva in 1 cell spun its cocoon between July 1 and 5 and was a darkened pupa by July 18, and a female bee eclosed by July 26. Eclosion of adults in 2 other nests took place as late as August 24-28. The adult bees overwintered in the cocoons, and emerged from the nests in the spring.

Parasites and predators. One of the nests contained an infestation of the mite *Chaetodactylus.* The hypopi varied in some details from those described as *C. krombeini* Baker from *Osmia lignaria* Say (Krombein, 1962). Another nest contained 2 adult female *Melit-*

tobia in 1 cell; it is not known whether this infestation originated in the field or in the laboratory.

Source material.

Rochester, N. Y. 1953 series: 9 b, 10 b. 1954 series: R 1. 1957 series: Bu 1.

Identifications by author.

OSMIA (CHALCOSMIA) GEORGICA Cresson

I have had only 1 nest of this bee, sent to me by K. W. Cooper who received it from D. L. Lindsley. The nest was provisioned at Oak Ridge, Tenn. No data are available on the habitat in which the trap was set.

Nest architecture. The nest was in a 6.4-mm. boring. There were 20 cells in the innermost 140 mm. of the boring, separated by partitions of masticated leaf pulp 0.5 mm. in thickness. The nest was capped by a series of 5 similar partitions, separated one from another by empty spaces of 2-3 mm.

Life history. Occupants of the nest had already spun cocoons when I received the nest during the summer of 1956. In the spring of 1957 I obtained 13 females and 2 males of *georgica* from the nest; occupants of the other 5 cells died as larvae or prepupae.

Source material.

Oak Ridge, Tenn. 1956 series: OR 2.

Identifications by author.

OSMIA (DICERATOSMIA) SUBFASCIATA SUBFASCIATA Cresson

I have had only 1 nest of this widely distributed form; it was in a 4.8-mm. boring. The trap had been set about a meter above the ground in the middle of a dense mesquite thicket at Scottsdale, Ariz.

Nest architecture. The nest was provisioned between March 21 and April 29. It contained 18 stored cells 6-10 mm. long and a vestibular cell of 16 mm. Male cells were 6-7 mm. long, and a single female cell was 10 mm. The cell partitions were made of masticated leaf pulp and were 0.2-0.3 mm. thick, except that the partition capping the outermost stored cell was 5 mm. thick. The closing plug was made of the same material and was 3 mm. thick.

Life history. When I opened the nest on May 9, the occupants of cells 1 to 7 were already in cocoons, the larva in cell 8 had just reached maturity, and there were successively younger larvae in cells 9 to 18. The larva in cell 18 reached maturity and began to spin its cocoon on May 17 or 18. Most, if not all, of the larvae pupated between July 1 and 29. By August 7 an adult male had eclosed in cell 3. I placed the cocoons in individual vials on that date. The occupants of all cells emerged from the cocoons between October 2 and November 6 or died during this period, except for 1 male which overwintered inside the cocoon. A small hole was made in the side of each cocoon to observe development; this may account for the premature fall emergence of the adults. The single female was reared from the innermost cell. The cocoon had an outer white silken layer conforming to the cell walls; the inner layer was ovoid, brown, varnished and brittle and had a small raised cap of dense white silk at the anterior end.

Parasites and predators. One cell had an infestation of *Melittobia* which originated in the laboratory.

Previous observations. Linsley (1946) reported that in southern California this bee nested in old burrows of wood-boring Coleoptera. He found the bee to be an effective pollinator of alfalfa. It has been reported as visiting a wide variety of flowers for nectar and pollen.

Source material.
    Arizona. 1961 series: H 67.

Identifications by author.

OSMIA (NOTHOSMIA) PUMILA Cresson

Next to *Osmia lignaria* Say this is the most common vernal bee in trap nests at Plummers Island. I obtained 39 nests of this species from 1958 through 1964; 14 additional nests probably were made by this bee. Thirty nests were in 4.8-mm. borings and 9 in 6.4-mm. borings; all but 1 of the questionable nests were in 4.8-mm. borings. I also received 5 *pumila* nests and 2 questionable *pumila* nests from Derby, N. Y.; 3 of these *pumila* nests were in 4.8-mm borings and 1 each in 3.2- and 6.4-mm borings. At Derby all but 1 of the nests were from stations on structural lumber containing abandoned borings of other insects; the single exception was from a station on a pine tree. Fifty-one of the nests from Plummers Island were from stations on standing dead tree trunks, dead limbs, or a woodpile, and 2 from stations on limbs of live trees; none of these nests came from stations on structural lumber. The preference for 4.8-mm. borings as a nesting site probably is partly a result of competition with *lignaria,* which prefers the 6.4-mm. borings, and partly because *pumila* is a smaller bee.

Supersedure and competition. The pompilid wasp *Auplopus mellipes* (Say) nested in the outer end of a boring in which *pumila* began a nest. However, this was not a case of competition, because the pompilid did not nest in the boring until several weeks after the bee had abandoned it.

Nest architecture. In most of the nests at Derby the mother bee placed a little masticated leaf pulp at the inner end of the boring or constructed a partition of this material some distance from the inner end. This was also true in 26 of the 39 *pumila* nests at Plummers Island; in the 13 remaining nests the bee began to store pollen and nectar at the inner end. Table 32 summarizes measurements of the length of stored and vestibular cells, and of the thickness of closing plugs and cell partitions.

An empty vestibular cell was present in all but 6 of the 31 borings completely stored by *pumila*. In 4 nests the vestibular cell was divided into 2 sections by a cross partition. There were no empty intercalary cells. The partitions between cells, and the closing plugs were made from masticated leaf pulp. The fairly thin cell partitions were flexible until the rather moist pollen-nectar masses were consumed, after which they became quite stiff. It was observed in 1 nest that before she stores any pollen and nectar in a cell the mother constructs a narrow annulus of leaf pulp at the point where the closing partition will be placed.

An analysis was made of 18 completely stored nests from Plummers Island in which there was no empty space at the inner end of the boring. Sixteen nests in 4.8-mm. borings contained a mean of 14 stored cells (range 2-21) and an empty vestibular cell. Four nests in 6.4-mm. borings contained a mean of 18 stored cells (range 6-27) and a vestibular cell. All the nests which contained more than a dozen cells produced bees of both sexes. The single *pumila* nest in a 3.2-mm. boring contained 6 stored and 1 vestibular cell and produced only male bees.

Life history. There is a single generation a year. Adult bees may be active in the Washington area from April 10 until early in June. However, the majority of nests are provisioned in a 3-week period beginning late in April or early in May. Three cells were stored as early as April 25, 1961, and in 1962 1 female completed her nest June 2. The occupants overwinter in their cocoons as adult bees and leave the nest for the first time the following spring. Nests were provisioned in Derby from late May until early July.

I did not obtain any information on the duration of provisioning flights or on the number of loads of pollen and nectar required to store a single cell. Very limited data from egg hatch indicate that 2 or 3 cells may be stored on a favorable day. A nest with 27 provisioned cells was constructed by May 19 in a 6.4-mm. boring set out on April 28. It is not known how soon the mother bee began to use this boring after it was set out.

The pollen-nectar mass is much moister than that of *lignaria*. These masses are subtruncate at the inner end where they are

TABLE 32.—*Dimensions (in mm.) of cells, partitions, and plugs in nests of Osmia pumila Cresson*

Locality	Boring diameter	Sex	Length of stored cells			Length of vestibular cells			Cell partitions		Closing plug	
			No.	Range	Mean	No.	Range	Mean	Range	Mean	Range	Mean
N.Y.	3.2	♂	4	7-8	7.8	1	—	15	—	0.2	—	7
	4.8	♀	15	7-9	7.6	1	—	55	—	0.5	—	5
		♂	11	5-7	6.3							
	6.4	♀	9	5-6	5.3	—	—	—	—	0.5	—	—
Md.	4.8	♀	142	6-10	7.2	23	9-132	50.7	0.1-0.5	0.3	4-17	8.7
		♂	56	5-7	5.7							
	6.4	♀	63	4-7	5.2	6	5-115	53.5	—	0.3	1-11	5.4
		♂	20	4-7	4.9							

in contact with the partition closing the preceding cell. The main part of the mass is cylindrical to conform with the boring walls. The outer end is oblique and slopes downward and outward. In the single nest in a 3.2-mm. boring from Derby the pollen-nectar masses for the male cells were 4-5 mm. long. In 4.8-mm. nests from Plummers Island these masses had a mean length of 4.4 mm. for female bees (range 4-6 mm.) and a mean length of 3 mm. for male bees.

The egg is opaque white and slightly curved and ranges from 2.3 to 2.5 mm. long by 0.8 to 1.0 mm. wide. The posterior end of the egg is slightly embedded in the pollen mass, and the egg is at a low angle to the mass with the anterior half or two-thirds free. Sometimes the mass is so moist that almost the entire length of the egg is in contact with it.

The egg of *pumila* has a shorter incubation period than that of *lignaria*; it hatches in 3 to 4 days. The larvae begin to void fecal pellets 7 to 9 days after eclosion from the egg. The entire larval feeding period requires 27-29 days for eggs hatching early in May and 14-21 days for those hatching later in May and in June. The cocoon is spun as soon as feeding is completed. Pupation takes place early in the summer. In 1 nest from Plummers Island the egg hatched on May 7, the larva completed feeding on June 3, and pupation occurred on June 24. In a nest from Derby 2 larvae completed feeding on June 30 and pupated about July 15-16. A female in 1 nest pupated July 14-21 and eclosed August 7-15. Emergence from the cocoons does not take place until the following spring. Very high adult mortality took place in overwintering trap nests, but this may also occur in normal nests, because the species does not appear to be extremely abundant.

The cocoon consists of 2 layers. The relatively thick outer layer is composed of loosely woven, coarse white strands and is roughly cylindrical in shape because it is spun against the walls and ends of the cell; it can be removed from the next layer with relatively little difficulty. The inner cocoon is usually ovoid in shape. At the anterior end is a small cap of dense white fibers which covers the nipple. The inner cocoon is a single layer of thin, leathery, light tan, varnished silk. The nipple consists of a thick circular disk of varnished silk beneath which are several layers of fine, closely woven, white silk, only the innermost of which is varnished. In the center of this innermost varnished layer is a small central pore of coarse, loose mesh, unimpregnated fibers.

The cocoons in 4.8-mm. nest from Derby were about 1.5 mm. shorter than the cells, but in Plummers Island nests they completely filled the space between the cell partitions. Female cocoons were longer than male cocoons because they were in longer cells.

Fifty-eight stored cells in nests from Derby yielded 24 females and 15 males, whereas 464 stored cells in Plummers Island nests yielded 205 females and 71 males. Quite evidently a preponderance of females is produced. The data from Plummers Island suggest a probable 3:1 sex ratio, whereas the nests from Derby were too few to permit an accurate calculation of the sex ratio in that area. Only males were produced in the single nest in a 3.2 mm. boring from Derby, but a preponderance of females was produced in the 4.8- and 6.4-mm. borings from both localities.

An accurate determination was made of the arrangement of sexes in 24 mixed nests in 4.8-mm. and 6.4-mm. borings, either by placing the cocoons in individual vials for rearing, or by opening the cocoons and recording the sex of the occupants. In 19 of the nests (18 from Plummers Island and 1 from Derby) the females were always in the innermost cells and males in the outermost. In 2 of these nests there were as many as 13 females in the innermost cells before there was a sequence of 5 or 6 males in the outermost cells. There were 4 nests from Plummers Island and 1 from Derby in which the arrangement of sexes departed from the normal. These are shown in table 33 where x represents a cell in which the bee failed to develop.

It may be argued, as for *lignaria,* that the random arrangement of sexes in these 5 nests may be due to several factors. When we consider the size of the cells, it appears that females should have developed in cell 3 of R 25, cell 9 of M 11, and cells 6 and 9 of M 40; the production of males in these cells may have been due to failure of the sperm to fertilize the egg. The development of males in cells 12 and 13 of M 40 and cells 14 to 16 of M 49 might have been due to temporary "fatigue" of the muscles controlling the spermetheca thus inhibiting the release of sperm. It will be noted that there was a sequence of 13 females in nest M49 before several males were produced. The same situation also developed in 2 other nests containing females at the inner end and males at the outer end. These limited data suggest that the mother may be incapable of fertilizing more than 13 consecutively laid eggs.

Parasites and predators. The most important parasite of *pumila* is the sapygid *Sapyga centrata* Say. It parasitized 23 of 120 stored cells in 11 nests at Plummers Island. Probably the same species parasitized 5 of 31 stored cells in 3 additional *pumila* nests from this locality, but the larvae were preserved for taxonomic study or died from natural causes.

The chrysidid *Chrysura pacifica* (Say) parasitized 4 cells in an 8-celled nest at Plummers Island. Probably this same cuckoo wasp attacked 4 cells in a 6-celled nest from the same locality supposedly

TABLE 33.—*Sequence of sexes in certain nests of Osmia pumila Cresson*

Nest and diameter		1	2	3	4	5	6	7	8	9	10	11	12	13	14	15	16	17	18	19	20	21	22	23	24	25	26	27
R25 4.8	cell	?	8	7	7	8	6	6	6	7	7	5	6	6	6													
	sex	X	♀	♂	X	♀	♂	♂	♂	♂	♂	♂	X	♂	♂													
M11 4.8	cell	9	8	8	7	8	7	7	7	7	7	7	7	6	6	5	6	6										
	sex	X	♀	♀	X	X	♀	♀	♀	♂	♀	♀	♀	♂	♂	♂	♂	♂										
M40 6.4	cell	6	6	6	6	5	7	6	5	6	5	5	5	5	4	5	5	5	5	5	5	4	4	5	4	4		
	sex	♀	♀	♀	♀	X	♂	♀	♀	♂	♀	♀	♂	♂	♀	♀	♀	♀	♀	♀	♂	♂	♂	♂	X	X		
M49 6.4	cell	6	6	5	4	4	5	5	6	5	5	4	5	5	5	4	4	4	4	4	5	5	7	5	4	4	5	4
	sex	♀	♀	♀	♀	♀	♀	♀	♀	♀	♀	♀	♀	♀	♂	♂	♂	♀	♀	♀	♀	♀	♀	♀	♀	♀	X	♂
Z21 6.4	cell	5	5	5	5	5																						
	sex	X	X	♂	X	♀																						

stored by *pumila;* neither bees nor parasites were reared from this nest.

There was a primary infestation by *Melittobia chalybii* Ashmead in 1 cell each of 7-celled and 11-celled nests from Plummers Island. Secondary infestations by this parasite occurred in the laboratory in 4 other nests.

A sarcophagid fly, presumably a species of Miltogrammini, destroyed a 4-celled nest at Derby probably built by *pumila.*

An unknown mite, possibly a species of *Chaetodactylus,* was noted in 2 cells of an 11-celled nest from Derby. This mite behaved the same as *C. krombeini* Baker in nests of *Osmia lignaria.* Possibly the same mite infested 1 cell of a 2-celled nest at Plummers Island presumably constructed by *pumila.*

The parasitic mite *Pyemotes ventricosus* (Newport) occurred as a secondary infestation in the laboratory in a nest presumed to have been stored by *pumila.*

Source material.
>   Derby, N. Y. 1957 series: G 22 (?), 39. 1958 series: R 2, 25, 64. 1961 series: L 2 (?), 4.
>   Plummers Island, Md. 1958 series: S 33 (?), 42 (?), 47 (?), 48, 58 (?). 1959 series: Y 29, 33. 1960 series: E 9, 12 (?), 14, 17, 18, 19, 31 (?), 47 (?). 1961 series: K 8, 11, 12 (?), 21 (?), 23 (?), 25 (?), 60. 1962 series: M 11, 12, 13, 14, 15, 16, 19, 23, 24, 38 (?), 39, 40, 41, 48, 49, 53, 55, 57, 58 (?), 77. 1964 series: Z 3, 4, 5, 6, 7, 8, 9, 10, 11 (?), 12 (?), 21, 26.

Identifications. Hymenoptera by T. B. Mitchell, R. M. Bohart, and the author.

OSMIA (CHENOSMIA) GAUDIOSA Cockerell

Five nests of this species from Portal, Ariz., were available for study, 4 of them in 4.8-mm. borings and 1 in a 6.4-mm. boring. The nests came from 3 different stations, 2 from a yucca stem a meter above the ground, 2 from a mesquite branch ⅓ meter above the ground, and 1 from a mesquite branch 2 meters above the ground.

Supersedure and competition. Only 1 of the borings was completely stored by *gaudiosa.* In the other 4 nests the bees were superseded by other bees and wasps. Probably there was competition because there was no empty vestibular cell in the sections stored by *gaudiosa.* In 2 of the nests the supersedure was by an unknown vespid or vespids; in the other 2 the superseder was the megachilid bee *Ashmeadiella m. meliloti* (Cockerell).

Nest architecture. In 4 nests the bees began to store pollen and nectar at the inner end of the boring. In the fifth nest the bee left an empty space of 32 mm. at the inner end of the boring, then made a partition of leaf pulp 0.5 mm. thick, and then provisioned the first cell. Twenty-one female cells in 4.8-mm. borings were 6-10 mm. long (mean 7.1 mm.), and 5 male cells were 6-7 mm. long (mean 6.4 mm.). Ten cells in the single 6.4-mm. nest were 4-5 mm. long; female bees emerged from 8 cells, and the occupants of the other cells died as larvae.

The partitions capping the cells were of masticated leaf pulp and 0.25 mm. thick. The empty vestibular cell in the 1 nest completed by *gaudiosa* was 40 mm. long, and the leaf pulp plug closing it was 0.5 mm. thick.

The single completed nest was in a 4.8-mm. boring. It contained 13 stored cells 6-9 mm. long and a vestibular cell of 40 mm.; the outermost 20 mm. of the boring was empty. Females emerged from 11 of the cells, the occupant of the twelfth was preserved as a resting larva, and the occupant of the thirteenth was destroyed by a predator.

Larval food. The bee eggs in 2 cells died. The pollen-nectar masses in these cells were 4-5 mm. long, and still quite moist on July 19. The pollen was analyzed as 96 per cent Papillionoideae (cf. *Astragalus, Vicia,* or *Lathyrus*) and 4 per cent probably Scrophulariaceae (cf. *Stemodia*).

Life history. There is only a single generation a year. I do not know when the nests were stored, but occupants of all the *gaudiosa* cells were resting larvae in cocoons when I picked up the nests and opened them for study around July 19. Probably they were stored during May, because offspring of the vespid superseder in 1 nest developed and emerged as adults before the nest was picked up. Pupation took place between July 28 and August 20. There was a pale pupa in 1 cell on the latter date, which had darkened by the 27th. This bee died as a fully colored pupa, but an adult bee eclosed in an adjacent cell on August 31. Adult bees left the cocoons and emerged in individual glass vials the following spring.

The cocoons consisted of a delicate white outer sheath spun against the cell walls, and an ovoid, brown, varnished, tough inner layer with a small, low nipple of dense white silk on the anterior end. The inner cocoon spun by 21 female larvae was 4-7 mm. long (mean 5.4 mm.) and of 5 males was 5 mm. long.

I reared only females from 4 nests. In the fifth nest the arrangement of sexes was as follows, an X indicating mortality:

X-♀-♂-♀-♀-♀-X-♀-♀-♂-♂-♂-♂-X

Parasites and predators. I did not obtain any parasites or predators of *gaudiosa* in these nests. An unknown predator penetrated the 1 completed nest and destroyed the occupant of the outermost cell. In another nest there were 3 dead tenebrionid beetle adults whose relationship to the bee is uncertain. The beetles belonged to the tribe Eurymetaponini, and were identified as 2 *Metaponium* sp. and 1 *Telabis* sp. One beetle was found at the inner end of the boring among fragments of leaf pulp and some beetle frass (?). Then there were 2 *gaudiosa* cells with bee cocoons and then 2 more beetles in another *gaudiosa* cell. It seems probable that the beetles invaded the nest to feed on the stored pollen and died because they were unable to turn around in the boring. Linsley (1944) reported the occurrence of adults of several other genera of tenebrionid beetles in cells of bees belonging to the genera *Osmia, Megachile, Anthophora,* and *Xylocopa*.

Source material.
    Arizona. 1959 series: X 51, 52, 53, 55, 155.

Identifications. Osmia by C. D. Michener, other Hymenoptera by the author; Coleoptera by T. J. Spilman.

MEGACHILE (LITOMEGACHILE) GENTILIS Cresson
(Plate 20, Figures 99, 100)

This leaf-cutter bee was a frequent nester in borings in Arizona. I reared it from 8 nests at 5 stations from Portal in 1961 and 1963, from 4 nests at 3 stations at Scottsdale in 1961, and from 22 nests at 9 stations at Granite Reef Dam in 1961. Twenty-seven nests were in 6.4-mm., and 7 were in 12.7-mm. borings. The settings were on open deserts under live or dead branches of mesquite (15 nests), palo verde (9), *Lycium,* desert willow, and sycamore (3 each), and 1 was on a wooden fence post.

Supersedure and competition. M. gentilis was superseded in one boring by *Trypargilum tridentatum* (Packard). It was not evident whether or not this was a case of competition.

Nest architecture (figs. 99, 100). In 3 nests the *mendica* females left an empty space 4-6 mm. long at the inner end of the boring. In the other nests they began to place leaf cuttings to form the first cell right at the inner end.

Cells in 6.4-mm. borings were 9-15 mm. long (mean 10.6). There was no appreciable difference in size between male and female cells. Cells in 12.7-mm. borings had about the same range in length, but in most of the nests in those larger borings there was a second series of linear cells side by side with part of the first series (fig. 100). As a consequence there were more cells per unit of length in the larger borings.

There was an empty space 5-117 mm. long (mean 29) between the last stored cell and the closing plug in completed nests. Occasionally, there were some scattered leaf cuttings in this otherwise empty space. The closing plugs of circular leaf cuttings were rather tightly packed and 2-14 mm. thick (mean 6).

There were 2-13 stored cells (mean 11) per completed nest in 6.4-mm. borings (fig. 99). In 12.7-mm. borings there were 5-15 cells, but I am not sure that any of these nests was completed.

Life history. There were 2 or more generations a year. Most of the nests were picked up from April 29 to mid-May, and adults emerged from them May 23 to June 28. Adults emerged July 28 to August 14 from nests completed later in May or early in June. I received 2 nests stored later in the summer whose occupants overwintered as diapausing larvae and emerged as adults the following spring.

Adults emerged 5-6 weeks after the nests were stored in summer generation nests. In a single nest the members of 1 sex usually emerged on the same day or within a period of 1-5 days. Males usually emerged a day earlier than females in the same nest, although occasionally there was concurrent emergence.

Females were in the inner and males in the outer cells of all nests which contained both sexes. I reared 43 females and 203 males from 340 stored cells. Considering the position of the cells I believe it is probable that females would have developed in at least 5 and males in at least 39 of the 94 cells from which I failed to rear adults.

Parasites and predators. The chalcidoid *Tetrastichus megachilidis* Burks was described from material reared from these nests. It infested 20 of 52 cells in 6 nests at Granite Reef Dam in the field. Later, in the laboratory, it infested 3 cells in a 14-celled nest from Scottsdale and 1 cell in a 13-celled nest from Granite Reef Dam.

A clerid larva, possibly *Trichodes horni* Wolcott and Chapin, destroyed the resting larvae in 2 cells of a 3-celled nest from Portal.

I reared the bombyliid fly *Anthrax atriplex* Marston from 1 cocoon each in 2 nests from Granite Reef Dam. *Anthrax irroratus* Say was reared from a cocoon of *gentilis* in a nest from Scottsdale.

Previous observations. Bechtel (1958) reared *gentilis* in California from nests in stems of blue elderberry. He obtained 11 females and 12 males of *gentilis* from 5 nests, as well as 5 specimens of its social parasite *Coelioxys novomexicana* Cockerell. The parasites emerged several days earlier than the host bees.

Source material.
Portal, Ariz. 1961 series: G 122, 123, 124, 125, 196, 213, 343. 1963 series: T 13.
Scottsdale, Ariz. 1961 series: H 89, 132, 146, 204.
Granite Reef Dam, Ariz. 1961 series: H 96, 97, 99, 101, 105, 106, 107, 108, 109, 110, 111, 112, 122, 123, 141, 142, 143, 149, 199, 203, 207, 216.

Identifications. Anthrax by N. Marston; *Tetrastichus* by B. D. Burks; wasps and bees by the author.

MEGACHILE (LITOMEGACHILE) MENDICA Cresson

I reared this bee from 39 nests: 2 from 2 stations at Derby, N. Y., in 1956 and 1958; 3 from 3 stations at Plummers Island, Md., in 1956 and 1962; 10 from 8 stations at Kill Devil Hills, N. C., 1954-1956; and 24 from 18 stations at Lake Placid, Fla., 1957 and 1959-1961. One nest was in a 4.8-mm. boring, 32 in 6.4-mm. borings and 6 in 12.7-mm. borings. Most of the nests at Derby and Plummers Island were from settings at the edges of wooded areas or in open woods. Some of the Kill Devil Hills nests were in similar areas, but some were on the barrens. The Florida nests were from the sand scrub area of the Archbold Biological Station. The settings were mostly on limbs of living or dead pine, oak, and hickory.

Supersedure and competition. M. mendica superseded *Podium rufipes* (Fabricius) in 1 of the nests from Kill Devil Hills. All other supersedures occurred in the Florida nests. M. *mendica* superseded the vespid wasp *Euodynerus foraminatus apopkensis* (Robertson) in 3 borings. Probably there was no competition in these borings because the *mendica* females nested in them during June and July several weeks after the wasps probably nested in them. M. *mendica* also superseded 1 or more species of the megachilid bee *Chalicodoma* (*Chelostomoides*) in 3 borings and was superseded by that bee in 2 borings. In 1 of these borings *mendica* stored a single cell at the inner end, then the *Chalicodoma* stored 4 cells in which the eggs died, and then a leaf-cutter bee (*mendica?*) made 3 more cells in which the eggs died.

Nest architecture. In 7 borings used initially by *mendica* the bees left an empty space of 6-45 mm. at the inner end; occasionally there were a few loose, circular leaf cuttings in this otherwise empty space. M. *mendica* is a leaf-cutter bee and the females constructed a series of linear cells from leaf cuttings as described above under the family heading. The cells were 8-17 mm. long (mean 11.5). Apparently there were no significant differences in length between male and female cells. Thirty male cells were 8-17 mm. long (mean 11.3), and a single female cell was 15 mm. long.

The closures varied in the 24 nests sealed by *mendica* for which I made notes. There were spaces of 8-90 mm. (mean 32) beyond the terminal stored cells in these nests. In a few nests this space was mostly empty except for some circular leaf cuttings packed tightly into the outer 5-10 mm. of the boring. Occasionally this space was rather loosely filled with round, oval, or rectangular leaf cuttings before the usual closing plug of tightly packed circular cuttings.

There were 1-13 stored cells (mean 8.3) in the 27 borings completely stored by *mendica*.

Life history. There were at least 2 generations a year at Derby, Plummers Island, and Kill Devil Hills. Adults emerged the end of July or early in August from nests stored presumably late in June or early in July at Derby. At Plummers Island I obtained nests of the summer generation only. These were stored the last half of July and their occupants overwintered as diapausing larvae; the adults emerged the following spring. At Kill Devil Hills adults emerged July 31-August 7 from 2 nests stored June 21 to July 3. Other nests at this locality were stored during August and early in September; their occupants overwintered as diapausing larvae and adults emerged the following spring.

Apparently there was more or less continual breeding in Florida during the warmer months. I received nests stored in every month beginning with the latter half of March through mid-September. Adults emerged from them between April 18 and October 22.

In the 2 summer generation nests at Kill Devil Hills about 35-40 days elapsed between the completion of the nests and emergence of the adults. This period appeared to be about a week shorter in Florida nests, although it was longer in early spring and late summer nests than in those from mid-summer.

All the individuals of 1 sex usually emerged from a single nest on the same day or within a day of each other. In mixed nests the series of males usually emerged 1-5 days earlier than their sisters in the inner cells. On rare occasions some individuals of both sexes emerged on the same date.

There was some variability in the duration of the period between pupation and adult emergence in the several individuals for which I noted such data. In 1 female it was 11-13 days, and in another 19 days. In 1 male it was 17 days; another male was still a prepupa on July 18, but an adult emerged on the 31st.

Females were in the inner and males in the outer cells in nests containing both sexes. I reared 53 females and 129 males from a total of 271 stored cells. Judging from the position in the cells females would probably have developed in at least 3 and males in at least 23 of the 93 stored cells from which I failed to rear adults.

Parasites and predators. The parasitic megachilid bee *Coelioxys sayi* Robertson parasitized 8 of 30 cells in 4 nests at Lake Placid.

A bombyliid fly larva, *Anthrax* species, fed on a *mendica* prepupa in its cocoon in a nest from Lake Placid. Unfortunately, the *Anthrax* pupa was injured and died before eclosion of the adult; it may have been a specimen of *atriplex* Marston or *irroratus* Say which I have reared from *Megachile gentilis* Cresson in Arizona.

At Kill Devil Hills a female *mendica* died head inward in her nest after provisioning 1½ cells. Filling her abdomen was a dipterous puparium from which a conopid fly *Physocephala marginata* (Say) emerged the following spring.

An undescribed species of the saproglyphid mite *Vidia* infested 1 nest each at Kill Devil Hills and Lake Placid. This mite was presumed to be a symbiont.

In the laboratory the eulophid wasp *Melittobia chalybii* Ashmead and the grain itch mite *Pyemotes ventricosus* (Newport) each infested 1 nest from Lake Placid.

I found a caterpillar tunneling in a moldy pollen-nectar mass in 1 cell in a Lake Placid nest. Presumably the larva may have hatched in the nest from an egg on one of the leaf cuttings used in the nest construction. It probably destroyed the bee egg or young larva in its feeding activities.

Previous observations. Several years ago I noted (Krombein *et al.*, 1958, p. 244) that *mendica* had been reared from rose canes. More recently Medler (1965a) reported on 57 nests of *mendica* found in sumac traps in Wisconsin. He obtained most of his nests in 6.4-mm. borings, although he found that *mendica* would also accept 4.8- and 8.0-mm. borings. Several kinds of wasps, *Trypoxylon, Dipogon, Euodynerus* (recorded as *Rygchium*), and *Ancistrocerus,* superseded *mendica* in 5 borings and were superseded by the bee in 5 others.

The *mendica* cells were 10-14 mm. long. A vestibular cell of variable length was present, and occasionally this space was filled with loose leaf cuttings. The closing plugs were usually 3-4 mm. thick but sometimes much thicker. He found 5.7 ± 3.1 stored cells per nest (range 1-13).

Medler reported 2 generations a year in Wisconsin with adults emerging during July and August from the first generation nests. During August and September these adults stored nests whose occupants overwintered as diapausing larvae. He found that the larval feeding period was a week at 21° C. and that spinning of the cocoon required a day. The period between pupation and adult emergence was about 3 weeks. He obtained 99 males and 100 females from 325 stored cells. In nests containing both sexes females were in the inner and males in the outer cells in all nests except one, where there was a female in the middle of a series of male cells.

Medler reared 21 *Coelioxys sayi* Robertson and 2 *C. octodentata* Say and reported that the parasites had a life cycle 3-4 days shorter than that of *mendica.* He did not find a consistent pattern of parasitism by the *Coelioxys.* He also found *Melittobia chalybii* Ashmead in 10 cells and thought that these infestations originated in the laboratory rather than in the field.

Source material.
Derby, N. Y. 1956 series: J 45. 1958 series: R 57.
Plummers Island, Md. 1956 series: H 111, 156. 1962 series: M 74.
Kill Devil Hills, N. C. 1954 series: F 1, G 19. 1955 series: C 42, 316, 345, 382.
1956 series: C 57, 58, 340, 341.
Lake Placid, Fla. 1957 series: M 11, 248, 259, 264. 1959 series: V 113, 120.
1960 series: B 44, 55, 63, 107, 167, 169, 174, 176, 180, 205. 1961 series:
F 44, 67, 70, 120, 129, 240, 276, 319.

Identifications. Physocephala by C. W. Sabrosky; *Anthrax* by
W. W. Wirth; *Vidia* by E. W. Baker; *Coelioxys* by T. B. Mitchell;
other bees and wasps by the author.

MEGACHILE (MEGACHILE) CENTUNCULARIS (Linnaeus)

I received 1 nest of this bee from a setting at the edge of a
wooded area at Powdermill State Park near Rochester, N. Y. It was
in a 6.4-mm. boring.

Nest architecture. The cells were made from leaf cuttings in the
usual manner as described for the subgenus under the family heading. There were about a dozen cells each 10 mm. long in this nest.

Life history. The boring was set out on June 9, and the nest was
completed by June 23. I received it on July 20, and on the 23d
2 males and a female emerged from it. I split open the nest on
July 25 and removed another live female bee.

Parasites and predators. The eulophid wasp *Melittobia* infested
some cells in this nest.

Previous observations. Gentry (1874) reported 2 nests in Pennsylvania, 1 of 6 cells in a horizontal burrow 3 inches below the
ground surface and the other in abandoned cells of a mud-dauber
wasp. Packard (1874, pp. 136-137) quoted Putnam as recording
a nest of 30 cells arranged in several rows beneath a roof board.
Hicks (1926, p. 231) reared *centuncularis* (recorded as *infragilis*
Cresson, a synonym) from a boring in a dead stem in Colorado.
Michelbacher and Hurd (1954) found this species nesting over a
period of some years in a metal window frame in California.
Medler (1959) presented the most complete biological account of
centuncularis; he reported 1 nest in a rolled-up carpet and several
nests in sumac traps.

Gentry found the cells in the ground to be about 19 mm. long
and those in the mud-dauber cells to be about 38 mm. long. These
are larger than cells reported by other observers and it is possible
that he misidentified the bees. In the nest reported by Packard the
cells were apparently about 12 mm. long. The cells in Medler's
nests were apparently no more than 13 mm. long because he found
a maximum of 15 cells in a boring 200 mm. long. Medler found
that the nest occupants overwintered as diapausing larvae. He suggested the possibility that there was only a single generation a year

in Wisconsin because the bees did not nest in his traps until late July and August. I believe that this is an erroneous assumption based on the dates of storage and emergence from my single nest.

Packard reported *Melittobia megachilis* (Packard) as a parasite of *centuncularis,* and Medler reared *M. chalybii* Ashmead from his nests; the latter infestation may have arisen in the laboratory, Michelbacher and Hurd reared *Monodontomerus montivagus* Ashmead from their nests. Medler also reared *Coelioxys moesta* Cresson, *Dibrachys* sp., and *Ptinus* sp., probably *hirtellus* Sturm, from nests of *centuncularis.*

Source material.
    Rochester, N. Y. 1956 series: **C 1.**

Identifications by the author.

MEGACHILE (EUTRICHARAEA) CONCINNA Smith

I received 2 nests of this leaf cutting species in 6.4-mm. borings from Oak Ridge, Tenn., in 1954 and 1956. Later, in 1961, I received a nest in a 4.8-mm. boring from a setting under a small willow tree in the yard of a home in Scottsdale, Ariz.

Nest architecture. One of the Oak Ridge nests contained 10 stored cells about 9 mm. long, and the other contained 8 stored cells. The inner 58 mm. of the Scottsdale nest was empty; then there were 4 stored cells, each 9 mm. long, then an empty space of 50 mm., and finally a closing plug of circular leaf cuttings 4 mm. thick.

Life history. There were probably 2 generations a year in Tennessee. The earlier nest was stored August-September 1954, the occupants overwintered as diapausing larvae, and 6 males and 2 females emerged late the following spring, June 6-7. One male spent at least a week in its cocoon after eclosion. The later nest was probably stored the latter part of June 1956. Five males and 2 females emerged from it on July 25; the occupants of 3 cells were destroyed by a dermestid larva. The cocoons in the later nest were about 7 mm. long.

Undoubtedly there were 2 or more generations a year in Arizona. The Scottsdale boring was set out May 30, and the nest was completed on June 15. There were half-grown larvae in 2 of the cells when I opened the nest on the 19th; these larvae died as a result of desiccation. In 1 of the other cells there was a prepupa in its cocoon on June 27. Two males emerged from cells 1 and 3 on July 21.

Parasites and predators. A dermestid beetle larva destroyed 3 of 10 cells in one of the nests from Tennessee.

Previous observations. Butler and Wargo (1963) published some biological notes on *concinna* in Arizona. They found nests in tubular holes in wood or mortar, copper tubing, and ears and folds of fertilizer bags, and they induced the bee to nest in large soda straws and in wooden traps. They reported that the cells in straws had 2-4 circular leaf cuttings at the posterior end and 6-10 oblong pieces on the sides. In long straws there were as many as 15 cells, but usually fewer. Ordinarily the bees left an empty space 10-80 mm. long after the last stored cell and then capped the straw with an entrance plug made from 7-36 circular leaf cuttings. When held at temperatures that fluctuated between 80° F. and 117° F., adult bees emerged 21-26 days (mean 23) after the cells were completed. They recorded parasitism by *Tetrastichus megachilidis* Burks with rates of 20 per cent in nests early in July and 42 per cent in mid-September.

Butler and Ritchie (1965) published some additional notes on *concinna* in Arizona, particularly with reference to its use as a pollinating agent and its manipulation in flight rooms. They stated that bees from overwintering nests emerged over a lengthy period, April to June, and that first-generation adults might emerge early in July. Populations were highest during July and diminished to low levels by September. Parasitism was at a minimum during June and July. They recorded *Tetrastichus megachilidis* as the most important parasite; they also reported parasitism in both Arizona and California by the bombyliid, *Anthrax cintalpa* Cole. They found that a dermestid beetle, *Trogoderma* sp., infested both cells containing healthy brood and cells in which the bees had died or had already emerged.

Source material.
Oak Ridge, Tenn. 1954 series: OR 2. 1956 series: OR 5.
Scottsdale, Ariz. 1961 series: H 57.

Identifications by T. B. Mitchell and the author.

MEGACHILE (EUTRICHARAEA) ROTUNDATA (Fabricius)

I reared this Holarctic leaf-cutter bee from a nest in a 4.8-mm. boring set on a wooden sign post in an open field at Dunn Loring, Va., in 1954.

Nest architecture. The nest probably was stored late in August because when I opened it on September 9, there were half grown larvae in cells 1 and 2. These cells were 8 mm. long. A third cell of the same length had only a partial store of pollen and nectar.

Life history. There was an extended period of larval diapause over the winter. The female occupant of cell 1 pupated May 26-27, the adult eclosed June 14, and I removed it from its cocoon on the 17th. The female in cell 2 pupated May 28-31, eclosed on June 15, and I removed it also on the 17th.

Previous observations. Stephen and Torchio (1961) published biological notes made in Oregon and Idaho on this adventive species. They reported nests in a number of different kinds of apertures including holes from which nails had been removed, hollow tubing or plant stems, channels between stacked lumber, and even beneath a coat hanging on a wall. The cells were placed in a linear series in narrow apertures but in an irregular fashion beneath the coat. They found 2-17 cells in narrow apertures depending on the length of the aperture. They reported a single layer of 4 overlapping leaf cuttings in cell walls in 4.5-mm. apertures and 2 layers of larger overlapping leaf cuttings in larger diameter apertures. The interior cell dimensions averaged 4.5 mm. in diameter by 8 mm. in length. The cells were capped with 3-6 circular leaf cuttings. The nest entrances were usually plugged with 8-15 circular leaf cuttings, although sometimes as many as 33 were used. Adults were active from early in June until late in September, but there was only a single generation a year. The larvae completed feeding in 3 weeks, spun their cocoons, and entered a prolonged period of diapause over the winter.

Much of the data in the preceding paragraph was republished (Stephen, 1962) in an Experiment Station Bulletin on the management of *rotundata* for alfalfa seed production. It was noted that dermestid larvae destroyed the contents of many cells. Ants acted as predators, removing immature and mature larvae from cells, and earwigs occasionally fed on the stored pollen.

Later he noted (Stephen, 1965) that adult emergence normally occurred during the morning, but that a different periodicity could be induced by conditioning prepupae to fluctuations in temperature at critical times during the developmental cycle.

Laboratory studies (Stephen and Osgood, 1965a) showed that pupation and adult emergence occurred only within the temperature range 19-38°C, with 32° being the peak developmental temperature. Alternating temperatures resulted in delayed adult emergence and in delayed peak emergence dates even though the lower of the temperatures was within the favorable range.

In a later study (Stephen and Osgood, 1965b) they stated that sex ratios of 3♂:1♀ and 2♂:1♀ were obtained in borings having diameters of 5.5 and 6.0 mm. respectively. They also stated that these favorable sex ratios occurred in borings 50-100 mm. in length; borings less than 50 mm. long resulted in the production of more males. They also found that usually females developed in the inner and males in the outer cells. Observed deviations from this sequence were believed to be due to occupation of a boring by several females or to senility of the female.

Source material.
Dunn Loring, Va. 1954 series: C 20.

Identifications by T. B. Mitchell.

MEGACHILE (MELANOSARUS) XYLOCOPOIDES Smith
(Plate 20, Figure 98)

I reared this large black leaf-cutting bee from 7 nests in 12.7-mm. borings; 3 from 3 stations at Kill Devil Hills, N. C., in 1958; and 4 from 2 stations at Lake Placid, Fla., in 1959 and 1960. In addition, 7 more nests were almost certainly made by this species in 12.7-mm. borings, 2 at Kill Devil Hills and 5 at Lake Placid. These latter nests came from similar though different settings; the cell dimensions were the same as in nests of *xylocopoides* and considerably larger than those of any other leaf-cutting *Megachile*. The 5 stations at Kill Devil Hills were beneath dead limbs of loblolly pine in open wooded areas. The 7 stations at Lake Placid were in the sand-scrub area of the Archbold Biological Station beneath limbs of oak and hickory.

Supersedure and competition. M. *xylocopoides* superseded the vespid wasp *Monobia quadridens* (Linnaeus) in 1 nest at Lake Placid. Actually, there may not have been competition for this boring because the wasp had constructed an empty cell beyond its single stored cell at the inner end. However, in 1 of the Kill Devil Hills nests *Monobia* or some other vespid placed 4 paralyzed caterpillars at the inner end of the boring, which was then taken over by *xylocopoides*.

Nest architecture (fig. 98). The bees constructed cells at the inner end of all empty borings except in one where the female left an empty space of 53 mm. before building the first cell.

The cells were larger than those of any other leaf cutter which nested in these traps. Thirty-nine stored cells were 15-20 mm. long (mean 16). In 1 cell from a Kill Devil Hills nest I counted 15 rectangular leaf cuttings which formed the cell walls and inner end; the cell was capped by 3 circular disks. In 1 of the Lake Placid nests 1 cell had 19 rectangular cuttings 13-18 mm. by 11 mm.

The space beyond the terminal stored cell was filled with loosely shingled, rectangular to oval leaf cuttings capped by about half a dozen tightly packed circular leaf cuttings at the boring entrance (fig. 98). The plugs were 18-85 mm. long (mean 39).

There were 1-7 stored cells (mean 4) in the 14 nests. Two of the four 1-celled nests were parasitized by *Coelioxys dolichos* Fox; I failed to rear adults from the other 2 nests. It may be that they also were parasitized by *Coelioxys* and that the *xylocopoides* female closes a nest immediately once she is aware that her nest had been parasitized. The 1-celled nests had a normal type of closing plug as described above.

Life history. The nests at Kill Devil Hills were picked up on July 28. However, they must have been completed around July 1 because there were pale bee pupae in some cells on the 28th. The nests contained 31 stored cells (range 5-7) from which 1 male bee and 8 females emerged August 10-12; 4 additional adults emerged and escaped during this period. All cells in one 7-celled nest were parasitized by *Leucospis* and all cells in another 7-celled nest by *Melittobia*. Three cells in 2 other nests were also infested by *Melittobia,* and 1 bee prepupa died from an unknown cause. Almost certainly there were 2 generations a year at Kill Devil Hills.

Probably there are several generations a year at Lake Placid. Males emerged May 24-26 from 1 nest and a single female on June 4 from another nest; these nests were completed during the week of April 13. From another nest stored the week of June 8 3 males emerged on July 17 and a fourth male on September 7. Pupation of this latter individual may have been delayed because I made a slit in the cocoon. Several nests were completed later in the season, but the actual dates were not noted. In 1 of these later nests the diapausing larva was subjected to 2 months of chilly weather outdoors; it pupated about 3 weeks after it was brought into a heated room, and the adult emerged and died sometime during the next 4 weeks.

The pollen-nectar mass in 1 cell was 11 mm. long. The duration of the combined egg and larval feeding stages was about 2 weeks. The period between pupation and adult emergence was not calculated exactly; it was at least 14 days for 2 females and between 11 and 18 for 3 males.

Parasites and predators. An unidentified species of *Melittobia,* possibly *megachilis* (Packard), parasitized 10 cells in 3 Kill Devil Hills nests. The chalcidoid wasp *Leucospis a. affinis* Say parasitized all 7 cells in another nest from the same locality. The social parasite *Coelioxys dolichos* Fox was reared from two 1-celled nests undoubtedly stored by *xylocopoides* at Lake Placid.

An undescribed species of the saproglyphid mite *Vidia* infested several cells in 2 nests from Kill Devil Hills.

W. Rowland of Pompano Beach, Fla., sent me a *xylocopoides* nest made in a rolled-up screen of split canes. The nest was 50 cm. long and contained about 12 cells. The bee prepupae in cocoons in the innermost 4 cells were parasitized by *Testrastichus megachilidis* Burks, which was described from some of my nests of *Megachile gentilis* Cresson from Arizona.

Source material.
Kill Devil Hills, N.C. 1958 series: T 201 (?), 202, 205 (?), 209, 210.
Lake Placid, Fla. 1959 series: V 58 (?), 153. 1960 series: B 71, 103, 188, 191 (?), 233 (?). 1961 series: F 69 (?), 144 (?).

Identifications. Acarina by E. W. Baker; *Leucospis* by B. D. Burks; bees and wasps by the author.

MEGACHILE (SAYAPIS) INIMICA INIMICA Cresson

I reared this bee from a nest in a 6.4-mm. boring from Lake Placid, Fla., in 1960. It was from a station on the side of a pine tree in the sand-scrub area of the Archbold Biological Station. Typical *inimica* undoubtedly nested in another 6.4-mm. boring at the same station only 2 weeks later; this nest had cells of the same size and the partitions and closing plug were of the same unusual construction. Another similar nest in a 6.4-mm. boring was obtained from a setting beneath a dead oak limb at the station in 1959.

Nest architecture. The earlier nest in 1960 was completed the week of May 18. The inner 25 mm. of the boring was empty. Then there were 2 circular leaf cuttings arranged transversely and a plug 5 mm. thick of firmly agglutinated sand. Then there were 4 stored cells 22, 22, 22, and 31 mm. long in which male bees developed. The cell walls were unlined. Each of them was capped by a complex partition consisting of 1 or 2 circular leaf cuttings on the inner surface and 3-4 mm. of agglutinated sand which also formed the base of the next cell. Beyond the last stored cell was an empty space of 8 mm. and then a closing plug 17 mm. thick of loosely arranged, more or less circular leaf cuttings.

The later 1960 nest, believed to be that of typical *inimica*, was completed the week of June 1. It had 4 mm. of debris and sand at the inner end and then 4 unlined stored cells, 23, 25, 25, and 53 mm. long, capped by compound partitions 3-12 mm. thick, made as in the earlier nest except that occasionally some debris was incorporated with the sand. Beyond the fourth cell was an empty space of 14 mm. and then a hard closing plug 8 mm. thick mostly of agglutinated sand.

The 1959 nest had 2 mm. of agglutinated sand at the inner end of the boring. There were 8 provisioned cells capped by compound partitions 1.5-2 mm. thick. The partitions consisted of a circular leaf cutting at the inner end slightly larger than the boring diameter and then firmly agglutinated sand grains. There was no vestibular cell and the closing plug was 6 mm. thick.

Life history. In all cells there were small larvae which had not yet begun to defecate when I opened the first 1960 nest on May 26. The larvae completed feeding on June 10 and began to spin their cocoons, which were light tan, varnished, and tough. One cocoon was about 13 mm. long. The larvae entered a prolonged period of diapause. I subjected them to chilly weather outdoors from January 11 to March 24 and then brought them into my heated office. They pupated April 8-10 and adult males eclosed in all cocoons May 3-4. I removed 1 of the bees on the 12th to ascertain its identity, and the others emerged naturally on May 15.

When I opened the second 1960 nest on June 9, an egg in cell 1 and a small larva in cell 3 were already dead; cell 4 was incompletely stored and lacked an egg. The larva in cell 2 spun a cocoon before July 20 even though it had eaten only half of the pollen. It remained in prolonged diapause just as did the larvae in the other nest. It was still alive the next spring but died several weeks after I brought the nest into my office.

The other nest reached me in mid-December 1959, but obviously it had been stored some months previously. The larvae in cells 1-5 were dead and moldy, and there were diapausing larvae in cocoons in cells 6-8. There were mite hypopi on the outside of these cocoons, and it is possible that the mites may have caused the death of the bee larvae in the earlier cells. The nest was subjected to chilly weather outdoors for 2 months, but this did not break the diapause. I put the nest in a refrigerator for another 2 months and still there was no development. One of the larvae was infested by *Melittobia chalybii* following this exposure. The other died during the next winter while it was exposed outdoors to more chilly weather.

Developmental data from these nests indicate that typical *inimica* is normally univoltine.

Parasites and predators. The eulophid *Melittobia chalybii* Ashmead infested 1 nest in the laboratory. Unknown mites were also found in several cells of this nest.

Source material.
Lake Placid, Fla. 1959 series: V 119 (?). 1960 series: B 41, 177 (?).

Identifications by the author.

MEGACHILE (SAYAPIS) INIMICA SAYI Cresson

I reared this subspecies from 2 nests in 6.4-mm. borings from Portal, Ariz., in 1961. Both were from settings on the desert floor, one beneath the dead limb of a sycamore and the other from a wooden fence post. The nest of this bee is quite distinctive. Based on architectural details, it is possible to identify a nest in a 4.8-mm. boring and 3 others in 6.4-mm. borings as having been made by *sayi* at Portal in 1961. One each of these nests came from the same stations as the first 2 nests reported above; the other 2 were from 2 stations on dead mesquite.

Supersedure and competition. The bee superseded the sphecid wasp *Trypargilum tridentatum* (Packard) in 3 borings.

Nest architecture. In 1 nest where *sayi* superseded *Trypargilum* the bee made a plug sealing off the 2 wasp cells at the inner end of the boring. This plug was about 6 mm. thick and consisted of several circular leaf cuttings at the inner end, then a layer of small pebbles with interspersed gummy leaf pulp. Then there were 4 unlined stored cells 20, 17, 17, and 25 mm. long. Males developed in 1, 2, and 4 and the larva in 3 was preserved. The partitions capping cells 1-3 were 2-3 mm. thick and had several leaf cuttings at the inner end and then a layer of fine pebbles mixed with gummy leaf pulp. The partition closing cell 4 was about 10 mm. thick; it was similar to those capping cells 1-3 but had in addition a layer of coarser pebbles and a final section of very fine pebbles and leaf pulp. There was an empty space of 17 mm. and then a closing plug 5 mm. thick with leaf cuttings, pebbles, and leaf pulp.

In the other nest from which I reared *sayi* the mother bee put a thin layer of leaf pulp at the inner end. Then she stored 3 cells 23-24 mm. long; a female bee developed in cell 1 and a small larva and an egg died in the other cells. A fourth cell was incompletely stored, and the bee did not seal the nest. The partitions were 1.5 mm. thick and as described above. Pollen-nectar masses in cells 2 and 3 were 11 mm. long.

The 4.8-mm. nest supposed to have been stored by *sayi* came from the same station as the second nest described above. The female put a thin layer of leaf pulp at the inner end and then stored 2 unlined cells 27 and 42 mm. long capped by the usual compound partitions 4 and 12 mm. thick. There was an empty space of 72 mm. and a compound closing plug 10 mm. thick. The pollen-nectar masses were 15 mm. long; the young larvae died.

In the three 6.4-mm. nests supposed to have been stored by *sayi* the mother placed 2 mm. of pebbles sealed by leaf pulp at the end of 1 boring. In the other 2 nests the bees walled off a *Trypargilum* cell as described for the first nest. These 3 nests had 14 stored cells 16-33 mm. long (mean 22), capped by compound partitions 2-4 mm. thick as described above, except that the terminal stored cell in 1 nest had a plug 14 mm. thick. The pollen-nectar masses were 8-10 mm. long in 1 nest and 11-12 mm. long in a second. Each nest had a vestibular cell 22-34 mm. long. The compound closing plugs were 2-6 mm. long.

The nests of typical *inimica* Cresson and *i. sayi* were very similar in architecture, differing chiefly in that the former used agglutinated sand to form most of the partitions and closing plug whereas the latter used small pebbles intermixed with gummy leaf pulp, which hardened into a very firm plug. Both subspecies retained vestiges of the leaf-cutting habit and put a few cuttings at the inner surface of each cell partition.

Life history. All the nests were stored quite late in the season, sometime after September 9, and at least one about the middle of October. The 5 completed nests were picked up on October 18. I opened them on November 6. The occupants of 2 nests were already in cocoons, but there was a mature larva just beginning to spin its cocoon in a third nest. The eggs or larvae in the other nests were dead. Occupants of the 2 nests from which I reared *sayı* adults overwintered outdoors as diapausing larvae. Males in 1 nest pupated May 5-11 and the adults left the nest June 7-10. The female in the other nest was a dwarf individual which did not pupate properly. However, it developed to the point that it could be identified positively as *inimica sayi*.

The emergence dates of these adults suggest that there may be 2 generations of this bee in Arizona.

Source material.

Portal, Ariz. 1961 series: G 197, 330 (♀), 339 (♀), 381 (♀), 395 (♀), 410.

Identifications by T. B. Mitchell and the author.

MEGACHILE (SAYAPIS) POLICARIS Say
(Plate 19, Figures 92-97)

This species differs markedly from other known megachilid bees and, in fact, from almost all aculeate Hymenoptera in that several larvae develop amicably in a single large brood cell with no apparent cannibalism (figs. 93, 94).

I reared *policaris* from a single nest in a 12.7-mm. boring from Lake Placid, Fla., in 1962, and from 7 nests from 5 stations at Portal, Ariz., in 1959 and 1961, 2 in 6.4-mm. and 5 in 12.7-mm. borings. The presence of brood chambers in most nests and the combinations of tiny whole leaflets and leaf pulp in the cell partitions and closing plugs were diagnostic of *policaris* nests. Using these criteria, I determined that I had 11 other nests of *policaris* from Portal, Ariz., 1959-1961, from which I failed to rear adult bees. Three of these nests were from stations from which I also received nests in which *policaris* adults developed.

The single nest from Florida was from a setting beneath the branch of a live scrub hickory in the sand-scrub area of the Archbold Biological Station. At Portal all nests were from the desert floor, 8 from stations on wooden fences or posts, 3 on a dead yucca stalk, 2 each on a dead agave stalk and on branches of mesquite, and 1 each from a dead sycamore limb, a desert willow, and an acacia.

Supersedure and competition. *M. policaris* superseded *Anthidium* *maculosum* Cresson in 1 boring and was superseded in 1 boring each by *Ashmeadiella occipitalis* Michener, an unidentified species of gum-using megachilid and *Euodynerus guerrero* (Saussure).

Nest architecture (figs. 92, 95-97). In 9 borings in which *policaris* was the first occupant, the bees placed a thin layer of gummy leaf pulp at the inner end before beginning to store pollen and nectar; in 1 nest there were some fibers from the boring wall mixed in with the leaf pulp; in 5 nests the bees placed pollen and nectar at the inner end without a preliminary coating of leaf pulp. The walls of the brood cells were not lined with leaf pulp.

There were 3 nests in 6.4-mm. borings in which each cell contained only a single larva; these cells were 13-30 mm. long (mean 19). The other four 6.4-mm. nests had 2-4 brood cells or a combination of individual and brood cells (fig. 97). The brood cells, each 25-52 mm. long (mean 37), contained 2-3 larvae per cell. I measured a few pollen-nectar masses in 6.4-mm. nests in which the larvae failed to develop. These masses were 10-30 mm. long (mean 20), and they contained 1-3 eggs (mean 2).

All the cells in 12.7-mm. borings were brood cells in which 2-16 eggs were laid (figs. 92, 93). The brood cells were 17-78 mm. long (mean 38). Four pollen-nectar masses packed solidly into the borings were 9-50 mm. long (mean 24) and contained 3-16 eggs (mean 6.5). In 1 cell the bee packed pollen and nectar into the bottom half of the boring for a distance of 12 mm. and laid 2 eggs on the mass. There were 1-4 brood cells (mean 2.4) in 10 nests in 12.7-mm. borings (figs. 92-96).

Vestibular cells were lacking in most of the 17 nests completed by *policaris*. However, there were 2 such cells 25-47 mm. long in 6.4-mm. borings and 2 cells 20-35 mm. long in 12.7-mm. borings. One of the latter cells was divided into 2 sections by a partition 5 mm. thick.

The partitions between the provisioned cells were usually 0.5-5 mm. thick, although there were 2 of 8 and 12 mm., respectively. These were compound partitions consisting usually of 2 layers of small compressed leaflets 2-9 mm. long separated by thin septa of hardened, gummy leaf pulp. Occasionally in thicker plugs there were several alternating layers of these materials.

The closing plugs capping either the last stored cell or the vestibular cell, when one was present, were 5-25 mm. thick (mean 12). They were constructed of these same materials in alternating layers. One plug had 4 layers of leaflets 1-3 mm. thick separated by thin septa of tough, gummy leaf pulp. The leaflets used in constructing the plug in 1 Arizona nest were identified as coming from a species of *Prosopis* (mesquite), *Mimosa biuncifera* (cat claw acacia), *Eysenhardtia polystachya* (kidneywood), and an unidentified species of shrub. In 1 Arizona nest there were some flower petals in the partition and the closing plug as well as the usual leaflets and leaf pulp. In the single Florida nest the closing plug consisted of about 3 layers each of alternating leaf cuttings and small leaflets and hardened leaf pulp. This was the only specimen of *policaris* which made leaf cuttings from whole leaves; the Arizona bees used the small whole leaflets only.

Larval food. Pollen masses from 4 cells in 1 Arizona nest in which larvae failed to develop and from a cell in another Arizona nest were identified as being composed of 100 per cent *Prosopis* (mesquite).

Life history. An examination of the large pollen masses in brood cells in which the occupants died as eggs or young larvae showed the following method of provisioning: The bee stored several millimeters of pollen and nectar at the inner end of the cell. Then she made a small hollow at the side of this mass, probably by thrusting the tip of her abdomen into the soft pollen, and laid an egg in it. Then she gathered more pollen, made another egg chamber, and so on (fig. 92).

The single nest from Florida must have been completed during May, probably early in the month, because when I opened the nest on June 9 the larvae had finished feeding and were ready to spin their cocoons. Most of the bees pupated June 17-22. Some of the adults were eclosed but still in their cocoons on July 18. Four females and 10 males emerged from the nest July 21-24.

Most of the Arizona nests were also stored early in the season, 1 of them being completed by May 4. Adults emerged from these nests August 6-19. A few Arizona nests were stored between September 9 and October 18; there were still feeding larvae in 2 of these nests as late as November 3 while others were spinning their cocoons on that date. Occupants of these latter nests overwintered outdoors as diapausing larvae and adults emerged the following spring. The period between pupation and adult emergence was 33-34 days for 1 female in an overwintering nest.

The cocoons, 12-15 mm. long, were spun from delicate, white, opaque silk; they were not varnished (figs. 95-96).

In the 8 nests from which I reared *policaris*, females only were obtained from 2 nests, males only from 4 nests, and both sexes from 2 nests. It is quite likely that both sexes might have developed in more of the nests had there not been so much mortality of immatures. The cause of this mortality of eggs and young larvae was not determined, but it certainly was not due to cannibalism or to an insufficient store of food.

The arrangement of sexes was not noted in the 1 mixed nest from Arizona from which I reared adults. However, in the mixed nest from Florida both sexes developed in at least 3 of the 4 brood cells. There was concurrent emergence of both sexes from these 2 mixed nests.

There was another mixed nest from Arizona from which I failed to rear any adults. It contained three brood cells. Eleven bee pupae were injured and killed when *Leucospis affinis* adults emerged earlier from 5 other cocoons in these cells and made disoriented efforts to escape from the nest. However, I was able to ascertain that brood cells 1 and 2 contained both male and female bees.

Males emerged from 1 overwintering nest 4 days earlier than females from the other overwintering nest.

I reared 26 females and 42 males from approximately 75 eggs.

Parasites and predators. The parasitic bee *Coelioxys texana* Cresson parasitized 1 cell in each of 2 nests presumably stored by *policaris* at Portal.

The chalcidoid *Leucospis a. affinis* Say parasitized 5 of 17 bees in a nest from Portal.

An unidentified dermestid larva infested 2 cells of a nest in the field at Portal.

Melittobia chalybii Ashmead infested 1 of the Portal nests in the laboratory, and the grain itch mite *Pyemotes ventricosus* (Newport) infested an additional 4 nests in the laboratory.

Source material.
Lake Placid, Fla. 1961 series: F 135.
Portal, Ariz. 1959 series: X 161 (?), 162 (?), 164, 254, 255 (?), 256, 257. 1960 series: X 224 (?). 1961 series: G 116 (?), 117 (?), 126 (?), 136, 146 (?), 214 (?), 217 (?), 218, 390, 398 (?).

Identifications. Pollen by P. S. Martin; plant leaflets by W. Niles; *Leucospis* by B. D. Burks; bees and wasps by the author.

CHALICODOMA (CHELOSTOMOIDES) GEORGICA (Cresson)

I reared this bee from 17 nests from 13 stations at Lake Placid, Fla. Ten nests were in 4.8-mm., 4 in 6.4-mm., and 3 in 12.7-mm. borings. All the stations were in the sand-scrub area of the Archbold Biological Station. Eight nests were from settings beneath limbs of live scrub hickory, 4 on the side of pine trunks, 3 beneath oak limbs, and 1 each on an oak trunk and beneath a fallen dead limb.

Supersedure and competition. C. georgica superseded *Euodynerus foraminatus apopkensis* (Robertson) in 2 borings and was superseded by *Pachodynerus erynnis* (Lepeletier) in 2. There was no competition in the first 2 nests, but there was in at least 1 of the latter 2.

Nest architecture. The bees placed resin at the inner end of the boring in half of the nests, and in the other half they left an empty space 6-47 mm. long and then made a narrow resin partition.

The cell walls opposite the pollen-nectar masses were coated with resin in the 4.8- and 6.4-mm. nests; the coated portion occupied about the posterior two-thirds of the cell. The pollen mass was 7 mm. long in a female cell in a 4.8-mm. boring. In the 12.7-mm. borings all the cell walls and ends were made of resin.

Thirty-six stored cells in 4.8-mm. borings were 14-32 mm. long (mean 18); abnormally long female and male cells, 135 and 107 mm. long, respectively, were not included in the foregoing figures. Eleven female cells were 14-22 mm. long (mean 18) and a dozen male cells were 15-32 mm. (mean 20). There was an empty intercalary cell 33 mm. long between 2 stored cells.

Twenty-two stored cells in 6.4-mm. borings were 13-45 mm. long (mean 19). Five female cells were 14-45 mm. (mean 24), and 5 male cells were 13-20 mm. (mean 16).

There were 2 kinds of nests in the 12.7-mm. borings. In 1 boring the bee coated the walls with a very thick layer of resin and had 2 stored cells, end to end, in the inner 25 mm. In the other 2 nests the bees made the cell walls and ends from resin, but the walls were thinner and the cells were more or less side by side, or placed in an oblique series. In 1 nest there were 14 such cells in the inner 80 mm. sealed by a 15-mm. plug of resin. In the other there were 6 cells in the inner 50 mm. sealed by a 3-mm. plug of resin.

Vestibular cells 10-62 mm. long (mean 25) were present in 3 of the 7 completed nests in 4.8-mm. borings and in 2 of the 3 completed nests in 6.4-mm. borings. There were no vestibular cells in 12.7-mm. borings.

The cell partitions and closing plugs were made of resin. The partitions were usually 1-3 mm. thick, although occasionally they were as much as 8 mm. in thickness. The closing plugs were 2-18 mm. thick (mean 6).

There were 1-9 stored cells (mean 4) in eight 4.8-mm. borings completely stored by *georgica,* 4-6 cells in two 6.4-mm. borings, and 2-14 cells (mean 7) in three 12.7-mm. borings.

Life history. Nests were completed from early in June until late in November or early in December. Adults emerged July 15 to October 18 from nests completed by the end of August. Occupants of nests completed after mid-August went into prolonged larval diapause and required exposure to chilly weather for 2 months before they pupated and eclosed as adults. In 1 nest picked up and mailed to me in mid-December there were a nearly mature larva in cell 1 and smaller feeding larvae in cells 2 and 3 when I opened the nest on December 30.

The period between completion of the nest and emergence of adults was about 33-40 days in 2 nests stored during June and the first week in July. This period required 45-60 days in 2 nests stored during mid-July and mid-August.

A male egg hatched July 20 and the adult emerged from the nest on September 1. When I opened another nest on June 14, a small larva had just begun to void fecal pellets; by July 1 it was a pale pupa with black eyes; on July 11 a female eclosed and left the nest on the 15th. The period between pupation and adult emergence was 26-30 and 32-39 days for 2 females from 2 overwintering nests. Several adults spent 4-7 days in the cocoons after eclosion from the pupal exuvia.

The cocoons were spun from delicate, white, unvarnished silk. The walls were semitransparent to subopaque and the outer end was more opaque. Nine female cocoons in 4.8-mm. nests were 11-16 mm. long (mean 13) and 7 male cocoons were 10-14 (mean 11).

I reared 23 females and 23 males from 66 stored cells. In the 20 cells from which I failed to rear adults, females would probably have developed in at least 4 cells and males in at least 5 cells. I reared females only from 7 nests, males only from 4 nests, and both sexes from 6 nests. Females were in the inner and males in the outer cells in all mixed nests.

In individual mixed nests males emerged 2-10 days earlier than their sisters.

Parasites and predators. The parasitic bee *Coelioxys modesta* Smith parasitized 6 of 10 cells in 2 nests from a single station. Both nests might have been stored by the same mother *georgica* and parasitized by the same *modesta* female.

The chalcidoid *Leucospis affinis floridana* Cresson parasitized 3 of 11 cells in the other 2 nests.

Source material.

Lake Placid, Fla. 1957 series: M 252, 281. 1959 series: V 152. 1960 series: B 91, 146, 173, 219, 220, 223, 235, 237. 1961 series: F 220, 311, 313. 1962 series: P 41, 148, 212.

Identifications. *Coelioxys* by T. B. Mitchell; *Leucospis* by B. D. Burks; *Chalicodoma* and wasps by the author.

CHALICODOMA (CHELOSTOMOIDES) EXILIS PAREXILIS (Mitchell)

I reared this bee from 3 nests from 3 stations in the sand-scrub area of the Archbold Biological Station, Lake Placid, Fla., in 1962. Two were in 4.8-mm. borings and one was in a 6.4-mm. boring. Two were from stations beneath limbs of live scrub hickory and one was from the side of an oak trunk.

Nest architecture. In 1 nest the bee put a thin coating of resin at the inner end of the boring before storing pollen and nectar, and in the other nests the females left an empty space 43-88 mm. long and then made a resin partition before beginning to store pollen.

There were 4-7 stored cells 12-19 mm. long (mean 14) in the two 4.8-mm. nests. Four female cells were 15-19 mm. long (mean 17) and 3 male cells 12-14 mm. long (mean 13). The pollen-nectar masses of both female and male cells were 5 mm. long. The bee did not complete one of the nests. The other had a vestibular cell 17 mm. long with a compound closing plug 7 mm. thick consisting of a section of resin and then bits of leaf, bark and wood fiber.

The single nest in the 6.4-mm. boring had 4 stored cells 9-11 mm. long. One female was reared from a cell 11 mm. long. This nest had a vestibular cell 10 mm. long and a simple closing plug of resin 2 mm. thick.

The partitions capping the stored cells were of resin and were 0.5 mm. thick.

Life history. The first nest was probably completed the first week of August. When I opened it on the 8th, I found dead eggs in cells 3 and 4 and a small dead larva in cell 2. The occupant of cell 1 pupated before August 24, and I found a dead female *parexilis* in this cocoon on September 16.

The second nest was completed the week of October 16. When I opened it on October 24, there were a small larva in cell 1, successively smaller larvae in cells 2-5, and eggs in cells 6 and 7. The eggs, 3.8 mm. long and 1.0 mm. wide, were lying on top of the moist pollen mass with the lower end somewhat embedded. I exposed this nest to chilly weather outdoors from November 6 to December 10. In my office there was no development after this period, so I exposed it outdoors again from January 2 to February 10. After this second period of cold treatment at least 1 of the occupants pupated March 12-16, and another emerged as an adult on May 4.

The third nest in a 6.4-mm. boring was abandoned before completion on some undetermined date, mailed to me on December 31, and opened on January 5. On that date the occupants of the 3 cells were diapausing larvae in cocoons 9-10 mm. long. I placed the nests outdoors in chilly weather until March 5. Pupation took place in my office March 17-April 2, and 3 females emerged on April 30.

Source material.
   Lake Placid, Fla. 1962 series: F 25, 43, 91.

Identifications by the author.

CHALICODOMA (CHELOSTOMOIDES) CAMPANULAE
CAMPANULAE (Robertson)

I reared this bee from 2 nests from Rochester, N. Y., in 1954. These were in 6.4-mm. borings from a setting on the side of a wooden garage.

One nest was completed July 31, the other sometime before August 25.

Nest architecture. At the inner end of both nests the mother bee left an empty space of 53-70 mm., sealed by a resin partition. The 8 and 9 stored cells in the 2 nests were 8-14 mm. long (mean 9). Each nest had a vestibular cell 5 mm. long. The partitions capping the cells and the closing plugs were narrow and made of dark resin.

Life history. Occupants of the nests overwintered outdoors as diapausing larvae in their moderately tough white cocoons. Pupation took place late in April or early in May and adults emerged 28-30 days later.

Previous observations. Rau (1926, pp. 202-203) reported that 1 of these bees entered a burrow in a vertical clay bank in Missouri. He found a quantity of resinous material in the burrow when he excavated it but did not know whether the bee or some other insect was responsible for placing it there.

Source material.
Rochester, N. Y. 1954 series: R 5, 6.

Identifications by the author.

CHALICODOMA (CHELOSTOMOIDES) CAMPANULAE
WILMINGTONI (Mitchell)

I reared this resin-using bee from 2 nests from 2 stations at Kill Devil Hills, N. C., in 1956 and from 5 nests from 5 stations at Lake Placid, Fla., in 1959, 1961, and 1962. Four nests were in 4.8-mm. and 3 in 6.4-mm. borings. The North Carolina nests were from open wooded areas beneath dead limbs of hickory and loblolly pine. The Florida nests were from the sand-scrub area of the Archbold Biological Station, 3 of them beneath limbs of scrub hickory and 2 beneath living and dead oak limbs.

Nest architecture. In 3 borings the bees left an empty space 8-69 mm. long at the inner end and then made a narrow partition of resin. The walls on the inner half of each cell opposite the pollen-nectar mass were coated with resin.

Twenty-four stored cells in 4.8-mm. borings were 14-62 mm. long (mean 19); 4 female cells were 18-62 mm. (mean 30) and 4 male cells were 16-20 (mean 18). Fifteen stored cells in 6.4-mm. borings were 13-25 mm. long (mean 16); 4 female cells were 15-25 mm. (mean 19) and 3 male cells were 13-16 mm. (mean 14).

There were 6 completed nests. All but 1 of them had a vestibular cell 5-48 mm. long (mean 23).

The partitions capping the cells were made of light to dark resin and were usually 1-3 mm. thick, although occasionally the terminal stored cell had a thicker partition of 5-8 mm. The closing plugs, usually made of resin, were 0.3-3 mm. thick. However, in 1 nest this plug was thicker and made up of debris, mainly leaf bits and small pieces of bark. Perhaps this last boring was capped by some individual other than the bee which nested therein.

There were 4-9 stored cells (mean 6) in 4.8-mm. borings and 5-6 cells in 6.4-mm. borings.

Life history. The 2 nests at Kill Devil Hills were stored during August. When I examined the nests on September 9, their occupants, except for 2 nearly mature larvae, were already in cocoons. The occupants overwintered outdoors as diapausing larvae and adults emerged early the next summer.

The 5 nests at Lake Placid also were stored late in the season, during September and October. Their occupants also overwintered as diapausing larvae but were subjected to only 2 months of chilly weather before being brought into my warm office. Adults emerged 2-3 months later.

Evidence from these nests suggests that this bee may be univoltine. The period between pupation and adult emergence was 23 days for a female from North Carolina, 26-29 days for 2 males from Florida nests and 51-59 days for 1 female from a Florida nest.

Nine female cocoons were 10-18 mm. long (mean 12) and 5 males were 9-11 mm. The cocoons were delicate, white, and transparent to opaque and had a small dense, opaque white cap at the anterior end.

Females were in the inner and males in the outer cells in all mixed nests. There were several nests from which I obtained only females or only males. I reared 10 females and 7 males from 41 stored cells. In the 24 cells from which I failed to rear adults, females would probably have developed in at least 2 and males in at least 7 cells.

Parasites and predators. I reared *Coelioxys modesta* Smith from 11 of 20 cells in 3 nests at Lake Placid.

Source material.
    Kill Devil Hills, N. C. 1956 series: C 213, 244.
    Lake Placid, Fla. 1959 series: V 122 ,126. 1961 series: F 351. 1961 series:
        P 192, 213.

Identifications. Coelioxys by T. B. Mitchell; *Chalicodoma* by the author.

CHALICODOMA (CHELOSTOMOIDES) SUBEXILIS (Cockerell)

I received a single nest of this bee in a 6.4-mm. boring from a station beneath the limb of a pine tree above Oak Creek Canyon, Ariz., in 1957.

Nest architecture. The nest was still being stored when it was picked up on September 18. It contained 7 completed cells 13-15 mm. long, and the anterior end of an eighth cell 15 mm. long was delimited by an annulus of resin. The partitions capping the cells were of clear resin 0.2-0.5 mm. thick. There was a little resin at the inner end of the boring and some resin was smeared on the walls in streaks.

Life history. When I opened the nest on October 3, the occupants of cells 1-7 were already in delicate, silken, subopaque white cocoons 8-9 mm. long. The larvae in cells 1-6 had already entered diapause, but that in cell 7 was still active, and so I preserved it for taxonomic study. The nest was placed outdoors for the winter and brought indoors again early in April. Some of the larvae pupated May 5 and adults had eclosed by May 26. I removed these 5 females from their cocoons 2 days later. A sixth female in cell 1 was still a pupa on May 28; she emerged from the nest on June 9.

Previous observations. Hicks (1927) reported a 2-celled nest of *subexilis* in a burrow 7.5 cm. long in a vertical sandstone cliff in Colorado. There were 2 cells surrounded by resin 2-4 mm. thick, separated from each other by a thin resin partition. The plug at the burrow entrance, also of resin, was 5 mm. long and 5 mm. thick. He reared a *subexilis* from a thin cocoon in the outer cell and its parasite *Coelioxys gilensis* Cockerell from a thicker cocoon in the inner cell. The *gilensis* larva overwintered in diapause and Hicks thought it likely that the *subexilis* also had overwintered in that stage.

Source material.
Oak Creek Canyon, Ariz. 1957 series: Q 31.

Identifications by the author.

CHALICODOMA (CHELOSTOMOIDES) OCCIDENTALIS (Fox)

I reared this bee from 3 nests from 3 stations at Portal, Ariz., in 1959 and 1961 and from 1 nest at Granite Reef Dam, Ariz., in 1961. The Portal nests were in 6.4-mm. borings and the Granite Reef Dam nest was in a 4.8-mm. boring. All nests were from stations on the desert floor, 2 of them from a mesquite branch or trunk and 1 each from a branch of juniper and palo verde.

Supersedure and competition. The bee superseded *Trypargilum tridentatum* (Packard) in 1 nest at Portal, but this was not a result of competition.

Nest architecture. The cell ends and walls opposite the pollen-nectar masses were coated with resin.

There were 6 stored cells 14-16 mm. long in the 4.8-mm. boring, females in cells 1 and 2 and males in cells 3-6. The partitions capping the cells were of clear resin 0.5-0.75 mm. thick. The pollen-nectar masses were 6-7 mm. long. The nest had not been completed when it was picked up.

In the 6.4-mm. nests there were 10 stored cells 14-43 mm. long (mean 18); 5 female cells were 14-17 mm. and 4 male cells 14-18 mm. long. The abnormally long 43-mm. cell was only partly stored, and it did not contain an egg. The resin partitions capping these cells were 0.5-4 mm. thick. Each of the nests had a vestibular cell 15-72 mm. long (mean 41); 1 of the cells was divided into 2 sections by a cross partition of resin. The closing plugs were of clear resin 2-4 mm. thick, except in 1 nest where there was a little earth or other debris mixed with the resin.

Life history. Adults emerged July 21-25 from 2 nests stored late in May and early in June, and August 4 from a nest stored during the middle of June. Obviously, there are at least 2 generations a season in Arizona.

The period between pupation and adult emergence was 31 days for 3 males and 31-33 days for 2 females.

The cocoons were delicate, white, silken, and semitransparent except for the opaque anterior cap. Cocoons of 4 females were 11-12 mm. long and 6 males were 10-11 mm. long.

I reared 7 females and 7 males from 15 completely stored cells. Only females were reared from 1 nest and both sexes from 3 nests. Females were in the inner and both sexes in the outer cells in the mixed nests. Males emerged 1-3 days earlier than their sisters in individual mixed nests.

Previous observations. Mitchell (1956, p. 132) stated that Linsley had found a nest of *occidentalis* in an adobe wall in California.

Source material.
    Portal, Ariz. 1959 series: X 180. 1961 series: G 101, 262.
    Granite Reef Dam, Ariz. 1961 series: H 49.

Identifications by the author.

Family XYLOCOPIDAE

The only xylocopid bees using these traps were the 2 eastern races of the large carpenter bee *Xylocopa v. virginica* (Linnaeus) and *v. krombeini* Hurd. Their nest architecture differed from that of all other bees and wasps using these borings in that the partition sealing each stored cell was made from a long ribbon of cemented wood chips wound into a spiral closure (fig. 101). These bees were also unique in having a gigantic egg 20 mm. long, in having the mother sometimes (always ?) remain in the nest long after the cells were stored, and in having the pupae orient with their heads toward the inner end of the boring.

XYLOCOPA (XYLOCOPOIDES) VIRGINICA VIRGINICA (Linnaeus)

I obtained 1 nest of the large carpenter bee in a 12.7-mm. boring suspended from a porch rafter of the cabin at Plummers Island, Md., in 1958. The female *virginica* began to nest in it the week of May 29. When I probed the boring with a grass stem on June 4, I found her inside and discovered that she had stored cells in the inner 50 mm. of the boring. Apparently my probing caused her to abandon the nest because when I picked it up on June 8, I found a female *Osmia lignaria* inside. She had completed with mud the partition of wood fibers closing cell 3, which had been started by the *virginica* female, and had begun to provision the first of her own cells.

Nest architecture. The 3 *Xylocopa* cells were 21-22 mm. long. The partitions closing the first 2 cells were 3-4 mm. thick at the edges and somewhat thinner in the middle. They were made from tiny wood chips rasped from the boring walls and firmly cemented together, presumably by a salivary secretion. The inner surface of the partition was roughened and convex, the outer surface smooth and concave. The pollen masses in cells 1-3 were well saturated with nectar; they were 14 mm. long, flattened on top and they filled the lower half of the cell.

Life history. There were a newly hatched larva in cell 1, an egg in cell 2 which must have been laid June 4 or a day or two earlier, but no egg was present in cell 3. The egg was curved, 20 mm. long, and 2 mm. wide. The larva began to hatch from it at 1000 hours on June 9. The larvae were voracious feeders. The one in cell 2 began to void long, narrow fecal pellets on June 14, the other larva having begun to do this a day or two earlier. The larva in cell 1 completed feeding at noon June 19 and was preserved for taxonomic study. The larva in cell 2 finished feeding by 1600 on the same day. On June 25 the eye disks of the developing pupa were showing through the larval integument and pupation occurred on the 28th. The pupa was misoriented and lay with its head toward the inner end of the boring. The eyes were black by July 7; by the 14th the entire pupa was dark and the adult was presumably ready to eclose. An adult female emerged from the nest on July 18. She had been able to orient herself properly and did not chew through the partition closing cell 1 before emerging.

Previous observations. Balduf (1962) gave an excellent summary of the numerous earlier published notes on this carpenter bee in which he incorporated a number of his previously unpublished observations. *X. virginica* prefers to nest in sound structural timber or dead wood. Coniferous wood is preferred to that from deciduous trees, although the bee will nest in either. The burrows follow the grain of the wood and occasionally there are 2 or more subsidiary parallel branches. The carpenter bee prefers to use old borings and cleans out the debris from a previous nest. Colonies were observed using the same tunnels for as long as 14 years. The new tunnels are uniform in diameter, but they become larger and irregular as they are used in subsequent years because the bees rasp out wood chips from the boring walls to construct the cell partitions.

In constructing the cell partition the bee makes a long ribbon of wood pulp which she "winds spirally, ring within ring, until the intercellular space" is sealed. The inner face of the partition is concave and smooth, and the outer convex face is roughened by an additional coating of wood chips. This is the reverse of the situation as I observed it, where the inner face is convex and roughened because of the spiral ribbon, and the outer face concave and smooth, presumably shaped in this way by pressure from the bee's head.

Cells in natural situations are described as being cylindrical and about 18 mm. long. Several observers noted that the female works in a very leisurely fashion. Rau thought that an individual female probably stored no more than 6-8 cells during her lifetime.

Rau found that the egg hatches in 2 days, a much shorter period than seemed likely for the 1 example I noted. Inasmuch as the egg is so gigantic, it appears that a somewhat longer period than 2 days should be expected. No observations were made on the duration of the larval and pupal stages, nor were any estimates available on the length of the life cycle, egg to adult. My figure of 44-47 days for this period in a female *virginica* agrees with the 43-day figure cited for a female of the Palaearctic *X. valga* Gerstaecker in Russia.

Most observers noted only a single generation a year, with adults overwintering in the tunnels after having been active in the field for several weeks. However, Hubbard said that carpenter bees in Crescent City, Fla., bred without intermission throughout the year. It is probable that his observations were made on the Floridian race, *virginica krombeini* Hurd.

The only parasites recorded by earlier workers are the bombyliid flies *Anthrax sinuosus* Wiedemann and *A. simson* (Fabricius).

Source material.
    Plummers Island, Md. 1958 series: S 79.

Identifications by the author.

XYLOCOPA (XYLOCOPOIDES) VIRGINICA KROMBEINI Hurd
(Plate, 20, Figure 101)

The type series of this Floridian race of the eastern carpenter bee consisted almost entirely of the bees obtained from 4 nests in 12.7-mm. borings from Lake Placid, Fla., in 1960. The nests came from 4 different stations in the sand-scrub area of the Archbold Biological Station, 3 from settings beneath live limbs of scrub hickory and 1 from a setting on a dead oak tree.

Nest architecture. The nests were picked up on May 17, 24, 31, and June 28. The live mother bee was present in each nest when it was picked up. There were 18 stored cells 19-23 mm. long (mean 20); I reared male bees from 3 cells 19-20 mm. long and a female from a cell 22 mm. long. There were 1-6 stored cells in each of the 4 nests.

The partitions capping the cells were 2-3 mm. thick. They were made from tiny bits of wood rasped from the boring walls and tightly cemented together, presumably by a salivary secretion. The inner surfaces of these partitions (fig. 101) showed a spiral pattern, indicating the course of construction, and the outer surfaces were smooth and shallowly concave where the female bee had compacted the fibers by pressing them, presumably with her head.

Life history. The pollen masses were quite moist with nectar. They were 10-15 mm. long, flat on the upper surface, and filled the lower half of each cell.

Occupants of cells were mature larvae or well-colored pupae when I received the nests. This suggests that the mothers may remain with the nests for a considerable period after the cells are stored.

In a 5-celled nest picked up on May 17, the larvae in cells 4 and 5 finished feeding by May 19 or perhaps by the preceding day. They pupated May 27 and 2 adult males left the nest on June 20. If we assume a larval feeding period of the same duration as in typical *virginica*, it appears that those cells must have been stored about May 1 and that the eggs probably hatched around the 8th.

In a 6-celled nest picked up on May 24 a larva in cell 3 pupated June 11-20. The adult male emerged June 30.

All prepupae and pupae lay with their heads toward the inner end of the borings. However, the adults were always able to orient themselves properly for emergence from the nests without chewing through the partitions separating them from the blind inner end of the boring.

I reared only 3 males and 1 female from the 18 stored cells. The female came from 1 nest and the males from 2 others.

Parasites and predators. All the nests had infestations of the acarid mite *Horstia virginica* Baker, which also was described from these nests. There were dead eggs or small larvae of *krombeini* in 11 cells; and it seemed likely that this mortality was caused by the mites. However, adult bees did develop in a few cells infested by the mites; perhaps the mites did not gain access to these particular cells until the bee larvae were full grown or nearly so.

Source material.
    Lake Placid, Fla. 1960 series: B 66, 106, 189, 190.

Identifications. Acarina by E. W. Baker; *Xylocopa* by P. D. Hurd, Jr.

PARASITES AND PREDATORS

Order ACARINA

I obtained representatives of 5 families of mites in these trap nests. One of them was the pyemotid *Pyemotes ventricosus* (Newport), a general ectoparasite of insect larvae and a serious pest in laboratory cultures (fig. 108). The species of Acaridae and Anoetidae usually occurred just as scavengers in the nests although their activities sometimes resulted in the death of the wasp occupants of the mite-infested cells. Another family was the Chaetodactylidae in which the adult mites killed the bee egg or young larva. Most of the mite species belonged to the Saproglyphidae, in which the adult and protonymphal mites fed on the wasp prepupae and pupae but did not cause mortality, and the hypopial mites congregated in acarinaria or on other specialized areas on the adult wasps.

The acarinarium is a chamber, on or within the body of the adult wasp, in which the mite hypopi, the deutonymphal resting stage, congregate. In the vespids *Monobia* and *Stenodynerus (Parancistrocerus)* these chambers are located at the base of the second abdominal tergum and are covered by the apex of the first tergum when the abdomen extends straight backward (fig. 102). The vespid *Ancistrocerus* does not have such a chamber; its mites cluster on the lateral and posterior surfaces of the propodeum (*A. antilope*) or beneath the apices of some of the posterior abdominal terga (*A. tigris*). Occasionally, as in *Monobia quadridens* and *Ancistrocerus antilope*, these mites may also congregate in the male genital chamber or in the female sting chamber.

Histiostoma myrmicarum Scheucher (?) was the only anoetid mite. I found it once in a nest of *Podium rufipes* (Fabricius), where it may have caused the death of the wasp egg or young larva. It was apparently going through its life cycle on the decaying cockroaches stored as prey for the *Podium* larva. In Europe the mite is associated with ants. Presumably it may have been brought into the nest by the *rufipes* mother when she constructed the closing plug of the nest from debris obtained on the ground.

There were 4 species of acarid mites in these nests, *Tortonia quadridens* Baker, *Horstia virginica* Baker, *Lackerbaueria krombeini* Baker (Krombein, 1962a), and an unidentified species of

349

Tyrophagus. The hypopi of the first 3 acarid mites usually occurred at random on the body of the host wasp or bee, although *Tortonia* hypopi were found once in the acarinarium beneath the apex of the first abdominal tergum of the host wasp *Monobia quadridens* (Linnaeus). So far as observed these acarids have the usual life cycle of egg-larva-protonymph-deutonymph(=hypopus)-tritonymph-adult; occasionally the deutonymph stage was omitted. The *Lackerbaueria* mites were associated with several species of pemphredonine wasps; they killed the host egg or young larva before developing on the aphids stored as prey. *Horstia* mites sometimes killed the *Xylocopa* egg or young larva before developing on the nectar in the pollen-nectar mass stored as food for the bee larva; occasionally the bees were able to develop successfully in mite-infested cells, but these bee larvae may have reached maturity before their cells were invaded by mites. The *Tortonia* mites appeared to act as scavengers only and did not cause mortality of the *Monobia* eggs or larvae. The fourth acarid, *Tyrophagus* sp., was found in 1 or more nests of *Trypargilum striatum* (Provancher).

Chaetodactylus krombeini Baker was the only chaetodactylid on which extensive developmental notes were made (Krombein, 1962b). Its behavior was different from that of most other mites observed in these nests in that the adult mites searched out and killed the *Osmia lignaria* egg or young larva in the infested cells. The mites then went through a cycle egg-larva-protonymph-tritonymph-adult, developing on the nectar in the pollen-nectar mass stored as food for the bee larva (figs. 111, 112). When this supply of food was nearly or entirely exhausted, an apodous, encysted hypopial form developed within the protonymphal skin (figs. 113, 114); the mites overwintered in this form. In the spring when the adult bees in adjacent cells were ready to leave the nests, these hypopi transformed into the active hypopial form with 8 legs, which climbed onto the body of an adult bee as it passed through the infested cells.

The saproglyphid mites have become perfectly adapted to a parasitic existence on their host vespid wasps (Krombein, 1961). Although several stages of the mites sucked blood from the wasp prepupae and pupae, they never caused wasp mortality so far as I observed. The associations have reached such a state of intimacy in several genera that specialized internal chambers have been developed in the adult host wasps to house the hypopial stage of the mite (figs. 102, 110).

A composite life history of the saproglyphid mites, based mainly on the several species of *Vespacarus*, can be summarized as follows: One or more mite hypopi drop off the female wasp as she lays an egg or provisions the cell with prey. The hypopi presumably transform into a tritonymphal stage, though occasionally this stage may be omitted. Adult mites (figs. 27, 104) are present in the cells by the time the wasp larvae have spun cocoons and entered the prepupal period, roughly 10-12 days. The adult mites suck blood from the prepupa, as is evidenced by tiny black scabs marking the sites of feeding punctures.

K. W. Cooper advises me (*in litt.*) that the hypopus usually develops into a female mite. The female mite need not lay a parthenogenetic egg; a male may develop within the body of the female. After he is born he mates with his mother and she then proceeds to lay fertilized eggs on the newly transformed wasp pupa (fig. 106). Cooper's finding is confirmed by circumstantial evidence —one usually finds equal numbers of adult female and male mites in a single cell during the later stages of an infestation.

These eggs hatch in 2-12 days. Cooper finds that the female may retain the eggs in the abdomen for some days so that at times it appears that eggs hatch in a very short time after being laid and at other times they require a much longer time. The 6-legged larvae which hatch from the eggs transform in 1-2 days into 8-legged protonymphs (fig. 107), which also feed on the pupae of the wasp. As the time of eclosion of the adult wasp nears, these protonymphs cluster on the venter of the pupa along the legs, thoracic sternum, and mesopleuron (fig. 109). They transform to deutonymphs either just before or shortly after the wasp sheds the pupal exuvia. They remain with the exuvia as it is being shed, but during the next 24 hours they crawl back onto the wasp and enter the acarinarium or one of the other special surfaces, where they congregate (fig. 110). When an infested female wasp begins to nest, several of the hypopi drop off to begin the life cycle anew.

The generalized sketch above fits most species of the mite genus *Vespacarus*, whose members are host specific on species of *Stenodynerus* subgenus *Parancistrocerus* and *Ancistrocerus t. tigris*. All the species of *Parancistrocerus* have an acarinarium consisting of a depressed area at the base of the second abdominal tergum (fig. 102). This chamber is normally covered by the apex of the first tergum when the abdomen is straightened out. Although the morphology of these acarinaria has not been investigated, it appears that each wasp species has a slightly differently shaped chamber for reception of its specific mites. *Ancistrocerus t. tigris* does not have an acarinarium; the hypopi cluster in transverse rows beneath the apices of some of the posterior abdominal terga. So far as is known, both sexes of adult wasps are infested by *Vespacarus* in the individual cells in the nest. The mites are not transferred from male to female during mating, as happens in the saproglyphid mite *Kennethiella*, nor are the *Vespacarus* mites found in the genital chamber of the female or male wasp as in *Kennethiella* and *Monobiacarus*.

The saproglyphid species *Monobiacarus quadridens*, a symbiont of *Monobia quadridens,* differs in several details from the generalized sketch presented above. The hypopi congregate in the male genital chamber or on the genitalia, and in the female sting chamber or on the sting and associated structures. Presumably there may be venereal transfer of mites from infested males to mite-free females during mating. Although the adult mites are found on the mature wasp larvae (fig. 27), they apparently do not feed on it but leave it as soon as it becomes a prepupa. The mite eggs are laid on the walls and anterior end of the cell. I was unable to follow the life history further because the mite populations died of desiccation shortly after the nests were opened for study. It is presumed that the mite food consists of organic debris in the cell. It is also thought that the mite hypopi gain access to the male or female genital chamber within a day or two after eclosion of the adult wasp and before it leaves its cell.

The saproglyphid *Kennethiella trisetosa* is a symbiont of *Ancistrocerus a. antilope* and *A. spinolae.* It differs in certain details from the generalized biology discussed above, and the wasp also differs in the accommodations provided for the mite on the adult wasp and the reactions of the female wasp larva to the mite. When the adult wasps emerge from the nest, the females are mite-free or bear only a few hypopi probably picked up as they traverse infested male cells closer to the entrance. However, the males from infested cells bear large loads of hypopi on the specialized lateral and posterior surfaces of the propodeum. When the wasps mate, large numbers of hypopi leave the propodeum, crawl down the male abdomen, and enter the genital chambers of both wasps. After this venereal transmission of mites, hypopi can leave the infested female wasp as she provisions a cell.

Development of the immature *Kennethiella* mites progresses during the feeding period of the larval wasp, as detailed above. When the wasp larvae have consumed their store of caterpillars, the male larva in a mite-infested cell cocoons normally. However, the female wasp larva in a mite-infested cell will not spin her cocoon until she has searched out and eaten all of the mites in her cell. (This explains why newly emerged female wasps are mite-free.)

The immature *Kennethiella* mites differ in one other behavioral detail from *Vespacarus* mites. When the protonymphs are ready to transform to deutonymphs, they cluster on the anterior end of the cocoon wall for the molt.

An undescribed species of the saproglyphid mite *Vidia* was found in 2 nests of the leaf cutter bee *Megachile mendica* Cresson and in 2 nests of *M. xylocopoides* Smith. There were small dead bee larvae in some of the cells from which I recovered mites. It was not certain whether the mites had killed the bee larvae, but they had not fed on the stored pollen-nectar mass. In 1 nest, eggs, protonymphs and adults were found on the meconial pellets of the larval bee between the outer cocoon wall and the leaf cuttings forming the cell.

Family SAPROGLYPHIDAE

VESPACARUS ANACARDIVORUS Baker and Cunliffe

This mite was present in the 2 nests of *Stenodynerus* (*Parancistrocerus*) *perennis ancardivora* (Rohwer) which I received from the Archbold Biological Station, Lake Placid, Fla., in 1961. When I opened the nest for study, all the pupae in 1 nest contained immature mites. However, none of the adult wasps which emerged subsequently bore mite loads in the acarinarium.

Krombein and Evans (1955, pp. 228-229) reported finding a nest of *perennis anacardivora* in a twig at Paradise Key, Everglades National Park, Fla. The 2 completely stored cells in this nest were infested with mites. Three adult female mites were recovered from 1 cell and 1 female mite from the other.

Source material.
  Lake Placid, Fla. 1961 series: F 17, 18.

Identifications. Acarina by E. W. Baker; wasps by the author.

VESPACARUS FULVIPES Baker and Cunliffe
(Plate 21, Figures 102-107; Plate 22, Figures 109, 110)

This saproglyphid mite infested all 7 nests of *Stenodynerus* (*Parancistrocerus*) *f. fulvipes* (Saussure), 1 at Dunn Loring, Va., and 6 at Kill Devil Hills, N. C. The mites were found in 11 of the 15 cells in these nests.

I counted 1-24 adult mites (mean 10) in 9 cells. The largest actual number was 10 females and 11 males in 1 cell, although in another nest I estimated a dozen of each sex in a single cell. The ratio of female to male mites was apparently 1:1.

As usual, the wasp prepupae showed many feeding punctures of the adult mites. The gravid females began to lay eggs on the wasp pupae as soon as pupation took place (figs. 104, 105). The eggs were 152-168μ long and 93-110μ wide. Most eggs were laid on the mouthparts and along the legs and wing pads of the pupa (fig. 106).

A careful count was made of the mite progeny of 10 females in a 1-celled nest. Forty-three eggs, larvae, and nymphs were mounted for study; 42 were transferred to other nests; 32 were recovered from the pupal exuvia; 94 were recovered from the body of the adult wasp; and a few crawled off the wasp and were lost while the adult wasp was in the cyanide jar. Altogether 211 mites were accounted for, plus an unknown but small number that were lost. It seems likely that each adult female is capable of laying about 2 dozen eggs.

The mite hypopi were counted in the acarinarium of a wasp from another nest. The acarinarium appeared to contain its maximum load of mites, which amounted to 118.

The eggs hatched in 8-14 days in nests of the overwintering generation, in which development was slower than in other generations. In 1 summer generation nest they hatched in 3 days. The mite larvae were about 127μ long and 54μ wide. They transformed to protonymphs in 1-2 days (fig. 107). The molt to the deutonymphal or hypopial stage apparently took place just prior to or during eclosion of the wasp from the pupal exuvia.

I made rather detailed notes on the comparative development of the immature mites and of the host pupa and newly eclosed adult in 4 nests. The first mite eggs were laid immediately after host pupation, and oviposition continued for at least 4 days. The eggs hatched into 6-legged larvae by the time the thorax and first 2 abdominal terga of the wasp began to darken; this was 10-12 days after pupation in the overwintering generation and 3-4 days in the summer generation. Most of the mite larvae, and subsequently the nymphs, clustered on the face, antennae, and mouthparts, and along the legs and on the thoracic sternum of the pupa; all these parts are adjacent or in juxtaposition on the wasp pupa. The mite larvae transformed to 8-legged protonymphs in 1-2 days, by which time the pupal head, thorax, and basal abdominal segments were quite dark, leaving only the terminal abdominal segments and appendages pale. In the next 7-14 days the rest of the wasp pupa darkened except for those parts destined to become yellow markings on the adult. During most of this period the plump, whitish protonymphs remained clustered as described above (fig. 109), although in 1 wasp some congregated on the mesopleuron and in another on the postscutellum as well as on some other areas.

The protonymph mites became flattened and transformed into deutonymphs (= hypopi) just before 1 of the adults eclosed, but in the other nests this molt did not take place until 24-48 hours after eclosion of the adult wasp. In any event the mite nymphs were shed with the pupal exuvia at the time of eclosion. Those that had not transformed to deutonymphs remained on the pupal exuvia until they did molt.

Detailed notes were made on 1 wasp in a nest (C 477) in which all the mites had transformed to hypopi by 1600 hours on May 28, 1956. The adult wasp began to eclose at 1610. The head and thorax were free and the wings expanded by 1615. During the next several minutes, as the abdomen was beginning to be freed of the pupal exuvia, a few of the mites left the exuvia and crawled onto the wasp's abdomen; however, most mites were still on the exuvia, principally on the wings. By 1625 at least 1 mite had gotten into the acarinarium at the base of the second tergum. Mites were gradually crawling from the exuvia onto the wasp's abdomen at 1630, at which time only the tip of the abdomen was still covered by the exuvia. At 1645 quite a few mites had formed a patch on the second sternum and only a few were in the acarinarium. By 1655 all mites had left the exuvia and most of them appeared to be quiescent in patches on the second tergum and sternum. Most visible mites were on the second sternum at 1715 and again at 1725. They were not symmetrically arranged because at 1745 there was a patch of mites covering the yellow spot on the right side of the second tergum which was not duplicated on the spot on the left side.

At 1100 on May 29 quite a few mites were assembled in shingled rows on the second sternum. By 1145 there had been some dispersal and no longer any shingling. At 1300 there were still quite a few mites on the second sternum, but others had entered the acarinarium and there was now a transverse row of them lying with their head ends slightly protruding beyond the apex of the first tergum. When another mite tried to enter the acarinarium, it crawled forward across the second tergum to the edge of the first, turned around so that the apex of its abdomen faced the edge of the first tergum and then wedged its way into the acarinarium. Shingling occurred when there was already a complete row of mites across the acarinarium. The next mite to enter forced its way in by wedging its abdomen beneath the front edge of the mites already in the acarinarium. Presumably lateral shifting of hypopi took place as the acarinarium filled up so as to make a symmetrical load in the chamber. By 1415 there were more free mites on the second tergum than on the second sternum, and by 1515 most of the mites had left the second sternum. By 1715 apparently almost all of the mites had entered the acarinarium. The wasp did not leave the nest until June 1. I counted 105 hypopi in the acarinarium.

In the wasp discussed above it took just a little over 24 hours after eclosion for almost all of the mites to enter the acarinarium. This same observation was repeated in another nest (C 255), where the wasp eclosed between 0815 and 0915 on August 8, 1955, and almost all the mites had entered the acarinarium by 1000 on the following day (fig. 110).

Source material.
    Dunn Loring, Va. 1954 series: C 34.
    Kill Devil Hills, N. C. 1955 series: C 90, 92, 105, 255, 477. 1956 series: C 617.

Identifications. Acarina by E. W. Baker; wasps by the author.

VESPACARUS HISTRIO Baker and Cunliffe

This saproglyphid mite infested all 5 nests of *Stenodynerus* (*Parancistrocerus*) *histrio* (Lepeletier) at Kill Devil Hills, N. C., but was absent from 1 nest of that wasp at Lake Placid, Fla. The mite occurred in 13 of 15 cells in the Kill Devil Hills nests.

I recovered 1-9 adult mites (mean 3.3) from 10 cells. In 1 partially stored cell containing a newly hatched wasp larva and 1 caterpillar, there were 3 hypopi on the caterpillar. By the time the wasp larva was ready to spin, the adult mites were clustered on it.

As usual the wasp prepupae showed many feeding punctures of the adult mites. Gravid female mites laid eggs on the wasps as soon as the latter pupated. The eggs were about 175μ long and 100μ wide. One gravid female laid 47 eggs on 1 pupa, 37 mostly on the antennae and mouthparts, 8 on the mesopleuron, and 1 each on a leg and the abdomen. Egg hatch apparently took a rather lengthy period. On 1 pupa the first mite eggs were laid on April 28; larvae began to hatch May 11-12, on which dates the wasp pupa had just begun to color. A few days later the mite nymphs congregated on the head and thorax of a partially colored pupa. When the adult wasp was ready to eclose, the mites clustered on the thoracic sternum of 2 pupae, and on the mouthparts and legs of a third pupa. They were shed with the pupal exuvia, but clambered back on the wasp's abdomen and entered the acarinarium during the 3-day period which elapsed between eclosion of the adult and its emergence from the nest.

Baker and Cunliffe (1960, p. 224) noted that I found hypopi of *Vespacarus histrio* in the acarinarium of an adult *Stenodynerus* (*Parancistrocerus*) *fulvipes fulvipes* (Saussure). These were obtained February 18, 1959, from a wasp collected in the field at Kill Devil Hills. Conceivably such cross infestations could arise when a wasp species, not the normal host for a particular mite, nests in an old nest of the correct host wasp in which some viable hypopi may remain in the old cells.

Source material.
    Kill Devil Hills, N. C. 1954 series: F 5. 1955 series: C 281. 1956 series: C 117, 238, 367.

Identifications. Acarina by E. W. Baker; wasps by the author.

VESPACARUS PEDESTRIS Baker and Cunliffe

This symbiotic mite was present in 6 of 8 cells in the only 2 nests of *Stenodynerus* (*Parancistrocerus*) *p. pedestris* (Saussure), which I received from Derby, N. Y., in 1955. I made no notes on the life history of this mite and merely recorded 1-2 adult female mites per infested cell, that mite eggs and nymphs were present on the wasp pupae, and that adult wasps from infested cells in these nests had mite hypopi in their acarinaria when they left the nests.

Source material.

Derby, N. Y. 1955 series: D 11a, 12b.

Identifications. Acarina by E. W. Baker; wasps by the author.

VESPACARUS SAECULARIS Baker and Cunliffe

This symbiont was found in 73 of the 76 nests from which I reared *Stenodynerus* (*Parancistrocerus*) *saecularis rufulus* Bohart. The wasps made an average of 3 cells per nest, and most of the cells in mite-infested nests had a population of mites.

I counted 1-16 adult mites (mean 7) in 16 cells in 8 nests. One nest contained 16, 9, 8, 9, and 4 adult mites respectively in cells 1-5, and another contained 2, 5, 3, and 4 adult mites respectively in cells 2-5. The ratio of female to male mites was 2:1.

Wasp prepupae showed many feeding punctures of the adult mites. Gravid female mites were 600μ long and 400μ wide. They began to deposit eggs as soon as the wasps pupated and continued to lay eggs for several days. Most of the eggs were deposited on the antennae, legs, and lower parts of the mesopleuron. The mite eggs were 143-167μ long and 75-101μ wide. Precise data were not obtained on duration of the egg stage, but mite larvae 200μ long and 117μ wide were present on some wasp pupae 4-7 days after the eggs were laid. They transformed to protonymphs 250-300μ long and 150-167μ wide in 2-3 days. When the adult wasps were about ready to shed the pupal exuvia, the mite nymphs clustered on the thoracic sternum and lower part of the mesopleuron. After the adult wasps eclosed, the mite hypopi clambered back on the abdomen and entered the acarinarium during the period of 3-4 days which elapsed between eclosion and departure of the wasp from its cell.

Source material.

Lake Placid, Fla. 1957 series: M 142, 143, 171, 186, 242, 251, 285. 1959 series: V 76, 83, 121, 123, 133, 137, 138. 1960 series: B 86, 114, 118, 149. 1961 series: F 22, 28, 29, 52, 93, 94, 115, 145, 150, 159, 166, 168, 178, 182, 183, 195, 200, 203, 205, 208, 209, 212, 216, 222, 237, 243, 255, 263, 264, 280, 288, 291, 294, 320, 334, 336, 350. 1962 series: P 20, 51, 87, 94, 96, 103, 107, 114, 164, 175, 179, 180, 185, 199, 200, 201, 215.

Identifications. Acarina by E. W. Baker; wasps by the author.

VESPACARUS TIGRIS Baker and Cunliffe

This saproglyphid mite was described from specimens collected from nests of *Ancistrocerus t. tigris* (Saussure). I found it in 8 nests, 4 from Derby, N. Y., 2 from Plummers Island, Md., and 1 each from Dunn Loring, Va., and Kill Devil Hills, N. C. Mite hypopi or adults were found in 19 of 32 provisioned cells in 7 of these nests; detailed notes were not made on the eighth nest. *V. tigris* also occurred in 2 nests of *Ancistrocerus c. catskill* (Saussure) at Plummers Island, in which it infested 5 of 9 cells.

I did not make detailed notes on the development, but the life cycle is presumed to be quite similar to that reported for most other saproglyphids. Apparently only a few hypopi dropped off in each cell as it was being provisioned by the mite-infested mother wasp. I recovered 2-4 adult mites from 1 cell each in 3 nests.

The first eggs were laid on the wasp pupae 2-3 days after pupation occurred. Six-legged mite larvae hatched in 2-3 days. Protonymphs were present a day later. I made no notes on the later stages of the nymphal mites in the *tigris* nests. However, when most adult *tigris* or *catskill* wasps emerged, the hypopi were clustered in 1 or 2 rows, side by side with their heads outward, beneath the apices of abdominal terga 3 and 4. On 2 wasps they assembled beneath the apex of tergum 2, and on 2 other wasps they clustered in patches on the propodeal surfaces as is normal for hypopi of *Kennethiella trisetosa* (Cooreman) on adults of *Ancistrocerus a. antilope* (Panzer) and *A. spinolae* (Saussure); these 2 types of hypopial orientation occurred on both *tigris* and *catskill*.

Source material.
　Derby, N. Y. 1955 series: D 7a. 1958 series: R 6. 1959 series: W 15, 32.
　Plummers Island, Md. 1960 series: E 73. 1963 series: U 4.
　Dunn Loring, Va. 1954 series: D 27.
　Kill Devil Hills, N. C. 1956 series: C 424.

Identifications. Acarina by E. W. Baker; Hymenoptera by the author.

VESPACARUS TOLTECUS Baker and Cunliffe

This was one of the most successful saproglyphid mites encountered during this trap nest study. It infested all 19 nests of *Stenodynerus (Parancistrocerus) toltecus* (Saussure) in Arizona, 10 from Portal, 5 from Granite Reef Dam, 3 from Scottsdale, and 1 from Molino Camp in the Santa Catalina Mountains. Not only was it successful in parasitizing all the nests, but also it was able to infest many of the cells in each nest. My notes show that at least 60 of 89 cells in 17 nests were infested with the mites. This number was probably substantially higher insofar as the number of cells originally infested was concerned. For instance, these mites are killed off in cells parasitized by chrysidid wasps, and 8 cells in mite-infested nests were parasitized by *Chrysis* (*C.*) *arizonica* Bohart. As a matter of fact, in an 11-celled nest from Portal mite-infested *toltecus* females emerged from cells 1-5 and mite-free *arizonica* males and females emerged from cells 6-11; it is unreasonable to suppose that cells 6-11 were all mite-free when the nest was stored.

I made no developmental notes on the mite, and it is presumed to be like other species of *Vespacarus* in the essential details of its life history. When they emerged from the nest, most of the adult wasps were infested with mites clustered in the acarinaria. However, I noted that in 2 adult wasps the mites were clustered on the apex of tergum 2. These wasps left the nest when I opened it, and the mites probably would have entered the acarinaria before the wasps emerged had I not opened the nest, thus allowing premature emergence.

Source material.
> Portal, Ariz. 1959 series: X68. 1961 series: G 9, 43, 52, 60, 87, 92, 250, 321, 323.
> Scottsdale, Ariz. 1961 series: H 4, 32, 83.
> Granite Reef Dam, Ariz. 1961 series: H 13, 60, 74, 91, 194.
> Molino Canyon, Santa Catalina Mountains, Ariz. 1961 series: H 124.

Identifications. Acarina by E. W. Baker; wasps by the author.

UNIDENTIFIED SPECIES OF VESPACARUS

Three presumed new species of *Vespacarus* were found in nests of 3 other species of *Stenodynerus* subgenus *Parancistrocerus*.

One of these occurred in a 1-celled nest of *vogti* Krombein at Plummers Island, Md. Three adult mites in this cell laid eggs on the wasp pupa, but none of them developed into hypopi. The vespid is known only from the unique female reared from this cell. I preserved an adult mite from the nest. However, species discrimination in the Saproglyphidae is based on characters of the hypopi; so a specific name cannot be assigned to this mite at the present time.

Another mite was found on 1 wasp in a 3-celled nest of *texensis* (Saussure) from Granite Reef Dam, Ariz.

A third mite species was found in all 3 cells of 2 nests of *bicornis cushmani* Bohart from Portal, Ariz. Mites in 2 of the cells developed into the hypopial stage and entered the acarinaria of the adult wasps prior to their emergence from the nests.

Source material.
> Plummers Island, Md. [nest of *Stenodynerus* (*Parancistrocerus*) *vogti* Krombein]: 1957 series: P 155.
> Granite Reef Dam, Ariz. [nest of *Stenodynerus* (*Parancistrocerus*) *texensis* (Saussure)]: 1961 series: H 19.

Portal, Ariz. [nests of *Stenodynerus* (*Parancistrocerus*) *bicornis cushmani* Bohart]: 1960 series: X 123, 223.

Identifications by the author.

KENNETHIELLA TRISETOSA (Cooreman)

This unusual saproglyphid mite has been the subject of intensive investigation by Cooper, who has published an introductory study (1955) of the biology and behavior of the hypopial stage of the mite and its relationship to the adult host wasp, *Ancistrocerus antilope* (Panzer).

I found the mite in 77 nests of *Ancistrocerus a. antilope*, 69 of 111 nests from Derby, N. Y., and 8 of 11 nests from Plummers Island, Md. The same mite, or a species so close as to be indistinguishable by modern taxonomic study, was also found in all 4 nests of *Ancistrocerus spinolae* (Saussure) which I obtained at Kill Devil Hills, N. C. *A. spinolae* and *antilope* are very closely related, and are the only North American members of this particular species group of *Ancistrocerus*.

It is possible that some of the other nests from Derby, from which I reared only female *antilope* wasps, may also have been infested by *trisetosa* mites at the time that they were provisioned. Female wasp larvae are known to destroy all mites in their cells before they spin cocoons. Consequently, those nests which I did not open until female larvae had cocooned, would show no signs of a mite infestation which might have been present earlier. In examining some nests I noted mites in some inner cells with feeding wasp larvae. Later, after these wasps had cocooned, no trace could be found of the mites, and the wasp occupants of these cells always transformed into female wasps. Cooper advised me (*in litt.*) that he was able to recover mite remains from the feces of the larval wasp, proving indisputably that the female larva does devour any mites in the cell.

When male wasps from infested cells emerge from the nest, they bear large numbers of mite hypopi on the lateral and posterior surfaces of the propodeum. Newly emerged virgin female wasps do not bear any mites. Cooper observed copulation of a newly emerged mite-infested male wasp with a mite-free virgin female. As soon as intromission occurred, many mites left the propodeal surfaces, streamed downward on the male abdomen and entered the genital chambers of both wasps. After one mating 69 hypopi were found in the female genital chamber and 90 in the male genital chamber. In a later observation involving a previously mated male with mites in the genital chamber and another virgin female, he noted that the hypopi transferred directly from the male genital chamber to that of the female.

No observations have been made on the means used by the mites to leave the female genital chamber and enter the cell as it is being provisioned. Cooper speculated that some hypopi might be forced out of the genital chamber either during stinging or during oviposition. However, the act of stinging is a very brief one, and it is unlikely that the mites could escape at that time. Hartman (1944) observed that the vespid egg is extruded gradually. This relatively slow process would give some hypopi a chance to escape from the genital chamber, and it is most probable that infestation of the cell takes place at this time and in this manner.

Apparently relatively few hypopi leave the genital chamber and enter each cell. I found 1-4 hypopi (mean 2.3) in 14 infested cells. My notes on activities of the mites in the cells are quite fragmentary. It is presumed, but not certain, that the hypopus (=deutonymph) transforms to a tritonymph soon after the cell is provisioned. The tritonymph then transforms to the adult, assuming a turgid, more or less rounded body form. At any rate adult mites are to be found in the cells by the time the wasp larvae are only partially grown, so that only a few days are required for a mite to transform from the hypopial to the adult stage. The nongravid adult mites are flattened animals about 700μ long with prominent dorsal setae. They suck blood from the wasp after the latter attains the shriveled, flaccid prepupal stage and soon they lose their flattened shape.

Within 2 days after pupation of the wasp the gravid female mite, 1080μ long and 830μ wide, began to lay eggs which were 190-203μ long and 110-113μ wide. Most eggs were deposited on the side of the thorax of the wasp pupa, but occasionally some were laid elsewhere on the body or even on the cocoon wall. In an individual nest eggs were laid over a period of at least 7 days. They hatched into 6-legged larvae about 200μ long in 2-3 days during the summer but in 4-5 days in the spring in overwintering nests. Within a day or two the mite larvae transformed into 8-legged protonymphs. By this time the wasp pupae were beginning to develop the adult color pattern. Two days after changing to protonymphs the mites molted to the deutonymphal (=hypopial stage. They clustered on the anterior end of the cocoon to molt. Sometimes the hypopi then returned to the wasp pupa and sometimes they continued to cluster on the cocoon wall until the adult male wasp eclosed. During the 2-3 days that the adult male wasp remained in the cocoon, the hypopi left the cocoon walls and reassembled in shingled rows to form dense mats on the lateral and posterior surfaces of the propodeum. Usually there were approximately equal numbers on the 2 lateral surfaces and a smaller number on the posterior surface. I made no counts of the number of hypopi on newly emerged male wasps, but Cooper found a mean propodeal load of 134 hypopi with as many as 407 on a single wasp.

Occasionally I found a newly emerged female wasp with a few hypopi on the propodeum. It is probable that these rare infestations arose secondarily as the previously mite-free female traversed the boring through infested male cells in which a few hypopi remained on the cocoon walls.

A species near *K. trisetosa* also infested both cells of a 2-celled nest (R63) of *Ancistrocerus c. catskill* (Saussure) at Derby. The mite hypopi arranged themselves on the propodeum of each of the male wasps in this nest just as they did on *antilope*.

Source material.

> Derby, N. Y. 1954 series: 2 unnumbered nests, I A, V B, IX B. 1956 series: J 2, 3, 10, 12, 16, 24, 26, 29, 38, 41, 51, 60, 63, 65, 68, 73, 78, 80, 91, 94, 97. 1957 series: G 1, 6, 7, 12, 41, 46, 51, 59, 65, 75, 81, 89, 96, 99, 100. 1958 series: R 7, 9, 12, 16, 31, 34, 42, 63. 1959 series: W 23, 27, 40, 49, 53, 54, 56, 59, 60. 1960 series: D 21, 43, 49, 51, 58, 59, 69. 1961 series: L 42, 55, 88, 89, 90.
>
> Plummers Island, Md. 1957 series: P 285, 286, 288, 289. 1960 series: E 23, 168. 1961 series: K 114. 1962 series: M 101.

Identifications. Acarina by E. W. Baker, wasps by author.

MONOBIACARUS QUADRIDENS Baker and Cunliffe

(Plate 7, Figure 27)

This saproglyphid symbiont of *Monobia quadridens* (Linnaeus) was described from material collected from trap nests during this study. I preserved mites from 3 nests from Kill Devil Hills, N. C., in 1956 and 1958, and from 8 nests from Lake Placid, Fla., in 1957, 1959, 1961, and 1962. The mites were found in 23 of 34 stored cells in these nests. *Monobiacarus* undoubtedly occurred in a number of other *Monobia* nests from Kill Devil Hills and Lake Placid, as noted in the biological account of that wasp host.

The adults (♀, 1025-1450μ long, and 600-690μ wide; ♂, 770μ long) are the largest mites associated with wasps or bees in any of these nests, not an inappropriate size considering that their wasp host is also a veritable giant (fig. 27). However, the other stages are not larger than those found in other species of saproglyphid mites. The eggs are ovoid, 186-194μ long and 101-126μ wide. Hypopi are 233-255μ long.

The hypopi usually congregated on the adult wasps either in the male genital or female sting chamber, and on the male genitalia or female sting capsule. However, I have also found them on the free apical part of the inner surface of the apparent fifth sternum. Presumably the hypopi may transfer from an infested male to an uninfested female during mating. Undoubtedly some of the hypopi leave the female when she deposits an egg in the nest. Also, presumably, these hypopi transform to tritonymphs and then to adults within a period of 10-14 days, because I found mite eggs by the time the wasps became resting larvae. There was no evidence that any stage of the mite fed on the wasp larva, prepupa, or pupa. Probably they behaved as scavengers, feeding on organic matter such as fecal pellets or products resulting from prey decomposition.

The mite eggs were laid on the cell walls, usually on the varnished sections at the anterior end, but occasionally they were scattered among the frass pellets of the caterpillar prey. I was unable to discover how soon the eggs hatched, because they shriveled from desiccation soon after the nests were opened.

Neither the duration of the larval nor of the protonymph stages was ascertained. These 2 stages combined cannot last more than 24-28 days, because I found hypopi clustered on wasp prepupae and recently transformed pupae. The hypopi usually congregated in dense patches on the prepupae either on the head or on the dorsum of one of the segments near the head, though I did find them near the tail end of 1 prepupa. They were shed with the larval pelt when the wasp pupated. The hypopi then crawled back onto the wasp pupa. I observed their position on only 1 pupa over a period of 10 days. On January 27 they were on the abdomen in several clusters, some on the middle of the third and fourth abdominal terga and some near the base and sides of the second sternum. As the wasp neared eclosion on February 5, most of the hypopi were dispersed singly over the body mostly on the abdomen, but some in pockets behind the wing bases. I do not know whether this dispersal, was in response to the developing adult within the pupal skin or because of my frequent opening of the nest. The hypopi were shed with the pupal exuvia and then climbed back on the wasp's body. They entered the genital chamber during the several days while the adult wasp remained in the cell to harden.

Source material.
    Kill Devil Hills, N. C. 1956 series: C 707. 1958 series: T 206, 223.
    Lake Placid, Fla. 1957 series: M 150, 190. 1959 series: V 56, 69, 136. 1961 series: F 136. 1962 series: P 65, 67.

Identifications. Mites by E. W. Baker; wasps by the author.

UNDESCRIBED SPECIES OF VIDIA

I found infestations of this mite in 1 nest each of *Megachile mendica* Cresson from Kill Devil Hills, N.C., and Lake Placid, Fla., and in 2 nests of *M. xylocopoides* Smith from Kill Devil Hills.

The 4-celled nest of *mendica* from Kill Devil Hills was stored during August or early in September. There was a cocoon in cell 4 when I examined the nest September 22. On May 4 there was a pale, brown-eyed male pupa in this cocoon. Three days later it was covered with numerous mite hypopi. There were a few mite hypopi on the propodeum and declivous surface of the first tergum of the adult male when it left the nest on May 16. A male bee from cell 3 had some hypopi similarly arranged.

The *mendica* nest from Lake Placid had 11 cells; 2, 3, 5, 7, and 8 were infested with the mite and the other cells were not. Adult male bees emerged from cells 1, 2, 3, 5, 7, and 8, and there were small dead bee larvae in the other cells. The mites did not develop on the pollen-nectar masses in the cells with dead bee larvae, and I do not know whether they caused the death of the young larvae in those cells. The mite hypopi were found principally on the propodeum of the adult when it left the nest or in the postscutellar pits near the wing bases. I recovered protonymphs and adults from the cell of 1 bee; they occurred principally on the fecal pellets between the outside of the cocoon and the leaf cuttings. They may have fed on the yellowish fecal pellets of the bee.

No developmental notes were made on the mites in the *xylocopoides* nests. In one 5-celled nest 1 bee died as a prepupa and 2 bee prepupae were infested by *Melittobia*. When adult bees emerged from the other 2 cells, each bore a number of mite hypopi on the posterior surface of the propodeum and the anterior declivous surface of the first abdominal tergum. The other nest also had 5 cells; 1 pupa was infested by *Melittobia*, and when it emerged 1 of the 4 adult bees carried a few hypopi on the propodeum.

The mite eggs were ovoid, 100μ long and 50μ wide. Protonymphs were 167μ by 67μ; hypopi were $167\text{-}255\mu$ by $100\text{-}142\mu$. An adult female was 367μ long and 150μ wide.

Source material.

Kill Devil Hills, N. C. 1955 series: C 42. 1958 series: T 202, 209.
Lake Placid, Fla. 1961 series: F 44.

Identifications. Vidia by E. W. Baker; bees by the author.

Family ACARIDAE

LACKERBAUERIA KROMBEINI Baker

I found this mite in 6 nests in 3.2-mm. borings from settings on the wooden wall of an old cowshed at my home in Arlington, Va., 1960-1962. All nests were of the pemphredonine wasp *Diodontus atratus parenosas* Pate, and the mites occurred in 23 of the 54 stored cells. *Lackerbaueria* infested 40 percent of the nests built by *Diodontus* at my home.

The wasp egg was dead in each of the cells infested by mites. Inasmuch as there was no egg mortality in the adjacent mite-free cells, it is certain that the tritonymphal or adult mites must have killed the wasp eggs during the 2-3 day period following egg deposition and before they would have hatched.

Adult females were $531-574\mu$ long and $350-363\mu$ wide, and adult males were $337-427\mu$ by $186-261\mu$. In 1 nest females began to lay eggs on the aphid prey about 6 days after the nest was completed or perhaps about 13 days after a particular cell was infested. The eggs were ovoid, $143-160\mu$ long and $110-118\mu$ wide. They hatched into 6-legged larvae in 2 days, and in another 2 days they transformed into 8-legged protonymphs. Futher development was not noted because of mortality caused by desiccation.

Presumably hypopi would be produced by the time adult wasps in adjacent cells were ready to emerge from the nest. The hypopi would attach to a mite-free wasp as it passed through the infested cell. The infested cells in these nests occurred as follows (m= mite-infested cell, w= wasp adult):

A 5:   m-m-m-m-w-m-w-w
J 1:   m-m-w-m-w-w-m-w-w
J 4:   m-w-w-w-m-w-w-m-w-m
J 5:   w-w-w-w-m-w-m-w-w-w
J 11: m-m-m-m-m-w-w-w
N 2:   m-m-m-w-w-w-w-w

Obviously, the mites in only the innermost cells, as in the last 2 nests, would not have a chance of attaching to wasps as the latter emerged from the nests. However, in each of the first 4 nests 1 or more wasps would have had to pass through 1 or more mite-infested cells. Presumably the infestations are normally transmitted in this manner. However, it is also possible that if hypopi in the inner cells remain viable for sometime, they may infest cells in a nest built subsequently in the same boring by another female.

Previous observations. A few years ago (Krombein, 1962a) I published notes on nests obtained in 1960-1961, remarking that 25 percent of the adult *Diodontus* which I captured on the cowshed wall bore an average of 7 *Lackerbaueria krombeini* hypopi distributed at random on the body. I found that some females of several other aphid-storing pemphredonine wasps, *Stigmus americanus* Packard, *Passaloecus annulatus* (Say), *P. cuspidatus* Smith, and *P. relativus* Fox, captured on this cowshed wall bore hypopi of *L. krombeini* and were the probable hosts of the mite. I also found a single hypopus each on *Spilomena pusilla* (Say), *S. barberi* Krombein, and *Trypoxylon backi* Sandhouse, which perhaps represented just chance contaminations; none of these last 3 wasps stores aphids.

Source material.
    Arlington, Va. 1960 series: A 5. 1961 series: J 1, 4, 5, 11. 1962 series: N 2.

Identifications. Acarina by E. W. Baker; wasps by the author.

HORSTIA VIRGINICA Baker

I recovered this acarid mite from 3 nests of the carpenter bee *Xylocopa virginica krombeini* Hurd. The nests were in 12.7-mm. borings taken from 3 stations at the Archbold Biological Station, Lake Placid, Fla., in 1960.

The mites occurred in 16 of the 17 stored cells in these nests. There was a dead *Xylocopa* egg in 1 infested cell and 11 small dead bee larvae in 11 of the other infested cells. Presumably this mortality was due to attack by the mites. However, the mites did not always kill the host egg or young larva, because I found live, fully grown bee larvae in 2 mite-infested cells. Adult bees developed in these cells, but the mites died perhaps from desiccation.

I did not obtain much information on the life cycle of this mite, but I did determine that it developed on the nectar in the pollen-nectar mass stored for the bee larva. I placed several of these masses from infested cells in glass vials for pollen analysis. Four or 5 weeks later I found the vials teeming with mites in all stages except the deutonymph, so apparently the mites will continue to breed so long as a supply of food is available. The eggs were ovoid, 167μ long and 84μ wide. The adult female was 478μ long by 248μ wide, and an adult male was 350μ long by 190μ wide.

No information was obtained on the manner of infestation of adult bees. Presumably bees from noninfested cells would become infested as they passed through an infested cell during their emergence from the nest. Or, it may be that live hypopi may remain in the old nest and infest new cells when another female uses the old boring.

Previous observations. A few years ago (Krombein, 1962a) I published some notes on these same nests.

Source material.
    Lake Placid, Fla. 1960 series: B 66, 106, 189.

Identifications. Acarina by E. W. Baker; bees by P. D. Hurd, Jr.

TORTONIA QUADRIDENS Baker

This acarid scavenger in nests of *Monobia quadridens* (Linnaeus) was described from material obtained from 2 nests from Kill Devil Hills, N. C., during this study. I also obtained specimens in a nest from Plummers Island, Md. The mites occurred in 9 of 11 cells in these 3 nests. Probably *T. quadridens* occurred in other nests from these localities and possibly also from Lake Placid, Fla., as noted in the biological account of the wasp host.

The hypopi occurred at random on the body of the adult wasp. I found them scattered on the thorax and abdomen, but never more than about a dozen per wasp. On 1 wasp there were 3 hypopi beneath the apex of the first abdominal tergum.

Not many life history details were noted. I did not find any mortality or feeding injury caused by mites in these 3 nests. Presumably this is a scavenger species that feeds on organic debris in the nests. Eggs may be laid on the cell walls because I noted that most adult and immature mites were found there. However, immature mites occurred on the prepupae in 1 nest.

It is possible that the *Tortonia* in the Plummers Island nest represent a different species. Dr. Baker noted a slight difference in length of the body setae of the Maryland specimens as compared with those from North Carolina.

Previous observations. A few years ago (Krombein, 1962a) I published a few biological notes based on the nests discussed above.

Source material.
    Plummers Island, Md. 1961 series: K 129.
    Kill Devil Hills, N. C. 1956 series: C 706, 727.

Identifications. Mites by E. W. Baker; wasps by the author.

Family CHAETODACTYLIDAE

CHAETODACTYLUS KROMBEINI Baker

(Plate 23, Figures 111-114)

I found Krombein's hairy-fingered mite in a dozen nests of the megachilid bee *Osmia (O.) l. lignaria* Say at Plummers Island, Md., in 1958, 1959, 1961, 1962, and 1964. The mites infested only 19 of 114 stored cells in these dozen nests. Furthermore, the mites infested only 8.5 percent of the available *lignaria* nests.

The mite was unique among those encountered during this study in that the hypopi occurred in 2 forms, one the ordinary migratory form with functional legs and the other an apodous encysted form within the skin of the protonymph.

The migratory form of the hypopus occurred at random on the body of adult bees. Several probably dropped off in the cell as the mother bee stored it with pollen and nectar. The hypopi were presumed to transform rapidly into tritonymphs and then into adults.

It is possible that only female mites developed from these hypopi, and that each of these females produced a single parthenogenetic male which mated with its mother; thereafter she would lay fertilized eggs. Females were 542-699μ and males 453-478μ long.

The adult mites attacked and fed on the host egg or young bee larva, sucking the fluid from the egg so that it soon shriveled or sucking blood from the larva. Then, the females laid fertilized eggs on the cell walls. These eggs were ovoid, 170-185μ long and 110-120μ wide. They hatched in 4-5 days into 6-legged mite larvae 223-250μ long and 160μ wide. The larvae transformed into 8-legged protonymphs 319-414μ long. Both the larvae and protonymphs had well-developed mouthparts and fed on the nectar in the pollen-nectar mass provided as food for the bee larva. It seemed probable that so long as there was an adequate food supply these protonymphs transformed directly into tritonymphs 408-427μ long, bypassing the deutonymph (=hypopus) stage as is known to happen in several other species of mites including *Horstia virginica* Baker. These tritonymphs transformed into adults.

Apparently there was continuous breeding throughout the summer so long as any nectar remained in the food mass. When the mites had exhausted the nectar supply, there remained in the cell just a mass of loose dry pollen grains (fig. 111). As the food supply became reduced, encysted hypopi (figs. 113, 114) were formed within the bodies of protonymphal mites. These encysted forms overwintered and some of them transformed to the migrating form of the hypopus in the spring about the time that the adult bees were leaving the nest.

In 3 nests the mites infested only the innermost cell or cells, but in the other nests they occurred in 1 or 2 of the intermediate or outermost cells.

It is presumed that the migrating hypopi would attach to an adult bee as the latter passed through an infested cell on its way out of the nest. Inasmuch as most mite-infested cells occurred at random within the nests, there was reasonable assurance that one or more adult bees would usually have to pass through one of the infested cells.

However, it is also possible that encysted hypopi remaining in the old nest might transform into active mites when another bee nested in the old boring, thus giving the mite a chance to parasitize the same or other species of bees.

Previous observations. A few years ago (Krombein, 1962b) I published an extended account of the biology of this mite based on most of the nests reported above.

Source material.
    Plummers Island, Md. 1958 series: S 17, 18, 29. 1959 series: Y 44, 65, 66. 1961 series: K 37, 40, 41. 1962 series: M 5, 26. 1964 series: Z 23.

Identifications. Acarina by E. W. Baker, bees by the author.

Family ANOETIDAE
HISTIOSTOMA MYRMICARUM Scheucher (?)

I found an infestation of this scavenger mite in a completed nest of the sphecid wasp *Podium rufipes* (Fabricius) from Lake Placid, Fla., in 1960. The nest was stored early in November. When I opened it on the 18th, I found numerous active immature mites and a few adults. Apparently the mites may have caused the death of the wasp egg or young larva, while going through their life cycle on the decaying, paralyzed cockroach nymphs and adults, *Cariblatta minima* Hebard, stored as prey for the wasp larva. My opening of the nest caused the death of the mite population from desiccation on the following day.

H. myrmicarum is a European species associated with ants of the genera *Myrmica, Lasius, Camponotus,* and *Formica,* on whose workers the mite hypopi occur. The mites are presumed to be scavengers in the nests of the ants. This is the first report of the possible occurrence of this mite in North America.

I presume that the infestation in the *Podium* nest arose from mite-infested debris placed in the nest by the host wasp to form a closing plug. I have reported the use of such materials as decaying wood pulp, ground debris, spider webbing, and cockroach feces in these plugs. It is not too farfetched to speculate that the wasp might have carried into the nest a dead ant infested with viable hypopi of this anoetid.

Source material.
Lake Placid, Fla. 1960 series: B 232.

Identifications. Acarina by C. G. Jackson; host wasp by the author.

Family PYEMOTIDAE
PYEMOTES VENTRICOSUS (Newport)
(Plate 22, Figure 108)

This grain itch mite was a serious pest in laboratory cultures of these trap nests. I found infestations which unquestionably originated in the field as follows: In 1 nest in 1954 from Arlington, Va.; in 4 nests in 1955 from Kill Devil Hills, N. C.; in 3 nests in 1956, 1 each from Arlington, Kill Devil Hills and Plummers Island, Md.; in 5 nests from Arlington in 1958; in 1 nest each from Arlington in 1959 and 1960; in 1 nest from Portal, Ariz., in 1961; in 3 nests from Lake Placid, Fla., in 1961; and in 1 nest from Granite Reef Dam, Ariz., in 1963. No infested nests were found in 1957, 1962, and 1964. The host wasps and bee were as follows: *Trypargilum clavatum* (Say) in 7 nests; *Trypoxylon frigidum* Smith, *Trypargilum t. tridentatum* (Packard), *T. tridentatum archboldi* (Krombein), and *T.* species in 1 nest each; *Diodontus atratus parenosas* Pate in 2 nests; *Euodynerus foraminatus apopkensis* (Robertson) in 2 nests; *Stenodynerus krombeini* Bohart in 1 nest; unidentified vespids in 2 nests; and *Osmia* sp. in 1 nest.

In addition *Pyemotes* infestations were discovered in many nests a week to several months after the nests were first examined. Undoubtedly some of these infestations occurred in the field and the mites were overlooked during the first examination by being concealed among the specimens of prey. However, most of these infestations took place in the laboratory after the nests had been received and examined. The unengorged female mites are slender, relatively rapidly moving animals. They are able to leave an infested nest after the host insects have been sucked dry and enter adjacent nests through the breached entrance plugs and cell partitions or between the split halves of the traps. These subsequently discovered infestations were found in 150 nests as follows: In 3 nests each from Arlington and Kill Devil Hills in 1954; in 6 nests from Kill Devil Hills in 1955; in 2 nests from Arlington and 1 nest from Kill Devil Hills in 1956; in 1 nest from Kill Devil Hills in 1958; and in 1961 in a dozen nests from Derby, N. Y., 37 nests from Plummers Island, 21 nests from Lake Placid, and 64 nests from several localities in Arizona. *Pyemotes* is a very widely distributed mite, and it is quite likely that some of the nests from Derby, N. Y., were infested in the field.

I destroyed infested nests or cells as soon as the infestations were discovered. In 1961 I received such a tremendous number of nests that it was not possible to examine many of them a second time before secondary infestations became widespread.

It is possible that field infestations might be prevented by coating the outside of the traps with a persistent miticide. I did not try this technique because the *Pyemotes* infestations were never serious until the disastrous season of 1961. In subsequent years I set out fewer traps, and so there was no problem in checking them frequently. Any treatment with a miticide would have to be done carefully to insure that symbiotic mites were not destroyed also.

I did not obtain any information on how these nests were infested in the field. Presumably wandering, unengorged female mites entered the nests while they were being stored by the host wasps and were walled up in a stored cell when it was capped. Normally, infestations in nature in nests of this type could be expected to terminate in the eventual death of the entombed mite's progeny unless the partition was breached by emergence of an adult wasp from an earlier uninfested cell in the linear series. In 7 nests infested in the field the female mites first attacked the host eggs, in 1 nest they attacked the host larva, in 4 nests the host prepupae (fig. 108), in 4 nests the paralyzed prey stored by the wasps, (an aphid,

2 spiders, and a caterpillar), and in 3 nests I did not note what they attacked. It is possible that mites did not gain access to the nests in which prepupae were attacked until after the hosts had reached that stage; these particular nests may have been in pre-split traps which afforded the mites ingress to the nests after the entrances were sealed.

Previous observations. Baker and Wharton (1952, pp. 165-167) gave a brief account of the life history of this pest. It is an ecto-parasite of various insect larvae, but it is not an important bio-logical control agent. Laboratory colonies of various insects are sometimes completely eradicated by the mite. The slender, adult fertilized female attaches to a suitable host, begins to suck blood from it, and the tip of her abdomen becomes greatly swollen (as in fig. 108). Eggs develop and hatch within this swollen sac. The mites complete all immature stages within the body of the female and transform to adults therein. Adult males emerge first, pierce the swollen sac with their mouthparts to obtain food, and remain near the genital opening. They fertilize the virgin females as they emerge from the mother's body. A female may produce as many as 300 offspring.

Source material (primary infestations only).
Plummers Island, Md. 1956 series: H 168.
Arlington, Va. 1954 series: A 6. 1956 series: K 3. 1958 series: U 1, 2, 7, 8, 12.
    1959 series: A 23. 1960 series: C 7.
Kill Devil Hills, N. C. 1955 series: C 265, 366, 425, 452. 1956 series: C 612.
Lake Placid, Fla. 1961 series: F 15, 36, 270.
Portal, Ariz. 1961 series: G 106.
Granite Reef Dam, Ariz. 1963 series: T 19.

Identifications. Acarina initially by E. W. Baker; host wasps and bees by the author.

Order THYSANOPTERA

Family PHLAEOTHRIPIDAE

HAPLOTHRIPS AMERICANUS (Hood)

This predaceous thrips was found in a single nest in a 6.4-mm. boring from Kill Devil Hills, N. C., in 1958. The nest was in a setting suspended from the partially shaded, dead limb of a living white oak in open woods. Although I did not rear any adult wasps from the nest, it must have been that of a vespid, a species of either *Stenodynerus* (*Parancistrocerus*) or *Ancistrocerus*. The wasp prey consisted of lepidopterous larvae, and there were saproglyphid mites on 1 of the wasp prepupae similar in appearance to mites associated with those 2 groups of Vespidae.

The nest contained 6 cells. When I opened it on July 28, I discovered that cells 4-6 had been infested by larvae of Miltogrammini which had already left the nest. There were living wasp prepupae in cells 1-3. During the next 2-3 weeks small moniliform bombyliid larvae belonging to the genus *Anthrax* were found feeding on these wasp prepupae. On September 12 one of the *Anthrax* larvae was nearly full grown. On that date I also found in cell 3 an adult female thrips and some immature stages in webbing on the cell wall; these thrips had fed on the wasp prepupa in that cell.

Miss K. O'Neill stated that the adult female thrips was definitely *americanus*. There were also 3 nymphs of 1 kind and 3 nymphs and 1 pupa of a different kind, but she could not determine whether these differences represented sex, stadium, species, or genus. She stated that *americanus* was predaceous and that it was ordinarily collected from the bark of living trees. I surmise that this female just used the wasp nest as a retreat in which to lay eggs and that the feeding on the wasp prepupa was purely fortuitous.

Source material.
    Kill Devil Hills, N. C. 1958 series: T 143.

Identifications. Thysanoptera by K. O'Neill; other insects by author.

Order COLEOPTERA

Family DERMESTIDAE

TROGODERMA ORNATUM (Say)

Prior to my studies it was thought that *ornatum* was predatory on the eggs and spiderlings of snare-building spiders beneath bark. However, I found a number of wasp nests in wooden borings from Plummers Island, Md., infested with 1 or several *Trogoderma* larvae. R. S. Beal was able to rear adults or to identify larvae of *ornatum* from 7 of these nests in 1956, 1957, and 1959. Five of them were of spider-storing wasps belonging to *Trypargilum,* 3 of *T. clavatum* (Say) and 1 each of *T. striatum* (Provancher) and *T. collinum rubrocinctum* (Packard), and 2 were of caterpillar-storing vespid wasps, 1 of *Monobia quadridens* (Linnaeus) and 1 of another unidentified vespid. The 3 infested *clavatum* nests came from settings on a rafter of the cabin porch; the other nests were from 4 stations on dead tree trunks or suspended from dead branches in the open woods.

When I opened them for examination shortly after they were completed, 2 of the *clavatum* nests and the 1 *striatum* nest were infested with *ornatum* larvae. Dermestid infestations were not found in the other 4 nests until completion of the overwintering period of diapause. It is possible that some of these latter nests were infested secondarily after being brought into the laboratory, though it is also possible that eggs or small dermestid larvae were hidden beneath the prey in the nests when I brought them in from the field.

The first infested *clavatum* nest was picked up on July 19, 1956. It had 8 stored cells and was not completed because the mother wasp was still in the nest. There were small feeding larvae of *clavatum* in cells 2-4 and 6-7, but cells 1, 5, and 8 each contained a shriveled wasp egg and 1 or more small *ornatum* larvae. Although I did not see an *ornatum* larva feeding on a wasp egg, the appearance of the eggs was consistent with their having been sucked dry. No other biological agents were found in these cells which could have caused this egg mortality. A day later I found a freshly killed *clavatum* larva in cell 3 with a newly molted *ornatum* larva. Four days later there were dead wasp larvae and live *ornatum* larvae in cells 6 and 7, and a newly spun wasp cocoon in cell 4. I examined this resting wasp larva through a small hole I made in the cocoon wall on October 5 and found it healthy. Next May, after the nest had overwintered outside, I found no wasp larva in the cocoon; but there were 4 live *ornatum* larvae in it and many cast dermestid skins.

The second infested *clavatum* nest, also incomplete, contained only 3 stored cells when I brought it in from the field on July 24, 1957. On that date there were newly hatched wasp larvae in cells 1 and 2 and a healthy wasp egg in 3. Two days later cell 1 contained a dead wasp larva and a small *ornatum* larva. I assumed that the *ornatum* larva had killed the wasp larva, but I could find no evidence of injury or that it had fed on the wasp.

The infested *striatum* nest was completed before mid-August. When I opened it on August 23, I found wasp cocoons with healthy resting larvae in each of the 6 cells; cell 1 also contained 2 small *ornatum* larvae which had fed on the spider remains in that cell but had not breached the cocoon wall. After the nest overwintered outdoors, I found that the *ornatum* larvae had completely devoured the wasp larva in cell 1.

I found infestations of dermestid larvae in more than 25 other nests from Plummers Island, Md., Arlington, Va., and Portal and Granite Reef Dam, Ariz. It is presumed that most of these were infestations by *ornatum*, but it is possible that 1 or more other species of *Trogoderma* were involved because some of the nests were those of megachilid bees.

There were 17 other nests at Plummers Island from 1956 through 1962 in which I found dermestid larvae at the time I first examined the nests or shortly thereafter. Eleven of these were nests of *Trypargilum*, 6 of *striatum*, 1 of *clavatum*, and 4 from which no host wasps were reared. One infestation occurred in a nest of a species of *Dipogon,* another spider-hunting wasp. Three were vespid nests, 1 each of *Monobia quadridens* (Linnaeus) and *Symmorphus canadensis* (Saussure), and 1 from which no host wasp was reared. I recorded another nest merely as being that of a wasp. The last nest was of the megachilid bee *Osmia lignaria* Say; there was a dermestid larva in cell 1, but the bee egg was gone when I examined this nest on May 16; 11 days later the beetle larva was in cell 2 and that bee larva was dead. Four other nests from Plummers Island were found to have secondary (?) dermestid infestations after overwintering outdoors; 2 nests were of *Trypargilum striatum,* 1 of *T. clavatum* and 1 of *Osmia lignaria.* Seventeen of this group of Plummers Island nests came from settings on structural timber on the cabin porch or an old canoe shed, and 5 were from settings on dead tree trunks.

The single *ornatum*-infested nest from Arlington, Va., was from a setting on an old cowshed wall containing numerous abandoned borings of anobiid beetles in which a number of solitary wasps nested. This nest was made by a species of *Trypoxylon,* possibly *backi* Sandhouse or *frigidum* Smith. When I examined the nest on July 21 there was a shriveled wasp egg in 1 cell and a small dermestid larva which probably had sucked the egg dry. I was unable to rear either the dermestid larva or the wasps in the other 2 cells.

The 4 infested nests from Arizona may all have been secondary infestations arising some time after the nests were stored or after they were brought into the laboratory. The host wasps and bees were the vespid wasps, *Ancistrocerus tuberculiceps* (Saussure) and *Pachodynerus astraeus* (Cameron), and the megachilid bees, *Ashmeadiella occipitalis* Michener and *Megachile* (*Sayapis*) sp., possibly *policaris* Say. Although I received numerous nests of *Trypargilum tridentatum* (Packard) from Arizona, not a single one had a dermestid infestation.

Previous observations and my own data suggest that *ornatum* is very closely associated with spiders. No information is available as to how the beetles gain access to the wasp nest. However, the fact that *ornatum* infestations are found so commonly in the nests of spider-storing wasps and rarely, if at all, in nests of caterpillar-storing vespid wasps or megachilid bees, suggests that the infestations probably do not arise from chance wandering by *ornatum* larvae. If this were the case, we would expect to find more infestations in nests of vespid wasps and megachilid bees which are proven secondary hosts and which are quite common on the cabin porch at Plummers Island. Perhaps an adult female of *ornatum* seeks out and oviposits in the cell of a spider-storing wasp during the period the wasp brings in the 6-24 spiders commonly stored in a single cell. This behavior would be consistent with my findings in some nests, where I did not notice a dermestid infestation shortly after the nest was stored but did find one a few days later. Another possibility is that the newly hatched dermestid larvae might be carried on the body of the wasp or of its spider prey during transport from the spider's retreat to the wasp's nest.

Evidence from a number of nests suggests that *ornatum* larvae are predaceous at least in their early instars. The finding of shriveled wasp eggs or of dead young wasp larvae in cells infested with dermestid larvae is striking circumstantial evidence that predation has been practiced. After the death of the host egg or larva, the *ornatum* larva feeds on the spiders which may be still paralyzed or dead. The dermestid larva is not always predaceous because I have occasionally found one that was able to obtain enough sustenance from the spider remains and left the host larva intact in its cocoon. If the dermestid larvae do not obtain enough food in one cell, they will migrate into adjoining stored cells.

The later instars of the dermestid also may be predaceous. In 1 nest of a *Trypargilum* species from Plummers Island a dermestid larva devoured the resting larva of a cuckoo wasp parasitic on the *Trypargilum*. Two weeks later I confined this dermestid larva in a cell in another nest containing a cocoon of *Trypargilum clavatum* in which I had made a small hole; there was a live resting wasp larva in the cocoon. Four days later the dermestid had pulled part of the resting wasp larva through this hole and had fed on it. A week later the wasp larva was almost entirely devoured and the dermestid larva was inside the wasp cocoon. Subsequently, I placed this dermestid larva with another live resting larva of *clavatum* in its cocoon; it fed extensively on this wasp larva also.

Several times in overwintering nests I found that the dermestid larva had bored right through the solid wood wall of the trap in order to get out. Presumably the dermestid behaves in this way when it is ready to pupate, because I never found beetle pupae inside of the wasp nests.

Previous observations. Auten (1925) found larvae of this beetle feeding on egg masses of *Epeira foliata* (Fourcroy) and *E. undata* (Olivier) [reported respectively as *Aranea frondosa* Comstock and *Epeira sclopetaria* Emerton] under bark in Ohio.

Beal (1960) included some of my early biological data. He mentioned that *ornatum* larvae fed on living wasp larvae of *Trypargilum clavatum* (Say) and *Monobia quadridens* (Linnaeus), and that *ornatum* larvae also were found in nests of *T. striatum* (Provancher), *T. collinum rubrocinctum* (Packard), and an unidentified vespid. Beal reported that *ornatum* was able to subsist on cereal foods alone, and he maintained laboratory cultures of the beetle on a diet of dog meal.

Source material.
   Plummers Island, Md. 1956 series: H 120, 141 (?). 1957 series: P 24 (?), 105,
      106, 125 (?), 130, 141, 156. 1958 series: S 6 (?), 99 (?), 103 (?), 106 (?), 114 (?).
      1959 series: Y 36 (?), 68, 92 (?), 108 (?), 114 (?), 115 (?), 124 (?), 147 (?). 1960
      series: E 42 (?), 45 (?), 103 (?), 114 (?), 139 (?). 1962 series: M 59 (?).
   Arlington, Va. 1956 series: K 20 (?).
   Portal, Ariz. 1961 series: G 100 (?), 117 (?), 171 (?).
   Granite Reef Dam, Ariz. 1961 series: H 92 (?).

Identifications. Dermestidae by R. S. Beal; wasps and bees by
the author.

THYLODRIAS CONTRACTUS Motschulsky

Larvae of this dermestid museum pest infested possibly 2 nests
of the vespid *Euodynerus foraminatus apopkensis* (Robertson) from
the Archbold Biological Station, Fla., in 1960. Both infestations
occurred in diapausing nest material and undoubtedly originated
in the laboratory. Larvae identified definitely as this species fed
on and killed 2 live diapausing larvae of the vespid in a 5-celled
nest. A larva of similar appearance killed 1 prepupa in another
6-celled nest of the same host.

Source material.
   Lake Placid, Fla. 1960 series: B 89, 135(?).

Identifications. Dermestidae by P. J. Spangler; wasps by the
author.

Family CLERIDAE
TRICHODES HORNI Wolcott and Chapin

I reared this species from 2 nests of megachilid bees from Portal,
Arizona. Both nests were from a single station on a fence post on
the desert floor at about 4,000 feet elevation. Both were completely stored during late April and early May and were taken up
on May 4, 1961.

One nest contained 17 cells made by the megachilid bee *Ashmeadiella (A.) m. meliloti* (Cockerell) in a 4.8-mm. boring. When
I opened this nest on May 13, there were nearly mature bee larvae
in many of the cells in the inner section of the boring. There was
also a small clerid larva in cell 17 (the outermost cell); it had
killed the bee larva in that cell. I did not examine the nest again
until June 10. On that date the clerid larva was a much larger pink
form; it had devoured all the prepupae, pupae, and adult bees in
their cocoons in the other 16 cells. Enough male adult bee fragments were present so that the host bee could be identified as
typical *meliloti,* a species which I reared from 2 other nests from
this same station stored during the same period. Between June 16

and 22 the clerid larva rasped a lot of fibers off the boring wall and made a plug 6 mm. thick between it and the boring entrance; between itself and the inner end of the boring it secreted a brittle, yellowish, transverse partition, 0.1 mm. thick. During the period June 30-July 11 it secreted a similar partition between itself and the plug of wood fibers that it constructed earlier, so that now it lay head inward between these two thin partitions. The clerid larva remained quite active into the fall and I placed the nest outdoors for the winter of 1961-1962. The larva remained active in its cell all through the following spring, summer, and fall; and I again placed the nest outdoors for the winter of 1962-1963. I brought the nest inside on March 1, 1963. Between April 30 and May 31 the clerid larva turned around in its cell and transformed to a pink pupa with its head toward the boring entrance. On May 31 the eyes of the clerid pupa were black. The clerid transformed to an adult male, which was ready to leave the pupal cell on June 15.

The other nest in a 6.4-mm. boring contained 18 cells of the megachilid bee *Ashmeadiella* (*A.*) *occipitalis* Michener, a larger bee than typical *meliloti.* I opened this nest also on May 13, on which date there were small, feeding bee larvae in all cells except 16, where a small clerid larva had killed and fed on the bee larva. On June 10 the clerid larva had eaten the bee larvae in cells 13-18; the bee larvae in cells 1-12 were already spinning cocoons or had completed them. Between June 16 and 22 the clerid fed on the bee prepupae in cells 8-12, and was now as large as the clerid larva in the *meliloti* nest. I placed a cork between the remaining bees and the clerid larva to prevent any further predation. The bees began to pupate on June 30 and adults had eclosed by July 29. I removed the adult bees on this date so that they would not injure the clerid larva when they attempted to leave the nest. The clerid larva molted to another (fourth ?) instar between July 29 and August 21. It also remained in the larval state from the summer of 1961 through the spring of 1963, and was treated during that period in the same way as the clerid in the other nest. This larva pupated between July 6 and August 13, 1963. The adult became fully colored but was unable to shed the pupal exuvia; it finally died about October 2. Development had progressed sufficiently so that it could be positively identified as a specimen of *horni.*

Previous observations. There have been no previously published notes on *T. horni.* Linsley and MacSwain (1943) published some observations on *T. ornatus* Say. They reported finding about a dozen megachilid bees serving as hosts in California, as well as 1 species each of *Ceratina, Euodynerus* [reported as *Odynerus*], and *Pseudomasaris.* They stated that the eggs were laid on flower heads frequented by the adult beetles for pollen. The mode of access to the host bee or wasp nest was not determined. They found that the primary larvae usually did not begin feeding until the host larvae had reached the prepupal stage. They reported 3 feeding instars in the larva and 2 nonfeeding instars. The fourth instar larva overwintered, transformed to a fifth instar larva in the spring, and then pupated either within a few weeks or occasionally not until the summer of the second or third year. The pupal period lasted 20 days in the laboratory. They were able to rear *ornatus* larvae on a diet of pollen alone.

Source material.
    Portal, Ariz. 1961 series: G 45 ,94.

Identifications. Beetle by G. B. Vogt; bees by C. D. Michener and the author.

CYMATODERA UNDULATA Say

A full-grown larva of this species crawled into an empty 4.8-mm. boring attached to the dead limb of a pine tree at Kill Devil Hills, N.C., in 1956. It rasped some wood fibers from the boring wall and constructed a plug to close off a cell about 20 mm. long in which it pupated. Later a female of the sphecid wasp *Podium rufipes* (F.) stored a cell in the outer part of the boring. When I opened the nest on July 29, the clerid was already a pale pupa with black eyes. It transformed to an adult and left its cell on August 13, chewing through a cork I placed between it and the *Podium* cell; the *Podium* larva died after failing to spin a proper cocoon.

Balduf (1935, p. 108) stated that *C. undulata* fed on the immature stages of various Cynipidae and Chalcidoidea in galls of the cynipid *Disholcaspis mamma* (Cresson). He also reported a combined prepupal and pupal period of 23 days in *undulata*. Balduf's rearing record is anomalous, and I wonder if it is not more likely that *undulata* would usually be predaceous on various solitary wasps and bees that nest in abandoned galls of Cynipidae than on the actual gall-makers and their parasites.

Source material.
    Kill Devil Hills, N.C. 1956 series: C 137.

Identifications. Beetle by G. B. Vogt, wasp by the author.

UNKNOWN SPECIES OF CLERIDAE

I found live clerid larvae, which died subsequently, in 11 other nests from Maryland, Florida, and Arizona. Some of them were probably larvae of the same species of Cleridae discussed on the preceding pages, but undoubtedly some were larvae of still other species. I am recording brief notes on these few nests to show the wide host range and the small percentage of nests attacked.

Four nests were from Plummers Island, Md., in 4 different years. The hosts involved were 2 vespid wasps, *Monobia quadridens* (Linnaeus) and an unidentified smaller species, the sphecid wasp *Trypargilum clavatum* (Say), and the megachilid bee *Osmia pumila* Cresson. In the first 3 nests, stored during July and August, the clerid larvae fed on the larvae or prepupae of the host wasps. In the bee nest, stored during mid-May, there was a small dead clerid larva at the inner end of the boring walled off by a partition of leaf pulp constructed by the mother bee.

A 7-celled vespid nest, almost certainly made by *Euodynerus foraminatus apopkensis* (Robertson), from the Archbold Biological Station, Fla., contained a clerid larva which fed on the prey and resting wasp larvae in several cells.

The 6 nests from Arizona were 2 of unidentified wasps, 1 of a species of *Stenodynerus* (*Parancistrocerus*), 1 of *Ancistrocerus tuberculiceps* (Saussure), 1 of the megachilid bee *Megachile gentilis* Cresson, and another probably made by the same species of *Megachile*. In all but the last nest the clerid larvae fed on some of the wasp or bee prepupae in their cocoons. When I first examined the last nest, the bee eggs or young larvae were dead and the clerid larva was feeding on the pollen-nectar mass in 2 of the cells.

Most of the nests from Arizona discussed above were probably attacked by larvae of *Trichodes horni* Wolcott and Chapin, although the clerid larva that fed on the stored pollen in 1 nest could have been a different species. The nests from Maryland and Florida could not have been attacked by *T. horni* because the known range of that species is southern Arizona and Baja California. The nests from Maryland and Florida could have been attacked by other species of *Trichodes,* or possibly even *Cymatodera.*

Source material.
    Plummers Island, Md. 1956 series: H 21. 1957 series: P 49. 1959 series: Y 114. 1962 series: M 24.
    Lake Placid, Fla. 1957 series: M 116.
    Oak Creek Canyon, Ariz. 1957 series: Q 3.
    Portal, Ariz. 1961 series: G 81, 196, 209, 248, 328.

Identifications. Host wasps and bees by the author.

Family RHIPIPHORIDAE

MACROSIAGON CRUENTUM CRUENTUM (Germar)

(Plate 24, Figures 115-118)

I reared this beetle from 1 cell each in a nest from Kill Devil Hills, N. C. (1956), Archbold Biological Station, Fla. (1957), Portal,

Ariz. (1961), and Granite Reef Dam, Ariz. (1961). All nests were in 6.4-mm. borings and were made by several species of vespid wasps. The North Carolina nest was that of *Euodynerus m. molestus* (Saussure) from a setting in a tree hole in a sweet gum in open woods. The Florida nest was that of *E. foraminatus apopkensis* (Robertson) from a setting suspended beneath the dead limb of an oak in the Highlands Ridge sand-scrub area. The nest from Portal was that of an unidentified vespid from a setting beneath the branch of a partially dead mesquite on the desert floor; the host vespid had nested in the old nest of a megachilid bee, but the host's identity as a vespid was confirmed by the finding of lepidopterous head capsules attached to the host cocoon. The nest from Granite Reef Dam was that of *Pachodynerus astraeus* (Cameron) from a setting beneath the limb of a mesquite in moderately dense growth near the river's edge.

My nests did not afford any information on the early stages of the beetle. Presumably the primary first instar rhipiphorid larva gains access to the nest by attaching to the body of the host wasp when the latter visits flowers for nectar (Linsley, MacSwain, and Smith, 1952). The beetle larva is then presumed to enter the body of the newly hatched wasp larva and to undergo one or more endoparasitic phases before emerging from the resting larva of the host at the time pupation is to occur and molting to the second instar.

In the nests from Florida and Granite Reef Dam I noted the small second (?) instar rhipiphorid larva on the host larva shortly after the parasite had emerged from the host body. The parasite was curled around the anterior ventral thoracic region of the host, as shown by Linsley *et al.* (1952, pl. 9, fig. 3) for *Rhipiphorus smithi* Linsley and MacSwain. In 1 specimen 9 days elapsed between my first observation of the small parasitic larva on its host, and the completion of feeding and voiding of feces by the full grown rhipiphorid larva. However, this parasite larva may have left the host body as many as 4 days before my first observation of it, because this period elapsed between my successive examinations of the nest. Linsley *et al.* recorded about 14 days for a similar period of feeding by the second through sixth instars in *R. smithi.*

Linsley *et al.* stated that the host of *Rhipiphorus smithi* was still recognizable as a bee larva although its abdomen was greatly contracted and its thorax strongly compressed. However, the larvae of *Macrosiagon cruentum* leave no recognizable remains of the host larva, as is evident in fig. 115 in which the rhipiphorid larva has nearly completed feeding on the host larva.

In 1 specimen, pupation (figs. 116-118) occurred 5 days or a little less after the *cruentum* larva completed feeding; Linsley *et al.* cited 4-7 days for this period in *R. smithi.* I did not ascertain the exact length of the pupal period. The specimen of *cruentum* from Florida pupated January 16-21, probably closer to the later date, and the adult male eclosed on the 31st. The specimen from Granite Reef Dam, Ariz., pupated March 21-27, probably closer to the earlier date, and an adult female eclosed April 16; this pupa was photographed on March 27 (fig. 116) and April 14 (figs. 117, 118). The pupal period in *smithi* appears to be shorter; Linsley *et al.* reported 13-14 days for this stage early in the season, and 11-12 days later in the season. Three of the *cruentum* adults remained in their cells 4-6 days after eclosion until the integument had hardened.

The endoparasitic first instar *cruentum* larvae apparently left the resting larvae of the host about the time that pupation occurred in unparasitized wasps in adjoining cells. In some of the nests from which I reared host wasps and beetle, the wasps pupated 19-22 days before the beetle pupated, and the adult wasps emerged 13-20 days before the adult beetle.

It seems possible that the hormonal changes preceding pupation of the host wasp may be the triggering mechanism causing emergence of the first instar rhipiphorid larva from its host. This theory could not be proved in the nest of the North Carolina wasp, which was one of the summer generation with no larval diapause. However, the nest from Florida was that of a univoltine wasp having an extended larval diapause of about 11 months. The first instar *cruentum* larva in this Florida nest did not emerge from its host larva until the wasp larvae in adjoining cells pupated; this was many months after the onset of diapause. Both of the Arizona nests were stored late in the season, and all of the wasp occupants overwintered as diapausing larvae; the *cruentum* larvae emerged from their host wasp larvae the following spring concurrently with pupation of the remaining wasp population.

Previous observations. Snelling (1963) reported rearing *cruentum* in Georgia from a nest of the vespid *Ancistrocerus campestris* (Saussure) in an old mud-dauber nest. He speculated that this mud-dauber, *Sceliphron caementarium* (Drury), might actually be the normal host of *cruentum,* and that parasitism of the vespid was accidental. My own experience definitely establishes that vespids are the preferred, and perhaps the only, hosts of *cruentum.* Tiphiid and bembicine hosts of several other American species of *Macrosiagon* have been reported; one African species of *Macrosiagon* is known to parasitize solitary vespid wasps.

Source material.
> Kill Devil Hills, N. C. 1956 series: C 236.
> Lake Placid, Fla. 1957 series: M 224.
> Portal, Ariz. 1961 series: G 202.
> Granite Reef Dam, Ariz. 1961 series: H 279.

Identifications. Rhipiphoridae by T. J. Spilman; wasps by the author.

Family MELOIDAE
NEMOGNATHA (PAURONEMOGNATHA) NIGRIPENNIS LeConte

A specimen of this parasitic beetle was reared from each of 2 4.8-mm. nests from Portal, Ariz., in 1959 and 1961. The earlier nest was in a setting on a corral fence, and the later came from a setting on a mesquite trunk. Both stations were on the desert floor at about 4,000 feet elevation.

The 1959 nest was that of the megachilid bee *Ashmeadiella (A.) occipitalis* Michener. There were black-eyed bee pupae in cells 1-6 and 13 when I picked up and examined the nest on July 19. Cell 7 contained a parasitic meloid larva inside exuvia of the fourth and fifth instar larvae of the parasite; the parasitic larva apparently gained access to the nest during construction by the bee of cell 12 because it fed on the contents of cells 8-12. The parasite pupated by July 28 inside the puparium formed by these larval exuvia. On August 13 a male bee emerged from cell 13, and a female of the rufous phase of *Nemognatha nigripennis* emerged from cell 7 on the 16th. Occupants of cells 1-6 failed to develop beyond the pupal stage.

The 1961 nest was made by the megachilid bee *Dianthidium ulkei perterritum* Cockerell. It was mailed to me on October 18, but probably the nest had been completed some weeks earlier because when I examined the nest on November 6, all the bees were already in cocoons. There was a 6-legged fourth instar meloid larva in cell 1, and cocoons of the bees were in cells 2 and 3. Probably between November 6 and 17, the meloid molted to the apodous fifth instar larva whose skin formed a tough brown puparium enclosing the apodous sixth instar prepupa. I set this nest outside for the winter on November 17 and brought it back indoors on March 3. Between May 5 and 11 the sixth instar prepupa emerged from the puparium through an even, longitudinal split in the integument. Between May 16 and 17 this sixth instar meloid pupated as a free pupa not enclosed in the puparium. An adult male of the dark phase of *nigripennis* eclosed on May 27 and left the cell 2 days later. Adult female bees emerged from the cocoons in cells 2 and 3 on May 24 and 29.

The sixth instar of the 1961 meloid left the puparium to pupate;

this is unique except for the specimen of *N. nemorensis* Hentz recorded on the following pages. In the 1959 nest the adult meloid chewed her way out through the tough puparium formed from the fifth instar derm. J. W. MacSwain wrote me that all meloids observed by him also had transformed to pupae within the puparia. Perhaps this unusual behavior was induced by my repeated opening of the nest to observe developmental details.

Previous observations. Enns (1956, p. 779) summarized the known rearing records for *nigripennis* and listed as hosts the megachilid bees *Dianthidium* sp., *Chalicodoma pratti* (Cockerell), *Megachile brevis* Say, and *Hoplitis biscutellae* (Cockerell). No life history details were given in connection with these host records.

Source material.
Portal, Ariz. 1959 series: X 63. 1961 series: G 315.

Identifications. Nemognatha by W. R. Enns; bees by the author.

NEMOGNATHA (PAURONEMOGNATHA) NEMORENSIS Hentz

I reared a female of this meloid from the nest of a species of *Chalicodoma* (*Chelostomoides*) from the Archbold Biological Station, Lake Placid, Fla., in 1961. The host bee was probably either *campanulae wilmingtoni* (Mitchell) or *georgica* (Cresson), the only species of this resin-using subgenus that I reared from Floridian nests. The nest was in a 4.8-mm. boring from a setting hung beneath the limb of a living scrub hickory in the Highlands Ridge sand-scrub area.

The nest was mailed to me on August 15, and I opened it for study on the 17th. It contained only a single bee cell. A small 6-legged meloid larva in the cell had just devoured the bee egg. It continued to feed on the pollen-nectar mass stored for the bee larva until about September 10. The fourth instar skin was shed between September 18 and 25, and the light tan fifth instar puparium was also shed during that period. Pupation as a free pupa not enclosed in the puparium took place September 26-27; this is probably abnormal behavior as noted above for *nigripennis*. The body began to darken between October 6 and 9. The adult female beetle was eclosed and at the entrance plug of the nest on October 13.

Previous observations. Enns (1956, p. 782) examined an adult of *nemorensis* pinned with a pupal case in a resinous bee cell from Florida. This host could also have been a species of *Chalicodoma* (*Chelostomoides*), but was more likely to have been that of one of the resin-using Anthidiini if it was a free cell. There are no other references to the biology of this species.

Source material.
    Lake Placid, Fla. 1961 series: F 301.

Identifications. Meloidae by P. J. Spangler; bee by the author.

NEMOGNATHA species

In 1961 I received from Portal, Ariz., 1 nest of *Ashmeadiella* (*A.*) *bucconis denticulata* (Cresson) which was infested by a *Nemognatha* larva. The nest was in a 4.8-mm. boring from a station on a partially dead mesquite on the desert floor. The nest was mailed to me on May 15, and I opened it on the 24th. There were small bee larvae feeding on pollen-nectar masses in cells 1 and 4. Cell 2 contained only a pollen-nectar mass but no bee egg or larva. In cell 3 there was a small dead meloid larva which had sucked dry the bee egg in that cell. This larva was identified subsequently as that of a species close to, but distinct from, *nigripennis* LeConte. An adult bee emerged from cell 1 July 30-31.

Source material.
    Portal, Ariz. 1961 series: G 55.

Identifications. *Nemognatha* larva by R. B. Selander; bee by the author.

Family STYLOPIDAE
PSEUDOXENOS HOOKERI (Pierce)
(Plate 25, Figures 119-122)

A heavy infestation of *P. hookeri* was found in 1957 in traps from the Highlands Ridge sand-scrub area of the Archbold Biological Station, Lake Placid, Fla., that contained nests of the vernal, univoltine vespid wasp *Euodynerus foraminatus apopkensis* (Robertson). The infestation was not discovered until the adult wasps emerged during January 1958. Many of the notes that follow were based on the stylopized wasps that emerged from 23 of the 1957 nests. Additional information was obtained from 8 stylopized nests received in 1959, 7 nests in 1960, and 18 nests in 1961. All the infested nests were of *apopkensis* except for one of the *apopkensis-parvirudis* intermediate. Most of the nests were stored by different female wasps because the 1957 nests came from 18 different stations, the 1959 nests from 6 stations, the 1960 nests from 4 stations, and the 1961 nests from 11 stations.

Most stylopized nests were stored by the host wasps from about mid-March to mid-April. I received 4 stylopized nests during the summer, but the *Euodynerus* females had stored only a few cells at the inner end of these borings and had been superseded by *Podium rufipes* (Fabricius) or *Megachile mendica* Cresson. Presumably these borings were partially stored by *Euodynerus* early in the spring, but were not taken up until they had been completely filled by *Podium* or *Megachile* during the summer.

Most of the wasps were in the late larval feeding or resting stages when I opened the nests in Washington immediately after receipt. There was no external evidence of stylopid infestation at that time or during any of my subsequent examinations of the nests during the summer and fall. I chilled some of the 1957 nests at 42° F. from July 15 to August 15 in an unsuccessful attempt to break the extended larval diapause. All the 1957 nests were placed outdoors in Arlington, Va., from October 12 to December 22 and were brought inside only during periods of freezing weather. These periods of chilling were sufficient to break diapause.

The wasps in the 1957 nests transformed to pupae from about December 28 to January 6. Male wasps emerged from the nests between January 13 and 17, and almost all the females between January 20 and 24. The occupants of the 1959 nests transformed to pupae from January 9 to 18; male wasps emerged January 26-29 and females February 4-10: Occupants of the 1960 and 1961 nests transformed to adults during April 1961 and February 1962 respectively after 2 months of exposure outdoors except during periods of freezing weather.

Life history. On January 14, 1958, I found that 3 newly emerged, freshly killed male wasps had 1 or 2 puparia of male stylopids protruding between some of the abdominal terga. After that time I examined each wasp that emerged from the 92 nests of *apopkensis.* Those that showed no evidence of infestation were killed at once, while those that contained exserted puparia of male stylopids were kept alive in an attempt to rear adult parasites. Twenty parasitized wasps, 14 males and 6 females, that emerged between January 14 and 21 were held in individual glass vials and fed on a solution of sugar in water. The vials were kept on my desk during the day under artificial light.

Meager observational data from one 1957 nest indicated that the puparium of the male stylopid did not extrude until after the adult wasp eclosed in the nest. I was able to confirm this in the 1959 nests by covering the cells with a sheet of cellophane so that development could be observed daily. In the 3 wasps that had exserted male stylopids the puparia were exserted from 2 to 4 days after eclosion of the adult wasp, usually just prior to emergence of the host from the nest. The conjecture by Linsley and MacSwain (1957) and earlier workers in Europe, that the male stylopids exsert while the hymenopterous host is in the pupal state, is not substantiated by my observations.

On January 17, 1958, I removed the anterior end from a male

stylopid puparium in a moribund wasp that emerged January 14. The stylopid at that time was a pale pupa with dark eyes and was oriented so that its venter was against the uppermost surface of the puparium. Two adult male stylopids emerged from other wasps on January 21 and 7 more from January 22 to 27. The time of emergence was from somewhat earlier than 0900 hours until 1535, but the majority of stylopids emerged between 0900 and 1000. The male stylopids emerged from the puparia 6 to 11 days (mean 8 days) after the host wasps left the nests.

I observed eclosion of the adult male stylopid only once. This male was almost entirely out of the puparium except for the wing tips and apical abdominal segments. The host wasp was uneasy and stroked the sides of its abdomen with its hind tarsi but could not dislodge the stylopid. Finally, the stylopid suddenly shot out of the puparium, perhaps by sudden inflation of the abdomen with air. Rotation of the stylopid in the puparium, so that the venter is down, apparently takes place just prior to emergence of the adults. In 1 moribund wasp 2 adults nearly ready to emerge were still venter up in their puparia.

The behavior of the adult male stylopids is marked by constant activity, as noted by other observers. The captive males ran incessantly with their wings vibrating for as long as 3 hours after eclosion from the puparium. After this they collapsed, but could move their appendages spasmodically for as many as 3 hours longer and faintly so for an additional 2 hours. Not all of the males were active for so long a period, and under normal conditions a male probably would not be capable of finding a female on another wasp and mating with her more than 1 to 3 hours after eclosion from the puparium. Gauss (1959) in southern Germany reported that death occurred 5-5½ hours after eclosion in males of *Xenos vesparum* Rossi, a stylopid parasite of *Polistes gallicus* (Linnaeus). Linsley and MacSwain found that males of *Stylops pacifica* were very active for a little less than 2 hours. After this the male collapsed and then exhibited vibrations of the appendages for 5 hours longer before death.

On the 17th, in an attempt to force emergence of the male stylopids, several of the wasps that emerged January 14, 1958, were exposed in their glass vials to bright sunlight for 3 minutes. No males eclosed, but a few minutes later the cephalothorax of a female was exserted from one of the wasps between the fifth and sixth abdominal terga to the right of the midline. When first exserted, the cephalothorax was soft, strongly flattened, opaque and white, with an elongate dark spot on each side anteriorly. It changed to dark brown in an hour and a quarter but was still soft. Female stylopids exserted the cephalothorax in 2 other wasps 5 days after those wasps left the nests. In the 1959 nests 2 female stylopids exserted 8 to 9 days after eclosion of the adult wasp. This delayed extrusion of the female cephalothorax possibly explains why Linsley and MacSwain found that females failed to extrude properly more frequently than males. Should the host already have 2 male puparia exserted, a female might not be able to extrude properly.

I tried twice to induce mating. A newly emerged male stylopid was kept in the vial with its host wasp, which also had an exserted female stylopid. The male tried to mate repeatedly for 20 minutes but was unsuccessful, perhaps because the wasp was so active. The male stylopid was moribund at the end of this period. Another newly emerged male was placed with a moribund wasp containing an exserted female stylopid, but it did not attempt to mate. Linsley and MacSwain found that mating in *Stylops pacifica* took place on flowers or on the ground at the nesting site when the host bee, *Andrena complexa* Viereck, was temporarily inactive during periods of overcast. Perhaps mating of *Pseudoxenos* can take place only under similar conditions of host inactivity in the open. Linsley and MacSwain, as well as Gauss, were successful in obtaining copulation by *Stylops* and *Xenos* respectively under laboratory conditions. Gauss reported that copulation by 2 *Xenos* males lasted only half a minute, while Linsley and MacSwain stated that 1 act by *Stylops* lasted for 2¼ minutes.

Stylopized wasps occurred sporadically in the 1957 nests containing more than 1 parasitized wasp. In one 9-celled nest stylopized wasps developed in cells 1 and 4, stylopid-free adults in cells 2 and 5-9, an apparently nonstylopized but dead wasp larva was in cell 3. In a 10-celled nest stylopized wasps developed in cells 5 or 6, 7 and 10, nonstylopized adults in cells 1-4, 5 or 6, and 8, and an apparently stylopid-free, dead wasp larva in cell 9. In a 12-celled nest there were stylopized adult wasps in cells 1, 2, 7, 10-12, stylopid-free adults in cells 4, 6, and 8, and an apparently unstylopized but dead wasp larva in cell 9.

I cannot offer any data on development of the eggs and young larvae within the female stylopid, inasmuch as I was unsuccessful in obtaining mating under controlled conditions and had no opportunity for field studies at the proper time. Presumably, as reported for *Stylops pacifica* by Linsley and MacSwain, the triungulinid larvae would be produced in enormous numbers, perhaps 9,000-10,000, within the body of the female and would emerge from her body over a period of 3 weeks about a month after copulation.

I do not know how first instar larvae of *Pseudoxenos* gain entry to the nest of the host wasp. It has been thought that larvae of some species of *Stylops* cling to body hairs of bees when the bees visit flowers and are then carried back to the nest. However, Linsley and MacSwain were able to demonstrate that the host *Andrena* took larvae of *Stylops pacifica* into the alimentary canal with nectar from the flowers and then regurgitated the nectar and stylopid larvae onto the pollen mass in the cell just prior to oviposition. Nesting behavior in *Euodynerus* differs from this sequence; the wasp oviposits first in the empty cell, then brings in a number of paralyzed olethreutid or tortricid larvae and then seals the cell with a partition of firmly agglutinated sand grains. Then, the wasp proceeds to construct and store a linear series of additional cells. Presumably the fluid used to agglutinate the sand grains is a salivary secretion. Adults of *Euodynerus* visit flowers for nectar and they might ingest the stylopid larvae at that time and regurgitate them when the cell is sealed, or perhaps the stylopid larvae merely cling to the body of the wasp when it visits flowers and gain access to the nest in that way.

The meager available evidence suggests that the triungulinid larvae of *Pseudoxenos hookeri* penetrated the host egg soon after they gained access to the host cell. Linsley and MacSwain found that larvae of *Stylops pacifica* entered eggs of *Panurginus melanocephalus* (Cockerell), a nonhost bee, and presumed that the larvae behaved similarly with eggs of *Andrena complexa*. They found that only the anterior part of the first instar larva penetrated the chorion; the stylopid then molted, and the second instar larva completed penetration of the egg leaving the first instar exuvia attached to the bee egg. When I first examined the nests in March and April 1957, I found a mortality rate of almost 12 percent in eggs of *apopkensis*. Altogether there were 83 dead eggs in all the nests of this wasp. At the time I supposed that this mortality, which was much higher than that found in any other species of wasp or bee in these nests, might have been caused by abnormally low temperatures in Florida prior to hatching of the eggs or to shock suffered in transit. However, the demonstration by Linsley and MacSwain that the first instar larvae of *Stylops pacifica* may enter the host egg suggested that some of this high egg mortality in *apopkensis* might have been due to penetration of the chorion by *Pseudoxenos* triungulinids. There was no opportunity to test this hypothesis with the 1957 nests, because the dead eggs were no longer available for examination when I discovered that some of the nests were stylopized. In 1959 there were 14 dead eggs and 12 dead newly hatched wasp larvae in nests of *apopkensis*. Detailed examination of these ova and larvae revealed tiny stylopid larvae in 2 of the eggs and in 1 of the larvae. One of the eggs had the exuvia of a triungulinid larva attached to the chorion and a tiny stylopid larva 0.169 mm. long inside the wasp larva; the latter was almost ready to hatch. The other egg (fig. 119) contained 5 stylopid larvae about 0.183 mm. long, inside the embryo. These could be identified as first instar triungulinid larvae because they had legs (figs. 120, 121); there were no triungulinid exuvia attached to the chorion of this egg. The first instar wasp larva contained only 1 tiny stylopid larva. There were some dead wasp prepupae in these nests, but none contained demonstrable stylopids.

I am unable to contribute much information on the development of *hookeri* within its host. In 1957 I preserved a number of wasp larvae of *apopkensis* just after they had completed feeding on the paralyzed caterpillars; presumably this was about a week after the eggs were laid. Fifteen of the wasp larvae came from nests from which I subsequently reared stylopized wasps. I dissected all the wasp larvae from stylopized nests, and I found only 1 parasitic larva, presumably that of a stylopid in the second instar. It floated free when I opened the body wall of the host larva; so I do not know exactly where it was located, though it definitely was not inside the gut. It was 0.21 mm. long, pale testaceous, apodous, and apparently lightly chitinized and bore 4-6 moderately short, scattered setae on most of the 11 body segments and a pair of elongate setae at the apex of the terminal segment (fig. 122). The small size of this larva indicates that it undergoes no growth while the host larva is feeding. Presumably the parasitic larva develops during the prolonged aestivation of the resting larva of the host and then undergoes a period of diapause. However, it is also possible that the stylopid makes no growth during the prolonged diapause of the host larva, but that it completes its larval development during the period of 18-33 days between the termination of diapause in the host prepupa and eclosion of the adult wasp.

Location of stylopids in adult host. There were 37 wasps with exserted stylopids in the 23 infested nests in 1957. Twenty-three of the wasps emerged from the nests successfully, but 14 were unable to cut their way through all the partitions and died in the nests. This mortality was probably not due to parasitism by stylopids, for 82 nonstylopized adults also died in the nests without being able to cut their way through all the partitions. The stylopized wasps contained 52 exserted parasites, 48 males and 4 females. Twenty-two of them contained only a single exserted stylopid, and 15 contained 2 stylopids each. In the wasps containing a single parasite the latter was exserted on the right or on the left side of the midline in equal numbers. In all cases of multiple parasitism 1 of the parasites was exserted to the left of the midline and 1 to the right. In 8 wasps the pair of stylopids was exserted side by side, and in 7 wasps the parasites were extruded between successive segments but on opposite sides of the midline. Table 34 summarizes the location of the exserted stylopids in wasps from the 1957 nests; the column heading 3-4 and so forth means that the stylopid was exserted between abdominal terga 3 and 4, and so on.

There were also some unexserted stylopids in wasps from stylopized nests in 1957. Thirteen of the wasps that contained exserted stylopids also had 1 or 2 unexserted parasites, and 5 wasps contained 1 unexserted stylopid and none exserted.

There was considerable variation in the location of exserted stylopids in the 4 parasitized wasps from the 1959 nests. One male had a pair of male stylopid puparia between terga 3 and 4, and a single male puparium on the left side between *sterna* 3 and 4. The other male wasp had an exserted male puparium on the right side between terga 4 and 5 and an unexserted male stylopid. In

TABLE 34.—*Location of exserted stylopids in adult wasps.*

Pseudoxenos: Sex and numbers	Male wasps			Female wasps		
	3-4	4-5	5-6	3-4	4-5	5-6
♂	5	12	0	1	4	0
♂♂	3	7	0	1	10	1
♂♀	2 ♀	3 ♂	1 ♀	1♀,1♀	0	0

1 female wasp a female cephalothorax was extruded on the right side between terga 4 and 5. In the other female wasp there was a male puparium on the right side between terga 3 and 4, another on the left side between terga 4 and 5, and a pair between terga 5 and 6; 5 days later a female cephalothorax exserted between *sterna* 2 and 3. One male wasp had an unexserted stylopid female. In addition there were 2 dead wasp eggs and a dead newly hatched wasp larva each of which contained 1 or more triungulinid larvae.

All the exserted stylopids in the 1960 nests were male puparia occurring in female wasps. One wasp had 2 puparia, side by side, between terga 4 and 5. In 7 other wasps the single puparium was exserted on the right or left side, and between terga 3 and 4 in 2 individuals, between terga 4 and 5 in 4 individuals, and between terga 5 and 6 in 1. Later I dissected all the wasps from the nests containing stylopized wasps and found that there were no unexserted stylopids in the abdomens.

In the stylopized nests in 1961 there were 7 male wasps and 8 females each with a single male stylopid exserted on 1 side of the midline or the other, between terga 4 and 5. One of each sex had a pair of male stylopids side by side between terga 4 and 5. One female wasp had a male stylopid exserted on the left side between terga 3 and 4, and another exserted on the right side between terga 5 and 6. As I killed the wasps from the 1961 nests as soon as they emerged, female stylopids did not have time to exsert. Later I dissected all the wasps from nests that had 1 or more occupants with exserted male stylopid puparia. I found that 9 males and 2 females each had a single internal female stylopid, but no males exserted or unexserted. A moribund female wasp pupa contained an unexserted male puparium.

Summarizing the data for the location of exserted stylopids in all 4 years, we find that in male wasps there were 12 stylopids of both sexes exserted between terga 3 and 4, 32 between 4 and 5, and 1 between 5 and 6; while in female wasps there were 8 stylopids of both sexes between terga 3 and 4, 32 between 4 and 5, and 5 between 5 and 6. Although male wasps have 7 exposed abdominal segments and females only 6, there was only 1 stylopid exserted between terga 5 and 6 in the males and none between terga 6 and 7. This is undoubtedly due to the massive genital capsule which occupies much of the space in the apex of the male abdomen. The female sting and associated structures do not occupy as much space; and so more stylopids were able to exsert between terga 5 and 6 in female wasps.

Sex ratio of stylopids in adult wasps. Exserted and unexserted females and males of *Pseudoxenos hookeri* were found in adult wasps in stylopized nests as follows:

$\male$ in 39 wasps
$\male\male$ in 10 wasps
$\male\male\male$ in 1 wasp
$\male\female$ in 8 wasps
$\male\male\female$ in 6 wasps
$\male\male\female\female$ in 2 wasps
$\male\male\male\male\female$ in 1 wasp
$\female$ in 17 wasps

This gives an overall ♀:♂ sex ratio of 1:2.5. However, analyzing the parasitism rates year by year we obtained the following figures:

1957—23♀, 50♂
1959— 2♀, 8♂
1960— 0♀, 9♂
1961—11♀, 21♂

These figures suggest that the actual ♀:♂ ratio is more likely 1:2. The 1957 and 1961 samples were adequate; the 1959 and 1960 samples were obviously too small to be meaningful.

It may be argued that the unexserted stylopids should not be included in arriving at these ratios. However, it must be remembered that many of the wasps were killed before the female stylopids had time to exsert, and that most of the unexserted stylopids were females. For example, if we counted only exserted stylopids we would have a 1:12 ratio in the 1957 nests and a 0:21 ratio in the 1961 nests.

Linsley and MacSwain (1957) thought that the sex ratio of *Stylops pacifica* was probably 1:1, though they admitted that satisfactory data were difficult to obtain. Gauss (1959) reported ♀:♂ sex ratios for *Xenos vesparum* of 3:2 in 1958 for 16 parasitized *Polistes* and 1:2.5 in 1959 for 53 parasitized wasps.

The preponderance of *hookeri* in male wasps (29:13) in 1957 is undoubtedly a reflection of the skewed sex ratio in the *apopkensis* population, rather than an indication that the stylopids are able to develop more successfully in male wasps. The 1957 nests parasitized by stylopids yielded 101 adult male wasps and 33 females. The total number of wasps reared in 1957 from the 92 nests of *apopkensis* was 295 females and 118 males. Linsley and MacSwain found in their examination of flower-visiting bees in 1954 and 1956 that the 2 sexes of *Andrena complexa* were nearly equally infested with exserted *Stylops pacifica*. Gauss reported finding only 9 stylopized *Polistes gallicus* males as against 58 stylopized females during the 2 years of his study. However, the situation in *Polistes* is different, because many more female wasps are produced, and males are found only late in the season.

Parasitism rates. It is impossible to calculate accurate parasitism rates because of the mortality of immature stages due to unknown causes. As mentioned earlier some, if not all, of the abnormally high mortality rates among eggs and newly hatched larvae of *apopkensis* are due to penetration by the triungulinid larvae.

Table 35 summarizes the pertinent findings from nests of *apopkensis* parasitized by *Pseudoxenos hookeri*. From these data we can calculate the following *minimum* parasitism rates of adult wasps for each of the 4 seasons:

Item	1957	1959	1960	1961
	Percent	*Percent*	*Percent*	*Percent*
Available nests (d/a)................	25	42	11	25
Available adults (h/c)...............	10	7	5	8
Adults in stylopized nests (h/g)......	33	15	33	27

The percentage of parasitized available adults shows a seasonal fluctuation in parasitism rates. This set of figures is comparable to the rates of 9 to 16 percent cited by Linsley and MacSwain for *Andrena complexa* adults collected at flowers in 1954 and 1956, respectively.

If we assume that all the eggs and young larvae in stylopized nests killed by some agent (table 35, items f 1 and 2) were actually killed by triungulinid larvae of stylopids, we can calculate new parasitism rates for stylopized nests which are probably more accurate than those based on adult parasitism alone. The rates for these 4 years, calculated by adding juvenile mortality (f 1-2) to the total number of stylopized adult wasps (h) and dividing by the number of cells in stylopized nests available for *Pseudoxenos*

TABLE 35.—*Parasitism by* Pseudoxenos hookeri *in nests of* Euodynerus foraminatus apopkensis *and* apopkensis-parvirudis *intermediates.*

Item	1957	1959	1960	1961
a. Number of nests provisioned	92	19	63	17
b. Number of provisioned cells in nests	705	148	468	538
c. Number of adult wasps examined	413	73	175	388
d. Number of stylopized nests	23	8	7	18
d 1. Number of nests with one stylopized adult wasp	13	5	6	8
d 2. Number of nests with two stylopized adult wasps	5	0	1	8
d 3. Number of nests with three stylopized adult wasps	3	0	0	1
d 4. Number of nests with four stylopized adult wasps	1	0	0	1
d 5. Number of nests with six stylopized adult wasps	1	0	0	0
e. Number of cells provisioned in stylopized nests	181	57	46	150
e 1. Cells destroyed by other parasites	6	3	4	7
e 2. Number of mature wasp larvae preserved	15	2	0	0
e 3. Number of wasp larvae accidentally killed	3	1	4	7
f. Cells in parasitized nests available for development of *Pseudoxenos* (e minus e 1-3)	157	51	38	136
f 1. Number of eggs killed by some agent	11	6	0	2
f 2. Number of newly hatched larvae killed by some agent	1	6	10	4
f 3. Number of young diapausing larvae killed by some agent	3	1	0	0
f 4. Number of old diapausing larvae killed by some agent	6	5	4	17
f 5. Number of adults escaped and not examined	2	0	0	0
f 6. Number of adults too fragmented to determine presence of stylopids	5	0	0	0
g. Number of adult wasps examined in stylopized nests (f minus f 1-6)	129	33	24	113
g 1. Number of adults with exserted stylopids	37	4	8	18
g 2. Number of adults with exserted and unexserted stylopids	13	1	0	0
g 3. Number of adults with unexserted stylopids only	5	1	0	12
h. Total number of stylopized adult wasps (g 1 plus g 3)	42	5	8	30

(f) are as follows: 1957—34 percent; 1959—33 percent; 1960—47 percent; and 1961—26 percent.

It is also possible that some of the mortality in resting larvae of *apopkensis* was caused by stylopid parasites. However, there was some mortality during this stage in the nests of all trap-nesting wasps and bees, and so not all, if any, of it in *apopkensis* can be ascribed to stylopization.

Miscellaneous. I obtained 1 other specimen of *Pseudoxenos hookeri* from trap nest material. This was in a nest of *Euodynerus f. foraminatus* (Saussure) provisioned at Plummers Island, Md., between August 14 and 22, 1957. The nest was picked up when only 1 cell had been completely stored. The female wasp which emerged from this cell on May 5, 1958, bore an exserted male stylopid puparium, identified subsequently as *hookeri* by R. M. Bohart. I did not find exserted or internal stylopids in 17 specimens of this same wasp from the 5 other nests from Plummers Island in 1957.

Previous observations. Bohart (1941) lists *Euodynerus a. annulatum* (Say) [as *Rygchium verus* Cresson], *E. annulatus arvensis* (Saussure) [as *arvensis*],and *E. annulatus sulphureus* (Saussure) [as *sulphureus*] as hosts of species of *Pseudoxenos* now considered to be synonyms of *hookeri* and advises me (*in litt.*) that he has also identified this stylopid from *E. foraminatus blandinus* (Rohwer).

Source material.
   Lake Placid, Fla. 1957 series: M 4, 6, 8, 12, 13, 26, 27, 56, 64, 86, 104, 134, 147, 151, 153, 158, 177, 181, 184, 199, 207, 229, 236. 1959 series: V 4, 12, 24, 45, 48, 80, 88, 98. 1960 series: B 55, 85, 96, 102, 122, 123, 163. 1961 series: F 19, 35, 39, 41, 47, 98, 102, 104, 111, 116, 119, 120, 126, 128, 155, 170, 175, 177.
   Plummers Island, Md. 1957 series: P 254.

Identifications. Stylopidae by R. M. Bohart; wasps by the author.

PSEUDOXENOS ERYNNIDIS Pierce

This stylopid was found in an adult of the vespid wasp *Pachodynerus erynnis* (Lepeletier) in each of 2 nests from the Archbold Biological Station in 1961. Both nests were from a single station beneath the limb of a live hickory in the Highlands Ridge sand-scrub area. As 1 nest was stored 4 weeks later than the other, it is unlikely that the same female wasp provisioned each. Unfortunately, both stylopized wasps were killed before I realized that they bore exserted male puparia of a stylopid. However, the development of 1 male had progressed enough to enable R. M. Bohart to identify it as a specimen of *erynnidis*.

The earlier 3-celled nest was stored in mid-June. Two females and a male of *erynnis* emerged from it July 17-18. The exserted stylopid protruded on the left side of the abdomen of 1 of the females between the fourth and fifth terga. There were no internal stylopids in these 3 wasps.

The later 2-celled nest was stored in mid-July. Cell 1 was destroyed by a miltogrammine maggot; a male of *erynnis* emerged from cell 2 on August 16. It bore 3 exserted male stylopid puparia,

2 between abdominal terga 4 and 5, and 1 on the right side between terga 3 and 4.

Source material.

Lake Placid, Fla. 1961 series: F 224, 257.

Identifications. Stylopidae by R. M. Bohart; wasps by the author.

Order DIPTERA

Family BOMBYLIIDAE

The parasitic flies of this family which I have reared from trap nests exhibit interesting diversity in host preferences and in the behavior of the larval stages. I obtained 4 species of *Anthrax*, 2 of *Toxophora*, and 1 of *Lepidophora*.

So far as host preferences are concerned, *Toxophora* is apparently the most restricted, for it was reared from nests of solitary vespids only. One species, *amphitea* Walker, was reared from 22 nests of vespids, and the same species probably parasitized 6 other vespid nests. The other species, *virgata* Osten Sacken, was reared from 3 vespid nests and probably parasitized 4 other vespid nests. The first instar *Toxophora* larva begins to feed on the host prepupa, or, in the case of *virgata*, on the host pupa also.

I reared *Lepidophora lepidocera* (Wiedemann) from 4 vespid nests. It may also have been present in 1 sphecid nest, that of *Trypargilum tridentatum archboldi* (Krombein), because a bombyliid larva fed on the spiders stored for the host wasp rather than on the host prepupa or pupa. This anomalous behavior of the larval parasite seems to be normal for *Lepidophora* because in 3 nests its larva fed on the caterpillars stored for the vespid host. However, in the fourth vespid nest it fed on the wasp prepupa in 1 of the cells. *L. lepidocera* was unique in one other way, namely because its larva usually fed on the contents of several cells in a linear series. It is a larger bombyliid than any of the others I reared, and the contents of 1 cell were rarely sufficient for it to reach larval maturity.

Anthrax atriplex Marston was reared only twice, each time from a nest of *Megachile gentilis* Cresson; the bombyliid larva fed on the host prepupa. However, the other 3 species of *Anthrax* were not so restricted in prey preferences. *A. aterrimus* (Bigot) and *argyropyga* Wiedemann were reared from 37 nests of species of *Trypargilum* and *Isodontia* (Sphecidae) and several species of solitary Vespidae. In Arizona *irroratus* Say was reared from 3 nests of megachilid bees, 1 nest of a colletid bee, and 1 vespid nest. It may also have parasitized a megachilid nest in Florida. In the literature *irroratus* is reported as a parasite in megachilid and vespid nests. The larvae of these 4 species of *Anthrax* usually fed on the host prepupae. However, a few larvae of *irroratus, aterrimus,* and *argyropyga* developed on the host pupae.

Bombyliids infested 26 other nests. They died as small larvae, unidentifiable to genus, in 14 of these nests. Pupae of *Anthrax* are easily recognizable, and I was able to identify them in the 12 other nests from which the adult parasites failed to emerge. Eleven of the nests containing *Anthrax* pupae were of species of *Trypargilum* or of various vespids, but the twelfth was in a nest of the pompilid, *Dipogon* sp. probably *sayi* Banks. It is most unfortunate that this particular bombyliid pupa was attacked by *Melittobia,* because it might have been a specimen of still another species of *Anthrax*.

I did not observe oviposition by any of the bombyliids. Presumably it is effected in the same manner as in *Anthrax limatulus fur* (Osten Sacken), a parasite of mud dauber wasps or other wasps and bees using abandoned mud nests as a nesting site (Marston, 1964, p. 94). The female bombyliid hovers in front of the nest entrance and projects eggs into it by flipping the tip of the abdomen downward and forward toward the entrance. Upon hatching the slender, filiform, motile larva makes its way into a host cell. The larvae of *Anthrax* and *Toxophora* await attainment of the prepupal or pupal stage by the host before attacking it. However, the larvae of *Lepidophora* customarily begin to feed at once on the prey stored for the host and each may require the contents of several cells to reach maturity. Ordinarily the bombyliid larva completes feeding a couple of weeks after the host larva finishes feeding on the stored prey, but in 2 nests attacked by *A. irroratus* and 1 nest attacked by *T. virgata,* the bombyliids overwintered either as eggs or tiny larvae and attacked the host prepupae or pupae the following spring.

Anthrax and *Toxophora* pupate within the host cocoon, and *Lepidophora* pupates within a host cell or cells. The bombyliid pupa bears a crown of heavy, sharp teeth, a transverse comb of short, close-set sclerotized rods with recurved ends on many abdominal terga, and a transverse row of long setae on many of the abdominal segments. The crown of teeth enables the pupa to cut through the host cocoon and mud partitions or leaf rolls by rotating its body in the cocoon or cell. The transverse rows of setae and sclerotized rods enable the pupa to move toward the nest entrance. When the adult fly is ready to eclose, the pupa cuts through the cocoon and cell walls and takes up a position at the nest entrance with its head and thorax outside of the boring. Eclosion then takes place in a few minutes.

The success of *Anthrax aterrimus* and *A. argyropyga* in parasitizing 22 nests of various species of *Trypargilum* merits special comment. In this group of wasps the male stands guard at the nest entrance while the female hunts for spiders. However, he is a very timid creature and backs into the burrow when a human appears near the entrance. Presumably he might behave similarly when a parasite appears at the entrance. Under these circumstances he would provide no defense against a bombyliid fly that hovered in front of the nest entrance and flipped eggs into or near the boring. He could be effective only if he emerged from the nest and chased off the intruder. Since these 2 species of *Anthrax* parasitized only 14 nests of other wasps in which the male did not stand guard at the entrance, it can be assumed that *Trypargilum* males offer no defense against attack by bombyliid or miltogrammine parasites which oviposit at the nest entrance.

In a number of nests I noted that the wasp occupant of the innermost cell was parasitized by a bombyliid. This does not necessarily imply that oviposition by the bombyliid must have taken place at the time that the host wasp began to nest in that particular boring. The mechanics of oviposition considered, bombyliid eggs could have been present around the entrances of several of the borings at a single station. They might have been deposited earlier in an attempt to parasitize another nest at the same station, and then one of the larvae entered the later nest. This circumstance might account for some of the seemingly anomalous host records noted below.

ANTHRAX ARGYROPYGA Wiedemann

I reared this bombyliid from 10 nests of sphecid wasps belonging to *Trypargilum* and from 9 nests of solitary vespids. It was reared from a nest of *Trypargilum collinum rubrocinctum* (Packard) at Cropley, Md., in 1955. At Plummers Island, Md., it was reared from 3 nests, 1 each in 1957, 1959, and 1962. Two of them were nests of *Trypargilum striatum* (Provancher), and 1 was of *Ancistrocerus c. catskill* (Saussure). It was reared from 1 nest of *Stenodynerus f. fulvipes* (Saussure) at Dunn Loring, Va., in 1954. At Kill Devil Hills, N. C., it was reared from 3 nests of *Trypargilum collinum rubrocinctum* and 1 nest of an unidentified vespid in 1956 and 1958. I reared it from 10 nests at Lake Placid, Fla., in 1957, 1959, 1961, and 1962, 3 of *Trypargilum c. collinum* (Smith), 2 each of *Stenodynerus pulvinatus surrufus* Krombein and *S. saecularis rufulus* Bohart, and 1 each of *Trypargilum tridentatum archboldi* (Krombein), *Stenodynerus beameri* Bohart, and *Pachodynerus erynnis* (Lepeletier).

Most of the stations in Maryland, Virginia, and North Carolina were in or at the edges of open wooded areas. The 3 stations at Plummers Island were on the sides of dead standing tree trunks.

The infested nest at Cropley was from the side of an old wooden shed, and that at Dunn Loring was from a setting in a pile of cut firewood. The 4 stations at Kill Devil Hills were on dead limbs of oak, pine, and hickory. The 9 stations at Lake Placid were in the Highlands Ridge sand-scrub area of the Archbold Biological Station, and were suspended from oak, pine, and scrub hickory limbs, or on the side of pine trunks. The parasitized nests were in 4.8-and 6.4-mm. borings, except for a nest of *Stenodynerus beameri* in a 3.2-mm. boring and one of *Trypargilum striatum* in a 12.7-mm. boring.

I made 1 field observation which affords some information on the length of time between nesting activities of the host wasp and emergence of the bombyliid adults from the nest. At Kill Devil Hills in 1958 a female of *Trypargilum c. rubrocinctum* was nesting on July 28. It is presumed that oviposition by the bombyliid female must have taken place about this date. A female *argyropyga* emerged from the innermost cell in this nest on September 7, about 6 weeks after oviposition by its mother. I did not obtain any information on the duration of the egg stage. However, data were obtained from 2 of the summer generation nests on the period between attachment of the first-instar bombyliid larva to the host prepupa or pupa and the emergence of the adult parasite. For a female bombyliid this period was 28 days and for a male 29 days. The data from these 3 nests suggested that about 2 weeks may be required for hatching of the egg and attachment of the first-instar larva to its host.

In the discussion of *Anthrax aterrimus* which follows I mention that the bombyliid larva may remain in the first instar for nearly 2 months if a suitable host is not available. I made an interesting observation which demonstrates this capability in *argyropyga*. This nest was made by *Trypargilum c. rubrocinctum* at Kill Devil Hills about mid-July 1958. When I opened the nest on July 28, I found a small bombyliid larva feeding on each of the wasp prepupae in cells 1 and 2. These bombyliids pupated between August 1 and 10. When I examined the nest on the latter date, I noted a small bombyliid pupa in cell 2. This tiny bombyliid larva must have been about 4 weeks old at that time. Males of *argyropyga* emerged from these 2 pupae on August 18, so this small bombyliid larva was unable to develop on its sibling pupa.

I observed that *argyropyga* larvae fed on the host prepupa in a dozen nests and once on the host pupa. I did not note the stage of the host attacked in the other nests, but it was either the prepupal or pupal stage. It required 8 days for a female *argyropyga* larva to completely suck dry a host prepupa.

A few observations were made on duration of the pupal stage.

In nests of the summer generation 3 females spent 13-16 days (mean 14) in the pupal stage, and 2 males spent 16-19 days (mean 17). Similar data from overwintering nests were quite variable because the pupal development occurred in my office from January through May. The pupal stage was 13-34 days for 3 females and 17-38 days for 3 males. In 1 summer generation nest I noted a period of 27 days between completion of feeding by the bombyliid larva and eclosion of an adult male *argyropyga*. This suggests that the prepupal period in the summer generation is about 10 days. In a nest of an unidentified vespid at Kill Devil Hills, a bombyliid pupa killed the prepupa of a chrysidid wasp in its efforts to leave the nest.

Fragmentary notes were made on the development of pupal coloration in 3 individuals of the summer generation. The eyes turned light tan 8-9 days after pupation, and were black a day later. The head and wings darkened in still another day, and on the 12th day there were dark stripes across the abdominal terga. Eclosion of the adults took place 2 days later.

In 6 nests of the summer generation the host wasps emerged 3-10 days before the bombyliids in the same nests. The *Trypargilum* hosts in 2 nests were out 3-7 days before *argyropyga*, and vespid hosts in 4 nests were out 6-10 days earlier than the flies. In a seventh nest (*Stenodynerus fulvipes*) the bombyliid emerged in mid-September, but the wasp in the adjacent cell overwintered as a diapausing larva and emerged the following spring. In one *Trypargilum* nest an *argyropyga* female in cell 1 and 4 wasps in cells 2, 6, 7, and 8 emerged in September; but a bombyliid in cell 3, presumably also an *argyropyga*, overwintered as a diapausing larva. It lived for several weeks the following spring but died before pupating. The wasp larvae in cells 4 and 5 in this nest died. In another nest (*Pachodynerus erynnis*) the host wasp emerged late in November, but an *argyropyga* in an adjacent cell overwintered as a diapausing larva and emerged the following spring.

In 3 other nests both the wasps and bombyliids overwintered as diapausing larvae. The host wasps emerged 13-14 days before the flies in nests of *Ancistrocerus c. catskill* and *Stenodynerus saecularis rufulus*, and 13-14 days *later* than the *argyropyga* in a nest of *Trypargilum striatum*, a species in which pupation occurs considerably later in the springtime.

I reared 4 *argyropyga* females and 1 male from the 5 nests from the Washington metropolitan area. At Kill Devil Hills I obtained 1 female and 4 males, and in Florida I reared 3 females and 8 males. A single specimen of *argyropyga* was present in 14 nests, and 2 specimens were present in each of 2 nests. Three other nests contained 2 bombyliids. One specimen of *argyropyga* emerged from each of these, and the other specimen in each nest died as a pupa. I also reared 1 specimen of *Anthrax aterrimus* from 1 of the 14 nests from which I reared a single *argyropyga*. *A. argyropyga* was present in the innermost cell in 11 nests, in the outermost cell in 1 nest, and in each of these cells in 1 nest. It occurred in intermediate cells in the other nests.

Source material.

Cropley, Md. 1955 series: B 25.

Plummers Island, Md. 1957 series: P 199. 1959 series: Y 131. 1962 series: M 37.

Dunn Loring, Va. 1954 series: C 34.

Kill Devil Hills, N. C. 1956 series: C 268. 1958 series: T 42, 61, 134.

Lake Placid, Fla. 1957 series: M 107, 162, 178, 251, 266, 286, 287. 1959 series: V 83. 1961 series: F 77. 1962 series: P 98.

Identifications. Anthrax by W. W. Wirth; wasps by the author.

ANTHRAX ATERRIMUS (Bigot)

(Plate 26, Figures 126, 127)

A. aterrimus was reared from 2 nests of *Trypargilum striatum* (Provancher) at Plummers Island in 1956 and 1960 and from 1 nest of *Isodontia auripes* (Fernald) in 1958. At Kill Devil Hills it was reared from 14 nests in 1955, 1956, and 1958, 6 of *Trypargilum clavatum* (Say), 3 of *T. collinum rubrocinctum* (Packard) (fig. 126), 2 of *Euodynerus megaera* (Lepeletier), and 1 each of *Monobia quadridens* (Linnaeus), *Ancistrocerus spinolae* (Saussure), and of an unidentified vespid. All the infested nests came from stations in partially or entirely shaded settings in open woods. At Plummers Island the stations were on a standing dead tree trunk, on a cabin porch rafter, and in the crotch of a dead sapling. The 10 stations at Kill Devil Hills were beneath dead limbs of oak, pine, and hickory except for 1 setting beneath the limb of a living oak. The nests were in 4.8-and 6.4-mm. borings, except those of *Monobia* and *Isodontia,* which were in 12.7-mm. borings.

I obtained no data on the duration of the egg stage, or on how many days may elapse before the first instar *aterrimus* larva attaches to the host prepupa or pupa. Developmental data from summer generation nests suggest that 5-6 weeks elapse between completion of the host nest and emergence of the bombyliid adults, and so the life cycle of the bombyliid from egg deposition probably is a minimum of only 1-3 days longer.

I obtained a first instar larva of what is presumed to be either this species or *A. argyropyga* from a nest of a solitary vespid at Kill Devil Hills in 1958. There were 2 other bombyliids in this nest. Neither of them reached maturity, but 1 progressed to the pupal stage and was readily identifiable as a species of *Anthrax.*

This first instar larva was 2.1 mm. long and resembled in gross details Clausen's figure (1940, p. 381) of *Hyperalonia oenomaus* Rondani. There were 12 body segments, the ninth abdominal being very much shorter than that figured by Clausen. The head was about two-thirds retracted into the prothorax. The 3 thoracic segments each bore a long seta on each side. The second to sixth and eighth abdominal segments each had a pair of short, small, fleshy ventral pseudopods. The last (ninth) abdominal segment had a pair of short conical protuberances at the apex dorsally, each of which bore a seta about one-sixth as long as the body. There were no anterior spiracles, but there was a pair of dorsal posterior spiracles near the apex of the eighth abdominal segment.

The bombyliid larva may remain in the first instar for a considerable period if no suitable host is available. The nest mentioned in the paragraph above was completed about mid-July and picked up on the 28th. Between August 11 and 22 the resting wasp larvae in cells 1-3 were each attacked by a single bombyliid larva. On September 12 there were in cell 2 the resting larva of a bombyliid and a small, live first-instar bombyliid larva. On this date I prepared a slide mount of the first-instar larva from which the description above was prepared. It must have been nearly 2 months old at that time.

I noted that the bombyliid larvae attacked host prepupae in 7 nests and host pupae in 3 nests. In the other infested nests I made no record as to whether the prepupa or pupa was attacked.

In 1 nest a period of 27 days elapsed between the date when the *aterrimus* larva began to feed on the host prepupa and the date when the adult female bombyliid eclosed. The pupal period was 15 days for another female *aterrimus* of the summer generation, and so the larva of the first female probably spent 12 days in feeding and as a prepupa. The pupal period during the summer generation was 15 days for a single female, and 12 and 18 days respectively for 2 males. In the overwintering generation the pupal period of 1 female was between 16 and 19 days and of 2 males 19 and 23 days.

The development of pupal coloration in *aterrimus* was noted in 3 nests. The eyes became light tan 8 days after pupation in one summer nest and 11-15 days after pupation in 2 overwintering nests. In the latter 2 nests the head, wings, and thorax were black 2 days later, and in another day black bars had developed across the abdominal terga. Eclosion of the adults occurred 2-3 days later.

In 4 summer generation nests *Trypargilum* wasps in adjacent cells emerged 1-2 days before *aterrimus* adults from the same nests. In 3 vespid nests the hosts emerged 14-16 days before *aterrimus* adults from the same nests. These emergence dates correlate with the shorter life cycle of the vespid wasps and the longer one of the species of *Trypargilum*.

The bombyliids overwintered as diapausing larvae in the other nests. The host wasp emerged 27 days before the *aterrimus* adult in the *Ancistrocerus spinolae* nest, 11-12 days before in a *Trypargilum clavatum* nest, 10 days before in the *Isodontia auripes* nest, concurrently in a *T. striatum* nest, and 3 days later in a *T. rubrocinctum* nest.

I reared 2 *aterrimus* females and 1 male from the Plummers Island nests and 8 females and 7 males from the Kill Devil Hills nests. There was only a single *aterrimus* in 15 of the nests parasitized by that species. One of these 15 nests contained an *aterrimus* in cell 9 and an *argyropyga* in cell 3. I reared 2 adults of *aterrimus* from a sixteenth nest. In still another nest there were 2 *Anthrax* pupae; an *aterrimus* adult emerged from one and the other pupa died. *A. aterrimus* was present in the outermost cell in 6 nests, in the innermost cell in 2 nests, and in both of these cells in a ninth nest. In the other 7 nests it parasitized 1 or 2 of the intermediate cells.

There are no published host records for this species. There is in the National Museum collection a nest of the sphecid wasp *Isodontia* (*I.*) *philadelphica* (Lepeletier) in the rotten stub of a tree branch collected by J. C. Bridwell at Vienna, Va. In addition to the wasps, Bridwell reared a specimen of *aterrimus* from this nest.

Source material.

Plummers Island, Md. 1956 series: H 60. 1960 series: E 46.

Kill Devil Hills, N. C. 1955 series: C 175, 177, 249, 421, 422. 1956 series: C 268. 1958 series: T 55, 62, 89, 145, 151, 155, 162, 206.

Identifications. *Anthrax* by W. W. Wirth and N. Marston; wasps by the author.

ANTHRAX ATRIPLEX Marston

I reared a specimen of this bombyliid from each of 2 nests of *Megachile* (*Litomegachile*) *gentilis* Cresson from Granite Reef Dam, Ariz., in 1961. Each nest was suspended beneath the dead limb of a mesquite at 2 different stations on the open desert.

The first nest contained 7 cells, was completed late in April, and was picked up and mailed to me on the 29th. I put the bee cocoons in individual glass vials on May 18. Adult bees emerged May 31-June 2 from the cocoons in cells 1-3. A female of *atriplex* emerged from cell 4 on June 13; the bombyliid larva fed on the bee prepupa in its cocoon. Bee larvae in the other cells died naturally or were parasitized by *Tetrastichus megachilidis* Burks.

The other nest contained 11 cells, was stored early in May, and was mailed to me on May 29. Bees emerged from cells 2-11 during transit, and when I opened it on June 7 they were loose in the shipping container. On that date there was a fully colored bombyliid pupa in the bee cocoon in cell 1. The bombyliid larva had fed on the resting bee larva. The adult bombyliid eclosed on June 8. There are no published host records for this species.

Source material.
Granite Reef Dam, Ariz. 1961 series: H 101, 107.

Identifications. Anthrax by N. Marston; bee by the author.

ANTHRAX IRRORATUS Say

I reared adults of this bombyliid from 4 nests from Portal, Ariz., and 1 nest from Scottsdale, Ariz. Each of 4 nests came from a different station on the open desert: 1 was suspended from an oak limb; 1 was in a partly dead mesquite bush; 1 was on a branch in a dense mesquite thicket; and 1 was suspended from a wire fence. The fifth nest was from a setting near the laboratory at the Southwest Research Station. *A. irroratus* also possibly parasitized 1 nest set on a pine tree trunk in the Highlands Ridge sand-scrub area at Lake Placid, Fla.

The hosts were as follows: The megachilid bee *Megachile gentilis* Cresson at Scottsdale; and the megachilid bees *Dianthidium heterulkei fraternum* Timberlake and *Ashmeadiella bucconis denticulata* (Cresson), the colletid bee *Hylaeus asininus* (Cockerell and Casad), and an unidentified vespid wasp at Portal. The host bee in the supposed infestation in Florida was *Megachile mendica* Cresson.

The *gentilis* nest was stored the latter half of April and had 15 cells. I preserved the bee prepupa in cell 15 for taxonomic study. Host bees emerged from cells 1-13 from May 25 to June 1. On June 9 I observed in the cocoon in cell 14, a large bombyliid larva which had sucked dry the megachilid pupa. The bombyliid pupated on June 10, and an adult female eclosed on the 28th.

There was only 1 cell in the vespid nest which must have been completed in late June or early July. When I opened the nest on July 20 there was a full-grown bombyliid larva in the delicate vespid cocoon. It had fed on the host prepupa. There could be no confusion as to the identity of the host in this nest, for the cocoon bore head capsules of the lepidopterous larvae stored for the host vespid. The bombyliid pupated between July 21 and 24, and an adult female eclosed on August 17.

The nests of *Dianthidium, Ashmeadiella,* and *Hylaeus* parasitized by *irroratus* apparently were stored later in the summer. The hosts in all nests were diapausing larvae when I first examined the nests in mid-October or late in December. The nests were then placed outdoors in chilling temperatures for 2 months to break diapause.

The *Ashmeadiella* nest had 25 cells. The occupants of all but 4 cells died as small larvae shortly after hatching or as resting larvae during the winter. Male bees emerged early in April from cells 15 and 24. A small bombyliid larva began to feed March 10-16 on each of the bee prepupae cells 7 and 25. They completed feeding on March 23. One of them pupated March 29 and an adult female eclosed on April 13. The other pupated between March 31 and April 2 and an adult female eclosed on April 20.

There were about a dozen cells in the *Hylaeus* nest. The bees in 2 cells pupated March 13-16, and a female bee left cell 1 when I examined the nest on April 3. On that date in cell 2 there was a pale bombyliid pupa whose larva had sucked dry the bee pupa. An adult male of *irroratus* eclosed on April 12.

I examined the *Dianthidium* nest on December 26. It contained 6 cells with diapausing bee larvae in cocoons in cells 1-5 and a diapausing bombyliid larva in the bee cocoon in cell 6. The bees in cells 3 and 4 and the bombyliid pupated between April 19 and 27. A female bombyliid eclosed May 15, and male bees emerged from cells 3 and 4 on the 31st. The bees in cells 1 and 2 did not pupate until June 1-10, and a female and male emerged on July 2.

These limited data from the Arizona nests establish that the pupal period for females is 18-24 days during the summer and 15-20 days in the laboratory for overwintering stock. The data also indicate that the first instar bombyliid larva may attack either the host prepupa or pupa, and that the bombyliid may overwinter either as an egg or tiny unfed larva as in the *Hylaeus* and *Ashmeadiella* nests, or as a diapausing larva as in the *Dianthidium* nest.

The *mendica* nest from Florida contained 6 cells. It was completed early in June, and I opened it for study on June 9. There was a small bee larva in cell 6 on that date; it died a few days later probably as a result of desiccation. I placed the other cells in individual glass vials on June 20 without further examination. Adult male and female bees emerged from cells 1, 3, 4, and 5 on July 1. On July 6 I cut open the bee cocoon in cell 2, injuring slightly the head of a live bombyliid pupa in the process. This pupa continued to develop and became fully colored, but died on the 22d. I assume that it may have been a specimen of *irroratus* because of the host; the pupa was definitely identifiable as that of *Anthrax*.

Previous observations. Brooks (1952, p. 370) reported *Megachile nivalis* Friese as a host of *irroratus* in Saskatchewan. Baker (1895, p. 173) recorded it [as *Argyramoeba oedipus* (Fabricius)] as a parasite in nests of *Odynerus* spp. in Colorado. *Odynerus* in the modern sense does not occur in North America; as used by

Baker it includes species of solitary vespids now assigned to half a dozen or so genera. Cooper (1954, pp. 281-282) reared *irroratus* from pupae of *Euodynerus foraminatus foraminatus* (Saussure) [recorded as *Rygchium rugosum* (Saussure)].

Source material.

    Portal, Ariz. 1959 series: X 233. 1960 series: X 315. 1961 series: G 189, 374.
    Scottsdale, Ariz. 1961 series: H 146.
    Lake Placid, Fla. 1960 series: B 63 (?).

Identifications. Anthrax by W. W. Wirth; bees and wasps by the author.

TOXOPHORA AMPHITEA Walker

(Plate 26, Figures 123-125)

I reared this bombyliid parasite of solitary vespid wasps from 18 nests from Lake Placid, Fla., 1959 through 1962, and from 4 nests from Plummers Island, Md., in 1961 and 1962. The Florida nests came from a dozen different stations in the Highlands Ridge sand-scrub area. Most of them were suspended from limbs of living scrub hickory, but a few came from similar settings on living oaks. The Plummers Island nests came from 3 stations in open woods, 2 of them on the side of standing dead tree trunks and 1 beneath a dead branch.

The host wasps in the Florida nests were as follows: 5 nests of *Pachodynerus erynnis* (Lepeletier); 5 nests of 1 or more species of unidentified vespids; 3 nests of *Stenodynerus lineatifrons* Bohart; 2 nests each of *S. beameri* Bohart and *Euodynerus megaera* (Lepeletier) (figs. 123-125); and 1 nest of *S. saecularis rufulus* Bohart. The Plummers Island *amphitea* were reared from 1 nest each of *Euodynerus schwarzi* (Krombein) and *Ancistrocerus campestris* (Saussure) and from 2 nests of 1 or 2 species of unidentified vespids.

What was undoubtedly this same species of *Toxophora* parasitized 2 additional Plummers Island nests made by unidentified vespids. The nests were from the same standing dead tree trunk where *amphitea* had attacked 2 other nests. Furthermore, the bombyliid pupae were unquestionably *Toxophora*, and *amphitea* is the only species of that genus occurring as far north as Maryland. A species of *Toxophora* parasitized 4 additional nests at Lake Placid, Fla., 2 of *Euodynerus foraminatus apopkensis* (Robertson) and 1 each of *Stenodynerus beameri* and *S. saecularis rufulus*. It is likely that *amphitea* was the parasite in these nests also because it attacked so many other nests at Lake Placid. However, it is not the only species of *Toxophora* occurring in Florida.

In 4 nests from Plummers Island from which I reared 2 females and 2 males of *amphitea*, 30-33 days elapsed between the dates on which the nests were completed and the emergence of adult bomby-liids. Inasmuch as oviposition by the mother bombyliid may have occurred 1 to several days prior to completion of the nests by the wasps, we can estimate a life cycle of 31-35 days for the summer generation of *amphitea* in Maryland. Comparable data are not available for nests from Florida but are probably identical.

I did not obtain any information on the duration of the egg stage or how many days may elapse before the tiny *amphitea* larva attaches to the resting host larva. However, probably about a week elapses between deposition of both the host and parasite egg and the attainment of full growth of the host larva, at which time the bombyliid larva may attach to the vespid. The period between maturity of the host larva and emergence of the adult bombyliid was 25 days for a female *amphitea* from Plummers Island and 29 days for a male. Similar data for 6 *amphitea* females from Florida were 21-29 days and 37 days for a single male; the latter period was for a late season nest when development may have been considerably slower. These data are somewhat misleading because the dates of host larval maturity and attachment of the parasite larva may not coincide. Developmental data suggest that *amphitea* males emerge 4-7 days earlier than females.

The tiny bombyliid larvae attached themselves transversely, usually on the dorsum of the host prepupa on one of the segments near the head (fig. 123). I recorded 16 *amphitea* larvae feeding on wasp prepupae and none on pupae. They sucked blood from the host prepupa (fig. 124), eventually reducing it to a collapsed shape-less mass, and reached larval maturity in less than a week. Pupa-tion of Florida specimens took place 3-5 days later (fig. 125). The pupal period for Florida material was 16-19 days for 3 fe-males and 11-12 days for 2 males. Usually wasps from adja-cent cells emerged 2-6 days (mean 4 days) earlier than *amphitea* adults in the same nests, but in 3 nests there was concurrent emer-gence of hosts and parasites.

I reared 12 females and 9 males of *amphitea* from Florida nests and 3 females and 2 males from Plummers Island nests, and so the probable sex ratio is 1:1. The parasites were distributed at random in the nests, some being in the first cells stored, some in the last cells stored, and some in intermediate cells. There was 1 *amphitea* in each of 14 nests and 2 specimens in each of 7 nests. One gets the impression that a female *amphitea* visits a nest only once and deposits 1 or several eggs during that visit.

Previous observations. Osten Sacken (1877, pp. 265-266) reported that Glover had found *amphitea* in a *Eumenes fraternus* nest, feed-ing either on the caterpillars stored for the wasp larva, or on the wasp larva itself.

Source material.

Plummers Island, Md. 1961 series: K 35, 46, 126, 154 (?), 171 (?). 1962 series: M 62.

Lake Placid, Fla. 1959 series: V 104, 106, 116. 1960 series: B 209. 1961 series: F 26 (?), 103 (?), 193 (?), 197, 203 (?), 212, 235, 261, 269, 279, 290, 296, 306, 324, 340, 341. 1962 series: P 7.

Identifications. Toxophora by W. W. Wirth; wasps by the author.

TOXOPHORA VIRGATA Osten Sacken

I reared adults of *virgata* from 3 nests from Portal, Ariz. One nest of an unidentified vespid was from a setting beneath a cedar branch along a dry wash in 1960. The other 2 were made by the vespid wasp *Stenodynerus toltecus* (Saussure) in 1961. They came from a single setting on a barbed wire fence on the open desert and may have been parasitized by the same *virgata* female, because both nests were picked up on May 22.

In addition, what was in all probability the same bombyliid parasitized 4 other vespid nests at Portal. The bombyliids in these nests died as pupae, but the species of *Toxophora* have a very distinctive pupa, and *virgata* was the only member of that genus that I bred from Arizona nests. One of these nests, taken in 1959 from a setting on a post beneath a concrete bridge, was made by an unidentified vespid. The other 3 in 1961 came from separate settings on a wooden fence post, from the branch of a partly dead mesquite, and from the branch of a desert willow; the first of these nests was made by *Euodynerus pratensis* (Saussure) and the other 2 by *S. toltecus*.

The 1960 nest of the unidentified vespid had 3 cells and was stored late in the summer. I did not open it until December 23, on which date there was a dead vespid larva in cell 1, a live, diapausing vespid larva in cell 2, and a dead vespid egg in cell 3. I placed this nest outdoors in chilling temperatures for 2 months to break the diapause. On April 18 in cell 2 I noted a small bombyliid larva 2 mm. long resting transversely on the back of the vespid prepupa on the second segment behind the head. The bombyliid larva fed on the prepupa and pupated by April 27. An adult male *virgata* eclosed on May 15.

The two 1961 *toltecus* nests parasitized by *virgata* had 12 and 6 cells respectively. Probably the nests were stored in mid-May, because they were mailed to me on the 22d and I opened them on June 1. There were pale wasp pupae in several cells on that date and other vespids pupated June 2-6. On June 1 I noted a small bombyliid larva on the back of the female wasp pupa in cell 1 of the 12-celled nest; the bombyliid completed feeding June 7-9, pupated on the 10th and a male *virgata* emerged on the 24th, 5 days after the female and male wasps emerged from cells 2-12. In the 6-celled nest I noted on June 2 a small bombyliid larva on the back of the wasp prepupa in cell 2; it completed feeding on the 9th, pupated on the 13th and a male *virgata* emerged on the 29th, 9-10 days after the wasps in adjacent cells.

In the nests probably parasitized by *virgata* there was 1 bombyliid in each of 2 nests and 2 each in the other 2 nests. In 1 nest the bombyliid fed on the wasp prepupa and in another the 2 bombyliids were each on the vespid pupa. In 2 nests the bombyliid pupae in outer cells were killed when wasps emerged from the inner cells. The bombyliids in these 4 nests occurred in random positions: One was in cell 1 of a 2-celled nest of an unidentified vespid; 2 were in cells 2 and 3 of a 9-celled *toltecus* nest; 2 were in cells 1 and 3 of a 10-celled *toltecus* nest; the position of the last bombyliid in a 5-celled *pratensis* nest was not ascertained.

Previous observations. Hall (1954, p. 145) reported that *virgata* was bred in California from old nests of *Sceliphron caementarium* (Drury) from which 3 vespid wasps also were bred, *Stenodynerus minimoferus* Bohart, *Euodynerus foraminatus blandinus* (Rohwer) (recorded as *Rygchium*) and *Ancistrocerus tuberculiceps sutterianus* (Saussure). Townsend (1893, p. 455) recorded it as having been reared in Colorado from the nest of a species of *Odynerus*. *Odynerus* sens. str. does not occur in North America, and any one of half a dozen genera of solitary vespids might have been the host wasp in this Colorado rearing.

Source material.
    Portal, Ariz. 1959 series: X 171 (?). 1960 series: X 166. 1961 series: G 43, 52 (?), 92, 323 (?), 409 (?).

Identifications. Toxophora virgata by W. W. Wirth; wasps by the author.

LEPIDOPHORA LEPIDOCERA (Wiedemann)

Two males of this rare bombyliid were reared from nests of solitary vespids from Lake Placid, Fla., in 1957, and 2 females in 1959. The nests came from 4 widely separated stations in the Highlands Ridge sand-scrub area of the Archbold Biological Station. One was tied to the side of the trunk of a small dead tree, 1 was on top of a pine stump, and 1 each was suspended beneath a limb of live scrub hickory and oak. Two nests had a boring diameter of 4.8 mm. and 2 of 6.4 mm. A fifth nest, probably parasitized by this species, was in a 4.8 mm. boring tied to the trunk of a pine tree.

The host wasp in 1 nest was almost certainly *Euodynerus foraminatus apopkensis* (Robertson), in a second nest it was *Stenodynerus saecularis rufulus* Bohart, and an unidentified vespid not *apopkensis* in the other 2 nests. The host in the fifth nest, probably parasitized by *Lepidophora,* was *Trypargilum tridentatum archboldi* (Krombein).

The first, an 8-celled nest, was received on April 2, 1957. Cells 1-5 contained only lepidopterous prey and shriveled wasp eggs, cells 6 and 7 contained a large bombyliid larva and scarcely any lepidopterous remains, and cell 8 contained a wasp larva in a newly spun cocoon. The bombyliid in this nest fed only on prey stored by the wasp because about 24 of the 46 caterpillars in cells 2 to 7 were shriveled and sucked dry. Apparently the bombyliid bored through the partitions closing cells 2 to 6 as it fed, but it fed mostly on the contents of cells 6 and 7. It transformed to a pupa 16 mm. long on April 15, and I transferred it then to an empty boring so that it would not kill the resting wasp larva in cell 8 when it emerged. The bombyliid pupa wriggled into the nylon emergence sleeve around the boring entrance at 1300 hours on April 24 and a male *lepidocera* eclosed a few minutes later. I was unable to rear the wasp in cell 8; it remained alive in the larval state until October 2 and died during exposure to low temperatures during the next 2 months. I expect that it was a specimen of *Euodynerus foraminatus apopkensis* because that was the only vespid with such a prolonged larval diapause in the nests from Lake Placid, Fla.; also, it was the only vespid that stored the olethreutid larvae found in this particular nest.

I received the second nest on November 26, 1957. It was 2-celled and contained a healthy resting larva of a vespid in cell 1. The second cell contained a full-grown vespid larva that had been sucked dry. The active bombyliid larva had bored through the outer end of the wasp cocoon after feeding, through the partition of agglutinated sand that capped cell 2 and it came to rest at the partition closing the vestibular cell. It became a quiescent, diapausing larva by December 5. I placed this nest outside my office window except during freezing temperatures from December 5 to February 5. The bombyliid transformed to a pupa on February 28 and a male *lepidocera* eclosed on March 13. The wasp in cell 1 transformed to a pupa a few days before February 13 and the adult *saecularis rufulus* left the cell when I opened the trap on February 24.

The third, received October 12, 1959, was a 1-celled vespid nest which contained a half-grown bombyliid larva and paralyzed lepidopterous larvae of the host wasp. The bombyliid pupated by October 24, and a female emerged November 6.

The fourth nest, received October 15, 1959, contained a large bombyliid larva in cell 3 feeding on a vespid larva, cell 4 was empty, and cells 5 and 6 contained mature wasp larvae. The bombyliid larva had previously fed on lepidopterous larvae in cells 1 and 2, boring through the partitions of agglutinated sand that capped these cells. On October 24 there was a bombyliid pupa in cell 3, a dead wasp prepupa in 5, and a black-eyed vespid pupa in 6 which died several days later. The adult female bombyliid emerged November 9.

A 7-celled nest of *Trypargilum tridentatum archboldi* (Krombein) was probably attacked by this species also. When I opened this nest on September 19, 1961, I found a mature bombyliid larva and spider remains in cell 4. The bombyliid had sucked all the body fluids from the spiders stored in cells 2 and 3 also. Apparently it began feeding in cell 2 and bored through the partitions capping cells 2 and 3 to get at the spiders stored in cells 3 and 4. Unfortunately this larva died before pupating. However, inasmuch as *Lepidophora* is the only known bombyliid that feeds on the prey or host larva in more than 1 cell, it seems very likely that this was a larva of that genus.

There are no published host records for this species.

Source material.
> Lake Placid, Fla. 1957 series: M 142, 237. 1959 series: V 86, 91. 1961 series: F 303 (?).

Identifications. Lepidophora by P. H. Arnaud and W. W. Wirth; wasps by the author.

Family PHORIDAE

MEGASELIA ALETIAE (Comstock)

I reared these scavenger flies from 1 nest each from Derby, N. Y., Plummers Island, Md., Kill Devil Hills, N. C., and Lake Placid, Fla. The host wasps were, respectively, *Trypargilum striatum* (Provancher), *T. collinum rubrocinctum* (Packard), *Podium rufipes* (Fabricius), and *Pachodynerus erynnis* (Lepeletier). In addition, I found a live mother *aletiae* with 3 small larvae in a 1-celled nest of *Stenodynerus a. ammonia* (Saussure) at Lake Placid, Fla. These 5 nests came from stations on live or dead branches or tree trunks in or at the edge of open wooded areas.

In addition, I found 45 nests infested by phorid larvae which probably were of this same species. These nests came from the 4 localities listed above. They were also from the same kinds of stations except that some were on structural timber. The host wasps in 44 nests were several species of *Trypargilum* (*striatum* (Provancher), *c. collinum* (Smith), *collinum rubrocinctum* (Packard), *clavatum* (Say)), *Trypoxylon frigidum* Smith, *Isodontia* sp., *Euplilis coarctatus modestus* (Rohwer), *Pachodynerus erynnis* (Lepeletier), *Stenodynerus saecularis rufulus* Bohart, *Monobia quadridens* (Linnaeus), *Symmorphus* spp., unidentified vespid spp., and *Dipogon* sp. I found phorid maggots also in 1 nest of a *Megachile* sp.

The prey stored by the host wasps listed above consisted of spiders, lepidopterous or coleopterous larvae, cockroaches, tree crickets, and adult midges.

The occurrence of *aletiae* (?) larvae in the single *Megachile* nest requires some comment. The *aletiae* larva are scavengers and normally feed on the prey stored for the host wasp larvae. *Megachile* stores a pollen-nectar mixture for its larvae. However, in this nest infested with phorids, the fly larvae did not feed on the pollen-nectar mixture, but apparently invaded the nest later and fed on the bee pupae in 2 of the cells.

The female *aletiae* enters the nest while it is being stored. In the nest in which I recovered a live female and 3 small larvae, it seemed probable that the female deposited living larvae rather than eggs. However, it may be that the egg stage is of very short duration. The larvae ordinarily behave as scavengers, feeding on the paralyzed prey stored for the host wasp larvae. The specimens of prey die soon after they are attacked by the phorids, so that actually most of the larval feeding is on carrion. However, some evidence accumulated during this trap nest study indicates that the phorid larvae may also attack the host wasp. In several nests I noted that the wasp eggs in cells infested by phorids were dead. In fact, in one *Symmorphus* nest from Plummers Island I observed a phorid larva sucking fluid from the host egg. Also, in several nests, including one from which I reared adults of *aletiae,* the maggots attacked the host prepupae or pupae in their cocoons. The phorid larvae can penetrate the partitions between cells, so that frequently several adjacent cells in a linear series were destroyed by them.

I did not obtain a great deal of life-history data. Adults of *aletiae* emerged from 1 nest 19-21 days after the mother phorid probably entered the nest. In another nest the pupal stage of *aletiae* lasted 4-5 days.

In the 4 nests from which I reared adults of *aletiae* their maggots destroyed 10 of 15 cells. In 30 additional nests probably infested by *aletiae* the maggots destroyed 55 of 107 cells.

Parasites and predators. I reared specimens of a braconid, *Synaldis* sp., from puparia of *aletiae* from the Derby nest.

Previous observations. The type series of *aletiae* was reared from pupae of the cotton leafworm *Alabama argillacea* (Hübner), and the phorid was presumed to be a parasite of the pupae. However, Riley (1885, pp. 116-119) cited field observations by Schwarz to the effect that *aletiae* developed as a scavenger in other dead and decaying insects as well as in decaying pupae of the cotton leafworm. Malloch (1912, p. 462) reported that it was reared from garbage and later (1914, p. 57) stated that it was reared from pupae of *Taeniocampa alia* Guenée, from breeding cages containing *Lachnosterna* larvae, and from rotting sugar beets.

Balduf (1928) contributed the most detailed life history notes on *aletiae*. He found phorid eggs on the body of a possibly diseased larva of the spindle stalk-borer, *Achatodes zeae* (Harris), a noctuid borer in corn stalks. The duration of the egg stage was not observed because some larvae had already hatched when the host larva was found. He stated that the phorid larvae entered the anus of the caterpillar and fed mostly on the tissue in the posterior third of the body. The larval stage was estimated as 11-15 days and the pupal stage as 7-11 days.

Krombein (1964a, pp. 108-109) found *aletiae* to be a serious pest in nests of the hibiscus wasp, *Ectemnius paucimaculatus* (Packard), where it fed on the decomposing adult flies stored as prey by the wasp. He reported that the phorid maggots destroyed 30 of 93 provisioned cells in 18 nests. The pupal stage lasted 11 days in a nest infested in July, and 15 days in a nest infested late in September. He also reported twice observing adult phorids attending the host wasp while the latter chewed out a nest entrance through the side of the hibiscus stem.

Source material (Megaselia aletiae)
  Derby, N. Y. 1958 series: R 56.
  Plummers Island, Md. 1958 series: S 35.
  Kill Devil Hills, N. C. 1958 series: T 40.
  Lake Placid, Fla. 1959 series: V 28. 1962 series: P 8.

Identifications. Megaselia by W. W. Wirth; *Synaldis* by C. F. W. Muesebeck; host wasps by author.

Source material (Megaselia sp., probably aletiae (Comstock)).
  Derby, N. Y. 1956 series: J 88, 107. 1957 series: G 126. 1958 series: R 65a. 1961 series: L 74.
  Plummers Island, Md. 1956 series: H 2, 31, 65, 96. 1957 series: P 14, 81, 90, 95, 273. 1958 series: S 7, 50, 61, 88, 91, 92. 1959 series: Y 71. 1960 series: E 101, 102. 1961 series: K 67, 132, 135, 177, 266. 1962 series: M 54, 94, 97.
  Kill Devil Hills, N. C. 1955 series: C 426, 439. 1958 series: T 213, 226.
  Lake Placid, Fla. 1957 series: M 63, 188, 216, 289. 1959 series: V 41, 42, 82, 138. 1962 series: P 87, 160.

Identifications. Flies and hosts by author.

Family CONOPIDAE

PHYSOCEPHALA MARGINATA (Say)

The discovery and rearing of this conopid from a trap nest were a matter of pure chance inasmuch as it was a parasite of the nesting bee and not of the brood. A female of the leaf-cutter bee *Megachile (Litomegachile) mendica* Cresson began a nest in a 6.4-mm. boring suspended beneath a dead hickory limb in open woods at Kill Devil Hills, N. C., in late July or August of 1955. I picked up the nest on September 18 and opened it for study on the 26th. I found that the bee had completely stored 1 cell at the inner end of the boring and had begun to store a second cell. She died facing inward at that point. Some days or weeks later the sphecid wasp *Podium rufipes* (Fabricius) began a nest in the outer end of the boring and made a closing plug near the entrance.

A dipterous puparium filled the abdomen of the bee. I kept it in a glass vial outdoors over the winter. An adult conopid emerged from it on May 27, but its wings failed to expand properly. However, it was readily identifiable on other characters as a specimen of *P. marginata*.

Previous observations. Van Duzee (1934, p. 315) recorded *marginata* (reported as *dakotensis* Van Duzee, a synonym) as having been reared from the honey bee, *Apis mellifera* Linnaeus. There are no other rearing records for this species. Presumably the *marginata* female pounces on the host bee during flight or while it visits flowers and oviposits between 2 of the abdominal segments.

Source material.
   Kill Devil Hills, N. C. 1955 series: C 382.

Identifications. Physocephala by C. W. Sabrosky; bee by the author.

Family Milichiidae

EUSIPHONA COOPERI Sabrosky

I reared some of these flies from the nest of a leaf-cutting bee, *Megachile* sp., probably *mendica* Cresson, from Plummers Island, Md., in 1959. The nest was in a 12.7-mm. boring from a station on a rafter of the cabin porch. I set out this boring on May 28, and the female bee completed her nest in it by June 4. There were 11 cells in the nest. Adult bees emerged from cells 4-11 on June 28 and escaped by cutting holes in the nylon emergence sleeve I had fastened around the nest entrance. I think it is almost certain that these bees were *mendica,* because that was the only leaf-cutter I reared from Plummers Island nests.

There had been no emergence from cells 1-3 by June 30, and so I opened them on that date. While unrolling the leaf cuttings forming the cell walls, I found a number of small dipterous puparia among them. There were 11 puparia in each of the leaf rolls of cells 1 and 3 and 13 in cell 2. The dipterous larvae had fed on the stored pollen rather than on the bee eggs or larvae, though the hosts were destroyed during the process. On July 7 I opened 1 of the puparia and found in it a live pale pupa. Late in August I opened

2 other puparia and found a live pale pupa in 1 and a dead shriveled pupa in the other. There was no emergence of adult flies from the other puparia by November 9, and so I placed all of them outdoors in a glass vial for the winter. I brought them back into my office on March 20. An adult of *cooperi* emerged from 1 of the puparia on April 29. On that date I placed 15 of the remaining puparia on damp sand and kept the other 15 in a glass jar without added moisture. On May 2, I opened 2 of the puparia; 1 contained an adult fly ready to eclose, and the contents of the other were moldy. There was no further emergence by May 18, and I found that the occupants of the other puparia were either desiccated or moldy.

In his description of this species Sabrosky (1955) gave a few life history notes made by K. W. Cooper in New York. The latter worker recovered a number of puparia and dead adult flies from the leaf rolls of a 5-celled nest of a species of *Megachile* in a wooden boring. The sixth cell was that of the vespid wasp *Ancistrocerus a. antilope* (Panzer), whose mud partitions prevented emergence of the adult flies. Cooper mentioned that all the bees perished, but he did not note whether the *Eusiphona* had fed on the bee larvae or on the pollen stored for them. His nest was stored during July, and live flies emerged in May of the following year. It was not determined whether the dead flies found in the leaf rolls had emerged the previous fall or in the spring before the nest was first opened for study on May 3.

The evidence from my nest establishes that oviposition by the mother *Eusiphona* must take place while the nest is being stored by the host bee. It will be recalled that only the innermost 3 cells of a total of 11 in my nest had been parasitized. If the fly deposited eggs after the nest was completed and sealed, then some of the outermost cells should have been infested. Also, the fact that the *cooperi* larvae in my nest fed on the stored pollen shows that they must have been active before or shortly after hatching of the host egg. The evidence from my nest also suggests that in *Eusiphona cooperi* there must be a very prolonged *pupal* diapause lasting more than 11 months.

Source material.
    Plummers Island, Md. 1959 series: Y 112.

Identifications. Eusiphona by C. W. Sabrosky; bee by the author.

Family SARCOPHAGIDAE

Maggots of scavenger flies belonging to the tribe Miltogrammini infested 208 wasp nests during the course of this study. Adults were reared from 45 nests. Forty-four of the nests were infested by 3 species of *Amobia, distorta* (Allen), *erythrura* (Wulp), and *floridensis* (Townsend), and 1 nest was infested by 1 specimen of *Senotainia trilineata* (Wulp). Species of *Amobia* have been reared previously from mud nests of wasps or from nests of wasps in stems. They have never been found in nests of ground-nesting wasps. On the other hand, the species of *Senotainia* have been reared frequently from ground-nesting wasps, and, aside from my single anomalous record here, have never been found in nests in wooden borings. Probably the infestation arose because this particular trap was from a setting on a concrete block in a basement area beneath the laboratory building at the Archbold Biological Station.

I have no observational data as to how *Amobia* females locate the wasp nest. However, Chapman (1959), working on the African species *A. africa* (Curran), found that females trailed the prey-laden *Eumenes* host female back to her nest. Presumably our American species behave in a similar manner, although it is strange that such behavior has not been observed. *Amobia* females have areas of enlarged facets on the eyes which presumably make possible this "shadowing" technique.

Once a female *Amobia* locates a nest in the process of being provisioned, she darts inside and deposits a clutch of small maggots among the specimens of prey stored by the host wasp (Myers, 1927). Limited evidence suggests that the host wasp may plug the nest and abandon it if she discovers this infestation. However, ordinarily it appears that she either ignores or fails to detect the maggots among the prey and may continue to store additional cells.

Myers (1927) found that *Amobia* maggots seek out and destroy the host egg before beginning to feed on the prey stored for the host. This behavior has been observed also for several species belonging to other genera of Miltogrammini. If there is insufficient prey in the original cell, the maggots invade adjacent cells to obtain enough food. The mud or sand partitions between the cells are readily breached by the maggots. Their presence in a cell certainly results in the rapid death of the host egg or larva and of the paralyzed prey. Infested nests have the typical odor of decaying flesh, and unquestionably the maggots do most of their feeding on carrion.

In heavy infestations the contents of all the cells may be destroyed by the maggots. In lighter infestations only the outermost cells in the nest are destroyed. This suggests that the larvae usually progress from the innermost or intermediate cells toward the outermost cells. When they have completed feeding, they usually congregate at the closing plug and transform to puparia there. Rarely, they penetrate the plug and wriggle outside to pupate. The fact that without fail the maggots pupate toward the nest entrance suggests that they may orient themselves by the same clues used by the wasp larvae, that is the convexity and roughness of the inner side of the cell partition. When the adults eclose, they breach the remainder of the plug and escape from the nest.

Chapman (1959) recorded a larval feeding stage of 4-8 days for the African species *A. africa,* and a pupal stage of 12-20 days depending on the temperature. He surmised that adult flies escaped from the mud cells of the host *Eumenes* by rasping or boring a hole with the ptilinum.

AMOBIA DISTORTA (Allen)

This species infested 13 nests at 9 stations at Derby, N. Y., in 1954, 1956, 1957, 1958, and 1960, and 1 nest at each of 7 stations at Plummers Island, Md., 1957-1961. Thirteen nests were on structural timber, 5 were on dead tree trunks, limbs, or cut firewood, and only 2 were suspended from branches of living trees. Most of the infested nests were in 4.8- or 6.4-mm. borings, except for 1 in a 3.2-mm. boring and 4 in 12.7-mm. borings.

The host wasps at Derby were vespids in 10 nests (5 of *Symmorphus c. cristatus* (Saussure), 4 of unidentified spp., and 1 of *Ancistrocerus c. catskill* (Saussure)), and sphecids in 3 nests (1 each of *Trypargilum clavatum* (Say), *T. striatum* (Provancher) and *T.* sp.). At Plummers Island the hosts were sphecid wasps in 6 nests (3 of *Trypargilum striatum,* 1 of *Trypoxylon frigidum* Smith, and 2 of a trypoxylonine sp. (or spp.)), and an unidentified vespid in 1 nest.

Adults of *distorta* emerged from several Plummers Island nests 16-20 days after the nests were completed by the host wasps. As 3 specimens from different nests were in puparia 12-13 days before emergence of the adults, the duration of the larval feeding stage appears to be 3-5 days. Adults of *distorta* emerged July 7 to August 23 from nests stored at Derby from mid-June to late July or early August. In 1 Derby nest stored the latter half of August *distorta* overwintered in the puparia and emerged the following spring. At Plummers Island *distorta* adults emerged June 26 to August 20 from nests stored by the host wasps from early in June until the latter part of July. From a vespid nest stored September 13-19 at Plummers Island a pair of *distorta* adults emerged on October 5; 7 additional flies overwintered in puparia and 2 females and 5 males emerged the following spring. It is not known whether the progeny from this nest represented a single clutch of larvae with divided adult emergence or whether 2 *distorta* females deposited clutches of 2 and 7 larvae, respectively.

Seventy-seven *distorta* maggots destroyed 33 of 57 cells in a dozen nests. In most of the Derby nests the ratio was about 1 maggot per infested cell, although 23 maggots developed on the contents of 4 cells of a large unidentified vespid in a 12.7-mm. boring. In the Plummers Island nests 2-3 maggots developed per infested cell, except in the nest of the small *Trypoxylon frigidum* in a 3.2-mm. boring, where 1 maggot required the contents of 2 cells to reach maturity. I reared 30 *distorta* females and 36 males from 86+ maggots.

Previous observations. Allen (1926, p. 16) reported males of *distorta* as having been reared from the mud "pipe organ" nests of *Trypargilum politum* (Say) at Plummers Island. Myers (1927) published some notes on what I presume is *distorta* under the name *Pachyophthalmus signatus* (Meigen) in Massachusetts. The female fly dashed into the nest of an *Ancistrocerus catskill* female just before the wasp brought a caterpillar into the nest; the fly paid another visit to the nest after the wasp left it. On the following day Myers found 4 small miltogrammine maggots on 2 of the caterpillars; the wasp egg was collapsed and emptied of its contents, presumably as a result of attack by the maggots. Three of the maggots matured on the caterpillars stored as prey in the 1 wasp cell. They pupated 9-11 days after larviposition, and adult flies emerged from the puparia 15-16 days later.

Source material.
  Derby, N. Y. 1954 series: 1 b. 1956 series: J 7, 18, 19, 54, 58, 71, 99. 1957 series: G 27. 1958 series: R 24, 51. 1960 series: D 32, 86.
  Plummers Island, Md. 1957 series: P 35, 210, 223. 1958 series: S 91. 1959 series: Y 148. 1960 series: E 51. 1961 series: K 73.

Identifications. Amobia by W. L. Downes; wasps by the author.

AMOBIA ERYTHRURA (Wulp)

I reared specimens of this fly from 1 nest each from Kill Devil Hills, N. C., in 1954, and Portal, Ariz., in 1961, and from 8 nests from the Archbold Biological Station at Lake Placid, Fla., during 1957, 1959, and 1961. The maggots destroyed the entire contents of the nests from North Carolina and Arizona. However, the presence of lepidopterous prey remains in these nests established that the wasp hosts must have been species of Vespidae. The host wasps in the Florida nests were also all Vespidae and consisted of *Euodynerus foraminatus apopkensis* (Robertson) in 5 nests and *Monobia quadridens* (Linnaeus), *Pachodynerus erynnis* (Lepeletier), and an unidentified vespid in 1 each of the other nests. All the nests were in 4.8- or 6.4-mm. borings except for that of *Monobia* which was in a 12.7-mm. boring. The North Carolina nest was suspended from the branch of a live Spanish oak on the barrens, and that from Arizona was suspended beneath the limb of a live mesquite on the desert floor. The nests from Florida were all from the Highlands

Ridge sand-scrub area; they were suspended from limbs of live scrub hickory or oak except for 1 suspended from a dead limb of a living oak.

Since I did not examine any infested nests while the maggots were small, I have no precise information on the duration of the larval stage. In 2 nests from Florida there were mature active maggots on March 27. They transformed to puparia and the adult flies emerged 17-21 days later. Since these nests were completed between March 19 and 25, the larval feeding period of the *Amobia* must have been between 2 and 8 days. These limited data indicate that the life cycle from larviposition to adult eclosion is probably 21-25 days. Adults of *erythrura* emerged from mid-March to mid-September from nests that were stored in Florida from early in February until mid-August. Eclosion of *erythrura* adults from a single clutch normally took from 3-4 days, although the 8 *erythrura* females from a single clutch emerged on the same day.

Forty-seven *erythrura* maggots destroyed 31 of 53 cells in 7 of the 8 nests infested by this species at Lake Placid. I reared 8 *erythrura* females from the eighth nest but neglected to record the number of cells in that nest. Normally a single cell contained enough prey to bring 1 or 2 maggots to maturity. However, in the nest of *Monobia*, which is a larger wasp, 8 maggots matured on the contents of 3 cells. I reared 33 *erythrura* females and 16 males from 55 maggots in the 8 infested nests. Both sexes of *erythrura* were present in all nests from which I reared more than a single specimen except for the 1 nest from which I obtained 8 females.

Source material.
    Kill Devil Hills, N. C. 1954 series: E 26.
    Lake Placid, Fla. 1957 series: M 67, 192. 1959 series: V 8, 40, 46, 95. 1961
        series: F 133, 170.
    Portal, Ariz. 1961 series: G 264.

Identifications. Amobia by W. L. Downes; wasps by the author.

AMOBIA FLORIDENSIS (Townsend)

This species infested 10 nests at 9 stations at the Archbold Biological Station, Lake Placid, Fla., in 1957, 1959, 1960, and 1961, 2 nests at Portal, Ariz., in 1961, and 3 nests at Scottsdale, Ariz., in 1961. All the nests were in 4.8- or 6.4-mm. borings. Eight of the Florida nests were from settings beneath living or dead scrub hickory and oak limbs in the Highlands Ridge sand-scrub area, and 2 were from a setting on a concrete block in a basement area beneath the laboratory. The 2 stations at Scottsdale were in a mesquite thicket on the desert floor, while those at Portal were suspended from limbs of a dead sycamore and a live desert willow along a dry stream bed.

The host wasp in all the Arizona nests was the sphecid *Trypargilum t. tridentatum* (Packard). In Florida the host wasps were vespids in 6 nests, 3 each of *Euodynerus foraminatus apopkensis* (Robertson) and an unidentified vespid (or vespids), and sphecids in 4 nests, 2 each of *Trypargilum johannis* (Richards) and *T.* sp. (or spp.).

Adults of *floridensis* emerged from parasitized nests 18-25 days after the nests were stored by the host wasps in Florida. The elapsed time between completion of larval feeding and adult emergence was 17-18 days for 2 females. The elapsed time between formation of the puparium and emergence of the adult was 14-15 days for 2 other specimens. These data suggest that the larval feeding period may normally be about 4-7 days. Adults of *floridensis* emerged from mid-April until late in June from nests stored in Florida from mid-March until early in June. Precise dates were not available for storing of the Arizona nests, but *floridensis* adults emerged from them from late in May until late in July. Emergence of adults from a single clutch required 1-3 days.

Sixty-three *floridensis* maggots destroyed 59 of 91 cells in 15 nests. In 4 nests a single maggot destroyed the contents of 3 to 5 cells. In these particular nests the infestations undoubtedly originated in an intermediate cell, and the maggot destroyed the contents of more than 1 cell, not for food but to reach the boring entrance. In most other nests the contents of 1 cell provided sufficient food for a single maggot, although as many as 11 maggots matured in a 5-celled nest in a 6.4-mm. boring. I reared 19 *floridensis* females and 26 males from the 63 maggots. Both sexes were present in all nests containing more than a single maggot.

Previous observations. Allen (1926, p. 11) recorded *Sceliphron caementarium* (Drury) and *Isodontia mexicana* (Saussure) [as *harrisi*] as hosts of *floridensis*. However, these records need confirmation, because the taxon treated as *floridensis* by Allen is now considered to represent both *floridensis* and *erythrura*.

Source material.
    Lake Placid, Fla. 1957 series: M 46, 83, 112, 308, 311. 1959 series: V 19, 74. 1960 series: B 175. 1961 series: F 213, 218.
    Portal, Ariz. 1961 series: G 68, 376.
    Scottsdale, Ariz. 1961 series: H 38, 178, 193.

Identifications. Amobia by W. L. Downes; wasps by the author.

UNIDENTIFIED SPECIES of AMOBIA

Miltogrammine maggots, undoubtedly several species of *Amobia*, infested 163 nests (69 from Derby, N. Y., 33 from Plummers Island, Md., 31 from Kill Devil Hills, N. C., 20 from Lake Placid, Fla., 5 from Portal, Ariz., and 1 each from Cropley, Md., Oxford, N. C., and

Camp Verde, Scottsdale, and Granite Reef Dam, Ariz.) in addition to the 45 nests reported on the preceding pages. I discarded many of these infested nests without attempting to rear the parasites, because the maggots had destroyed all the cells so that specific host identifications were impossible. In other nests the adult flies had already emerged, or I was unsuccessful in rearing them. I presume that all these infestations were by the 3 species of *Amobia* discussed in detail above. However, inasmuch as 2 or more species of *Amobia* may be present in any of these areas, it is not possible to say, for example, that all the Derby and Plummers Island nests were infested by *distorta* or that all the Kill Devil Hills nests were infested by *erythrura*.

The host wasps at Derby included: Vespidae—7 of *Ancistrocerus a. antilope* (Panzer), 2 of *A. c. catskill* (Saussure), 3 of *Symmorphus c. cristatus* (Saussure), 1 of *S. canadensis* (Saussure), and 39 of unidentified species; and Sphecidae—5 of *Trypargilum striatum* (Provancher), 2 of *T. collinum rubrocinctum* (Packard), and 9 of several *T.* spp. The host wasp was not noted for 1 nest.

In the Washington metropolitan area the infested nest at Cropley was that of a *Trypargilum* sp., while those at Plummers Island included the following: Vespidae—1 of *Ancistrocerus a. antilope* and 4 of several unidentified species; and Sphecidae—11 of *Trypargilum striatum*, 3 of *T. clavatum* (Say), 2 of *T. collinum rubrocinctum,* and 12 of several *T.* spp.

In North Carolina the host wasp in the single Oxford nest was a *Trypargilum* species, while at Kill Devil Hills the hosts were: Vespidae—2 of *Monobia quadridens* (Linnaeus), 2 of *Stenodynerus ammonia histrionalis* (Robertson), 1 of *S. krombeini* Bohart, 1 of *S. f. fulvipes* (Saussure), 1 of *Ancistrocerus spinolae* (Saussure), and 15 of several unidentified species; and Sphecidae—5 of *Trypargilum t. tridentatum* (Packard), 1 each of *T. clavatum, T. collinum rubrocinctum,* and an unidentified *T.* sp., and 1 of an *Isodontia* sp.

The host wasps in the Florida nests were: Vespidae—3 of *Euodynerus foraminatus apopkensis* (Robertson), 2 of *Stenodynerus saecularis rufulus* Bohart, 1 of *S. pulvinatus surrufus* Krombein, 1 of *Pachodynerus erynnis* (Lepeletier), and 11 of several unidentified species; and Sphecidae—2 of *Trypargilum johannis* (Richards).

In Arizona the host wasps were *Trypargilum t. tridentatum* in 1 nest each from Portal, Granite Reef Dam, and Scottsdale, and 1 or more species of unidentified vespids in 4 nests from Portal and 1 nest from Camp Verde.

Source material.

    Derby, N. Y. 1955 series: D 7c, 12c, 13e. 1956 series: J 13, 14, 20, 21, 44, 55, 74, 81, 88, 107. 1957 series: G 9, 13, 18, 23, 24, 26, 29, 32, 59, 60, 64, 67, 68, 70, 71, 73, 77, 82, 84, 86, 91. 1958 series: R 49, 54, 59, 63a, 65a. 1959 series: W 10, 18, 20, 28, 33, 41, 43, 48, 52, 55, 57, 70. 1960 series: D 7, 11, 13, 55, 61, 66, 77, 85. 1961 series: L 9, 33, 47, 52, 57, 64, 71, 81, 84, 85.

Cropley, Md. 1955 series: B 39.

Plummers Island, Md. 1956 series: H 72. 1957 series: P 31, 41, 65, 101, 103, 115, 139, 140, 173, 205, 226, 229, 268. 1959 series: Y 48. 1960 series: E 119, 144, 167. 1961 series: K 16, 68, 92, 110, 139, 156, 173, 188, 198, 200, 204, 222. 1962 series: M 80, 85, 103.

Oxford, N. C. 1957 series: H 149.

Kill Devil Hills, N. C. 1954 series: E 38. 1955 series: C 9, 10, 11, 18, 30, 49, 145, 291, 356, 377, 446, 448, 451, 477, 510. 1956 series: C 683, 696, 714. 1958 series: T 16, 33, 49, 133, 143, 151, 155, 159, 160, 187, 207, 240.

Lake Placid, Fla. 1957 series: M 44, 96, 159, 176, 290, 298, 310. 1959 series: V 9. 1960 series: B 5. 1961 series: F 52, 147, 183, 253, 257, 289. 1962 series: P 10, 22, 74, 104, 116.

Camp Verde, Ariz. 1957 series: Q 33.

Portal Ariz. 1959 series: X 117, 153, 172, 217. 1960 series: X 152.

Scottsdale, Ariz. 1961 series: H 190.

Granite Reef Dam, Ariz. 1961 series: H 257.

Identifications. Amobia and wasps by the author.

SENOTAINIA TRILINEATA (Wulp)

I reared *trilineata* from a nest of *Stenodynerus fulvipes rufovestis* Bohart in a 6.4-mm. boring from Lake Placid, Fla., in 1957. The nest was on a concrete block in a basement area beneath the station laboratory.

The nest was stored the latter part of June. Three miltogrammine maggots developed in 1 cell and had transformed to puparia before I examined the nest on July 1. A single male of *trilineata* emerged from 1 of the puparia on July 10.

As mentioned earlier, this is an anomalous host record for *trilineata,* and the infestation undoubtedly occurred because of the position of the trap station. All previously recorded hosts for species of *Senotainia,* including *trilineata,* have been ground-nesting wasps.

Source material.

Lake Placid, Fla. 1957 series: M 306.

Identifications. Senotainia by W. L. Downes; wasp by author.

Order HYMENOPTERA

Superfamily ICHNEUMONOIDEA

Family ICHNEUMONIDAE

EPHIALTES SPATULATA (Townes)

I reared 2 females of this species from nests of Vespidae from Derby, N. Y., in 1958 and 1960. One nest was of *Euodynerus f. foraminatus* (Saussure) in a 4.8-mm. boring; the other was of *Symmorphus c. cristatus* (Saussure) in a 3.2-mm. boring. Both nests came from stations on a pile of cut firewood in full sunlight during part or all of the day.

The *Euodynerus* nest was completed in July 1958, and I opened it for study on August 11. It contained 6 stored cells and an empty vestibular cell. There were diapausing wasp larvae in delicate silken cocoons in cells 1-5, and a pale, black-eyed parasite pupa in the host cocoon in cell 6. The parasite had fed on the diapausing wasp larva. A female of *spatulata* was ready to eclose on August 15, and it left the nest on the 20th. The host wasps in adjacent cells overwintered as resting larvae and transformed to pupae and adults the following spring.

The *Symmorphus* nest was completed late in June 1960, and I opened it for study on July 13. It contained 3 stored cells and an empty vestibular cell. There were diapausing wasp larvae in opaque silken cocoons in cells 1 and 3. In the wasp cocoon in cell 2 was a pale parasite pupa, whose larva had fed on the diapausing wasp larva. A female of *spatulata* left the nest on July 21, injuring the wasp larva in cell 3 during her emergence, so that the wasp died subsequently. The occupant of cell 1 overwintered as a resting larva, and a female of typical *cristatus* emerged from it the following spring.

The parasite has a long ovipositor, and it is likely that oviposition takes place through the wooden side of the boring. There are no published life history notes on this species or on any North American members of the genus as restricted by Townes and Townes.

Source material.
Derby, N. Y. 1958 series: R 17. 1960 series: D 2.

Identifications. Ephialtes by H. K. Townes; wasps by the author.

POEMENIA AMERICANA AMERICANA (Cresson)

I reared this parasite from 2 nests of *Passaloecus* sp., undoubtedly *cuspidatus* Smith, from Derby, N. Y., in 1959 and 1960. A small parasite larva, identical in appearance with those of *Poemenia* in the first 2 nests, was found in each of 3 other nests of *P. cuspidatus* at Derby in the same years and at the same stations. All the nests were from stations on piles of cut firewood in the full sun. Four of them were in 3.2-mm. borings, and 1 was in a 4.8-mm. boring. The nests were stored during the latter half of June.

The first instar *Poemenia* larva is quite characteristic because its body bears many relatively long setae. Larvae having this appearance were present in several cells from which I failed to rear adult parasites. The cells in these five nests occurred as follows (W=adult wasp; P=adult *Poemenia;* p=larval *Poemenia* (?); x=larval wasp mortality):

```
W  3 :   ♀P---x---p
W 11:    x---p---♂W
D  4 :   p---♂W
D  8 :   ♂P---p
D 34:    p
```

The female *Poemenia* has a relatively lengthy ovipositor, and it seems probable that she oviposits through the wooden side of the boring. Her egg must be deposited either loose in the cell or else on the skin of the host larva, because the *Poemenia* develops as an ectoparasite. The early behavior of the *Poemenia* larva is apparently very similar to that described subsequently for several species of the cuckoo wasp *Chrysura* on megachilid bee larvae; that is, the first instar parasite larva attaches by its mandibles to the host body. It sucks some blood but does not increase greatly in size, nor does it molt to the second instar until the host larva has finished feeding.

The host larva in 1 cell was full grown on June 23, and the first instar *Poemenia* larva attached to the dorsum of the wasp larva was 1.9 mm. long. The host larva voided meconial pellets on June 27 and 28. By the latter date the *Poemenia* larva was 2.25 mm. long, but it had not yet molted to the second instar. It molted on July 1, and by the 10th it had reduced the host larva to about a third of its original size. The *Poemenia* larvae spun delicate, semi-transparent cocoons 8 (♂) and 12 (♀) mm. long. Both of these parasites overwintered as diapausing larvae, transformed to pupae and then to adults the following spring concurrently with *Passaloecus cuspidatus* adults from other nests from the same locality. The pupal period in *Poemenia* must be about 10 days. One of the specimens was ready to pupate on April 18, and the adult *americana* left the nest on the 30th, probably several days after it actually eclosed.

There are no published prey records for typical *americana*. *P. americana nebulosa* Habeck and Townes was reared from larvae of lepidopterous and coleopterous borers in pine cones.

Source material.
Derby, N. Y. 1959 series: W 3, 11 (?). 1960 series: D 4 (?), 8, 34 (?).

Identifications. Poemenia by L. M. Walkley; wasps by the author.

MESSATOPORUS COMPRESSIVENTRIS Cushman

I reared a single female of this ichneumonid from a nest of *Trypargilum collinum rubrocinctum* (Packard) from Plummers Island, Md. The nest was from a setting tied to a dead standing tree trunk in moderately dense woods. I set out the boring on June 9, 1962, and a nest had been completed in it by July 11. The inner 100 mm. of the boring was empty. Then there were 4 stored cells extending to the boring entrance, cell 4 being capped by a mud plug 4 mm. thick. When I opened the nest on the 12th the wasp larvae in cells 1 and 2 were almost mature; so the nest must have been stored during the first week in July. Cell 4 contained 8 spiders and a parasite larva sucking blood from the abdomen of

1 of the spiders. This larva fed on the remaining spiders, leaving most of the exoskeletons, transformed to a pupa on or before July 20, and a female *compressiventris* emerged on the 27th. The wasp larva in cell 2, and the diapausing wasp larvae in cells 1 and 3 were dead by July 20. However, the wasp was readily identified by the typical cocoons spun by the larvae in cells 1 and 3. Had these wasps lived, they undoubtedly would have overwintered as diapausing larvae.

There are no other host records for *compressiventris*, but other species of *Messatoporus* in North America have been recorded as parasitizing the free mud cells of mud-daubing spider wasps belonging to the genera *Auplopus* and *Phanagenia*. It has been assumed that the *Messatoporus* was parasitic on the resting wasp larvae in these mud cells. However, the evidence from my nest suggests that the newly hatched *Messatoporus* larva may destroy the host egg or larva and then proceed to feed on the prey stored for the host wasp. Inasmuch as other prey records are for mud-daubing wasps which construct free mud cells, it seems likely that in my nest the mother *compressicornis* oviposited into the outermost cell through the mud plug at the nest entrance rather than through the wooden side of the block itself.

Source material.
Plummers Island, Md. 1962 series: M 4.

Identifications. *Messatoporus* by L. M. Walkley; wasp by the author.

Superfamily CHALCIDOIDEA

Family EULOPHIDAE

TETRASTICHUS JOHNSONI Ashmead

This eulophid parasite of spider wasps infested 7 nests of *Dipogon s. sayi* Banks and *Dipogon* sp., probably *s. sayi*, at Plummers Island, Md., 1 nest in 1959 and 6 in 1961. The nests came from settings on 3 different standing dead tree trunks. Four of the 1961 nests were from a single station and were infested during mid-June, the end of July, and early in September.

The adult female *johnsoni* invades the nest while the wasp is storing it. The parasite is enclosed in a cell with the paralyzed spider bearing the wasp egg when the wasp constructs the closing plug of loose debris for that cell. I picked up 3 nests only a few days after they were infested and found an adult female in 1 cell in each nest. I killed 2 of the parasites at once, thinking that they were specimens of *Melittobia;* neither of the eggs in these cells had hatched at this time. I reared the wasps in these 2 cells to maturity, a definite indication that *johnsoni* does not oviposit in the wasp egg. In the third nest I observed a female *johnsoni* sitting on a newly hatched *sayi* larva on June 19, chewing at the larval skin. A day later this female *johnsoni* had gotten stuck to some tape used to hold the parts of the split trap together. However, she must have deposited eggs the day before because the wasp larva was later found to be parasitized. On June 21 I noted another female *johnsoni* sitting on the cell wall in another cell in this same nest. Although she died a day later, she also had parasitized the small wasp larva from which I reared her progeny later.

It is quite easy to overlook these female parasites in newly provisioned cells; they are small (1.2 mm. long) and can hide beneath the spider or among the particles of debris used to form the closing plug for each cell. My observations suggest that the female *johnsoni* has quite a short adult life and probably parasitizes only a single larva.

Presumably the eggs are deposited inside the host as is normal for other species of *Tetrastichus*. My observations suggest that oviposition takes place in the newly hatched wasp larva, not in the egg. I have no data on the duration of the egg stage, but probably it is very brief. The *johnsoni* larvae are endoparasitic and apparently complete their feeding just a day or two after the host larva spins its cocoon, or about 10-12 days after oviposition by the female *johnsoni*. When the *johnsoni* larvae are mature they are apparent through the host cocoon as yellow blobs, the yellow representing the accumulated waste material in the gut of each larva. The parasites completely fill the host larva at this time. Shortly thereafter they rupture the host pelt and leave it to pupate within the host cocoon. About 2 days after leaving the host larva the parasite larvae defecate, and pupation as free pupae takes place 3 days later. Adults eclose 5-8 days after pupation. In 2 cells of the summer generation the elapsed time between oviposition and pupation was 14 and 20 days, and in 4 cells the period between pupation and adult eclosion was 5-8 days (mean 6 days). Eclosion of adults lasted over a period of 2-3 days. In 4 cells the period between probable oviposition and eclosion of adults was 19-25 days (mean 21 days).

Adults of *johnsoni* emerged during the summer from 7 of the parasitized larvae and from the other 2 parasitized larvae after a prolonged period of larval diapause over the winter. In 1 *sayi* nest stored late in July *johnsoni* adults emerged August 18 from the wasp larva in cell 3, but not until the following spring from the wasp larva in cell 1.

Both sexes of *johnsoni* emerged from each host larva, though there was a substantial preponderance of females. Altogether from the 9 parasitized cells I obtained 543 ♀ *johnsoni*, 84 ♂, 11 ♀ pupae, 16 pupae of indeterminate sex, and 27 larvae, so the ♀:♂ ratio probably is 7:1. The maximum number of *johnsoni* obtained from a single larva was 102 (98 ♀, 2 ♂, 2 pupae), and the minimum number was 37 (16 ♀, 2♂, 5 ♀ pupae, 6 other pupae, 8 larvae).

Although it was not possible to determine definitely the sex of the host wasp larva, some reasonably reliable estimates as to the sex can be based on the length of the host cocoons. Male cocoons of *Dipogon sayi* have a mean length of 8 mm. (range 7-9 mm.), and female cocoons of 10 mm. (range 7-13 mm.). Based on these mean lengths 2 of the host larvae containing 37 and 42 parasites, respectively, were probably males, 5 of the host larvae containing 42-102 parasites (mean 81) were probably females, and 2 host larvae containing 51 and 77 parasites, respectively, were in cocoons falling between the 2 mean lengths.

Nests of *sayi* were infested by *johnsoni* as early as June 1 and as late as September 1. Adults of *johnsoni* emerged June 23 from the nest provisioned around June 1. Emergence of *johnsoni* from other nests of the summer generation occurred on July 8 and 16 and August 12, 17, and 18. These emergence dates and the relatively short life cycle suggests that *johnsoni* has 3 or more generations a season. There was concurrent emergence of hosts and parasites in the 4 nests from which I reared both.

Previous observations. Burks (1943, p. 527) reported that the type series of *johnsoni* was reared from mud cells of the spider wasp *Phanagenia bombycina* (Cresson), but he suggested that the wasp may not have been the primary host. However, my observations definitely establish *johnsoni* as a primary parasite of spider wasp larvae. It was the only parasite I reared from *Dipogon sayi*.

Source material.
  Plummers Island, Md. 1959 series: Y 54. 1961 series: K 100, 112 ,120, 122, 158, 238.

Identifications. Tetrastichus by B. D. Burks; wasps by the author.

TETRASTICHUS species

I reared this undescribed species from a single prepupa in a 7-celled nest of *Trypargilum t. tridentatum* (Packard) from Granite Reef Dam, Ariz. The nest was in a 4.8-mm. boring suspended beneath a mesquite limb in moderately dense growth along the river. It was stored about mid-July 1961, picked up on the 19th, and I opened it for study on the 28th. On that date there were pale wasp pupae in cocoons in cells 5-7, small dead wasp larvae in cells 2-4, and a full-grown dead wasp prepupa in cell 1 containing a number of adult *Tetrastichus* just beginning to emerge from the host body. I recovered 43 females, 12 males, and 1 damaged specimen, probably a female. A few specimens may have escaped, and so the sex ratio can be estimated only tentatively as 4:1. Adult wasps emerged from cells 5-7 on August 10-11, just about 2 weeks after the parasites. Although I obtained numerous nests of *tridentatum* from several localities in Arizona, this was the only one parasitized by *Tetrastichus*.

Of the known species in the genus it is most closely related to *johnsoni* Ashmead. The hosts of the 2 species belong to different families of wasps. However, the close relationship of the 2 parasites becomes more meaningful when it is remembered that both of these genera of wasps store paralyzed spiders in their nests.

Source material.
   Granite Reef Dam, Ariz. 1961 series: H 62.

Identifications. Tetrastichus by B. D. Burks; wasp by the author.

TETRASTICHUS MEGACHILIDIS Burks

This eulophid parasite of leaf-cutting megachilid bees was described from material reared during this study from the nests discussed below. It infested 8 nests of *Megachile (Litomegachile) gentilis* Cresson, 7 from Granite Reef Dam, Ariz., and 1 from Scottsdale, Ariz. The Scottsdale nest and one of the Granite Reef Dam nests were secondarily infested by *megachilidis* in the laboratory in Washington. At Granite Reef Dam 1 nest was from a setting beneath a cottonwood limb near the river in moderately dense growth; the others were from 3 settings beneath limbs of palo verde and mesquite on the open desert. Three of the nests infested in the field were from a single station beneath a mesquite limb and were apparently stored at the same time.

The nests infested in the field were provisioned during the latter half of April. I did not realize that they were parasitized until a number of *megachilidis* adults emerged from several cells in 3 nests on May 18, 9 days after I first examined the nests. Presumably, the initial infestation in these megachilid nests took place as I indicated previously for *Tetrastichus johnsoni*; that is, the adult female parasite entered the nest while the bee was constructing and provisioning cells, or shortly after the nest was completed. If *megachilidis* behaved as did *johnsoni*, oviposition probably occurred after the host larva hatched. Primary emergence of *megachilidis* from these nests occurred May 18-24. Since I did not open any of the bee cells when I split the traps on May 9, I can only guess that the life cycle of *megachilidis* at that time of the year was probably about 25-30 days. I assume that oviposition by the parasites took place when the bee larvae hatched. The parasite larvae developed inside of the host larva, completely consumed it after it spun its cocoon, and then left the pelt of the larval bee to pupate within the bee cocoon as free pupae. When the adult parasites eclosed they chewed holes through the tough silken wall of the host cocoon and through the leaf rolls to escape from the nest.

When I discovered the emerging *megachilidis* adults on May 18 I immediately put all the remaining *gentilis* cocoons in individual corked glass vials, so that I could determine the number and sex of parasites per cell. Unwittingly, this procedure fortunately served also to prevent infestation of new cells. I found subsequently that a few of the *megachilidis* adults that escaped on May 18 must have entered some of the adjacent uninfested *gentilis* nests. They oviposited in several bees which must have been in the prepupal or pupal stages on that date. At any rate, early in June I found 5 well-colored male bee pupae and 1 bee prepupa in 3 nests; each of the bees contained prepupae or pupae of *megachilidis*. Emergence of adult parasites *from within* these bee prepupae and pupae occurred June 16-21, or 29-34 days after the *megachilidis* adults entered the nests. Presumably it would have taken the parasites several days to chew through the leaf rolls and tough silken cocoons, and so it seems probable that a 25-30 day life cycle was required for this second generation also. The pupal period in these secondary infestations was a minimum of 7 days, for I noted pale *megachilidis* pupae in 2 host bee pupae on June 9 and adult parasites emerged on the 16th.

In nests of the primary infestation the adult parasites emerged 2-13 days prior to emergence of adult bees from adjacent cells. This length of time explains why a secondary infestation could take place in these same nests, because many bees would still be in the pupal stage when the parasites emerged.

Presumably there are several generations of *megachilidis* a year, but I received no nests from the field parasitized later than the end of April.

Both sexes of *megachilidis* emerged from each host larva or prepupa except for 1 male bee prepupa from which 54 males and no females emerged. Over-all, counting both the primary and secondary infestations and including the 374 specimens from 5 cells that I recaptured on May 18, I obtained 1,232 females, 448 males, and a few immatures from 23 infested cells. The sex ratio, therefore, appears to be 3:1 and the mean number of parasites per host about 75. The maximum number of *megachilidis* obtained from a single larva in the primary infestation was 152 (110 ♀, 42 ♂), the minimum was 33 (25 ♀, 8 ♂), and the mean number per infested larva was 83. In the secondary infestations the maximum number of *megachilidis* was 82 (74 ♀, 8 ♂) from a male bee pupa, the minimum was 4 (2 ♀, 1 ♂, 1 larva), also from a male bee pupa, and the mean number per infested bee was 46.

It was possible to predict the sex of the host bee larva in many cases, because in a *gentilis* nest containing both sexes the females always developed in the inner cells and males in the outer cells. In the primary infestation there were 2 female larvae containing respectively 57 and 152 parasites (mean 105), while 5 male larvae contained 33 to 113 parasites (mean 82). Although these figures are scanty, they do correlate with the slightly larger size of the female bee.

I have the impression that a female *megachilidis* may parasitize only 1 larva in a nest in a 4.8-mm. boring where the leaf rolls are tighter but that she may parasitize several cells in a nest in a 12.7-mm. boring where the leaf rolls are looser and easier to penetrate. Cells in the 5 nests containing primary infestations were parasitized as follows: Cell 11 of an 11-celled nest; cell 7 of a 7-celled nest; cell 11 of an 11-celled nest; cells 2, 3, 4, 6, 7, 8, 9, 10 of a 10-celled nest; and cells 2, 4, 5, 7, 10, 11 of an 11-celled nest. The first 3 nests were in 6.4-mm. borings and the last 2 in 12.7-mm. borings. The infested nests in 12.7-mm. borings were from 2 stations. Emergence of *megachilidis* adults in the 10-celled nest began from 1 cell each on May 18, 19, and 21, from 3 other cells on the 23d, and from the last 2 cells on the 24th. In the 11-celled nest emergence of *megachilidis* adults began from 3 cells on May 18, from a fourth cell on the 21st, and from the other 2 infested cells on the 23d. These sequences of initial emergence dates suggest that oviposition in the infested cells took place over a period of 5-6 days if a single female was involved in each nest.

I also reared *megachilidis* from a nest of another leaf-cutting bee, *Megachile (Melanosarus) xylocopoides* Smith, from Pompano Beach, Fla., in 1961. The nest was not in a trap but had been built in a roll of a split cane screen on a porch. The nest was mailed to me on October 30, 1961, and I opened the 9 cells on November 10. Adults of *megachilidis* emerged from the cocoon in cell 1 when I breached its wall. The bee prepupae in cells 2-4 were also parasitized by *megachilidis* which were in the pupal stage on that date; adult parasites emerged from these 3 cocoons in isolated glass vials on November 13 and 20. The parasites developed in the mature bee larvae and left the skin of the latter to pupate inside the bee cocoon. An adult bee emerged from 1 of the noninfested cells the following March after undergoing a prepupal diapause of 2 months in chilling temperatures outdoors. As *Megachile xylocopoides* is a larger bee than *M. gentilis,* more parasites were able to develop in each prepupa. I found 318, 213, 227, and 73 parasites, respectively, in cells 1-4, for a mean of 208 per host. Altogether there were 428 females, 384 males, and 19 immature *megachilidis* of undetermined sex in these 4 cells; male and female parasites emerged from each host larva. Judged from the emergence dates these may have been the progeny of a single female, thus indicating a possible 1:1 sex ratio for the progeny of a single fertilized female in Florida, as contrasted to an overall 3:1 ratio in Arizona for the progeny of several females.

Previous observations. Butler and Wargo (1963, p. 205) reported parasitism of a small megachilid bee, *Megachile (Eutricharaea) concinna* Smith by *megachilidis* in Arizona. Working with artificial nesting sites provided by boxes full of soda straws, they observed a parasitism rate of 20 percent early in July 1962. They obtained 35-90 adults (mean 53) per parasitized cell. By mid-September 1962 the parasitism rate increased to 42 percent, with most of the parasitized cells being at the inner end of the nests. They found that parasitism rates in cells 1-8 ran 93 percent, 48, 38, 16, 10, 7, 4, and 0 percent. They commented that *megachilidis* adults were common around the nesting sites from early July to mid-September.

Source material.
  Granite Reef Dam, Ariz. 1961 series: H 99, 106, 107, 109, 141, 143, 199.
  Scottsdale, Ariz. 1961 series: H 132.
  Pompano Beach, Fla: unnumbered nest.

Identifications. Tetrastichus by B. D. Burks; bees by the author.

MELITTOBIA CHALYBII Ashmead

This eulophid parasite was a very serious pest in trap nests. It not only parasitized a number of nests in the field at several localities but also it caused serious secondary infestations in other nests in the laboratory. Adult females, with or without immature progeny, were found in 182 nests fresh from the field. In addition, secondary infestations developed in 89 other nests after they had been in the laboratory for some weeks or months.

I obtained the following overall parasitism rates in field-infested nests:

  Derby, N. Y.—8.5 percent of 555 nests, 1954-1961.
  Cropley, Md.—10.0 percent of 20 nests, 1955.
  Plummers Island, Md.—12.4 percent of 872 nests, 1956-1963.
  Kill Devil Hills, N. C.—4.2 percent of 382 nests, 1954-1956, 1958
  Lake Placid, Fla.—0.9 percent of 927 nests, 1957, 1959-1962.
  Portal, Ariz.—0.3 percent of 361 nests, 1959-1961.

There was noticeable annual fluctuation of these rates of parasitism at the 2 localities having the highest rates and longest period of consecutive years of trapping. At Plummers Island the 1956-1963 rates were 14.4, 11.5, 15.9, 3.9, 14.2, 18.3, 6.7, and 12.5 percent, respectively, while at Derby the 1954-1961 rates were 9.5, 4.6, 5.8, 6.8, 9.1, 13.2, 9.6, and 10.0 percent, respectively. The field parasitism rates at Kill Devil Hills were 0, 5.8, 0.7, and 7.7 percent, respectively, for 1954-1956 and 1958. At Lake Placid these rates were 1.9, 1.7, 0.6, 0.3, and 0 percent in 1957 and 1959-1962, respectively. In 3 seasons of trapping at Portal there was only 1 nest infested in the field for a rate of 0.4 percent in 1961.

The nests infested in the field were almost entirely from settings on structural lumber or on dead branches or tree trunks. All these sites contained abandoned borings of wood-boring insects. These natural borings were being used for nesting sites by the wasps and bees which also used the traps placed on or beneath these stations.

TABLE 36.—*Nests infested in the field by* Melittobia chalybii *at Derby, N.Y., Plummers Island, Md., and Kill Devil Hills, N.C.*

Species	N. Y.	Md.	N. C.
Monobia quadridens (Linnaeus)	0	1	1
Euodynerus f. foraminatus (Saussure)	1	0	0
" schwarzi (Krombein)	0	1	0
Ancistrocerus a. antilope (Panzer)	3	1	0
" campestris (Saussure)	0	1	0
" c. catskill (Saussure)	1	0	0
" t. tigris (Saussure)	0	2	0
Symmorphus albomarginatus (Saussure)	1	0	0
" c. cristatus (Saussure)	3	0	0
" sp. or spp. (*Chrysomela* storers)	3	0	0
Stenodynerus ammonia histrionalis (Robertson)	0	0	1
Vespid spp. (caterpillar storers)	7	4	2
Dipogon sp. or spp.	0	3	0
Trypargilum clavatum (Say)	1	11	2
" collinum rubrocinctum (Packard)	6	5	1
" striatum (Provancher)	8	67	0
Trypoxylon frigidum Smith.	3	0	0
Trypoxylonini spp.	1	4	2
Passaloecus sp. or spp.	4	0	0
Isodontia auripes (Fernald)	0	1	0
" sp.	0	0	1
Podium luctuosum Smith	0	1	0
Euplilis sp.	0	1	0
Hylaeus sp.	1	0	0
Osmia lignaria Say	0	3	0
" pumila Cresson	2	1	0
Megachile xylocopoides Smith	0	0	3
" sp.	1	1	0
Unknown wasp or bee	2	0	0

Melittobia has limited powers of dispersal, thus accounting for its presence in traps placed in these particular situations, rather than in traps suspended from branches of living trees. Although *Melittobia* females are winged, they apparently do not fly at all but merely hop a few inches or walk about on the substrate.

Table 36 lists the host species and number of nests parasitized in the field at Derby, N. Y., Plummers Island, Md., and Kill Devil Hills, N. C., At Cropley, Md., 1 nest each of *Trypargilum collinum rubrocinctum* (Packard) and *T. striatum* (Provancher) were parasitized in the field. Nests infested in the field at Lake Placid, Fla., were as follows: 3 of *Pachodynerus erynnis* (Lepeletier) and 1 each of *Stenodynerus fulvipes rufovestis* Bohart, *S. saecularis rufulus* Bohart, an unknown vespid sp., *Trypargilum johannis* (Richards), and an unknown wasp or bee. The single nest parasitized in the field at Portal, Ariz., was of *Stenodynerus toltecus* (Saussure).

I obtained no data on the life history because as soon as I discovered them I destroyed infested cells or nests to prevent contamination of adjacent cells or of other nests. The most complete account of the life history of *chalybii* may be found in Buckell (1928). He obtained his stock of *chalybii* from a nest of *Eumenes fraternus* Say and cultured it in a warm laboratory during the winter on diapausing larvae of *Sceliphron caementarium* (Drury). After mating, a female *chalybii* pierced the body of the wasp larva with her ovipositor and then fed on the blood exuding from the puncture. She deposited her first eggs on the wasp's body a short time after mating and feeding. The eggs were about 0.014 inch long and 0.002-.004 inch in diameter and hatched in 3-4 days. The larvae sucked blood from the host larva and were full grown in 11-15 days. No cocoon was spun, and the pupal period was 7 days for males and 18 days for females. Buckell found that the period from oviposition to emergence of the adult was 21 days for males and 37 for females. Females were produced in much greater numbers than males; only males were produced from unfertilized eggs. He mentioned that a single wasp larva served as food for several generations of the parasite.

Source material (field infestations only).

Derby, N. Y. 1954 series: XIV a, XV a. 1955 series: D 8d, 11d. 1956 series: J 32, 48, 85, 89, 97, 117, 133. 1957 series: G 10, 39, 44, 48, 53, 99. 1958 series: R 2, 27a, 50, 54, 58. 1959 series: W 27, 38, 58, 61, 66, 75, 76, 77, 78, 80. 1960 series: D 3, 43, 63, 65, 72, 79, 88. 1961 series: L 7, 11, 13, 15, 19, 27, 72, 83.

Cropley, Md. 1955 series: B 26, 35.

Plummers Island, Md. 1956 series: H 6, 8, 20, 22, 72, 85, 92, 99, 104, 105, 118, 122, 125, 168. 1957 series: P 3, 24, 32, 40, 44, 48, 53, 84, 107, 118, 131, 137, 139, 145, 151, 179, 226, 237, 242, 268, 284. 1958 series: S 30, 35, 36, 39, 49, 69, 106, 108, 112, 116, 117. 1959 series: Y 14, 68, 91, 124, 127. 1960 series: E 37, 42, 49, 51, 59, 69, 70, 75, 87, 91, 95, 96, 116, 130, 187. 1961 series: K 2, 6, 15, 16, 43, 55, 61, 68, 109, 128, 130, 134, 135, 136, 138, 141, 143, 144, 151, 160, 179, 194, 195, 200, 202, 203, 206, 208, 212, 215, 223, 224, 241, 248, 253. 1962 series: M 42, 55, 83, 85, 86, 119. 1963 series: U 4.

Kill Devil Hills, N. C. 1955 series: C 11, 12, 49, 153, 154, 242, 258, 292. 1956 series: C 423. 1958 series: T 33, 34, 44, 202, 205, 209, 213.

Lake Placid, Fla. 1957 series: M 143, 194, 299, 302. 1959 series: V 74, 96. 1960 series: B 201. 1961 series: F 97.

Portal, Ariz. 1961 series: G 52.

Identifications. Chalcidoid initially by B. D. Burks; wasps and bees by the author.

Family ENCYRTIDAE
COELOPENCYRTUS HYLAEI Burks

This tiny encyrtid, 1.0-1.1 mm. long, was described from material I reared from a nest of a species of *Hylaeus* in a 3.2-mm. boring at Plummers Island, Md., in 1956. This trap was from a setting beneath a plank in a woodpile about 30 cm. from the ground near the cabin.

I gathered this nest on July 18 and opened it for study that evening. At the inner end it contained a cell 10 mm. long of *Hylaeus.* The walls and ends of this cell were lined by a delicate clear membrane secreted by the mother bee as is customary in the family Colletidae. There was a rather liquid mixture of nectar and pollen in the inner 5 mm. of the cell. I could not see the bee egg, which, perhaps, was nearly submerged in this sirupy mixture. There was an empty space of 2 mm. between the mixture and the transverse delicate membrane. A small female *Coelopencyrtus* was resting in this space, clinging to the inner surface of the transverse membrane. The cell was capped by a plug 3 mm. thick of fine wood fibers rasped from the boring wall. There was an empty space of 44 mm. beyond this plug and then a second cell 12 mm. long with the walls and ends coated with the delicate clear membrane; this cell was not provisioned.

Two days later I observed a small bee larva feeding on the outer end of the food supply; the chalcid was still resting on the inner wall of the closing septum. On July 27 the bee larva had consumed almost the entire store of pollen and nectar; the chalcid had now moved to the inner end of the cell.

I did not examine the nest again until August 14, when the female chalcid was dead and the bee larva was greatly distended. Its body contained darkened chalcid pupae in individual cells. On August 17 the adult chalcids left the nest when I opened it for examination. There were 24 females and 1 male. Presumably, the mother chalcid oviposited in the mature bee larva around July 27.

Previous observations. Brandhorst (1962, p. 477) reported rearing *hylaei* from nests of *Hylaeus* sp., probably *cressoni* (Cockerell), in 2 abandoned galls of *Walshia amorphella* Clemens on *Amorpha fruticosa* Linnaeus in Nebraska. He obtained 60 females and 2 males from 5 bee pupae.

Source material.
Plummers Island, Md. 1956 series: H 73.

Identifications. Chalcidoid by B. D. Burks; bee by the author.

Family TORYMIDAE
MONODONTOMERUS OBSCURUS Westwood

The torymid is fairly common around the porch rafters and beams of the cabin at Plummers Island, Md. However, I reared it only once from a trap containing a nest of the vernal bee *Osmia lignaria* Say. This nest was from a setting on 1 of the cabin beams. I did not open it until July 18, on which date the bees had been in cocoons for some weeks. Early the following spring I opened the bee cocoons. Most of them contained dead bee prepupae or small larvae, but there was a live male bee in the cocoon in cell 8. Also, in the cocoon in cell 10 there was a dead bee prepupa and a pair of *Monodontomerus obscurus* which had died during the winter. *Monodontomerus* has a long ovipositor, and it is presumed that it oviposits through the boring walls into the bee larva.

Previous observations. Rau (1937a, p. 338) reared *obscurus* [reported erroneously as *M. montivagus* Ashmead and *M.* sp.] from cocoons of *Osmia lignaria* Say and *O. cordata* Robertson in Missouri. He reared 4 to 6 *obscurus* from *cordata* cocoons and 9 of the parasites from a *lignaria* cocoon.

Source material.
    Plummers Island, Md. 1961 series: K 38.

Identifications. Chalcidoid by B. D. Burks; bee by the author.

Family LEUCOSPIDAE
LEUCOSPIS AFFINIS AFFINIS Say

I reared specimens of typical *affinis* from 1 nest each from Kill Devil Hills, N.C., in 1958, and from Portal, Ariz., in 1959.

The North Carolina *affinis* came from a nest of a leaf-cutting species of *Megachile* in a 12.7-mm. boring suspended from the dead stub of a limb of a loblolly pine in open woods. The host bee was almost certainly *Megachile* (*Melanosarus*) *xylocopoides* Smith. It is the only *Megachile* at Kill Devil Hills that uses 12.7-mm. borings, and I reared it from 2 other stations in similar settings in open woods about a hundred meters distant. I picked up this nest July 28, 1958, when it contained 7 bee cocoons in cells made from leaf cuttings; there was a pale bee pupa in one of the outermost cocoons. A week later a parasitic larva had nearly sucked dry the bee pupa in this cocoon. On August 12 I opened 3 of the other cocoons and found a *Leucospis* pupa in each. Seven adult females of *affinis* emerged from the 7 cocoons on August 20-22.

The Arizona *affinis* came from a nest of a *Megachile* in a 12.7-mm. boring on the desert floor near Portal. The nest was from a setting on a sycamore tree along a dry wash. The host bee was probably *Megachile* (*Sayapis*) *policaris* Say, because the nest with its 3 brood cells, each containing several *Megachile* cocoons, was identical in appearance with other nests from this area from which I reared *policaris*. This is the only bee I found in traps at Portal that constructs a series of brood cells in which several larvae develop. I picked up this nest on July 19, when I observed pale bee pupae in some cocoons. On the following day a male *Leucospis affinis* emerged from one of the cocoons near the outer end. On July 21 a female *affinis* was just eclosing in another cocoon. Between July 24 and 28, 4 *affinis* females emerged from all 3 brood cells in this nest. In their struggles to emerge the *affinis* adults fatally injured all of the bee pupae.

Previous observations. Peck (1963) listed from the literature the following species of megachilid bees as hosts of typical *affinis: Anthidium emarginatum* (Say), *Dianthidium pudicum consimile* (Ashmead), *Hoplitis producta* (Cresson), *Megachile brevis* Say, *M. inermis* Provancher, *M. montivaga* Cresson, *M. relativa* Cresson, *Osmia atriventris* Cresson, *O. pumila* Cresson, *O. simillima* Smith, and *Stelis sexmaculata* Ashmead. He also listed a gall-making moth, *Ecdytolopha insiticiana* Zeller, as a questionable host. Undoubtedly this record is erroneous; probably the actual host was a megachilid bee that nested in an old gall of the moth.

Graenicher (1906) in Wisconsin reported on the life history of typical *affinis* in nests of the 3 *Osmia* species listed above. He observed the *affinis* female ovipositing into the cells through the side of the dead branch containing the nest. The chalcid required about 10 minutes to effect oviposition in a cell. Successive cells in the linear series were then parasitized in turn. The egg was attached to the inside of the cell wall or to the inside of the cocoon wall if the host larva had already spun a cocoon. He estimated that the egg hatched 66-72 hours after it was laid. The large-headed first instar *Leucospis* larva had very large mandibles and first searched for and killed any other *Leucospis* eggs or larvae in the same cell. Then it attached itself by its mandibles to the resting bee larva to suck some blood. The parasite larva molted to a small-headed second instar larva after 3 days. It continued to feed on the body fluids of the host until the latter was just an empty skin. The *Leucospis* larva completed feeding 12 days after hatching and pupated 5 days later. It did not spin a cocoon of its own but pupated within the host cocoon. The pupal stage in the summer generation lasted for 14 days. Graenicher found that *affinis* was bivoltine in Wisconsin. He also reported variability in size of *affinis* adults correlated with size of the host.

Medler (1958) also working in Wisconsin reported that *affinis* had a larval stage of 7-10 days and a pupal stage of 9-11 days under laboratory conditions at 27° C. He stated that in parasitized nests of *Megachile relativa* the rate was probably more than 80 percent. In nests containing both sexes of *affinis* he found that females usually occurred in the inner and males in the outer cells, though occasionally a male developed in the middle of a series of female cells. Medler confirmed Graenicher's findings as to the bivoltinism and the correlation of parasite and host size.

Source material.
    Kill Devil Hills, N. C. 1958 series: T 201.
    Portal, Ariz. 1959 series: X 255.

Identifications. Leucospis by B. D. Burks; bees by the author.

LEUCOSPIS AFFINIS FLORIDANA Cresson

Specimens of this Floridian race of *affinis* were reared from a dozen nests from the Archbold Biological Station in 1957, 1960, and 1961. The nests came from 9 stations in the Highlands Ridge sand-scrub area. They were suspended from limbs of live hickory or oak trees except for 3 nests from a single setting on the trunk of a partly dead oak tree. Three nests were in 4.8-mm. borings, 8 in 6.4-mm., and 1 in a 12.7-mm. boring.

The hosts of *affinis floridana* were all megachilid bees. In 2 nests the host was *Chalicodoma* (*Chelostomoides*) *georgica* (Cresson), a resin-using bee. Members of this same subgenus were hosts in 9 other nests. I reared no bees from these 9 nests, but the hosts probably were either *georgica, campanulae wilmingtoni* (Mitchell), or *exilis parexilis* (Mitchell), or perhaps all 3 species; these were the only species of this distinctive subgenus reared from traps in Florida. The host in the twelfth nest was a species of *Megachile* (*Sayapis*), possibly *policaris* Say.

The parasitism rate in the infested nests was 72 percent (31 of 43 stored cells). Altogether I reared 18 females and 13 males of *floridana* from the nests. Sex ratios are difficult to determine in *Leucospis* because only 1 parasite develops in each cell even though 2 or more eggs may be laid in the cell. There was no consistent arrangement of sexes of *Leucospis* in the nests from which both sexes of the parasite were reared. In the 6 mixed nests the arrangement of *Leucospis* was as follows (x = larval bee mortality):

M 251: ♀-♂
F 164: ♂-♀-♀-♀-♂-♀
F 259: ♀-♀-♀-♂-♀-♀
F 267: ♀-♂-♂-x
F 276: ♂-♀-x-♀
F 338: ♂-♀-x-♀-♂

Very scanty information was obtained on the behavior and duration of immature stages. In 1 *georgica* nest there were 2 large-headed, newly hatched *floridana* larvae in 1 cell on July 7. By the following day 1 of these parasitic larvae had killed the other and had attached itself to the resting larva of the bee in its cocoon. The *floridana* larva had completely sucked dry the bee prepupa on July 16, only 8 days after it began feeding. In 1 nest of a species of *Chelostomoides* a *floridana* larva attached to the resting larva of the host in its cocoon between October 29 and 31. It was almost mature by November 5 and had reduced the bee larva to an empty shriveled skin by the 8th.

The duration of the pupal stage was determined in only a few cases. The first *floridana* larva mentioned in the preceding paragraph pupated on July 19, and an adult male left the nest on August 8, probably 3-4 days after it shed the pupal exuvia. In several overwintering nests both males and females of *floridana* emerged 21-22 days after pupation.

Four of the nests were of the summer generation, and *floridana* adults emerged concurrently with or a few days before the host bees in 2 of the nests; no host bees were reared from the other 2. In 6 nests provisioned during October or later the nests had to be treated to 2 months of chilling temperatures outdoors to break the larval diapause of the parasites; no host bees emerged from these nests. In the last 2 nests there was divided emergence by the parasites, 1 *floridana* in each nest emerging before the nests were exposed to 2 months of chilling temperatures, and 1 or 2 *floridana* transforming to pupae and then to adults after this period of chilling.

Source material.
Lake Placid, Fla. 1957 series: M 251, 285. 1960 series: B 125, 173, 176. 1961 series: F 71, 164, 259, 267, 276, 313, 338.

Identifications. Leucospis by B. D. Burks; bees by the author.

Superfamily CHRYSIDOIDEA

Family CHRYSIDIDAE

The cuckoo wasps belonging to this family were among the most fascinating insects encountered in these trap nest studies. The brilliant metallic-blue or green adults are the most beautiful of the insects associated with these nests. The method of attack by the adult females, the degree of host specificity, comparative effectiveness of the various species as parasites, mode of attack by the chrysidid larvae, degree of synchrony in development with that of the hosts, and specificity of the cocoons were all of considerable interest.

Mechanics of parasitism by adult females. In all the cuckoo wasps which parasitized these nests in wooden traps the females deposited 1 or more eggs in the host cell as it was being stored. There was no evidence to show that the female of any species breached a completed nest and oviposited inside of the host cocoon as has been demonstrated for *Chrysis fuscipennis* Fabricius (Stage, 1960) in nests of mud-daubers.

Once a chrysidid female discovers a nest being stored by a suitable host she probably keeps it under frequent observation. I have noted a female *Chrysis coerulans* Fabricius waiting a few centimeters from the nest entrance of the vespid *Ancistrocerus a. antilope* (Panzer) at Lost River State Park, W. Va. The female cuckoo wasp tapped her antennae incessantly and rapidly against the substrate as the host wasp brought in caterpillar after caterpillar. Presumably oviposition by the cuckoo wasp is triggered when she observes the host bringing in pellets of damp mud to cap the stored cell. At this point in nest construction it is presumed that she rapidly backs into the boring while the host wasp is absent, and, by means of her long telescoped terminal abdominal segments, deposits an egg among the specimens of prey.

The occasional finding of more than a single chrysidid egg per host cell may indicate parasitism by 2 cuckoo wasp females or perhaps a single female may lay 2 or more eggs per cell as Ferguson (1962, p. 36) has recorded for the parasitic mutillid wasp *Photopsis orestes* (Fox). It may be mentioned at this point that only 1 parasite larva develops per cell, any others occurring in the cell being destroyed by cannibalism.

The finding of several parasitized cells in sequence in a number of nests attacked by cuckoo wasps, for example *Chrysura kyrae* Krombein, *Chrysis (Trichrysis) carinata* Say, *C. (T.) mucronata* Brullé, and *C. (C.) arizonica* Bohart, is a definite indication that many cuckoo-wasp females keep a nest under frequent surveillance once it has been discovered and that they oviposit in successive cells as they are stored.

Comparative effectiveness as parasites. Some species were more effective as parasites than others from the standpoint of their being able to parasitize a larger number of cells once they discovered a nest. This presumably related to their skill in concealing evidences of parasitism from the host wasps. For example, *Chrysura kyrae, Chrysis carinata, C. mucronata, C. inaequidens* Dahlbom, and *C. smaragdula* Fabricius were quite effective as parasites, whereas other species such as *Chrysogona verticalis* (Patton), *Chrysis nitidula* Fabricius, and *C. stenodyneri* Krombein were relatively ineffective. The first group of species often succeeded in parasitizing several cells per nest, whereas in the latter group there was rarely more than 1 cell parasitized per nest and many parasitized nests were closed prematurely by the host wasps as evidenced by abnormally long vestibular cells next to the single parasitized cell.

Chrysis coerulans Fabricius showed racial (?) differences in its effectiveness as a parasite. The population at Derby, N. Y., was relatively ineffective, with an average of only 1.4 cells parasitized per nest, and many nests gave evidence of premature closure by the presence of abnormally long vestibular cells. The Florida population, which may represent a discrete taxon at the subspecific level, was more effective. It parasitized 2.4 cells per nest, and this rate might have been higher except that there was a possibility that a single cuckoo wasp may have been parasitizing several nests at 1 station concurrently.

Host specificity. Varying degrees of host specificity were encountered in this study. The only cuckoo wasps thought to be species specific are *Chrysis* (*C.*) *cembricola* Krombein on the vespid wasp *Symmorphus canadensis* (Saussure) and *Chrysura kyrae* Krombein on the megachilid bee *Osmia* (*O.*) *l. lignaria* Say.

Several chrysidids apparently parasitized the species of a single host genus only. These were: *Chrysura sonorensis* (Cameron) on the megachilid bee *Ashmeadiella*; *C. pacifica* Say on the megachilid bee *Osmia*; *Chrysogona verticalis* (Patton) on the sphecids *Trypoxylon* and *Trypargilum* though principally on the former; *Chrysis* (*Trichrysis*) *carinata* Say and *C.* (*T.*) *mucronata* Brullé on *Trypargilum,* although there was 1 authentic but anomalous record of *mucronata* on the vespid *Euodynerus;* *Chrysis* (subg.?) *pellucidula* Aaron on *Trypargilum; Chrysis* (*C.*) *stenodyneri* on the vespid *Stenodynerus* (both subgenera); and *Neochrysis panamensis* (Cameron) on the sphecid *Podium*. Some of these species, such as *Chrysura pacifica, Chrysis smaragdula,* and *Neochrysis panamensis,* were reared from only a single host species; but consideration of their distribution suggests that other species of the host genera must be used in parts of the range.

Several other cuckoo wasps had a broader host range. Although I reared *Omalus aeneus* (Fabricius) from nests of the pemphredonine wasp *Passaloecus* only, it is known to parasitize the nests of other aphid-storing Pemphredonini such as *Pemphredon* and *Stigmus*. Several species of typical *Chrysis* parasitized caterpillar-storing vespid wasps as follows: *C. arizonica* was reared from nests of *Stenodynerus* and *Euodynerus; inflata* Aaron from nests of *Euodynerus* and *Ancistrocerus;* and *inaequidens* from nests of *Euodynerus, Monobia, Stenodynerus,* and *Pachodynerus*. The 2 closely related species in typical *Chrysis, coerulans* and *nitidula,* not only parasitized such caterpillar-storing genera as *Ancistrocerus, Euodynerus,* and *Stenodynerus* but also attacked *Symmorphus,* which stored coleopterous larvae belonging to the genus *Chrysomela*.

Life history. The first instar chrysidid larva is a highly modified form. It has a heavily sclerotized head capsule with long antennae and sharp piercing mandibles, the body frequently has long setae which may aid in locomotion, and the body terminates in a pair of forked, fleshy pseudopods which also assist in locomotion. When this larva molts to the second instar, it assumes the normal form of a wasp larva, rather maggotlike in appearance.

In most of the species encountered in these nests the chrysidid egg hatched a day or two before the host egg unless several days elapsed between oviposition by the host and the parasite. The newly hatched parasite larva then sought out the host egg or young larva, pierced the chorion of the egg or larval integument with its sharp mandibles, and sucked the host egg or young larva dry. Then it molted to the second instar and began to feed on the prey stored for the host wasp larva. Usually some of the specimens of prey remained untouched when the chrysidid larva spun its cocoon. The period between egg hatch and cocoon spinning was about a week. This type of larval behavior was noted in all species except those of *Chrysura* and *Chrysis* (subg.?) *pellucidula*.

In the genus *Chrysura* the chrysidid larva usually hatched a day later than that of the host bee, even though both eggs were presumably deposited on the same date. The newly hatched larva moved slowly over the pollen-nectar mass stored for the host bee; occasionally it appeared to imbibe a small amount of nectar. About 3-7 days after hatching the *Chrysura* larva attached itself by its mandibles to the feeding bee larva and began to suck a small amount of blood. The host bee larva began to spin its cocoon 17-31 days after it hatched. At this time the *Chrysura* larva was still attached to the bee larva by its mandibles; it had increased some in size and was turgid, but it had not molted.

As soon as the host cocoon was completed and the bee larva became quiescent, the *Chrysura* larva molted to the second instar and began to feed on the host larva which was usually devoured completely. The *Chrysura* larva then spun its cocoon inside that of the host bee. The period between egg hatch and cocoon spinning in *Chrysura* was nearly 2 months.

Cocoons. The cocoons of the Chrysidinae (*Chrysura, Chrysogona,* and *Chrysis*) were unique in that each had 1 or several small patches of dense unvarnished silk near the anterior end. The function of these patches is unknown, though it has been suggested that they may be of significance in supporting the larva during the spinning of the rest of the cocoon. The remainder of the cocoon proper usually consisted of tough, varnished, transparent to subopaque silk. Frequently the chrysidid first spun a transparent sheath attached loosely to the cell walls, and the cocoon proper was spun inside of this.

In most species the cocoons were ovoidal and not specifically diagnostic. However, the cocoons of 2 Chrysidinae differed in shape from the others. In *Chrysis (C.) stenodyneri* the wasp larva made a transverse septum across the boring to form the anterior end of the cocoon; the remainder of the cocoon was cylindrical or with walls tapering posteriorly, and the posterior end was rounded. *Chrysis* (subg.?) *pellucidula* made a transverse septum in the middle of the host cocoon and the rest of the cocoon was a single layer of delicate white silk spun against the anterior walls and end of the host cocoon.

The cocoons of the 3 species of Elampinae reared from trap nests were also distinctive. That of *Holopyga (?) taylori* was almost spherical. It had an outer layer of short fibers of white silk; the inner layer was honey-colored, varnished, and had a small pore at the anterior end covered by varnished silk. The cocoons of the 2 species of *Omalus* had thin, delicate silken walls and a truncate, poreless, anterior end constructed from a dense, thick spiral band of silk. In *iridescens* the anterior end was made of a narrower, darker band than in *aeneus*.

Synchrony in host and parasite development and emergence. In most of the species observed there was synchronous development and emergence within a few days of each other by the cuckoo wasps and host wasps or bees in adjacent cells or in nests stored at the same time. It is not difficult to see that this would be the case in those species of cuckoo wasps whose larvae destroy the host egg and then develop simultaneously with host wasps in adjacent cells.

Obviously, this synchrony would not normally occur where the host was univoltine and the cuckoo wasp was multivoltine. *C. coerulans* was a very puzzling species in this respect. The somewhat atypical Florida population of *coerulans* was multivoltine, but it parasitized vespid hosts of which the principal one was univoltine. When the *coerulans* adults emerged from inner or intermediate cells of this univoltine host, they destroyed the diapausing host larvae in the outer cells. The more typical northern populations of *coerulans* were multivoltine when they occurred on multivoltine hosts, but they were univoltine when they parasitized univoltine hosts. These data suggest that, at least in the more northern areas, we may have biological races of *coerulans* adapted to host periodicity.

In the species of *Chrysura* and in *Chrysis pellucidula* the development could not be synchronous with that of the host because the parasite larva did not begin to feed in earnest until the host larva had spun its cocoon. However, the adult emergence was synchronized. In the multivoltine *Chrysura sonorensis* the synchronous emergence was achieved because the pupal period of the cuckoo wasp was shorter than that of the host bee. In the univoltine

Chrysura kyrae both it and its host transformed to adults during the summer, but did not emerge from the cocoons until the following spring. In *Chrysis pellucidula* both it and its host overwintered as diapausing larvae.

OMALUS (OMALUS) AENEUS (Fabricius)

I reared this parasite of *Passaloecus cuspidatus* Smith from 2 nests in 3.2-mm. borings from Derby, N. Y., in 1957, and from Arlington, Va. in 1962. At Derby the nest was from a setting on the wall of a wooden house. The nest at Arlington was on the side of an old wooden cowshed at my home.

O. aeneus parasitized 2 of 4 cells in the Derby nest and 1 of 3 cells in the Arlington nest.

Life history. The Arlington nest was completed by *P. cuspidatus* on May 24, 1962. I did not notice that cell 1 was parasitized by a cuckoo wasp when I examined the nest on that date. The date of completion of the Derby nest was not noted; but, inasmuch as *cuspidatus* is univoltine, the nest was probably stored during June. *O. aeneus* also is univoltine and the parasites overwintered as diapausing larvae. A male *aeneus* pupated May 1-6 in the Arlington nest and the adult emerged on May 15. In the Derby nest a male *aeneus* emerged April 27, just a day before a male *cuspidatus* in the adjacent cell. I preserved 1 mature *aeneus* larva from the nest from Derby.

The cocoons were 5 mm. long. The walls were thin, delicate, white, and semitransparent; the anterior end was transverse and spun from soft, thick, white silk in a broad spiral band.

Previous observations. Bohart and Campos (1960, p. 240) reported a twig-nesting species of *Passaloecus* as being a host of *aeneus* in California. They also quoted Invrea as reporting the hosts of *aeneus* in Europe as *Stigmus*, *Passaloecus* and *Pemphredon* (*Cemonus*).

Source material.
    Derby, N. Y. 1957 series: G 110.
    Arlington, Va. 1962 series: N 6.

Identifications. *Omalus* by R. M. Bohart; Pemphredonini by the author.

OMALUS (OMALUS) IRIDESCENS (Norton)

I reared this cuckoo wasp from the nest of a *Passaloecus* species in a 4.8-mm. boring from Derby, N. Y., in 1956. The nest was from a setting in a pile of cut firewood. Cell 1 was made by a caterpillar-storing vespid wasp; cells 2 and 3 were made by an aphid-storing pemphredonine wasp, unquestionably a species of

Passaloecus because the cell partitions were made from resin; cells 4 and 5 were made by the spider-storing *Trypargilum collinum rubrocinctum* (Packard).

The date of storing by the *Passaloecus* was unknown except that it must have occurred after July 4, the date when the trap was set out, and before August 16, the date when the boring was sealed by *Trypargilum*.

When I opened the nest on September 6 the chrysidid was a diapausing larva in its cocoon among aphid remains in cell 2; the host pemphredonine larva in cell 3 did not develop. The cuckoo wasp overwintered as a diapausing larva and died the following spring as a fully colored male pupa which could be identified positively as a specimen of *iridescens*.

The cocoon was 7 mm. long and light brown, with delicate, subopaque walls. The anterior end was truncate and consisted of a dense, thick, tightly woven, narrow spiral band on the outer end.

Previous observations. Bohart and Campos (1960, p. 241) summarized previous rearing records which were all for aphid-storing Pemphredoninae, *Stigmus inordinatus* Fox, *S. americanus* Packard, and *Diodontus trisulcus* (Fox).

Source material.
    Derby, N.Y. 1956 series: J 72.

Identifications by the author.

HOLOPYGA (?) TAYLORI Bodenstein

I reared 1 specimen of this little cuckoo wasp from a nest of *Solierella affinis blaisdelli* (Bridwell) in a 3.2-mm. boring. The nest was from a setting on the side of a yucca stem on the desert floor near Portal, Ariz., in 1960.

The occupants of the nest were in cocoons when I examined the nest late in December, some months after it was completed. The chrysid cocoon was interspersed among some *Nysius* nymphs, prey of the *Solierella,* and several *Solierella* cocoons. The chrysidid cocoon was 3 mm. long and almost spherical. The outer surface was composed of short fibers of white silk; the inner surface was honey-colored and varnished; it had a small pore at the interior end silked over on the inside by varnished silk. The chrysidid overwintered presumably as a diapausing larva as did the host wasps, and a female emerged on May 7, 9 days after one of the host wasps.

Source material.
    Portal, Ariz. 1960 series: X 12.

Identifications by the author.

CHRYSURA KYRAE Krombein

(Plate 18, Figures 87, 88; Plate 27, Figures 128-130)

This species apparently is host specific on the megachilid bee *Osmia* (*Osmia*) *lignaria lignaria* Say, almost all the known specimens having been reared from that host or collected at stations where the bee was nesting. Adults of *kyrae* were reared from 20 *lignaria* nests at Plummers Island. Chrysidid larvae, undoubtedly of this same species, were found but not reared in another 14 *lignaria* nests. Altogether, this chrysidid apparently parasitized 78 of 313 cells in the 34 infested nests. It is the most important parasite of *lignaria* at Plummers Island where the over-all parasitism rate was 25 per cent of the available nests and 25 per cent of the available cells in the nests which it infested. Seven of 20 nests were infested by *kyrae* in 1958, 14 of 60 in 1959, 2 of 7 in 1960, 5 of 32 in 1961, and 6 of 21 in 1962. Twelve of the infested nests were in 4.8-mm. borings, 18 in 6.4-mm., and 4 in 12.7-mm. Thirty-one of the *lignaria* nests infested by *kyrae* were from stations on structural timber containing abandoned borings of other insects, and 3 nests were from 3 separate stations on standing dead tree trunks.

Actually the parasitism rate would have been higher still if *kyrae* females had deposited only 1 egg per cell and had placed the extra eggs in unparasitized cells. Occasionally I found as many as 3 chrysidid eggs in a single bee cell or 2 to 3 chrysidid larvae attached to 1 bee larva. Only one of these reached maturity in each cell. I counted 88 chrysidid eggs or larvae in the 78 infested cells, and undoubtedly I missed some eggs which were on a surface of the pollen-nectar mass not exposed by splitting the trap. It is not known whether this multiple oviposition is a result of several cuckoo wasps visiting the same nest or whether a single female may deposit more than 1 egg per cell. At least it is a virtual certainty that an individual female will keep a nest under surveillance and deposit at least 1 egg per cell in almost every cell in part of a linear series. Otherwise, how could one account for such sequences as the following?

Nest S 16—cuckoo wasps in cells 5, 8, 9, 10 of 11-celled nest
Nest Y 56—cuckoo wasps in cells 1, 3, 4, 5, 8 of 8-celled nest
Nest Y 65—cuckoo wasps in cells 7, 13, 14, 16, 23 of 23-celled nest
Nest Y 75—cuckoo wasps in cells 1, 2, 3 of 8-celled nest
Nest Y 76—cuckoo wasps in cells 2, 3, 5, 6 of 6-celled nest
Nest Y 91—cuckoo wasps in cells 5, 6, 7, 8, 10 of 10-celled nest
Nest Y 102—cuckoo wasps in cells 1, 3, 4, 5 of 5-celled nest
Nest K 41—cuckoo wasps in cells 4, 5, 6, 7, 9 of 11-celled nest
Nest K 42—cuckoo wasps in cells 1, 2, 5, 6, 7 of 7-celled nest
Nest M 5—cuckoo wasps in cells 1, 2, 3 of 9-celled nest
Nest M 6—cuckoo wasps in cells 2, 4, 5 of 5-celled nest
Nest M 31—cuckoo wasps in cells 4, 5, 6 of 11-celled nest

Life history. Adults of *kyrae* are active from early April until the end of May. My earliest record is sighting a specimen on a dead standing tree trunk on April 9, 1959. I found newly laid eggs of *kyrae* in *lignaria* nests as late as May 23, 1959. These data indicate a seasonal flight range of at least 6½ weeks. The actual oviposition period probably is the last month of the flight period, for the earliest egg I found was one laid about April 26.

Ordinarily the female *kyrae* deposits her egg along the side of the pollen-nectar mass (fig. 128), so that it is hidden from the sight of the host bee. Occasionally, I have found eggs in the empty space between the outer end of the pollen mass and the mud plug capping the cell; undoubtedly these eggs were deposited while the host bee was capping the cell. The egg is opaque white, 1.6 mm. long, and 0.5 mm. wide and has quite a tough chorion.

The chrysidid hatches about a day later than the host larva, or in 6 to 8 days after deposition. The newly hatched larva of *kyrae* (figs. 87, 129) has a very pale fulvous head capsule immediately after hatching, but in several days this darkens to a light tan. The chrysidid larva moves slowly along the side of the pollen mass, apparently mostly by pushing with its forked tail. About a week after hatching it reaches the host larva and attaches on the back or side by means of its mandibles. It imbibes a small quantity of blood because its body becomes somewhat distended (figs. 88, 130). However, it does not molt until after the host larva spins a cocoon. The chrysidid is shed with each successive molt of the bee larva, but it usually attaches again within a day or two.

The bee larva completes its feeding about 2½ to 4 weeks after hatching and spins a cocoon. Several days later it becomes a quiescent larva. At this time the attached chrysidid larva molts and then devours the entire bee larva. Inside the bee cocoon it spins a delicate transparent cocoon with a small patch of dense white silk near the anterior end, transforms to a pupa, and then to an adult early in August. It overwinters inside the 2 cocoons and emerges the following spring.

Chrysidids were not reared from all parasitized cells. I preserved a number of first instar larvae for taxonomic study. Others were lost by cannibalism, injury, attack by *Chaetodactylus krombeini* mites, or by failure to become reattached after the bee larva molted. There were also a few cases of unexplained chrysidid mortality, where adult bees emerged from cocoons spun by bee larvae which were observed to bear attached healthy chrysidid larvae the preceding spring. It appears that the sex ratio is probably 1:1, because I obtained 17 males and 19 females of *kyrae* in these rearings.

Source material.
    Plummers Island, Md. 1958 series: S 14, 15, 16, 17, 18, 29, 74. 1959 series:
    Y 56, 63, 65, 69, 75, 76, 84, 85, 91, 92, 99, 100, 102, 104. 1960 series: E 3,
    41. 1961 series: K 1, 37, 41, 42, 72. 1962 series: M 5, 6, 30, 31, 34, 69.

Identifications by the author.

CHRYSURA PACIFICA (Say)
(Plate 27, Figure 131)

I reared this species only once, from a nest stored by *Osmia*
(*Nothosmia*) *pumila* Cresson at Plummers Island. This nest was
in a 4.8-mm. boring from a set of traps fastened to the side of a
dead, standing tree trunk. The nest was not completed and the
mother bee was inside when I picked up the nest on May 3. By
this date the bee had stored 7 cells and was beginning to store
the eighth.

When I opened the nest on May 3 I noted 1 small chrysidid
egg on the side of the pollen mass in cell 4 and another egg on
the inner surface of the leaf pulp partition capping cell 6. I checked
the nest daily, and on May 7 I found a newly hatched chrysidid
larva in cell 4 and 2 newly hatched chrysidid larvae in cell 6
(fig. 131). These data suggest that the chrysidid egg hatches in
4 to 5 days. On the following day I noted recently hatched cuckoo
wasp larvae in cells 4 to 7. The larva in cell 4 had its mouthparts
applied against the moist pollen-nectar mass and may have imbibed
some nectar during the several days that it remained on the mass.
The *pacifica* larvae attached themselves by their mandibles to the
dorsum of the bee larvae 3 to 4 days after hatching. They imbibed
a small amount of blood and increased in size but did not molt
while the host larvae were feeding. The bee larvae began spinning
cocoons on June 3. I made small tears in the sides of 2 of the
bee cocoons to observe actions of the parasite larvae. On June 4
1 of the chrysidid larvae was 1.8 mm. long; a week later it was
2.3 mm. long. Another of the chrysidid larvae molted to the second
instar on June 13. On June 19 the chrysidid larva in cell 4 had
completely devoured the host larva and began to spin its cocoon
inside the host cocoon. The chrysidid larva in cell 5 did not complete feeding until June 27, and completed its cocoon on July 1.
The chrysidid in cell 4 pupated between July 15 and 17, and the
adult wasp eclosed between August 5 and 11. A female *pacifica*
developed in cell 4 and a male in cell 5; both died during the
winter. The full grown chrysidid larva in cell 6 was preserved for
taxonomic study, and that in cell 7 died without killing the host
larva.

Another 6-celled, incompleted nest in a 4.8-mm. boring, presumably stored by *Osmia pumila*, was recovered from this same station

on May 3. Cells 3 to 6 of this nest were parasitized by a chrysidid, presumably by the same female of *pacifica* that parasitized the other nest. These chrysidid eggs were 1.5 mm. long. There were 3 chrysidid eggs in cell 5 and 2 eggs in cell 6. In this nest the chrysidid eggs hatched in 5 to 6 days. I observed 1 of these larvae moving its mouthparts against the moist pollen-nectar mass and I felt reasonably certain that it was imbibing some nectar. The parasites attached to the host larvae 3 to 4 days after hatching. I noted that 1 *pacifica* larva voided a small, moist, unformed fecal mass several days after it attached to the bee larva; it did not molt. Several of the chrysidid larvae were preserved for taxonomic study shortly after they hatched; the others and all of the bee larvae died later.

The limited data from these 2 nests suggest that the parasitism rate by this species may be quite high once a chrysidid female locates a nest being stored by the bee. If it is assumed, as I think likely, that a single cuckoo wasp parasitized both of these nests, she deposited a total of 12 eggs in the 8 parasitized cells apparently within a period of 2-3 days.

I have collected adult females of *pacifica* as late as May 23 at Plummers Island.

There have been no previous observations on the biology of this species. The host record of *Osmia* (*Chalcosmia*) *georgica* Cresson in the Hymenoptera Catalog (Bodenstein *in* Muesebeck *et al.*, 1951, p. 721) was based on a misidentification of the cuckoo wasp.

Source material.
    Plummers Island, Md. 1958 series: S 47 (?), 48.

Identifications. Hymenoptera by T. B. Mitchell and the author.

CHRYSURA SONORENSIS (Cameron)

In my experience this cuckoo wasp has as its hosts several species of the megachilid bee *Ashmeadiella*. I reared it from 5 nests from Portal, Ariz., in 1961; 3 nests of *Ashmeadiella* (*A*). *occipitalis* Michener in 4.8- and 6.4-mm. borings; one 4.8-mm. nest of *Ashmeadiella* (*A.*) *bucconis denticulata* (Cresson); and one 3.2-mm. nest of an *Ashmeadiella* sp. Probably this same chrysidid parasitized another 3.2-mm. nest of an *Ashmeadiella* sp.; neither cuckoo wasp nor host bee was reared from this nest. Each of the host bees used leaf pulp in the nest construction.

All the stations from which the parasitized nests came were on the desert floor in open country. Three of the nests came from a single station on a dead mesquite branch, 2 from separate stations on fence posts, and 1 from the side of a yucca stalk.

The parasitism rate is very low. Altogether in 1961 I received from several localities in Arizona 138 nests of various species of *Ashmeadiella*, 70 of *occipitalis*, and 6 of *bucconis denticulata* from Portal. In 1958 I had 25 nests of species of *Ashmeadiella* from Portal; none of them was parasitized by *sonorensis*. However, in an individual parasitized nest the rate occasionally may be high, probably because an individual female chrysidid may continue to visit a nest under construction and oviposit in successive cells. Only 1 cell was parasitized in 4 nests containing respectively 3, 6, 12, and 16 completed cells; in 2 of these nests only the terminal cell was parasitized, and in a third the position of the chrysidid in the nest was not determined. In a 10-celled nest cells 4 and 6 were parasitized by sonorensis. In the 5-celled nest probably attacked by *sonorensis,* cells 2, 3, and 4 contained chrysidid larvae.

The 3 parasitized nests of *occipitalis,* provisioned between May 8 and 22, were from the single station on a dead mesquite branch. One of the nests, stored between May 15 and 22, had a first instar chrysidid larva attached to a small bee larva in cell 1 when I opened the nest on June 2. The host larva was almost mature on June 16, on which date the chrysidid was still in the first instar although it was distended from sucking some blood. The bee larva spun its cocoon from June 19 to 21. The chrysidid larva molted to the second instar on June 22. On June 30 the chrysidid larva was mature; it had just sucked the host larva dry and had not devoured the pelt. On this date the bees in cells 2 and 3 were ready to pupate. A male chrysidid eclosed on July 27; male and female bees emerged from the other cells July 27-31.

The other 2 parasitized nests of *occipitalis* were stored between May 8 and 15. A male chrysidid and 15 female bees emerged from 1 nest July 30-31. There were small bee larvae in the other nest on May 24. On June 22 there was a chrysidid larva 3.5 mm. long on the prepupa in cell 4 and a two-thirds grown chrysidid larva on the prepupa in cell 6. The chrysidid larva in cell 6 had spun its cocoon by June 27, it transformed to an entirely pale pupa by July 7, the adult eclosed by June 24, and a female *sonorensis* emerged from the nest on the 28th. Again, the host pelt was attached to the outside of the chrysidid cocoon. The larva in cell 4 was mature on June 30 and was preserved for subsequent taxonomic study. Bees emerged from several of the other cells July 31 to August 9.

The other 3 nests were collected in the field on October 18. I opened them for study early in November. In one 12-celled nest there were feeding bee larvae in all cells on November 3. A female *sonorensis* and 7 *bucconis denticulata* bees emerged from this nest the following spring; the chrysidid was from cell 12. In a second 5-celled nest, the bee larvae were mature on November

1. There was 1 small attached chrysidid larva on each of the bee larvae in cells 2 and 4 and a dead first instar chrysidid larva on the floor of cell 3. The chrysidid larvae were mature on November 6; 1 was preserved for further study and the other died during the winter. In the third 6-celled nest the bees were in cocoons by November 4. There was a chrysidid larva feeding on the resting bee larva in cell 6. A male *sonorensis* emerged from this cell the following spring, but the bees in the other cells were killed by *Pyemotes* mites.

The chrysidid cocoons were spun inside those of the host bee. Two of them were light tan with a small patch of dense white silk at the anterior end, 8 mm. long, and cylindrical with rounded ends.

Source material.
  Portal, Ariz. 1961 series: G 8 (?), 63, 67, 112, 266, 289.

Identifications. Hymenoptera by R. M. Bohart and author.

CHRYSOGONA VERTICALIS (Patton)

I reared this cuckoo wasp from 2 nests at Derby, N. Y., in 1956 and 1961 and from 1 nest each from Cropley, Md., in 1955, Plummers Island, Md., in 1960, and Arlington, Va., in 1959. The Derby nests were in 3.2-mm. borings, 1 from a pile of cut firewood and the other from the side of a wooden house. The Cropley, Plummers Island, and Arlington nests were from settings on old wooden sheds or a cabin; the first 2 were in 4.8-mm. borings and the last in a 3.2-mm. boring.

The host wasps at Derby were *Trypoxylon frigidum* Smith and *Trypoxylon* sp. At Cropley the host was *Trypargilum collinum rubrocinctum* (Packard). The Plummers Island nest was built by a species of *Trypoxylon* and that at Arlington was constructed by *Trypoxylon frigidum*. *C. verticalis* parasitized 8 of 22 cells in these nests.

In addition, 3 nests of *T. frigidum* at Arlington in 3.2-mm. borings were undoubtedly attacked by this same parasite, which occurred in 3 of 9 cells but was itself not reared to maturity.

Life history. The following data on egg and larval stages are from probable specimens of *verticalis*. One egg in a *frigidum* nest was 0.9 mm. long, 0.3 mm. across the middle and pointed toward the posterior end. One was on the thoracic sternum of a spider in the middle of the cell, and another was on the foreleg of the last spider in the cell. Two eggs hatched in 2-3 days, and 1 of the larvae completed feeding in 3-4 days. The newly hatched larva was 1.5 mm. long. The interval between egg laying and completion of feeding was 6 days for 1 specimen.

The period between completion of feeding and adult emergence in the summer generations was 15-16 days for 3 females. The period between pupation and emergence of an adult male was 8 days. The entire life cycle, egg to adult, in the summer was 18 days for 1 male and 25 days for a female.

The cocoons of 2 males from Derby and Arlington were 4 and 6 mm. long, ovoid, delicate, semitransparent, and with a dense white patch near the anterior end. A female cocoon from Cropley was 6.5 mm. long; it had an outer layer of fuzzy white silk and an inner layer of opaque, tan, varnished silk with a white patch near the anterior end.

Adults emerged June 10 to August 2 from nests stored from May 23 to early in July by the host wasps. Occupants of a nest stored around September 1 overwintered as diapausing larvae. Emergence of the parasites and host wasp was concurrent in the 1 nest in which both emerged successfully. There are undoubtedly several generations a year. At Plummers Island I have captured *verticalis* from May 5 to October 26.

Previous observations. The following spider-storing sphecid wasps have been reported as hosts of *verticalis*: *Trypoxylon fastigium* Fox and *T. frigidum* Smith (Bodenstein in Muesebeck *et al.*, 1951, p. 722), *Trypargilum* sp. (Krombein *et al.*, 1958, p. 95), and *Trypoxylon frigidum* and *T. backi* Sandhouse in Michigan (Thomas, 1962, 1963).

Thomas reported that the *verticalis* eggs were 1 mm. long, that they were deposited near the base of the host cell, and that the newly hatched larvae sought out and killed the host eggs before beginning to feed on the spiders. He stated that the egg hatched in 3 days, that the larva molted 3 times during the 3-day feeding period, and that cocoon spinning required 2 days. Pupation occurred a week after completion of feeding, the adult eclosed 9 days later and left the nest 3 days after eclosion.

Source material.
Derby, N. Y. 1956 series: J 125. 1961 series: L 15.
Cropley, Md. 1955 series: B 25.
Plummers Island, Md. 1960 series: E 4.
Arlington, Va. 1959 series: A 6, 16 (?), 19 (?), 23 (?).

Identifications by the author.

CHRYSIS (TRICHRYSIS) CARINATA Say
(Plate 28, Figures 132, 133 (?), 134)

In eastern North America there are 2 common species of *Chrysis* subgenus *Trichrysis* which formerly were confused under *parvula* Fabricius. Actually, *parvula* is a Central American species which does not occur in North America. I am using *carinata* for the smaller of the 2 species in eastern North America; it has the posterolateral angles of the second abdominal tergum edentate, a shorter first flagellar segment in the male, and its hosts are several species of *Trypargilum*. The larger species *tridens* (Lepeletier and Serville) has dentate or spinose posterolateral angles of the second tergum, a longer first flagellar segment in the male, and apparently it preys on mud-daubing, spider-storing wasps such as *Sceliphron* and *Chalybion*.

I found *C. carinata* to be the most common cuckoo wasp in trap nests. It occurred in 6 nests from Derby, N. Y., in 1955, 1956, 1959, and 1961; in 3 nests from Cropley, Md., in 1955; in 48 nests from Plummers Island, Md., 1956-1962; in 1 nest from Kill Devil Hills, N. C., in 1955; and in 2 nests from Lake Placid, Fla., in 1957.

At Derby the chrysidid parasitized 8 of 18 cells in the 6 nests. The host wasps were *collinum rubrocinctum* (Packard) in 3 nests, *clavatum* (Say) in 1 nest, and in 2 nests the trypoxylonine host was not identified because no adults were reared and no host cocoons were available.

T. c. rubrocinctum was the host in all 3 parasitized nests at Cropley. *C. carinata* parasitized 4 of 15 cells.

In the 48 parasitized nests at Plummers Island *rubrocinctum* and *striatum* (fig. 132) were hosts in a dozen nests each, *clavatum* (fig. 133 (?)) was the host in 6 nests, and in 18 trypoxylonine nests no host cocoons or adults were available. The cuckoo wasp occurred in 78 of 188 cells.

No trypoxylonine adults were reared from the single nest at Kill Devil Hills; 1 of 2 cells was parasitized by *carinata*.

At Lake Placid, Fla., *c. collinum* (Smith) was the host wasp in 1 nest, and no trypoxylonine adults were reared from the other nest. Three of 6 cells in the 2 nests were parasitized.

The numbers of parasitized cells recorded above reveal that *carinata* was a reasonably successful parasite once it found a host nest, because the overall parasitism rates were 27-50 per cent. At Plummers Island, where more nests were parasitized than at any other locality, the rate of parasitized cells was 41 per cent, but only 14 per cent of the available *Trypargilum* nests were parasitized.

The position of parasitized cells in the nests suggested that once a female *carinata* discovered a nest being stored, she continued to visit it and to lay eggs in successive cells (fig. 134). From 1 to 3 of the outermost cells were parasitized in 49 nests.

Furthermore, the data apparently indicated that the host wasp may complete the nest prematurely if she realizes that a cell has been parasitized. Many 1- and 2-celled nests were sealed by the host wasps after *carinata* had laid an egg in the first or second cell. However, occasionally the cuckoo wasp succeeded in placing her eggs in the nest without the host wasp being aware of the parasitism or perhaps occasional individual hosts did not react to nest parasitism by sealing the nest prematurely. For example, in an 11-celled nest at Plummers Island *carinata* parasitized cells 2, 3, 6, 7, 9, and 11, and in a 5-celled nest from the same locality *carinata* parasitized cells 2, 3, 4, and 5. Neither of these nests was sealed prematurely.

I noted as many as 3 *carinata* eggs in 1 *clavatum* cell at Plummers Island. These were in cell 5 of a 5-celled nest, 1 of them at the inner end and the others near the outer end; 1 of the latter was quite close to the host egg. I do not know whether these were all laid by the same female or by several females. The *carinata* larvae are cannibalistic and only 1 survives in a cell.

Life history. The egg of *carinata* is 1.6 mm. long and 0.45 mm. wide at the broadest section just before the tail end. It tapers gradually to a narrow rounded point at the anterior end and is 0.10 mm. wide just before the tip. I did not obtain exact data on duration of the egg stage, but the eggs usually hatched a day earlier than the host eggs (figs. 132, 133 (?)), and so the *carinata* eggs probably hatch in about a day.

Immediately after hatching the *carinata* larva sought out the host egg, sank its mandibles into it, and sucked out the fluid (fig. 132). In 1 larva the first molt occurred about 24 hours after the chrysidid attacked the host egg. The second instar *carinata* larva then moved onto 1 of the spiders stored as prey, usually the one on which the host egg was attached, and began to suck blood from the spider's abdomen. The second molt occurred about 12 hours after the first. The third molt took place in about 36 hours, and the fourth molt followed in about 12 more hours. Larvae of *carinata* in 4 different cells spent 4-6 days feeding on the host eggs and some or all of the spiders stored for the host. Usually the chrysidid larva left some of the prey untouched (fig. 134).

The spinning of the cocoon required 2-3 days. The cocoons were dirty white to light tan and opaque; they had 1 or 2 patches of dense white silk toward the anterior end. Male and female cocoons were about the same size. Sixteen cocoons in 4.8-mm. borings were 5-8 mm. long (mean 7) and 20 cocoons in 6.4-mm. borings were 7-9 mm. long (mean 8).

The period between pupation and adult emergence was 15-21 days (mean 17.5) for a dozen females in overwintering nests from Plummers Island. After eclosion adults remained in the cocoons 3-4 days.

Both in overwintering and in summer generation nests the parasites emerged 3-25 days (mean 13) before host wasps in adjacent cells of the same nests. However, in 1 *rubrocinctum* nest from

Plummers Island a *carinata* female emerged from cell 8 on July 16, a few weeks after the nest was completed, but the host wasps in the inner cells did not transform to adults until the following spring.

There is apparently a single generation a year at Derby and usually in the Washington area also. At Plummers Island *carinata* adults emerged the following spring from nests stored from the latter part of June until early in September. However, in 1 nest of *rubrocinctum* completed during June an adult *carinata* emerged July 16 and *rubrocinctum* adults July 19-20. In 1 of the Cropley nests of *rubrocinctum* a couple of *carinata* females emerged late in July. The single *carinata* from Kill Devil Hills overwintered as a diapausing larva. In 1 of the Florida nests stored during August adults of *carinata* and of its host *c. collinum* emerged in the latter half of September. These data suggest that *carinata* is usually univoltine in the more temperate part of its range and multivoltine in the Austral area.

At Plummers Island I reared 47 females and 4 males. Not enough adults were reared from other areas to permit any conclusions as to sex ratio. There were 6 females from Derby nests, 2 females and a male from Cropley nests, a male from Kill Devil Hills, and 1 female and 1 male from Lake Placid.

In an 11-celled *rubrocinctum* nest at Plummers Island there were *carinata* females in cells 2, 6, 7, 9, and 11; the *carinata* pupa in cell 3 was killed when the female in cell 2 started to cut its way out of the nest. If one assumes that this nest was parasitized by a single *carinata* female, it appears that a cuckoo wasp may lay a succession of fertilized female eggs.

Parasites and predators. I found a full-grown bombyliid larva in a *carinata* cocoon in a *clavatum* nest at Plummers Island. As it unfortunately died before pupating, a generic identification was not possible.

The eulophid *Melittobia chalybii* Ashmead infested 1 cell each in 3 nests parasitized by *carinata* in the field at Plummers Island and in 1 nest at Cropley. It also infested a cell parasitized by *carinata* in another nest after it was brought into the laboratory.

The grain itch mite *Pyemotes ventricosus* (Newport) infested a *carinata* cocoon in a Derby nest after the latter was brought into the laboratory.

Previous observations. A few years ago (Krombein, 1958c) I published notes under the name *parvula* on the Kill Devil Hills nest of *Trypargilum* parasitized by *carinata*. I presumed the host wasp to be *clavatum* (Say) or *collinum rubrocinctum* (Packard). Earlier host records for *parvula* (Bodenstein *in* Muesebeck *et al.*, 1951, p. 722) do not apply to *carinata*.

Source material.

Derby, N. Y. 1955 series: D 5b, 14c (?). 1956 series: J 5, 25, 72. 1959 series: W 81. 1961 series: L 43.

Cropley, Md. 1955 series: B 22 (?), 25, 35, 42.

Plummers Island, Md. 1956 series: H 2, 4, 6, 53, 77, 136. 1957 series: P 14, 46, 59, 71, 77, 91, 137, 159, 161, 162, 179, 207, 208, 222, 226, 248, 255, 257, 277. 1958 series: S 39, 44, 108. 1959 series: Y 132. 1960 series: E 21, 22, 44, 45, 46, 57, 58, 67, 83, 123, 181. 1961 series: K 29, 32. 1962 series: M 17, 43, 59, 65, 67, 119.

Kill Devil Hills, N. C. 1955 series: C 380.

Lake Placid, Fla. 1957 series: M 161, 162.

Identifications by the author.

CHRYSIS (TRICHRYSIS) MUCRONATA Brullé

This cuckoo wasp is rather similar in appearance to *Chrysis (Trichrysis) carinata* Say. It differs in minor morphological characters and appears to have a different sex ratio.

C. mucronata occurred in 17 nests from the desert floor at Portal, Ariz., in 1961. The host was the sphecid wasp *Trypargilum t. tridentatum* (Packard) except in 1 nest in which the host was the vespid *Euodynerus p. pratensis* (Saussure). *C. mucronata* parasitized cell 5 in the vespid nest; there were remains of caterpillars in that cell, and *pratensis* males were reared from cells 4 and 6. Consequently, this anomalous host record must be accepted as a positive one. No other boring at this station was being stored by *Trypargilum* at the time that *mucronata* parasitized the vespid nest. *C. mucronata* occurred in 24 of 68 cells in these 17 nests, giving a parasitism rate of 35 percent. However, it parasitized only 30 percent of the available *Trypargilum* nests at Portal during the period 1959-1962.

The position of parasitized cells in the nests suggested that once a female *mucronata* discovered a nest being stored she continued to visit it and to lay eggs in successive cells. From 1 to 3 of the outermost cells were parasitized in 13 nests. The occurrence of just a few *Trypargilum* cells and lack of a vestibular cell or the presence of abnormally long vestibular cells in some nests indicated that frequently the host wasps abandoned a nest or sealed it prematurely when parasitism by *mucronata* was discovered. However, this was not always true, because *mucronata* parasitized cells 1, 4, 5 and 6 in one 6-celled nest, and the host wasp did not seal this nest prematurely.

Life history. I did not obtain any data on duration of the egg and larval stages because all specimens of *mucronata* were mature larvae or prepupae in cocoons when I received the nests.

The ovoid cocoons were white to dark tan, semitransparent to opaque, and had 1 or 2 small patches of dense white silk near the anterior end. Seven of them in 4.8-mm. borings were 5-9 mm.

long (mean 6), and 9 in 6.4-mm. borings were 7-8 mm. long.

The period between pupation and adult emergence was 20-21 days each for 2 males and 2 females of the summer generation. In 1 nest 31 days elapsed between completion of larval feeding and emergence of the adult male of *mucronata,* and so the entire life cycle for summer emergents is probably 35-40 days.

The parasites emerged 3-21 days (mean 8) before the host wasps in adjacent cells of the same nests. Occupants of these nests, both parasites and hosts, emerged June 13 to August 11 from nests completed during the period from early May to mid-July, and so there are possibly 3 or more generations a year. In the 5 nests stored during September and October, *mucronata* and its hosts overwintered as diapausing larvae in 4 nests. In the fifth nest there was a dead, limp, fully colored *mucronata* pupa in cell 6 on November 6; the host wasps in the inner cells overwintered as diapausing larvae.

I reared 12 females and 5 males from the 24 parasitized cells.

In the closely related *carinata* Say the female:male ratio was about 12:1 at Plummers Island. Females of *mucronata* were reared from cells 1, 4, 5, and 6 of a 6-celled nest, and host wasps from the other 2 cells. If one assumes that this nest was parasitized by a single female, it appears that *mucronata* also can lay a succession of fertilized female eggs. This was the only nest from which I was successful in rearing more than a single *mucronata.*

Previous observations. Parker (1962) reported rearing *mucronata* from a cell of *Trypargilum tridentatum* (Packard) in an old mud nest of *Sceliphron caementarium* (Drury) in California.

Source material.
    Portal, Ariz. 1961 series: G 56 (?), 57, 102, 107, 172, 182, 247, 262, 306, 307, 329, 335, 339 (?), 343, 367, 383, 410 (?).

Identifications by R. M. Bohart and the author.

CHRYSIS (CHRYSIS) ARIZONICA Bohart

During 1961 I reared *arizonica* adults from 4 nests from 4 different stations at Portal, Ariz. and from 2 nests from a single station at Granite Reef Dam, Ariz. The host wasps at Portal were *Euodynerus guerrero* (Saussure) in two 6.4-mm. nests and unidentified vespids in two 4.8-mm. nests. At Granite Reef Dam the host wasp was *Stenodynerus (Parancistrocerus) toltecus* (Saussure), 1 nest in a 4.8-mm. and 1 in a 6.4-mm. boring.

C. arizonica parasitized 8 of 16 cells in both the Portal and Granite Reef Dam nests. It attacked the outermost cells in each nest. In 4 nests only the last cell was parasitized, but in an 8-celled nest from Portal cells 2, 3, 4, 6, and 8 were parasitized, and in an 11-celled nest from Granite Reef Dam cells 5-11 were attacked by *arizonica*. It appeared that the host wasp may have sealed 1 nest prematurely after the first and only cell was parasitized by *arizonica*.

Life history. The 2 nests from Granite Reef Dam were stored between April 29 and May 29. They may have been stored by the same *toltecus* female and parasitized by the same *arizonica* female because the development was concurrent. When I opened the nests on June 7, both the host wasps and the parasites were already in the pupal stage. Adults of *toltecus* and *arizonica* emerged June 14-20. (The chrysidid cocoons had been put into individual vials.) Emergence from 1 nest was June 14-19 and in the other nest June 19-20.

The Portal nests were stored during September or early in October. When I opened them November 3-6, the occupants were all diapausing larvae. The wasps overwintered in that stage and transformed to pupae and then to adults the following spring. The period between pupation and adult emergence was between 13 and 16 days for 1 *arizonica* female and 9-12 days (mean 11) for 3 males.

The female cocoons were transparent, light yellowish tan, and varnished; 9 of them were 6-12 mm. long (mean 8). Male cocoons were similar except that 1 was unvarnished and opaque; 4 of them were 7-11 mm. long (mean 9).

The *arizonica* adults emerged 4-6 weeks before the host wasps in the 2 overwintering *guerrero* nests, but the emergence was concurrent or a few days later than *toltecus* in nests of that species.

I reared 3 *arizonica* females and 2 males from the Portal nests and 7 females and a male from the Granite Reef Dam nests. In 1 Portal nest there was a female in cell 2 and a male in cell 4, and in 1 Granite Reef Dam nest there were females in cells 5-10 and a male in cell 11.

Parasites and predators. The grain itch mite *Pyemotes ventricosus* (Newport) attacked 1 *arizonica* pupa in the laboratory.

Source material.
   Portal, Ariz. 1961 series: G 80, 253, 259, 324.
   Granite Reef Dam, Ariz. 1961 series: H 60, 194.

Identifications. Chrysis by R. M. Bohart; other wasps by the author.

CHRYSIS (CHRYSIS) CEMBRICOLA Krombein

This rare little cuckoo wasp is thought to be host specific on the vespid *Symmorphus canadensis* (Saussure). I reared it from a 3.2-mm. nest at Arlington, Va., in 1956, and 6 years later I obtained chrysidid larvae presumed to be *cembricola* in 2 cells of another *canadensis* nest at Arlington.

The earlier nest was completed on June 28, and I opened it on the 30th. The vespid egg in cell 1 was already shriveled, but I did not note the *cembricola* larva which had presumably attacked it. However, on July 5 the *cembricola* larva began to spin its cocoon. It coated the walls and ends of the cell with transparent silk. Inside of this it constructed an ovoid transparent cocoon 6 mm. long with 2 patches of opaque, dense white silk near the anterior end. The parasite overwintered as a diapausing larva. There was a pale black-eyed pupa in the cell on April 22; an adult female left the cocoon when I opened the trap on April 29.

The second 3-celled nest was completed and opened on May 23. There was a chrysidid larva feeding on an *Apion* weevil larva in cell 1 and a newly hatched chrysidid larva attacking the *Symmorphus* egg in cell 2. I lost the larva in cell 2 when I attempted to preserve it for taxonomic study. The *cembricola* (?) larva in cell 1 completed feeding on May 27 and I preserved it for taxonomic study.

Previous observations. When I described this cuckoo wasp as a new species (Krombein, 1958b, pp. 53-58), I included the biological notes from the earlier nest discussed above. I also mentioned that adults of *cembricola* and *canadensis* were active on the same dates at Lost River State Park, W. Va., and at my home in Arlington; this tends to substantiate the belief that *cembricola* is probably host specific on *canadensis*.

Source material.

Arlington, Va. 1956 series: K 11. 1962 series: N 3 (?).

Identifications by the author.

CHRYSIS (CHRYSIS) COERULANS Fabricius

This cuckoo wasp parasitized 32 nests at 22 stations at Derby, N. Y., 1954-1961; 2 nests from 2 stations at Plummers Island, Md., 1961-1962; and 30 nests from 9 stations at the Archbold Biological Station, Lake Placid, Fla., 1960. At Derby there were 2 nests parasitized in 3.2-mm. borings, 14 in 4.8-mm., and 15 in 6.4-mm. borings, as well as a single one in a 12.7-mm. boring. There was 1 parasitized nest each in 4.8-and 6.4-mm. borings at Plummers Island. At Lake Placid there were 10 nests in 4.8-mm. and 20 in 6.4-mm. borings.

C. coerulans parasitized 46 of 109 stored cells in the nests from Derby. The host wasps were all Vespidae as follows: 12 nests from which I failed to rear adult hosts but which could be identified as vespids because of the caterpillar prey; 9 of *Ancistrocerus a. antilope* (Panzer); 4 of *A. t. tigris* (Saussure); 3 of *A. c. catskill* (Saussure); and 2 each of *Euodynerus f. foraminatus* (Saussure) and *Symmorphus c. cristatus* (Saussure).

At Plummers Island *coerulans* parasitized 4 of 8 stored cells.
The host vespid was not reared from 1 nest; in the other nest
it was *Symmorphus albomarginatus* (Saussure).

The host vespid was *Euodynerus foraminatus apopkensis*
(Robertson) in 25 nests at Lake Placid, Fla. In 2 nests it was
Euodynerus megaera (Lepeletier), and in 1 nest it was *Stenodynerus (Parancistrocerus) saecularis rufulus* Bohart. The host vespids were not reared in the other 2 nests. *C. coerulans* parasitized
69 of 222 stored cells in these nests from Florida.

At Derby there were nine 1-celled nests in which that single cell
was parasitized by *coerulans*. In 10 other nests only the outermost cell or two was parasitized by *coerulans*. These data suggest
that frequently the host wasp may have sealed the nest prematurely
when she became aware of the parasitism. *C. coerulans* parasitized
1-4 cells (mean 1.4) per nest at Derby or 40 per cent of the
available cells.

The Florida population of *coerulans* was atypical in having a
$1♀:2♂$ sex ratio instead of $2♀:1♂$ as in the Derby population.
It also differed in its relationship to the host wasps. In Florida
coerulans parasitized 1-6 cells (mean 2.3) per nest but only 30 per
cent of the available cells. This anomalous situation arose because
the host wasps never closed the nest prematurely. Either they reacted
differently to the parasitism, or the Florida *coerulans* were more
successful in concealing their eggs, so that the parasitism was not
noted by the hosts.

It was rather infrequently in Florida nests that *coerulans* parasitized a consecutive series of more than 2 cells in a nest. This
happened in only 3 nests where *coerulans* occurred in cells 1-6 of a
6-celled nest; in cells 1, 6, 7, and 8 of an 8-celled nest; and in
cells 3-6 of a 6-celled nest. In many of the other nests only 1 or
2 cells were parasitized and these occurred at random in the nests,
sometimes in the inner, sometimes in the outer, and sometimes
in the middle cells.

It is possible that some of this random parasitism happened
because a single chrysidid female parasitized 2 or 3 nests which
were being stored at the same time and station at Lake Placid.
During the week of March 29-April 4 at Station 7 *Euodynerus
foraminatus apopkensis* stored a 9-celled nest and *E. megaera*
stored a 7-celled nest; *coerulans* parasitized cells 5, 7, and 8 of the
first and cells 1 and 4 of the second. During the week of April 5-11
two 9-celled and one 7-celled nests were stored at Station 5 by
Euodynerus foraminatus apopkensis; coerulans parasitized cells 3,
6, 9 and cell 8 in the first 2 nests respectively and cells 2 and 7
in the third. At Station 7 during the week of April 5-11 *apopkensis*
stored two 9-celled nests and a 3-celled nest; *coerulans* parasitized

cell 6 and cells 3, 8, and 9 in the first 2 nests, respectively, and cell 1 in the third. Finally, during the week of April 12-18 at Station 7 *apopkensis* stored a 10-celled nest and *megaera* a 4-celled nest; *coerulans* parasitized cells 1, 2, 4, 5, 7, and 8 of the first and cells 3 and 4 of the second. These data suggest that the vespids were storing cells faster than the chrysidids could produce eggs.

Life history. I did not obtain information on the size of the egg or the duration of that stage. However, in 1 nest stored at Plummers Island 23 days elapsed between oviposition by the *coerulans* female and emergence of an adult male *coerulans* from the parasitized cell. In 6 nests stored during April at Lake Placid the cycle from egg to adult *coerulans* was 28-30 days.

The newly hatched *coerulans* larva sought out and destroyed the host egg. One larva spent 4 days feeding on some of the caterpillars stored for the host larva. The period between probable egg laying and completion of feeding was 10 days for 2 *coerulans* larvae from Derby.

Presumably spinning of the cocoon required 2-3 days. It was light tan to dark brown in color, transparent to subopaque, and varnished, and there was a patch or two of dense white silk near the anterior end. Male cocoons were a little shorter than female cocoons, and cocoons of the Derby population were a little shorter than those of the Florida population. At Derby 14 female cocoons were 7-9 mm. long (mean 8.1) and 5 male cocoons were 7-8 mm. long (mean 7.2) In the Florida nests 5 female cocoons were 8-12 mm. long (mean 10.6) and 19 male cocoons were 7-11 mm. long (mean 9.3).

Pupation occurred 5-7 days after completion of larval feeding during the summer generation. In 1 individual the eyes were black on the third day after pupation, the thorax began to darken on the fourth day, and eclosion of the adult took place on the seventh day. The period between pupation and emergence of the adult was 7-12 days for 5 individuals in midsummer, but 17-19 days for 8 specimens from Florida nests during April and May. The adults spent 2-4 days in the cocoon after eclosion.

I made a few notes on a pair from cells 5 and 8 of a nest from Lake Placid. I found them mating in the nylon emergence sleeve at 1145 hours on May 17 soon after their emergence from the nest. Shortly thereafter I transferred them to a large glass vial. Between then and 1445 they mated at least 6 times for periods of 5-10 minutes each. There was no courtship; the male just mounted the female and bent his extruded genital capsule forward beneath the apex of her third tergum to engage the partially exserted apical segment. During mating his head extended forward to the rear of her scutum. She was quiescent but he vibrated his antennae continually, tapping the back of her head. Occasionally he flirted his wings. Usually he held on to her with his fore and mid legs, the former clutching either her propodeal teeth or bases of her forewings and the latter grasping the sides of her second abdominal tergum in the middle. Sometimes he clutched the sides of her third tergum with his hind legs. Convulsive pumping movements of his genitalia occurred several times a minute.

I fed them sugar solution on a strip of blotting paper on May 17, 18, 20, and 23. I noted mating again on the 23d. The female died on May 26. On that date none of her eggs had developed even though she had fed on a vespid prepupa prior to her emergence from the nest and on sugar solution for several days after emergence.

The parasites emerged concurrently with host wasps from adjacent cells in all nests except those of *Euodynerus foraminatus apopkensis*. That wasp has only a single generation a year. Consequently the *coerulans* from those nests emerged about 11 months before their hosts. Frequently, cells parasitized by *coerulans* were in some of the inner cells in these *apopkensis* nests, so that any *apopkensis* larvae in the cells between the *coerulans* cells and the nest entrance were destroyed. Usually the *coerulans* adults fed on parts of these resting vespid larvae. Probably they would have been unable to chew through all of the mud partitions if they had not obtained some food in this way. Even so, some of them failed to penetrate all of the partitions and died in the nests.

At Derby there were 2 generations a year except where the host was the univoltine *Symmorphus c. cristatus*. In nests of other species stored from the first week in June to July 24 *coerulans* emerged June 29 to August 18; in nests stored later in the summer the *coerulans* overwintered as diapausing larvae as did the host wasps in adjacent cells. This also happened in 1 nest of *Ancistrocerus a. antilope* stored about June 28.

At Plummers Island the *Symmorphus albomarginatus* nest was stored June 3-6; both the host wasp and *coerulans* overwintered as diapausing larvae. The other nest was of a caterpillar-storing vespid. It was completed June 11, and a male *coerulans* emerged from the only cell on July 4.

Adults of *coerulans* emerged from the last week of April until May 24 from Florida nests stored by the host vespids during the month beginning the last week in March.

I reared 28 females and 13 males from Derby nests, 4 males from Plummers Island nests, and 19 females and 42 males from the Lake Placid nests. Enough specimens were reared at Derby and at Lake Placid to indicate that there was a 2♀:1♂ sex ratio at the former and a 1♀:2♂ ratio at the latter.

In almost all nests from Derby and Lake Placid from which I reared both sexes of *coerulans* there were 1 or more females in the inner cells and 1 or more males in the cells closer to the entrance. In the 2 Lake Placid nests from which I obtained the largest number of *coerulans* the sequence was as follows (x = mortality of vespid): ♀-♀-x-♀-♀-x-x-♂-x x and ♀-♂-♂-♂-♂-♂. In 1 nest from Derby and 1 from Lake Placid, respectively, the sequence was as follows: ♂-x-♀-x and x-x-♂-x-x-x x ♀ ♂. Altogether these data suggest that if a single *coerulans* female parasitizes several cells in a nest she lays female eggs in the inner and male eggs in the outer cells.

Reference has been made earlier to several anomalous characteristics of the Florida population. There was 1 additional peculiarity about it. It occurred in large numbers in a single year and in only the spring nests of that year. If there was emergence of *coerulans* during May from vespid nests in natural situations at Lake Placid, these individuals apparently did not attack any vespid nests in these borings later in the summer.

Parasites and predators. The eulophid *Melittobia chalybii* Ashmead parasitized a chrysidid prepupa in 1 Derby nest in the field; a specimen of *coerulans* was reared from another cell in this nest.

Cells 5-11 in a nest from Lake Placid were parasitized by both *Chrysis inaequidens* Dahlbom and *C. coerulans* Fabricius. Adults of the former were reared from cells 6, 7, 8, and 10 and of the latter from cells 5 and 9; the newly hatched chrysidid larva in cell 11 was preserved for taxonomic study. It is quite possible that eggs of both chrysidid species were laid in some or all of the parasitized cells, and that cannibalism occurred whenever there was multiple parasitism.

Previous observations. Walsh (1869, p. 135) reared *bella* Cresson, presently considered to be a synonym of *coerulans*, from the old cells of a *Sceliphron* mud dauber which he thought had been stored by *Eumenes fraternus* Say; the host identification was unquestionably erroneous because *Eumenes* builds its own nest, a little mud jug. Ashmead (1894, p. 79) reported rearing *coerulans* from mud cells of *Sceliphron*; almost certainly these were abandoned cells in which some other wasp nested. I contributed the first authentic rearing records several years ago (Krombein et al., 1958, p. 95) based on some of the nests reported above. Parker (1962) in California found *coerulans* parasitizing cells of *Ancistrocerus tuberculiceps sutterianus* (Saussure) in old *Sceliphron* nests. Medler (1964a, c, d) in Wisconsin reared *coerulans* from trap-nests in sumac twigs of the wasps *Euodynerus f. foraminatus* (Saussure), *E. leucomelas* (Saussure), *Ancistrocerus a. antilope* (Panzer), *A. c. catskill* (Saussure), and *A. t. tigris* (Saussure). In the parasitized nests of these species Medler (1964d) found that *coeru-*

lans parasitized 45 percent and 20 percent respectively, of the available cells in the 2 species of *Euodynerus,* and 45, 36, and 20 percent, respectively, of the available cells of the 3 species of *Ancistrocerus.*

Medler (1964d) found that there were 2 generations of *coerulans* in Wisconsin and that the parasites overwintered as diapausing larvae in the second generation nests. The life cycles of the vespid hosts and of the cuckoo wasp parasite were synchronized. A number of his nests contained 2 or more cells in succession parasitized by *coerulans,* but in other nests there was either random parasitism or parasitism of only 1 cell. He found no correlation between sex of the host and of the parasite. He also reported that the host wasp probably did not detect parasitism by the cuckoo wasp because parasitized and unparasitized nests contained the same total number of stored cells.

Source material.

   Derby, N. Y. 1954 series: IIc. 1955 series: D 3b, 9a, 9b. 1956 series: J 22, 23, 34, 40, 52, 67, 91, 94, 100. 1957 series: G 38, 51, 89, 99. 1958 series: R 32, 34, 36, 39. 1959 series: W 14, 17, 65. 1960 series: D 21, 43. 1961 series: L 22, 30, 31, 51, 60, 68.
   Plummers Island, Md. 1961 series: K 94. 1962 series: M 75.
   Lake Placid, Fla. (atypical). 1960 series: B 21, 22, 23, 26, 35, 36, 45, 46, 47, 48, 49, 50, 53, 54, 56, 57, 58, 85, 94, 98, 99, 100, 101, 102, 109, 111, 118, 124, 126, 128.

Identifications. Chrysis by R. M. Bohart (Florida series) and the author; host wasps by the author.

CHRYSIS (CHRYSIS) DERIVATA Buysson

I reared a female of this species from 1 cell of a 3-celled nest of *Euodynerus foraminatus apopkensis* (Robertson) in a 6.4-mm. boring from Lake Placid, Fla., in 1960. The nest presumably had been stored in April, but I did not receive and open it for study until August. At that time both the host and parasite were diapausing larvae in cocoons. After 2 months of exposure to chilling temperatures outdoors during the winter, the occupants of these cells transformed to pupae and then to adults.

Previous observations. Several years ago (Krombein, 1958c, p. 161) I published a few notes on what I supposed was a partially developed pupa of *derivata* in the nest of an unidentified vespid from Kill Devil Hills, N. C. The chrysidid cocoon was ovoid, 7 mm. long and 4.5 mm. wide, and spun of dense, opaque creamy silk.

Source material.

   Kill Devil Hills, N. C. 1955 series: C 449 (?).
   Lake Placid, Fla. 1960 series: B 91.

Identifications by the author.

CHRYSIS (CHRYSIS) INAEQUIDENS Dahlbom

I reared adults of *inaequidens* from 2 nests from a single station on the barrens at Kill Devil Hills, N. C., in 1956 and from 41 nests from 28 stations in the Highlands Ridge sand-scrub area of the Archbold Biological Station, Lake Placid, Fla., in 1957 and 1959-1962. In addition, I preserved 1 larva, presumably of this species, from another nest at Lake Placid. Twenty-four of the parasitized nests were in 4.8-mm. borings, 19 in 6.4-mm. borings, and a single one in a 12.7-mm. boring.

The host wasp in the Kill Devil Hills nests was *Euodynerus megaera* (Lepeletier). *C. inaequidens* parasitized 4 of 13 stored cells in these 2 nests.

At Lake Placid *inaequidens* parasitized 82 of 247 stored cells (33 percent) in the 42 nests. It occurred in 1-5 cells (mean 2) per nest. The host wasps were: *Euodynerus foraminatus apopkensis* (Robertson) in 27 nests; *E. megaera* (Lepeletier) in 1 nest; *Monobia quadridens* (Linnaeus) in 1 nest; *Pachodynerus erynnis* (Lepeletier) in 2 nests; *Stenodynerus pulvinatus surrufus* Krombein in 2 nests; *S. saecularis rufulus* Bohart in 1 nest; and unidentified vespids in 9 nests.

At Kill Devil Hills *inaequidens* parasitized cells 9 and 10 of a 10-celled nest and cells 1 and 2 of a 3-celled nest. At Lake Placid it parasitized the outermost cells in 20 nests, the innermost cells in 6 nests, and 1 or more intermediate cells in 16 nests. Occasionally, it was evident that the host wasp had sealed her nest prematurely, perhaps when she was aware of the parasitism. Two or more cells in sequence were parasitized by *inaequidens* in only 20 of the Florida nests and 3 or more cells in sequence in only 8 of those. Despite the random occurrence of *inaequidens* in many nests, there was little evidence that this was due to its concurrent parasitism of several nests at 1 station, as was evident in *Chrysis coerulans*.

Life history. Adults of *inaequidens* emerged 34-41 days after 2 nests were stored in mid-March in Florida. A month later *inaequidens* adults emerged 27-29 days after 2 nests were stored. I did not obtain any data on the duration of the egg stage or of the larval feeding period, but presumably 6-8 days would be required for these 2 stages. Twenty-two days elapsed between completion of larval feeding and emergence of 2 adult males from a midsummer nest. The period between pupation and adult emergence was 17 days for a Florida male during March and 13 days for a female in August. After eclosion the adults spent at least 3 days in the cocoon before emerging from the nest.

The cocoons consisted of 2 layers. There was a transparent, more or less colorless, varnished, silken sheath lining the cell walls and ends, and an inner ovoid, varnished, yellow to tan, transparent to subopaque cocoon. There was no difference in length of these inner cocoons so far as sex or boring diameter was concerned. Forty-seven of them were 7-11 mm. long (mean 9).

Adults of *inaequidens* and of the host wasps emerged more or less concurrently in most nests except those of *Euodynerus foraminatus apopkensis*. In nests of the latter stored from about mid-February to the last week of April *inaequidens* adults emerged March 21 to June 6, whereas the host wasps in adjacent cells did not emerge until the following spring. In 1 nest of *Stenodynerus pulvinatus surrufus* the chrysidid emerged December 16, but the host wasps in adjacent cells did not emerge until 3 months later after exposure to chilly weather to break the larval diapause. In a nest of *Pachodynerus erynnis* the host wasps pupated early in January, but the *inaequidens* did not pupate until nearly a month later.

The 2 nests from Kill Devil Hills were probably stored the latter half of August. All the occupants overwintered as diapausing larvae and transformed to pupae and adults the following spring. There are certainly at least 2 generations annually of *inaequidens* in coastal North Carolina where I have collected adults from June 28 to September 10.

Nests were stored in Florida from mid-February until the last week in November. There are undoubtedly a number of generations of *inaequidens* there with continual breeding during most of the year. Adults emerged as early as March 21 and as late as December 16. However, in 2 nests stored the last week in November or early in December the diapausing larvae of *inaequidens* required 2 months of exposure to chilling weather before they completed their life cycle.

In several nests of *foraminatus apopkensis* the *inaequidens* adults destroyed some of the diapausing host larvae lying in the cells between the *inaequidens* cells and the nest entrance. In most cases the cuckoo wasps sucked dry the host prepupae during this emergence. In 1 nest 2 *inaequidens* killed and fed on 6 *foraminatus apopkensis* larvae in an unsuccessful attempt to leave the nest.

I reared 3 females and 1 male from nests from Kill Devil Hills and 43 females and 28 males from Florida nests. Females were in the inner and males in the outer cells in most nests from which I reared both sexes. However, 2 nests had unusual sequence of sexes as follows (x=mortality or vespid): x-x-x-x-♂-x-♀-x-♀♀ and ♀-♂-♀-x. These nests may have been parasitized by 2 different female chrysidids, thus accounting for these unusual sequences.

Parasites and predators. I did not rear any parasites from cells which contained *inaequidens,* although I did find a newly hatched bombyliid larva on the wall of a cell containing a full-grown chrysidid larva; I preserved the latter for taxonomic study.

Cells 5-11 in a nest from Lake Placid were parasitized by both *Chrysis coerulans* Fabricius and *C. inaequidens*. Adults of the former were reared from cells 5 and 9 and of the latter from cells 6, 7, 8, and 10; the newly hatched chrysidid larva in cell 11 was preserved for taxonomic study. It is quite possible that eggs of both chrysidid species were laid in some or all of the parasitized cells and that cannibalism occurred whenever there was multiple parasitism.

Previous observations. Several years ago (1958c, pp. 161-163) I published notes on the 2 nests from Kill Devil Hills parasitized by *inaequidens*. I referred to the cuckoo wasp as *fabricii* Mocsary; that species is not now considered to be a member of the North American fauna and most U. S. records ascribed to it are referable to *inaequidens*. Moore and Parker (1962) reported *inaequidens* as a parasite of *Euodynerus foraminatus scutellaris* (Saussure) (recorded as *Rygchium*) in abandoned mud cells of *Sceliphron caementarium* (Drury) in California. They bred 14 males and 16 females of *inaequidens* from a number of *Euodynerus* cells.

Source material.
Kill Devil Hills, N.C. 1956 series: C 673, 675.
Lake Placid, Fla. 1957 series: M 31, 32, 57, 59, 99, 114, 123, 157, 166, 168, 179, 193 (?), 288. 1959 series: V 1, 18, 32, 79, 88, 101, 103, 111, 117, 147. 1960 series: B 15, 17, 20, 42, 82, 84, 94, 117, 135. 1961 series: F 27, 91, 184, 185, 253, 287, 292, 297. 1962 series: P 153, 215.

Identifications. Chrysis by R. M. Bohart and the author; host wasps by the author.

CHRYSIS (CHRYSIS) INFLATA Aaron

I reared *inflata* from 8 nests from 5 stations at Portal, Ariz., in 1959 and 1961. Seven of the nests were from settings on the desert floor, and 1 was from a setting on an old dead tree on a mountainside. Three nests were in 4.8-and 5 in 6.4-mm. borings.

C. inflata parasitized 12 of 26 stored cells in these nests. The host wasps were all vespids as follows: One or more unknown species in 4 nests, *Ancistrocerus t. tuberculiceps* (Saussure) in 2 nests, and *A. durangoensis* Cameron, and *Euodynerus guerrero* (Saussure) in 1 nest each.

The cuckoo wasp parasitized only a single cell in 6 of the nests. In a seventh 2-celled nest the female parasitized both cells and then was walled in dead or alive by the host wasp. In the last 6-celled nest *inflata* parasitized cells 2-5.

The innermost cell of 2- and 3-celled nests was parasitized in 3 nests, and the outermost 1 or 2 cells in three 2- to 4-celled nests. Intermediate cells were parasitized in the other 2 nests. It is possible that the host wasps closed a few nests prematurely with an abnormally long vestibular cell when they discovered that the nests were being parasitized.

Life history. I did not obtain any data on the duration of the egg and larval feeding periods. The time between pupation and emergence was 7-10 days for 6 males in overwintering nests and at least 13 days for 1 female in midsummer. This single female remained in the cocoon 6 days after eclosion before she left the nest.

Five male cocoons were 7-9 mm. long (mean 8.1) and 2 female cocoons were 10 mm. long. The cocoons were ovoid, varnished, brittle, and testaceous to dark brown in color.

C. inflata emerged concurrently with host wasps from adjacent cells in 1 nest, 3 days after the host wasp in another nest, and about 2 weeks before the host wasp in a third nest.

There were at least 2 generations a year. Adults of *inflata* emerged July 19 to August 3 from nests presumably stored by the host wasp between the latter part of June and the early part of July. In 3 nests presumed to have been stored in September, both *inflata* and the host wasps overwintered as diapausing larvae and transformed to pupae and adults the following spring.

I reared 4 females and 6 males of *inflata*. Four males emerged from cells 2-5 of a 6-celled nest, and only 1 cuckoo wasp was reared from each of the other nests.

Source material.

   Portal, Ariz. 1959 series: X 171, 172, 237. 1961 series: G 249, 313, 328, 336, 372.

Identifications by the author.

CHRYSIS (CHRYSIS) NITIDULA Fabricius

I reared *nitidula* from 7 nests from 5 stations at Derby, N. Y., 1956 and 1959-1961 and from another 7 nests from 5 stations at Plummers Island, Md., 1957, 1961 and 1962. Nine nests were in 4.8-mm. and 5 in 6.4-mm. borings. Seven nests were on wooden buildings, 3 on dead standing tree trunks, 2 in a pile of cut firewood, and 1 each on elm and sumac branches.

At Derby *nitidula* parasitized 7 of 18 stored cells and just the outermost cell in each nest. The presence of unusually long vestibular cells in each of these nests suggests that the host wasps sealed them prematurely as soon as the parasitism was discovered. The hosts were all vespid wasps as follows: *Ancistrocerus a. antilope* (Panzer) in 3 nests; *Symmorphus c. cristatus* (Saussure) in 1 nest; and unidentified species of caterpillar-storing vespids in 3 nests.

C. nitidula parasitized 8 of 23 cells in the 7 nests from Plummers Island. The cuckoo wasps were in the outermost cell or cells in all but 2 nests where they parasitized the penultimate cells.

Again, the evidence indicated that usually the host wasps sealed the nests prematurely when the parasitism was discovered, because of the presence of several unusually long vestibular cells. In 1 incompleted nest I caught a female *nitidula* lurking on top of the trap; she had laid an egg in completed cell 5 and was probably waiting to lay another egg in cell 6 which at that time contained only the vespid egg. The host wasps at Plummers Island were all vespids as follows: *Ancistrocerus a. antilope* (Panzer) in 3 nests; *Euodynerus schwarzi* (Krombein) in 1 nest; and unidentified caterpillar-storing wasps in 3 nests. Two of the latter were almost certainly nests of *antilope* also, because they came from the same station and at the same time as an *antilope* nest and contained mites which were undoubtedly *Kennethiella*.

All the host wasps preyed on caterpillars except *Symmorphus c. cristatus*, which stored beetle larvae (*Chrysomela* sp.).

Life history. I neglected to measure the chrysidid egg in the nest on which I caught the mother *nitidula*. I presume that this egg was laid the morning of June 23, when I captured the mother at 1330 hours. The vespid in the parasitized cell had already hatched. The *nitidula* egg hatched June 25 or 26 and the larva must have attacked the vespid larva because the latter appeared to have been bitten; it died a day later. I preserved the first instar *nitidula* larva for taxonomic study.

In another Plummers Island nest I noted a chrysidid egg on top of the caterpillars at the outer end of cell 1 and another chrysidid egg in cell 2 on the ceiling between the vespid egg and the inner end of that cell. There must have been 2 chrysidid larvae in cell 1, because even though I noticed a dead first instar chrysidid larva in that cell another *nitidula* developed in it subsequently.

One female larva pupated 6 days after she completed feeding. The adult female left this nest 7 days after pupation. In another female the period between completion of larval feeding and emergence from the nest was 14 days. In overwintering nests the period between pupation and adult emergence was 8 days for 2 males and 11 days for a female. One adult spent 2 days in the cocoon after eclosion. In 5 nests of the summer generation the period between sealing of the nest by the host vespid and emergence of the *nitidula* adults was 25-31 days (mean 27).

The cocoons were ovoid, transparent, varnished, and light to dark tan. Each had a small patch of pale, dense silk anteriorly. Three male cocoons were 7-8 mm. long, and 3 female cocoons were 8-11 mm. in length.

There were obviously at least 2 generations a year at Derby. The host nests were stored between June 10 and 27 and *nitidula* adults emerged July 8-18. Emergence of the host wasps from adjacent cells was from a day earlier to 3 days later in 3 nests and about 11 months later in the *Symmorphus* nest.

Probably there were 3 generations annually at Plummers Island, where nests were parasitized from the first week in June until mid-September. Both *nitidula* and the host wasps overwintered as diapausing larvae in nests stored after mid-July. In 1 nest stored early in June an *antilope* male in cell 1 killed a fully colored female *nitidula* pupa in cell 4 as the host male emerged from the nest on June 30. In several overwintering nests the *nitidula* adults emerged 1-12 days before host wasps in earlier cells. I have collected *nitidula* at Plummers Island from May 21 to September 4.

At Derby I reared 6 females and a male from the 7 parasitized cells, and at Plummers Island I reared 3 females and 4 males. There were 2 *nitidula* males in the only nest from which I obtained more than a single adult parasite.

Previous observations. Several years ago (Krombein *et al.*, 1958, p. 95) I reported hosts of *nitidula* [as *chalcopyga* Mocsary, a synonym] as being *Euodynerus f. foraminatus* (Saussure) [reported as *Rygchium*], *Ancistrocerus a. antilope* (Panzer), and *Symmorphus c. cristatus* (Saussure); these records were based on some of the nests reported above. Hobbs *et al.* (1961, p. 147) reared *nitidula* from nests of *Ancistrocerus c. catskill* (Saussure) in abandoned mud cells of *Anthophora occidentalis* Cresson in a clay bank in southern Alberta. Medler (1964a, d) working in Wisconsin, reared *nitidula* from trap-nests in sumac twigs; hosts were the vespid wasps *Ancistrocerus a. antilope* (Panzer), *A. c. catskill* (Saussure), *A. t. tigris* (Saussure), and *Euodynerus f. foraminatus* (Saussure). He reported (1964d) that *nitidula* parasitized 43, 31, 21, and 21 per cent, respectively, of the available cells in parasitized nests of these 4 species.

Medler (1964d) found that there were 2 generations of *nitidula* in Wisconsin and that the parasites overwintered as diapausing larvae in second generation nests. The life cycles of the vespid hosts and of the cuckoo wasp were synchronized. A number of his nests contained 2 or more cells in succession parasitized by *nitidula,* but in other nests there was either random parasitism or parasitism of only 1 cell. He found no correlation between sex of the host and of the parasite. He also reported that the host wasp probably did not detect parasitism by the cuckoo wasp because parasitized and unparasitized nests both contained the same total number of stored cells.

Source material.
    Derby, N. Y. 1956 series: J 92. 1959 series: W 39. 1960 series: D 16, 27. 1961
        series: L 42, 44, 62.
    Plummers Island, Md. 1957 series: P 283, 284, 286. 1961 series: K 97, 114.
        1962 series: M 59, 71.

Identifications by the author.

CHRYSIS (CHRYSIS) SMARAGDULA Fabricius

This large handsome cuckoo wasp is quite possibly host specific on members of the genus *Monobia*. All my reared material of it came from nests of *M. quadridens* (Linnaeus). Except for 1 specimen of *Chrysis (C.) inaequidens* Dahlbom, reared from a Florida nest of *quadridens*, *smaragdula* was the only cuckoo wasp reared from *Monobia*. However, *smaragdula* ranges more widely than *M. quadridens,* and it is probable that its host in the drier western part of its range is *M. texana* (Cresson).

I reared adults of *smaragdula* from 3 nests of *quadridens* from Plummers Island, Md., in 1957, from 3 nests from Kill Devil Hills, N. C., in 1956 and 1958, and from 1 nest from Lake Placid, Fla., in 1962. In addition *smaragdula* must have parasitized 5 other nests of *quadridens* at Kill Devil Hills in 1958. These determinations were based on finding the characteristically large chrysidid cocoons from which adults had already emerged in 4 of the nests and on the large preserved *smaragdula* larva from 1 cell in the fifth nest.

All the 12 nests parasitized by *smaragdula* were in 12.7-mm. borings. Most of the nests were at the edges of wooded areas or in open woods. Many of them were from stations beneath dead limbs of pine, oak, or hickory, but a few were on dead or living tree trunks. Three were on structural lumber, *i.e.*, a wooden fence, a cabin porch, or a pile of planks on the ground. Only 2 nests came from a single station, so it is probable that most of the nests were parasitized by different individuals of *smaragdula.*

The parasitism rate in the dozen nests was high. It ran 53 per cent (3 of 6 cells at Plummers Island, 15 of 29 cells at Kill Devil Hills, and 2 of 3 cells at Lake Placid). However, the over-all parasitism rates were quite low except at Kill Devil Hills. At Plummers Island *smaragdula* parasitized only 9 per cent of the available nests and 4 per cent of the available cells; at Kill Devil Hills these percentages were 29 and 25 per cent, respectively; and at Lake Placid the percentages were each 1 per cent.

C. smaragdula occurred in 2 or more cells in 4 nests at Kill Devil Hills and in the single nest at Lake Placid. In 3 of these nests either the chrysidids were in a series of adjacent cells in the outer end of the nest or they parasitized all the cells. In the fourth nest *smaragdula* developed in cells 1 and 2 and *Monobia* in cell 3. In the fifth nest *Monobia* developed in cells 1 and 4 and *smaragdula* in cells 2, 3, and 5. In the multicelled *Monobia* nests in which only a single cell was parasitized, the innermost cell in 3 nests and one of the intermediate cells in the other 3 nests were attacked. These data suggest that occasionally a female *smaragdula* continued to visit a nest once she discovered it, laying 1 or more eggs in each cell as it was provisioned.

Life history. K. W. Cooper kindly sent me some notes he made at Gainesville, Fla., on an egg of *smaragdula* in a *Monobia* nest. The chrysidid egg was 2.2 mm. long and 0.6 mm. wide, buff white, and elongate ovoid. The egg was held at a temperature of 72° F., and it hatched 44-55 hours after being laid. The newly hatched larva was preserved for taxonomic study.

I obtained limited data from 1 nest from Plummers Island which suggest that the feeding stage of the larva may be 4-5 days. In this nest I saw a recently hatched *Monobia* larva in cell 1 on July 17. On the 19th this larva was moribund, and I found in the cell among the caterpillar prey a small *smaragdula* larva. Presumably the latter had attacked the *Monobia* larva. The cuckoo wasp larva continued to feed on the caterpillars and began to spin a cocoon on the 22nd.

A period of at least 15 days elapsed between pupation and emergence of 1 adult male from the cocoon. This same period was at least 20 days for 1 female. A period of 3-4 days elapsed between actual eclosion of the adults and their emergence from the cocoons. These figures are from nests in which the chrysidids overwintered as diapausing larvae.

Emergence of *smaragdula* adults from 2 summer generation nests at Kill Devil Hills was more or less concurrent with that of the host wasps from the same nests. Two males of *smaragdula* emerged July 30 and 3 females of *quadridens* August 1-2 from 1 of the nests. In the other nest a *smaragdula* male emerged August 3, 2 *quadridens* females on the 4th, and 2 *smaragdula* females on the 4th and 6th. Since the exact elapsed time between egg hatch and adult female emergence of *Monobia* was 36-37 days in the summer generation, it is probable that both sexes of *smaragdula* require a similar period for their development.

The *smaragdula* larva spun a silken varnished sheath against the cell walls and ends. Inside of this it constructed the inner cocoon which was ovoid, light yellowish tan to dark brown, varnished, and brittle. This inner cocoon was 11-17 mm. long (mean 14) in 6 females, and 11-13 mm. long (mean 12) in 5 males.

C. smaragdula and its host overwintered as diapausing larvae in the Plummers Island nests which were stored in mid-July. It is probable that, like its host, the cuckoo wasp has a partial second generation at Plummers Island. There are 2 generations of *smaragdula* at Kill Devil Hills and presumably 2 or more at Lake Placid.

I reared 6 females and 5 males of *smaragdula* from these nests. In the 3 nests from which I reared more than a single parasite, I reared both sexes in 2 of them and 2 males in the third.

Previous observations. I published a brief account of the biology of this species (Krombein, 1958c, p. 163) based on the first parasitized nest obtained at Kill Devil Hills. Data from this nest are included in the more extended account on the preceding pages.

Rau (1931a, p. 199), reporting on a series of homing experiments, stated that a marked specimen was liberated a mile from its place of capture. It returned to the nesting site the next morning, 17½ hours later. The specimen, recorded by Rau as *Chrysis* (*Hexachrysis*) sp., with a dot of yellow paint on the thorax and bearing Rau's number 28, is in the collection of the U.S. National Museum; it is a female of *smaragdula* Fabricius.

Source material.
> Plummers Island, Md. 1957 series: P 132, 175, 204.
> Kill Devil Hills, N. C. 1956 series: C 228. 1958 series: T 213, 217, 221, 223, 224, 225, 230.
> Lake Placid, Fla. 1962 series: P 227.

Identifications by the author.

CHRYSIS (CHRYSIS) STENODYNERI Krombein

I reared this cuckoo wasp from 10 nests at 9 stations on the barrens at Kill Devil Hills, N. C., in 1955 and 1956 and from a single nest from the sand-scrub area of the Archbold Biological Station, Lake Placid, Fla., in 1959. All nests were in 4.8-mm. borings except 1 in a 6.4-mm. boring.

At Kill Devil Hills *stenodyneri* parasitized 12 of 33 cells (35 per cent). Its hosts were all vespids as follows: *Stenodynerus* (*S.*) *krombeini* Bohart in 3 nests; *S.* (*S.*) *lineatifrons* Bohart in 2 nests; *S.* (*S.*) *ammonia histrionalis* (Robertson) in 1 nest; *S.* (*Parancistrocerus*) *histrio* (Lepeletier) in 1 nest (based on identification of mite hypopi found in nests); and unidentified vespids, probably species of *Stenodynerus,* in 3 nests.

The host was an unidentified vespid in the Florida nest where *stenodyneri* parasitized cell 1 and miltogrammines parasitized the other 4 cells.

At Kill Devil Hills *stenodyneri* parasitized 1 or 2 cells at the outer end in 8 nests. It seemed likely that the host wasps abandoned many of these nests when the parasitism was discovered, because 6 of them contained only 2 or 3 stored cells.

Life history. I did not open any nests early enough to ascertain the duration of the egg or larval feeding stages. The period between pupation and adult emergence for individuals in overwintering nests was 17-21 days for 3 females and 17 days for a male. Adults remained in the cocoons 2-6 days after eclosion from the pupal exuvia.

The cocoons were distinctive in shape. The anterior end was a transverse septum across the boring. Occasionally the cocoon was cylindrical with a rounded posterior end, but usually it was narrower immediately behind the anterior end and tapered gradually to the rounded posterior end. It was transparent, light tan, brittle, and varnished and had 1-4 (usually 2-3 narrrow strips of dense, opaque pale silk on the sides near the anterior end. A dozen cocoons were 7-13 mm. long (mean 9). The adults escaped by cutting a circular hole in the transverse anterior end.

Males of *stenodyneri* emerged 2-17 days earlier than females. Usually the chrysidids emerged 1-28 days earlier than the host vespids in adjacent cells, although in 1 nest there was concurrent emergence by a female chrysidid and a male vespid.

It is probable that there are at least 2 generations a year at Kill Devil Hills. All the nests which I obtained there were stored between the last week in July and mid-September. One nest must have been stored about September 15 because the *stenodyneri* in 1 cell was spinning its cocoon on the 23d. The cuckoo wasps and host wasps overwintered as diapausing larvae and transformed to pupae and then to adults late in the following spring. I collected adults in the field at Kill Devil Hills July 3- August 5.

The single nest from Lake Placid was stored during the first week in April. The *stenodyneri* in cell 1 transformed to a pupa April 14-22, probably about the 16th. A female *stenodyneri* emerged from this nest on May 4. This early emergence date suggests the possibility of several generations annually in Florida. Three field-collected specimens from Florida included in the type series of *stenodyneri* were collected March 15, June 21, and "10-11" (presumably October 11, but possibly November 10).

I reared 7 females and 5 males from nests at Kill Devil Hills. There were 2 *stenodyneri* in only 2 nests. In one of these both parasites were females, and in the other there was a female in cell 6 and a male in cell 7.

Parasites and predators. It is possible that 1 or more *stenodyneri* might have been destroyed by miltogrammine maggots, *Amobia floridensis* (Townsend), in the nest from Florida. The cuckoo wasp parasitized cell 1 and the maggots ravaged cells 2-5. It is quite possible that the mother *stenodyneri* might have parasitized 1 or more of the 4 outer cells in this nest also.

Previous observations. Several years ago (Krombein, 1958c, pp. 155-160) I published an account of the biology of *stenodyneri* based on the 10 nests from North Carolina.

Source material.
    Kill Devil Hills, N.C. 1955 series: C 30, 70, 348, 447, 474, 475, 479. 1956 series: C 32, 60, 700.
    Lake Placid, Fla. 1959 series: V 74.

Identifications. Acarina by E. W. Baker; Miltogrammini by W. L. Downes, Jr.; wasps by the author.

CHRYSIS (subgenus?) PELLUCIDULA Aaron

I reared a single specimen of this uncommon species from the outermost cell of a 5-celled nest of *Trypargilum collinum rubrocinctum* (Packard) from Derby, N. Y., in 1957.

The nest was stored early in the summer, presumably in July, but I did not open it until September 6. There was a dead *rubrocinctum* larva in a cocoon in cell 1 and a live one in cell 4; the wasp eggs in cells 2 and 3 were dead. In cell 5 was a *rubrocinctum* cocoon, but the resting larva of the host had been parasitized by a cuckoo wasp. The latter did not consume the entire host body but had walled off the remains in the posterior end of the host cocoon by a clear, varnished, transverse septum. The *pellucidula* cocoon consisted of a single layer of delicate white silk spun against the walls and anterior end of the host cocoon. The transverse septum, which constituted the posterior end of the chrysidid cocoon, was not silked over. The *pellucidula* cocoon was 4.5 mm. long. The resting larva lay in it with its anterior end directed toward the transverse septum; when the adult eclosed, it reoriented itself properly and emerged from the anterior end of the host cocoon.

The chrysidid in cell 5 and the *rubrocinctum* in cell 4 overwintered as diapausing larvae. The parasite in cell 5 transformed to a pupa on April 25, 5 days before the host wasp pupated in cell 4. On April 28 the *pellucidula* pupa had light tan eyes. An adult male of *pellucidula* eclosed on May 7, but it did not emerge until the 14th, 6 days earlier than the host wasp in cell 4.

It is presumed that *pellucidula* is similar to the species of *Chrysura* in its manner of attacking the host; that is, while the host is storing the cell the chrysidid egg is deposited and when it hatches the larva attaches to the host larva and sucks a small amount of blood. The parasite does not molt to the second instar and feed in earnest on the host until the latter has spun its cocoon.

Previous observations. Hicks (1934, p. 267) reared *pellucidula* from a nest of *Trypargilum t. tridentatum* (Packard) in California.

Source material.
   Derby, N. Y. 1957 series: G 37.

Identifications by the author.

NEOCHRYSIS PANAMENSIS (Cameron)

This cuckoo wasp appears to be host specific on the cockroach-storing sphecid *Podium*. I have reared it from *rufipes* (Fabricius) at Kill Devil Hills, N. C., and Lake Placid, Fla. However, at Plummers Island, Md., I collected a female *panamensis* on a dead tree trunk in which *P. luctuosum* Smith nested; *P. rufipes* is not known to occur at that locality. Both *rufipes* and *panamensis* range from North Carolina southward to Florida and west along the coast to Mexico and south to Panama.

I found *panamensis* in 8 nests from 6 stations at Kill Devil Hills in 1955, 1956, and 1958 and in 21 nests from 13 stations at Lake Placid in 1957 and 1959-1961. Thirteen nests were in 4.8-mm. borings and 16 in 6.4-mm. borings. The North Carolina nests were in open wooded areas and those in Florida were in sand-scrub areas.

There was only a single host cell in all but 1 of the nests, as is customary in *Podium rufipes*. In the single exception there were 2 *rufipes* cells; I obtained a host wasp from cell 1 and a *panamensis* from cell 2. The host wasps in the other nests were identified by a combination of the cockroach prey and the characteristic closing plug of debris with an outer coating of resin.

Life history. I did not obtain any information on the size of egg or duration of the egg stage. The newly hatched *panamensis* larva first sought out and devoured the host egg. Then it began to feed on the dorsum of the abdomen of one of the cockroaches. If the cockroach was a winged adult, the *panamensis* larva got beneath the wings to feed. The chrysidid larva fed on the soft parts only, and usually it did not devour all the cockroaches placed in the cell for the host larva. The larval feeding period was rather long; in 1 specimen it required a week.

When the *panamensis* larva was ready to spin a cocoon it usually compacted the prey remains at 1 end of the cell and spun the cocoon adjacent to them. First, the larva spun a transparent silken sheath 10-25 mm. long loosely attached to the boring walls; occasionally in this sheath it incorporated wings or sclerites from some of the cockroaches. Then it spun an inner ovoid cocoon. In the Kill Devil Hills population this inner cocoon was brittle, varnished, dark brown, and subopaque with a small cap at the anterior end of dense, brown unvarnished silk. In the Florida nests the cocoon was white and subopaque to opaque. There was no difference in length between male and female cocoons. Eighteen inner cocoons were 7-15 mm. long (mean 10).

The period between completion of larval feeding and pupation is estimated to be 9-10 days for individuals of the summer generation. This time interval is based on a period of 28 days between completion of larval feeding and adult emergence for 2 males, and a period of 18-19 days between pupation and adult emergence for 4 males. For a female of the overwintering generation 21 days elapsed between pupation and adult emergence. One adult remained in the cocoon 3 days after eclosion.

There were at least 2 generations at Kill Devil Hills, where a *panamensis* adult emerged August 13 from a nest stored presumably early in July. In 2 other North Carolina nests stored later in the summer, *panamensis* overwintered as diapausing larvae and transformed to pupae and then to adults the following spring.

Adults of *panamensis* emerged April 29 to August 15 from nests stored in Florida from the latter part of March until mid-July. Two nests stored during September and October were parasitized by *panamensis;* the mature larvae were preserved for taxonomic study, and so I do not know whether they would have transformed at once to pupae and adults or entered larval diapause. However, in another nest stored during the first half of October, the *panamensis* larva did enter diapause and required 2 months of exposure to chilly weather outdoors in Arlington, Va., before it transformed to a pupa and adult. It appears that there must be several generations a year in Florida, because nests were stored during each month from March through October.

I reared 4 females and 1 male at Kill Devil Hills. At Lake Placid I obtained 3 females and 9 males. Several larvae died naturally or were preserved for taxonomic study.

Previous observations. A few years ago (Krombein, 1958c, pp. 147-149) I published biological notes on *panamensis* based on the nests obtained at Kill Devil Hills in 1955 and 1956. In that paper I referred to the parasite as *Chrysis alabamensis* Mocsary and to the host as *Podium carolina* Rohwer; these are now recognized to be synonyms of *Neochrysis panamensis* (Cameron) and *P. rufipes* (Fabricius), respectively.

Source material.
    Kill Devil Hills, N. C. 1955 series: C 136, 248, 381, 385. 1956 series: C 387, 627, 629. 1958 series: T 40.
    Lake Placid, Fla. 1957 series: M 18, 33, 56, 89, 117, 118, 120, 128, 129, 152, 271. 1959 series: V 124. 1960 series: B 202, 212, 215. 1961 series: F 219, 232, 241, 246, 254, 298.

Identifications by the author.

Superfamily SCOLIOIDEA

Family MUTILLIDAE

So far as is known females of this family oviposit on the resting larvae of other insects either in cocoons or in puparia. I obtained very few trap nests parasitized by mutillids, because usually the nests were picked up too soon after completion to permit this parasitism to occur.

In all the parasitized nests the closing plugs at the nest entrances and the partitions capping the cells were made of mud. The female mutillid gained access to the outermost cell by chewing a small hole through the plug and partition. Then she chewed a tiny hole in the anterior end of the host cocoon and oviposited on the resting larva of the host. It is not known whether the host larva was paralyzed by stinging, but this would not be necessary if it had reached the inert, flaccid diapausing stage.

After oviposition females of *Spaeropthalma pennsylvanica scaeva* (Blake) and *S. uro* (Blake) sealed the breach in the host cocoon with a small plug of mud fabricated from the closing partition. Usually females of these species did not reseal the holes they made in the cell partitions and closing plugs; this omission permitted other parasites, such as *Melittobia chalybii* Ashmead, to gain access to the nest subsequently. I did not note whether the female *uro*, which parasitized the caterpillar-storing vespid, resealed the breach in the delicate host cocoon; she did reseal the breach she made in the partition capping the parasitized cell.

The mutillids were not effective parasites of occupants of these trap nests, because they parasitized only the outermost cell. The host cocoons occupied so much of the boring that there was not sufficient room for the female mutillid to squeeze past the outermost cocoon to gain access to the penultimate stored cell.

Ferguson (1962, pp. 26-27 and table 9) pointed out that *S. unicolor* (Cresson) and *S. orestes* Fox were not host specific but parasitized a number of ground-nesting bees and their parasites, even including the same species of mutillid. His observations are confirmed by the recorded host preferences for the 2 identified species with which I worked. My own rearing records indicate that species of *Trypargilum* are the hosts, but previously published information (summarized by Krombein *in* Muesebeck *et al.*, 1951, p. 752) established that *S. pennsylvanica* (Lepeletier) parasitizes a number of species of mud-dauber wasps belonging both to the Pompilidae and Sphecidae, and *S. uro* Blake (recorded as *uro melanderi* (Baker)) was bred from *Dianthidium curvatum sayi* Cockerell (Fischer, 1951, p. 49).

SPHAEROPTHALMA (SPHAEROPTHALMA) PENNSYLVANICA SCAEVA (Blake)

(Plate 29, Figures 135-139)

I reared this mutillid or found evidences of parasitism by it in 7 nests from Plummers Island, Md., 1959, 1960 and 1962. Two nests were in 4.8-mm. borings and 5 in 6.4-mm. borings; all were from settings on standing, dead tree trunks.

All the hosts were sphecid wasps belonging to *Trypargilum* as follows: 4 of *striatum* (Provancher); 2 of *collinum rubrocinctum* (Packard); and 1 of *clavatum* (Say).

The mutillids parasitized only completed nests and only the outermost cell in each of 6 nests. In every nest the mother mutillid chewed a hole about 3 mm. in diameter through the center of the mud closing plug (fig. 135) to get into the vestibular cell; these closing plugs were 3-5 mm. thick. Then, to reach the host cocoon she chewed another hole through the partition capping the outermost stored cell; these partitions were 0.5-2 mm. thick. In 1 nest the vestibular cell was divided into two by a transverse mud partition so that the parasite had to chew through 3 layers of mud in that nest. In the seventh nest a female mutillid was at the closing plug when I picked up the nest on June 20, but she had not yet begun to breach this seal.

Next the mutillid chewed a small hole, perhaps 1 mm. in diameter, in the anterior end of the host cocoon and oviposited on the host larva. It is not known whether the host larva was stung before oviposition. Then the female sealed the breach in the host cocoon with some moistened mud from the closing plug (figs. 136-139).

The 4 nests in 1959 were stored and parasitized during a 6-week period while I was in Arizona. When I opened the nests on August 23 the mutillid larva had already devoured the host prepupa in each of the outermost cells and had spun its own cocoon inside that of the host. The mutillids and host wasps overwintered as diapausing larvae. One of the mutillids was parasitized in the laboratory by *Melittobia,* and male mutillids emerged from the other 2 nests late in the spring. The period between pupation and adult emergence was 15 days each for these 2 males.

The 2 nests in 1962 were stored and parasitized during a 3-week's period while I was in Florida. One of the mutillids was parasitized in the field by *Melittobia.* When I opened the nest on July 11 the other mutillid was just a small larva feeding on the straightened-out host prepupa (fig. 137). It finished feeding on the 13th, spun its cocoon (figs. 138, 139), and pupated July 22-24. An adult female emerged on August 9.

The mutillid cocoons were ovoid, white to light tan, semitransparent to opaque, and spun of soft, delicate silk. Three of them were 9-12 mm. long.

Parasites and predators. One mutillid was parasitized in the field by the eulophid *Melittobia chalybii* Ashmead; 2 mutillids were parasitized in the laboratory by the same species.

Previous observations. Rau and Rau (1918, pp. 88-89) reared it from nests of an *Auplopus* species (=*Pseudagenia*) in Missouri. Rau (1922, p. 8) reared *scaeva* from a cocoon of *Sceliphron caementarium* (Drury) in Missouri. Later (Rau, 1928, p. 437) he reported rearing it from nests of the pipe-organ wasp, *Trypargilum politum* (Say). Several years ago (Krombein *in* Muesebeck *et al.,* 1951, p. 752) I added as hosts the mud-daubing wasps

Auplopus architectus (Say) and *A. mellipes* (Say) based on reared material in the collection of the U. S. National Museum. Apparently it has as hosts a wide range of mud-daubers, but confines its attacks to those which store paralyzed spiders as prey.

Source material.

> Plummers Island, Md. 1959 series: Y 55, 57, 80, 120. 1960 series: E 58. 1962 series: M 42, 56.

Identifications by the author.

SPHAEROPTHALMA (PHOTOPSIOIDES) URO (Blake)

I reared a male of this mutillid from the outermost cell in each of 2 nests of *Trypargilum t. tridentatum* (Packard) at Portal, Ariz., in 1959 and 1961 and a female of *uro* from a cell of a caterpillar-storing vespid wasp from the same locality in 1961. What was presumed to be this same species parasitized a 1-celled nest of *tridentatum* at Portal in 1961; it was parasitized in the laboratory by the grain itch mite *Pyemotes ventricosus* (Newport).

As was noted for *S. pennsylvanica scaeva* (Blake) the mutillid mother chewed a small hole through the mud seals at the nest entrance. There was a vestibular cell in only 1 of the nests, and so in 2 nests the mutillid mother had to breach only a single partition. She then chewed a small hole in the anterior end of the host cocoon, oviposited on the diapausing host larva, and resealed the *Trypargilum* cocoon with mud from the partition; I did not note whether the breach in the vespid cocoon was resealed with mud.

I picked up the 1959 nest on July 19. All the occupants were prepupae in cocoons on that date; the mutillid was in its own cocoon inside the host cocoon in the outermost cell. The host prepupae were dead but a specific identification could be made from the distinctive cocoon. The mutillid pupated July 21 and an adult *uro* male emerged from the nest on August 3.

The second *tridentatum* nest was picked up on September 21, 1961. Presumably it had been stored several weeks earlier. The mutillid in the outermost cell pupated and emerged between that date and November 8, when I found it dead and dry in a glass vial in which I had placed the cocoon. The host wasps in the inner cells overwintered as diapausing larvae and transformed to pupae and then to adults the following summer.

The third *tridentatum* nest was stored between September 3 and October 18. The mutillid prepupa in the single *tridentatum* cocoon was attacked by *Pyemotes* mites in the laboratory.

The 3-celled nest of the caterpillar-storing vespid was presumably stored between September 3 and October 18, 1961. When I opened it on November 3 I discovered that the vespid occupant in cell 3 had transformed to an adult and left the nest before it was mailed

to me. There was a rhipiphorid larva, *Macrosiagon c. cruentum*
(Germar), in cell 1 and a mutillid cocoon containing a diapausing
larva in cell 2. The mother mutillid had chewed through the middle
of the mud partition capping cell 2, presumably after the adult vespid left cell 3; she then replastered this breach with mud after laying an egg on the resting vespid larva. After the mutillid larva
completed feeding, it spun an ovoid cocoon 9 mm. long, light tan
in color, and composed of tough, opaque silk. The mutillid overwintered as a diapausing larva and transformed to a pupa March
17-19. An adult female of *uro* eclosed on April 4 and left the
cocoon on April 6.

Previous observations. Fischer (1951, p. 49) reared a male of
uro (reported as *uro melanderi* (Baker)) from a cocoon of the
megachilid bee *Dianthidium curvatum sayi* Cockerell in Kansas.
The nest was from a burrow in a vertical gravel bank.

Source material.
    Portal, Ariz. 1959 series: X 69. 1961 series: G 199 (?), 202, 245.

Identifications. Sphaeropthalma uro by W. E. Ferguson; host
wasps by the author.

Family SAPYGIDAE
SAPYGA CENTRATA Say

I reared *centrata* adults from 1 nest at Derby, N. Y., in 1958,
and from a dozen nests from 10 stations at Plummers Island, Md.,
1958-1964. In addition, eggs or larvae, undoubtedly of this same
species, were found in another 5 nests from 5 more stations at
Plummers Island. Fourteen of the host nests were in 4.8-mm.-
borings, and 4 were in 6.4-mm.-borings. Fourteen of them were
from settings on dead standing tree trunks and 4 were from settings
on wooden buildings.

Osmia (Nothosmia) pumila Cresson was the host bee in 16
nests and *O. (Centrosmia) bucephala* Cresson was the host in the
other 2. Both of these species used leaf pulp in nest construction.
Significantly, *centrata* did not parasitize *Osmia (O.) lignaria* Say
at Plummers Island, although that bee nested concurrently and more
commonly in these borings than *pumila*. This finding may be correlated with the fact that *lignaria* uses mud rather than leaf
pulp in the nest construction.

S. centrata parasitized 2 of 10 cells in the 2 *bucephala* nests
and 32 of 172 cells in the 16 *pumila* nests for an over-all rate
of 19 percent. It parasitized 1-5 cells per nest. In most nests the
outermost cell or cells were parasitized, but occasionally the sapygid
attacked several cells in the middle or inner end of the nest.

I received the impression that a female *Sapyga* might parasitize a series of cells once she found a nest under construction. In 7 nests there were series of 2-5 consecutive cells (mean 3) all parasitized by *centrata*. Cells 1 and 5-7 were parasitized in 1 of these 7 nests, and so perhaps this nest was attacked by 2 different female *Sapyga*. There was no indication that sapygid parasitism caused the host bee to seal the nest prematurely.

I observed 2 sapygid eggs in 1 cell, one lying across the host egg and the other in the empty space between the food mass and the partition capping the cell. This nest possibly was attacked by 2 different *centrata* females, because the eggs must have been laid at about the same time.

Life history. The egg of *centrata* was slender and straight (not sausage shaped) but tapered toward the posterior end; it was 1.7 mm. long and 0.34 mm. wide. I did not obtain exact data on the duration of the egg stage; but it hatched 1-2 days earlier than the host eggs in adjacent cells, and so probably it was about 2 days.

A newly hatched sapygid larva was 1.8 mm. long. In about a day it sought out and began to suck fluid from the host egg. The latter was shriveled about a day later and the parasite larva was now about 2.6 mm. long and turgid. The first molt took place 3 days after the egg hatch and before the parasite began to feed on the pollen-nectar mixture stored for the bee larva. During the day following this first molt the *centrata* larva appeared to suck nectar only, but on the second day it began to feed on the pollen also.

About 4 days after the first molt and 8-11 days after attacking the host egg, it began to void fecal pellets. These were black, ovoid, and 0.42 mm. long and 0.25 mm. wide. The sapygid larva could always be distinguished from the host bee larva once this stage was reached, because the fecal pellets of the bee were cylindrical, light brown, and 0.76 mm. long and 0.25 mm. wide.

In 1 larva the second molt took place between 6 and 12 days after the first molt. In another 6 days the sapygid larva began to spin together some of the fecal pellets in a loose net of silk. It continued to feed on the pollen-nectar mass for about another week and presumably made a third molt during this period.

The *centrata* larvae devoured from one-third to two-thirds of the food stored for the host larvae, depending on whether *bucephala* or *pumila* was the host. In spite of this it took the sapygids 5-10 days longer to finish feeding than it did the bee larvae in adjacent cells. The entire feeding period for 5 *centrata* larvae was 26-31 days (mean 28); comparable feeding periods for *Osmia pumila* larvae at the same time were 14-21 days.

It took 1 larva 5 days to spin its cocoon. The cocoons were ovoid, white, and varied from semitransparent to opaque. The fecal pellets were attached to the outer surface. Cocoons in 4.8-mm. borings were 5 mm. long and those in 6.4-mm. borings 7-8 mm. long.

One female pupated July 22-28 and the adult eclosed August 7-15.

There was concurrent emergence of adult parasites and hosts in the spring from the 1 nest from which both did emerge. In other nests 1 or both died as adults during the winter.

The nest at Derby was apparently attacked by *centrata* the latter half of June. At Plummers Island *centrata* parasitized the *Osmia* nests from the last week in April until about May 20.

I reared 1 female and 1 male from the Derby nest. At Plummers Island I reared 14 females and 5 males.

In 3 different years and in 5 nests from both localities from which I reared 2 or more *centrata* adults, the sequence of sexes was as follows: ♀-♂; ♂-♂; ♀-♂-♂; ♀-♀-♀-♀; and ♀ ♀ ♂. If we assume that a single female *Sapyga* parasitized each of these nests, it appears likely that a female may lay first a series of female eggs and then one of male eggs.

Previous observations. Ashmead (1896, p. 179) described *Sapyga pelopaei*, now considered to be a synonym of *centrata*, and mentioned that it was bred from cells of the mud dauber, *Sceliphron caementarium* (Drury), at Toronto, Ontario. Unquestionably this wasp was not the host of the *Sapyga;* the true host must have been a megachilid bee which nested in the abandoned mud dauber nest.

Source material.
> Derby, N. Y. 1958 series: R 2.
> Plummers Island, Md. 1958 series: S 55. 1959 series: Y 33 (?). 1960 series: E 14, 18, 19, 65. 1961 series: K 21 (?). 1962 series: M 24, 48, 55 (?). 1963 series: U 19 (?). 1964 series: Z 3, 4 (?), 6, 7, 8, 12.

Identifications. Sapyga by R. M. Bohart; bees by the author.

Superfamily APOIDEA

Family MEGACHILIDAE

STELIS (PROTOSTELIS) COSTALIS FLORIDANA Graenicher

I reared this parasite of a resin-working megachilid bee from a nest in a 6.4-mm. boring from Lake Placid, Fla., in 1962. The trap was from a setting beneath the limb of a scrub hickory in the Highlands Ridge sand-scrub area of the Archbold Biological Station.

The inner end of the boring contained a plug of resin 7 mm. thick. There were 3 stored cells 16-17 mm. long, capped by resin partitions 1-2 mm. thick. The bottom half of the cell wall was coated with resin. There was no vestibular cell or closing plug.

The nest was picked up on December 31, and I opened it on

January 5. Obviously it had been stored much earlier, because the occupants of the cells were already in cocoons. The female cocoons in cells 1 and 2 were 11 and 12 mm. long. A male *floridana* cocoon in cell 3 was only 6 mm. long and was placed crosswise in the cell. The cocoons were dark brown and varnished and had the customary anthidiine nipple at the anterior end.

The occupant of cell 2 pupated March 12-16, and an adult female emerged May 6. A female emerged from the cocoon in cell 1 on the following day. A dwarfed, fully colored male pupa in cell 3 died.

Unfortunately all the cells were parasitized, so I am unable to name the specific host bee. The host was either 1 of the resin-using anthidiine bees or a species of *Chalicodoma* subgenus *Chelostomoides* in the Megachilini.

Source material.
    Lake Placid, Fla. 1962 series: P 195.

Identifications by the author.

COELIOXYS DOLICHOS Fox

This shiny black social parasite almost certainly has as its host *Megachile* (*Melanosarus*) *xylocopoides* Smith. I reared it from 2 1-celled nests in 12.7-mm. borings of a leaf-cutting species of *Megachile* from stations beneath an oak branch in the sand-scrub area of the Archbold Biological Station, Lake Placid, Fla., in 1959 and 1960. The size of the cells and details of the nest architecture were consistent with those features in *xylocopoides* nests from Lake Placid.

The first nest was sent to me in December 1959. It had been completed at some undetermined date earlier in the season. I opened it on December 16 and ascertained that there was a diapausing larva in the cocoon. The nest was subjected to chilly weather outdoors until February 13 when I brought it into my office. The female *dolichos* pupated February 27-29, and I found the adult dead but limp in its cocoon on March 20.

The other nest was sent to me early in January 1961. It also had been completed at an undetermined earlier date. When I opened the nest on January 9, there was a diapausing larva in its cocoon. I put this nest outdoors in chilly weather until March 24, when I brought it into my office. The female *dolichos* pupated March 25-30 and the adult eclosed on April 18; it left the cocoon a day later.

The *dolichos* cocoons were 13 mm. long and 7 mm. wide. One was cylindrical with rounded ends; the anterior end had a median patch of white silk. The other cocoon was ovoid and was surrounded by a thin (0.2 mm.) layer of hard packed pollen which had not been consumed by the *dolichos* larva. The cocoon had 2 layers: An outer one which was delicate, brittle, varnished, and dark brown; and an inner one which was closely applied to the outer and silken, light tan, delicate, and unvarnished.

Source material.

Lake Placid, Fla. 1959 series: V 58. 1960 series: B 233.

Identifications by the author.

COELIOXYS SAYI Robertson

I reared this parasitic megachilid bee from 4 nests of *Megachile* (*Litomegachile*) *mendica* Cresson from Lake Placid, Fla., at 4 different stations in 1957, 1959, and 1960. Three nests were in 6.4-mm. borings and 1 was in a 4.8-mm. boring.

C. sayi parasitized at least 8 of the 30 stored cells. There may have been a few additional parasitized cells in 1 of the nests from which 8 bees escaped and were not recovered.

In addition, there was a 5-celled nest from Lake Placid stored by a leaf cutter bee from which I preserved a first-instar *Coelioxys* larva from cell 5. The nest was almost certainly stored by *mendica*, and it is presumed that the parasite was *sayi*.

The 4 nests definitely parasitized by *sayi* were stored early in June, late in July, and at the middle and end of August. *C. sayi* parasitized cells 2 and 4 in a 6-celled nest, cell 5 in another 6-celled nest, 4 of 6 cells in a third 6-celled nest, and 1 or more cells in a 12-celled nest.

The parasite and host bees in individual nests emerged on the same day or within 2 days of each other. Emergence from the parasitized nests occurred from June 29 until late September, and so there are undoubtedly several generations a year of this parasite.

Source material.

Lake Placid, Fla. 1957 series: M 11. 1959 series: V 113, 120, 135 (?). 1960 series: B 167.

Identifications. Coelioxys by T. B. Mitchell; *Megachile* by the author.

COELIOXYS TEXANA Cresson

I reared 1 female of this parasitic bee from each of 2 nests of *Megachile* (*Sayapis*) *policaris* Say from the desert floor near Portal, Ariz. in 1960 and 1961. Although I did not rear the host bee from either nest, the large pollen-nectar masses and brood chamber, and the occurrence of compound partitions consisting of alternate layers of small whole leaflets and gummy leaf pulp left no doubt as to the identity of the host. One nest in a 6.4-mm. boring was from a setting beneath the dead branch of a live acacia; the other in a 12.7-mm. boring was from a setting on a mesquite trunk.

The nests were sent to me at the end of each year, and there was no information as to when they might have been stored. Occupants of the cocoons overwintered outdoors as diapausing larvae. In the 1960 nest the host bees had emerged from cells 1 and 3 the previous fall; a *Coelioxys texana* female in cell 2 pupated April 19-27, eclosed May 17-18, and emerged from the nest on the 23d. In the 1961 nest the host larvae in brood cells 1-4 died the previous fall; a *Coelioxys texana* female in brood cell 1 pupated May 12-18, and emerged from the nest June 10.

The cocoon was light brown with a varnished inner layer and a closely adherent outer layer, which appeared to be impregnated with a gummy substance. There was a dense, white silken cap at the anterior end. One cocoon was 12 mm. long.

Source material.
    Portal, Ariz. 1960 series: X 224. 1961 series: G 126.

Identifications by the author.

COELIOXYS MODESTA Smith

I reared this parasitic bee from 5 nests of *Chalicodoma* (*Chelostomoides*) from Lake Placid, Fla., in 1959 and 1961. The host bees were *campanulae wilmingtoni* (Mitchell) in 3 nests and *georgica* (Cresson) in 2 nests. Probably *modesta* parasitized 2 additional nests of *Chelostomoides* from Lake Placid from which I failed to rear either hosts or parasites.

The host nests were in 4.8-mm. and 6.4-mm. borings placed at stations in the sand-scrub area of Archbold Biological Station. The 5 nests from which I reared *modesta* were from 4 stations on a pine trunk and beneath hickory and oak limbs. The 2 nests supposedly parasitized by *modesta* were from another station beneath a live limb of a scrub hickory.

C. modesta was a very successful parasite; it was reared from 57 per cent of the cells in 5 nests. Apparently an individual female continued to visit a nest, once she found one under construction, and she oviposited in successive cells. If the host bees were aware of parasitism, they did not seal the nests prematurely. In the *campanulae wilmingtoni* nests *modesta* parasitized cells 1-4 of a 6-celled nest, cells 5-9 of a 9-celled nest, and cells 2-3 of a 5-celled nest; each of these nests was from a different station. In the *georgica* nests *modesta* parasitized cells 2-6 of a 6-celled nest and cell 1 of a 4-celled nest. These nests were from the same station and may have been stored by the same individual host bee and parasitized by the same individual parasite. In the 2 nests presumed to have been parasitized by *modesta, Coelioxys* larvae were present in all cells of the 3-celled nest and in cells 2 and 3 of another 3-celled nest. Both nests were from the same station and may have been stored by the same host bee and parasitized by the same individual of *Coelioxys.*

Apparently the female *Coelioxys* may deposit more than 1 egg per host cell. In 1 nest I found several dead first instar *Coelioxys* larvae in 2 cells, each of which contained a single live *Coelioxys* larva. Developmental data from 1 nest indicate that the larval feeding period of a *modesta* larva is about 10-12 days.

The *modesta* cocoons were silken, white, opaque, and somewhat tougher and more opaque than those of the host bees. The anterior end was of dense, white, opaque silk. Nine of them were 8-12 mm. long (mean 10).

All the nests were constructed and parasitized late in the season during September and October. Both host and parasite larvae entered diapause and had to be subjected to 2 months of chilly weather outdoors before they pupated and transformed to adults. The period between pupation and adult emergence was 25-28 days for a female *modesta* and 26-29 days for a male.

The emergence of host bees and parasites from a single nest usually occurred over a rather extended period. Sometimes there was concurrent emergence of some individuals, and at other times the host bees emerged as much as 18 days earlier.

I reared 5 females and 5 males of *modesta* from 17 parasitized cells in the nests definitely parasitized by that species. In the 2 mixed nests in which I determined the sequence of sexes, there were a female and male of *modesta* respectively in cells 2 and 3, and 2 females and 2 males of *modesta* respectively in cells 1-4.

Parasites and predators. Laboratory infestations by *Melittobia chalbyii* Ashmead occurred in several *modesta* cocoons in 1 nest and also in 1 of the nests presumed to have been attacked by *modesta.*

Previous observations. Fye (1965b, p. 876) recorded *modesta* as a parasite in nests of *Megachile* (*M.*) *relativa* Cresson in stem borings in northwestern Ontario. Graenicher (1927, pp. 233, 274) reported *modesta* as a parasite of *Megachile* (*M.*) *centuncularis* (Linnaeus) [recorded as *infragilis* Cresson, a synonym] in a nest in an upright hollow stem in Wisconsin. Almost certainly a *lapsus calami* is involved here. *M. centuncularis* is a leaf-cutting species, and judging from my observations *modesta* confines its attentions to resin-using bees of *Chalicodoma* subgenus *Chelostomoides.* Quite possibly Graenicher wrote *modesta* Smith when he actually should have written *moesta* Cresson. In support of this theory I found a specimen of *moesta* in the collection of the U.S. National Museum from Milwaukee, Wis., the locality where Graenicher made most of his collections and observations, but no specimens of *modesta* with that label. Furthermore, Medler (1959), also working in Wisconsin, reared *moesta* from a nest of *centuncularis*.

Source material.
    Lake Placid, Fla. 1959 series: V 122, 126. 1962 series: P 21 (?), 41, 183 (?), 192, 212.

Identifications. Coelioxys by T. B. Mitchell; *Chalicodoma* by the author.

REFERENCES

AINSLIE, C. N.
1924. Note on the nesting habits of *Chlorion elegans*. Canadian Entomol., vol. 56, pp. 269-270.

ALLEN, H. W.
1926. North American species of two-winged flies belonging to the tribe Miltogrammini. Proc. U. S. Nat. Mus., vol. 68, art. 9, pp. 1-106, 5 pls.

ASHMEAD, W. H.
1894. The habits of the aculeate Hymenoptera. Parts 1-4. Psyche, vol. 7, pp. 19-26, 59-66, and 75-79.
1894-95. Notes on cotton insects found in Mississippi. Insect Life, vol. 7, pp. 25-29, 240-247, 320-326.
1896. Descriptions of new parasitic Hymenoptera. Trans. Amer. Entomol. Soc., vol. 23, pp. 179-234.

AUTEN, M.
1925. Insects associated with spider nests. Ann. Entomol. Soc. Amer., vol. 18, pp. 240-250.

BAKER, C. F.
1895. Biological notes on some Colorado Diptera. Entomol. News, vol. 6, pp. 173-174.

BAKER, E. W.
1961. Some Acaridae from bees and wasps. Proc. Entomol. Soc. Washington, vol. 63, pp. 1-10, 6 pls.
1962. Natural history of Plummers Island, Maryland. XV. Descriptions of the stages of *Chaetodactylus krombeini*, new species, a mite associated with the bee, *Osmia lignaria* Say. Proc. Biol. Soc. Washington, vol. 75, pp. 227-236, 24 figs.

BAKER, E. W., and CUNLIFFE, F.
1960. Notes on saproglyphid mites associated with solitary wasps. Proc. Entomol. Soc. Washington, vol. 62, pp. 209-231, 119 figs.

BAKER, E. W., and WHARTON, G. W.
1952. An introduction to acarology. 465 pp., 377 figs. New York.

BALDUF, W. V.
1928. Notes on the habits of *Aphiocheta aletiae*. Ohio Journ. Sci., vol. 28, pp. 237-245, 4 figs.
1935. The bionomics of entomophagous Coleoptera. 220 pp., 108 figs. St. Louis.
1961. Insects from tunnels of *Xylocopa virginica*. Bull. Brooklyn Entomol. Soc., vol. 56, pp. 81-85.
1962. Life of the carpenter bee, *Xylocopa virginica* (Linn.) Ann. Entomol. Soc. Amer., vol. 55, pp. 263-271, 3 figs.

BEAL, R. S.
1960. Descriptions, biology and notes on the identification of some *Trogoderma* larvae. U. S. Dept. Agric. Tech. Bull. 1228, 26 pp., 7 figs.

BECHTEL, R. C.
1958. Notes on emergence and a parasite of *Megachile gentilis* Cresson. Pan-Pac. Entomol., vol. 34, p. 12.

BEQUAERT, J.
1925. The genus *Ancistrocerus* in North America, with a partial key to the species. Trans. Amer. Entomol. Soc., vol. 51, pp. 57-117.

1939. *Odynerus annectens* de Saussure and related species, with additional notes on *Odynerus hidalgo* de Saussure. Ann. Entomol. Soc. Amer., vol. 32, pp. 58-69.

1944. The North American species of *Ancistrocerus* proper. Entomol. Amer., vol. 23, pp. 225-286.

BLACKMAN, M. W., and STAGE, H. H.
1924. On the succession of insects living in the bark and wood of dying, dead and decaying hickory. N.Y. State Coll. Forestry Tech. Publ., vol. 17, pp. 3-269, 14 pls.

BOHART, G. E.
1955. Gradual nest supersedure within the genus *Osmia*. Proc. Entomol. Soc. Washington, vol. 57, pp. 203-204, 1 fig.

BOHART, R. M.
1941. A revision of the Strepsiptera with special reference to the species of North America. Univ. Calif. Pubs. Entomol., vol. 7, pp. 91-160, 8 text figs.

BOHART, R. M., and CAMPOS, L. E.
1960. A review of the genus *Omalus* Panzer in North America. Ann. Entomol. Soc. Amer., vol. 53, pp. 235-250, 30 figs.

BOYCE, H. R.
1946. Larvae of *Spilonota ocellana* (D. & S.) used to provision nests of a eumenid wasp. Entomol. Soc. Ontario, 76th Ann. Rept., pp. 35-37.

BRANDHORST, C. T.
1962. The microcommunity associated with the gall of *Walshia amorphella* on *Amorpha fruticosa*. Ann. Entomol. Soc. Amer., vol. 55, pp. 476-479, 1 fig.

BROOKS, A. R.
1952. Identification of bombyliid parasites of Phalaenidae of the Prairie Provinces of Canada, with descriptions of six other bombyliid pupae. Canadian Entomol., vol. 84, pp. 357-373, 46 figs.

BRUNSON, M. H.
1938. Influence of Japanese beetle instar on the sex and population of the parasite *Tiphia popilliavora*. Journ. Agric. Res., vol. 57, pp. 379-386.

BUCKELL, E. R.
1928. Notes on the life history and habits of *Melittobia chalybii* Ashmead. Pan-Pac. Entomol., vol. 5, pp. 14-22, 3 figs.

BUCKLE, J. W.
1929. *Ancistrocerus capra* and the larvae of *Epargyreus tityrus*. Canadian Entomol., vol. 61, pp. 265-266.

BURKS, B. D.
1943. The North American parasitic wasps of the genus *Tetrastichus*—a contribution to biological control of insect pests. Proc. U. S. Nat. Mus., vol. 93, pp. 505-608.

BUTLER, G. D., and RITCHIE, P. L., JR.
1965. Additional biological notes on *Megachile concinna* Smith. Pan-Pac. Entomol., vol. 41, pp. 153-157.

BUTLER, G. D., and WARGO, M. J.
1963. Biological notes on *Megachile concinna* Smith. Pan-Pac. Entomol., vol. 39, pp. 201-206.

CHANDLER, L.
1958. Biological interrelationships in mud-dauber nests with special reference to *Osmia cordata* Robt. Proc. Ind. Acad. Sci., vol. 68, pp. 199-204.

1962. Interspecific competition in *Osmia lignaria* Say—*O. cordata* Robt. nesting associations. Proc. North Central Branch, Entomol. Soc. Amer., vol. 16, pp. 18-19.

CHAPMAN, R. F.

1959. Some observations on *Pachyophthalmus africa* Curran, a parasite of *Eumenes maxillosus* De Geer. Proc. Roy. Entomol. Soc. London, vol. 34, pp. 1-6.

CLAUSEN, C. P.

1940. Entomophagous insects. 688 pp., 257 figs. New York.

COOPER, K. W.

1953. Biology of eumenine wasps. I. The ecology, predation and competition of *Ancistrocerus antilope* (Panzer). Trans. Amer. Entomol. Soc., vol. 79, pp. 13-35.

1954. Biology of eumenine wasps. IV. A trigonalid wasp parasitic on *Rygchium rugosum* (Saussure). Proc. Entomol. Soc. Washington, vol. 56, pp. 280-288.

1955. Biology of eumenine wasps. II. Venereal transmission of mites by wasps, and some evolutionary problems arising from the remarkable association of *Ensliniella trisetosa* with the wasp *Ancistrocerus antilope*. Trans. Amer. Entomol. Soc., vol. 80, pp. 119-174, 1 pl., 6 text figs.

1957. Biology of eumenine wasps. V. Digital communication in wasps. Journ. Exp. Zool., vol. 134, pp. 469-514, 2 pls.

COPPEL, H. C.

1961. An unusual habitat for *Ancistrocerus tigris* (Saussure). Entomol. News, vol. 72, pp. 246-248, 2 figs.

CUSTER, C. P., and HICKS, C. H.

1927. Nesting habits of some anthidiine bees. Biol. Bull., vol. 52, pp. 258-277.

DAVIDSON, A.

1899. *Sphex elegans*. Entomol. News, vol. 10, pp. 179-180.

DAVIS, D. R.

1964. Bagworm moths of the Western Hemisphere. U. S. Nat. Mus. Bull. 244, pp. 1-233, 12 maps, 385 figs.

ENGELHARDT, G. P.

1929. An observation on the breeding habits of *Chlorion harrisi* in Texas. Bull. Brooklyn Entomol. Soc., vol. 23, pp. 269-271.

ENNS, W. R.

1956. A revision of the genera *Nemognatha*, *Zonitis* and *Pseudozonitis* of America north of Mexico, with a proposed new genus. Univ. Kans. Sci. Bull., vol. 37, pp. 685-909.

EVANS, H. E.

1953. Comparative ethology and the systematics of spider wasps. Syst. Zool., vol. 2, pp. 155-172, 5 figs.

EVANS, H. E., and YOSHIMOTO, C. M.

1962. The ecology and nesting behavior of the Pompilidae of northeastern United States. Misc. Bull., Entomol. Soc. Amer., vol. 3, pp. 67-119.

FERGUSON, W. E.

1962. Biological characteristics of the mutillid subgenus *Photopsis* Blake and their systematic values. Univ. California Pubs. Entomol., vol. 27, pp. 1-92, 7 pls., 2 text figs.

FERNALD, H. T.

1906. The digger wasps of North America and the West Indies belonging to the subfamily Chlorioninae. Proc. U. S. Nat. Mus., vol. 31, pp. 291-423, 5 pls.

FISCHER, R L.
    1951. Observations on the nesting habits of megachilid bees. Journ. Kans. Entomol. Soc., vol. 24, pp. 46-50, 2 figs.
FLANDERS, S. E.
    1962. The parasitic Hymenoptera: Specialists in population regulation. Canadian Entomol., vol. 94, pp. 1133-1147.
FROST, S. W.
    1944. Notes on the habits of *Monobia quadridens* (Linn.). Entomol. News, vol. 55, pp. 10-14, 1 pl.
FYE, R. E.
    1965a. The biology of the Vespidae Pompilidae, and Sphecidae from trap nests in northwestern Ontario. Canadian Entomol., vol. 97, pp. 716-744, 9 figs.
    1965b. Biology of Apoidea taken in trap nests in northwestern Ontario. Canadian Entomol., vol. 97, pp. 863-877, 6 figs.
    1965c. Methods for placing wasp trap nests in elevated locations. Jour. Economic Entomol., vol. 58, pp. 803-804, 4 figs.
GAUSS, R.
    1959. Zum Parasitismus der Fächerflügler. Mitt. bad. Landesver. Naturk. and Naturschutz, vol. 7, pp. 331-347, 6 figs.
GENTRY, T. G.
    1874. Notes on *Megachile centuncularis*. Canadian Entomol., vol. 6, pp. 171-175.
GRAENICHER, S.
    1906. On the habits and life history of *Leucospis affinis* Say, a parasite of bees. Bull. Wisconsin Nat. Hist., vol. 4, pp. 153-159, 6 figs.
    1927. On the biology of the parasitic bees of the genus *Coelioxys*. Entomol. News, vol. 38, pp. 231-235, 273-276.
HALL, J. C.
    1954. Notes on the biologies of three species of Bombyliidae, with a description of one new species. Entomol. News, vol. 65, pp. 145-149.
HARTMAN, C. G.
    1905. Observations on the habits of some solitary wasps of Texas. Bull. Univ. Texas, vol. 65, 74 pp., 4 pls.
    1955. How *Odynerus* suspends her egg. Psyche, vol. 51, pp. 1-4.
HICKS, C. H.
    1926. Nesting habits and parasites of certain bees of Boulder County, Colorado. Univ. Colo. Studies, vol. 15, pp. 217-252.
    1927. *Megachile subexilis* Ckll., a resin-working bee. Entomol. News, vol. 38, pp. 17-21.
    1934. Some reared insect parasites and their hosts. Univ. Colorado Studies, vol. 21, pp. 265-271, 1 pl., 1 text fig.
    1936. *Tracheliodes hicksi* Sandhouse hunting ants. Entomol. News, vol. 47, pp. 4-7.
HOBBS, G. A., NUMMI, W. O., and VIROSTEK, J. F.
    1961. *Anthophora occidentalis* Cress. and its associates at a nesting site in southern Alberta. Canadian Entomol., vol. 93, pp. 142-148, 3 figs.
HUNGERFORD, H. B., and WILLIAMS, F. X.
    1912. Biological notes on some Kansas Hymenoptera. Entomol. News, vol. 23, pp. 241-260, 3 pls.
HURD, P. D., JR.
    1959. Beefly parasitism of the carpenter bees belonging to the genus *Xylocopa* Latreille. Journ. Kansas Entomol. Soc., vol. 32, pp. 53-58, 1 fig.

ISELY, D.
  1913. The biology of some Kansas Eumenidae. Kansas Univ. Sci. Bull., vol. 8, pp. 233-309, 4 pls.
IWATA, K.
  1939. Habits of seven species of Pompilidae in Japan. Mushi, vol. 12, pp. 17-24.
JAYAKAR, S.D.
  1963. "Proterandry" in solitary wasps. Nature, vol. 198, pp. 208-209.
JONES, F. M.
  1904. Pitcher-plant insects. Entomol. News, vol. 15, pp. 14-17, 2 pls.
KASTON, B. J.
  1948. Spiders of Connecticut. Connecticut Geol. Nat. Hist. Surv. Bull. 70, pp. 1-874, 2144 figs.
KOERBER, T. W., and MEDLER, J. T.
  1958. A trap-nest survey of solitary bees and wasps in Wisconsin, with biological notes. Proc. Wisconsin Acad. Sci., Arts, Letters, vol. 47, pp. 53-63.
KROMBEIN, K. V.
  1952. Preliminary annotated list of wasps of Lost River State Park, West Virginia, with descriptions of new species and biological notes. Proc. Entomol. Soc. Washington, vol. 54, pp. 175-184, 6 figs.
  1953. Kill Devil Hills wasps. Proc. Entomol. Soc. Washington, vol. 55, pp. 113-135.
  1954. Wasps collected at Lost River State Park, West Virginia, in 1953. Bull. Brooklyn Entomol. Soc., vol. 49, pp. 1-7.
  1955a. Miscellaneous prey records of solitary wasps. I. Bull. Brooklyn Entomol. Soc., vol. 50, pp. 13-17.
  1955b. Some notes on the wasps of Kill Devil Hills, North Carolina, 1954. Proc. Entomol. Soc. Washington, vol. 57, pp. 145-160, 4 figs.
  1956a. Miscellaneous prey records of solitary wasps. II. Bull. Brooklyn Entomol. Soc., vol. 51, p. 42-44.
  1956b. Biological and taxonomic notes on the wasps of Lost River State Park, West Virginia, with additions to the faunal list. Proc. Entomol. Soc. Washington, vol. 58, pp. 153-161, 3 figs.
  1958a. Miscellaneous prey records of solitary wasps. III. Proc. Biol. Soc. Washington, vol. 71, pp. 21-26.
  1958b. Additions during 1956 and 1957 to the wasp fauna of Lost River State Park, West Virginia, with biological notes and descriptions of species. Proc. Entomol. Soc. Washington, vol. 60, pp. 49-64, 6 figs.
  1958c. Biology and taxonomy of the cuckoo wasps of coastal North Carolina. Trans. Amer. Entomol. Soc., vol. 84, pp. 141-168, 2 pls.
  1958d. Biological notes on some wasps from Kill Devil Hills, North Carolina, and additions to the faunal list. Proc. Entomol. Soc. Washington, vol. 60, pp. 97-110.
  1959a. Three new wasps from Florida and taxonomic notes on allied forms. Proc. Entomol. Soc. Washington, vol. 61, pp. 145-153, 1 fig.
  1959b. Biological notes on Prochelostoma philadelphi (Robertson). Entomol. News, vol. 70, pp. 135-136.
  1961. Some symbiotic relations between saproglyphid mites and solitary vespid wasps. Journ. Washington Acad. Sci., vol. 51, pp. 89-93, 6 figs.
  1962a. Biological notes on acarid mites associated with solitary wasps and bees. Proc. Entomol. Soc. Washington, vol. 64, pp. 11-19.
  1962b. Natural history of Plummers Island, Maryland. XVI. Biological notes on Chaetodactylus krombeini Baker, a parasitic mite of the mega-

chilid bee, *Osmia* (*Osmia*) *lignaria* Say. Proc. Biol. Soc. Washington, vol. 75, pp. 237-249, 2 pls.

1964a. Natural history of Plummers Island, Maryland, XVIII. The hibiscus wasp, an abundant rarity and its associates. Proc. Biol. Soc. Washington, vol. 77, pp. 73-112, 18 figs.

1964b. Miscellaneous prey records of solitary wasps. V. Bull. Brooklyn Entomol. Soc., vol. 53, pp. 118-120.

1964c. Results of the Archbold Expeditions. No. 87. Biological notes on some Floridian wasps. Amer. Mus. Novitates, no. 2201, pp. 1-27, 1 fig.

KROMBEIN, K. V., and EVANS, H. E.
    1954. A list of wasps collected in Florida, March 29-April 5, 1953, with biological annotations. Proc. Entomol. Soc. Washington, vol. 56, pp. 225-236.

    1955. An annotated list of wasps collected in Florida, March 20 to April 3, 1954. Proc. Entomol. Soc. Washington, vol. 57, pp. 223-235.

KROMBEIN, K. V., *et al*.
    1958. First supplement to synoptic catalog, Hymenoptera of America north of Mexico. U. S. Dept. Agr., Agr. Monogr. 2, pp. 1-305.

LEVIN, M. D.
    1957. Artificial nesting burrows for *Osmia lignaria* Say. Journ. Econ. Entomol., vol. 50, pp. 506-507, 4 figs.

LIN, C. S.
    1962. Biology and nesting habits of hunting wasp *Isodontia Harrisi* Fernald. Tex. Journ. Sci., vol. 14, pp. 429-430.

LINSLEY, E. G.
    1944. Natural sources, habitats, and reservoirs of insects associated with stored food products. Hilgardia, vol. 16, pp. 187-222.

    1946. Insect pollinators of alfalfa in California. Journ. Econ. Entomol., vol. 39, pp. 18-29.

LINSLEY, E. G., and MACSWAIN, J. W.
    1943. Observations on the life history of *Trichodes ornatus*, a larval predator in the nests of bees and wasps. Ann. Entomol. Soc. Amer., vol. 36, pp. 589-601, 2 pls.

    1957. Observations on the habits of *Stylops pacifica* Bohart. Univ. California Pubs. Entomol., vol. 11, pp. 395-430, 3 pls., 1 text fig.

LINSLEY, E. G., MACSWAIN, J. W., and SMITH, R. F.
    1952. The life history and development of *Rhipiphorus smithi* with notes on their phylogenetic significance. Univ. Calif. Pubs. Entomol., vol. 9, pp. 291-314, 6 pls., 3 text figs.

MALLOCH, J. R.
    1912. The insects of the dipterous family Phoridae in the United States National Museum. Proc. U. S. Nat. Mus., vol. 43, pp. 411-529, 7 pls.

    1914. Notes on Illinois Phoridae with descriptions of three new species. Bull. Brooklyn Entomol. Soc., vol. 9, pp. 56-60.

    1933. Review of the wasps of the subfamily Pseninae. Proc. U. S. Nat. Mus., vol. 82, art. 6, pp. 1-60, 2 pls.

MALYSHEV, S. I.
    1911. Zur Biologie der *Odynerus*-Arten und ihrer Parasite. Hor. Soc. Entomol. Ross., vol. 11, no. 2, 58 pp., 20 figs.

MARKIN, G. P.
    1965. Notes on the use of soda straws as nesting sites by *Rygchium foraminatum*. Ann. Entomol. Soc. Amer., vol. 58, pp. 132-133, 1 fig.

MARSTON, N.
 1964. The biology of *Anthrax limatalus fur* (Osten Sacken), with a key to and descriptions of pupae of some species in the *Anthrax albofasciatus* and *trimaculatus* groups. Journ. Kansas Entomol. Soc., vol. 37, pp. 89-105, 6 figs.

MATTHEWS, R. W.
 1965. The biology of *Heriades carinata* Cresson. Contrib. Amer. Entomol. Inst., vol. 1, no. 3, pp. 1-33, 23 figs.

MATTHEWS, R. W. and FISCHER, R. L.
 1964. A modified trap-nest for twig-nesting Aculeata. Proc. North Central Branch, Entomol. Soc. Amer., vol. 19, pp. 79-81, 1 fig.

MEDLER, J. T.
 1958. Parasitism of bees in trap-nests by *Leucospis affinis* Say. Entomol. News, vol. 69, pp. 21-24.
 1959. A note on *Megachile centuncularis* (Linn.) in Wisconsin. Canadian Entomol., vol. 91, pp. 113-115, 1 fig.
 1964a. Biology of *Rygchium foraminatum* in trap-nests in Wisconsin. Ann. Entomol. Soc. Amer., vol. 57, pp. 56-60.
 1964b. A note on *Auplopus* Spinola in trap-nests in Wisconsin. Entomol. News, vol. 75, pp. 189-191.
 1964c. A note on *Rygchium leucomelas* (Saussure) in trap nests in Wisconsin. Entomol. News, vol. 75, pp. 26-27.
 1964d. Parasitism of Eumeninae by cuckoo wasps in trap-nests in Wisconsin. Proc. Entomol. Soc. Washington, vol. 66, pp. 209-215.
 1965a. A note on *Megachile mendica* Cresson in trap-nests in Wisconsin. Proc. Entomol. Soc. Washington, vol. 67, pp. 113-116.
 1965b. A note on *Ancistrocerus tigris tigris* (Saussure) in trap-nests in Wisconsin. Jour. Kansas Entomol. Soc., vol. 38, pp. 314-316.
 1965c. Biology of *Isodontia* (*Murrayella*) *mexicana* in trap-nests in Wisconsin. Ann. Entomol. Soc. Amer., vol. 58, pp. 137-142, 4 figs.

MEDLER, J. T., and FYE, R. E.
 1956. Biology of *Ancistrocerus antilope* (Panzer) in trap-nests in Wisconsin. Ann. Entomol. Soc. Amer., vol. 49, pp. 97-102, 2 figs.

MEDLER, J. T., and KOERBER, T. W.
 1957. Biology of *Dipogon sayi* Banks in trap-nests in Wisconsin. Ann. Entomol. Soc. Amer., vol. 50, pp. 621-625, 6 figs. 3 tables.

MICHELBACHER, A. E., and HURD, P. D., JR.
 1954. *Monodontomerus montivagus* Ashmead, a parasitic of *Megachile centuncularis* (Linnaeus). Pan-Pac. Entomol., vol. 20, p. 146.

MICHENER, C. D.
 1953. The biology of a leafcutter bee (*Megachile brevis*) and its associates. Univ. Kansas Sci. Bull., vol. 35, pp. 1659-1748, 31 figs.

MITCHELL, T. B.
 1956. Notes and descriptions in the megachilid subgenus *Chelostomoides*. Pan-Pac. Entomol., vol. 32, pp. 129-138.

MOORE, C. G., and PARKER, F. D.
 1962. A host of *Pyria inaequidens* (Dahlbom). Pan-Pac. Entomol., vol. 38, p. 14.

MUESEBECK, C. F. W., KROMBEIN, K. V., TOWNES, H. K., *et al.*
 1951. Hymenoptera of America north of Mexico—Synoptic catalog. U. S. Dept. Agr., Agr. Monogr. 2, pp. 1-1420, 1 map.

MUMA, M. H., and JEFFERS, W. T.
 1945. Studies of the spider prey of several mud-dauber wasps. Ann. Entomol. Soc. Amer., vol. 38, pp. 245-255, 2 pls.

MYERS, J. G.
  1927. A sarcophagid "parasite" of solitary wasps: *Pachyophthalmus* parasitizing *Ancistrocerus.* Entomol. Mo. Mag., vol. 63, pp. 190-196.
NYE, W. P., and BOHART, G. E.
  1964. Equipment for making nesting holes for the alfalfa leaf-cutting bee. Utah State Univ. Agric. Exp. Stat. Circ. 145, 7 pp., 6 figs.
OSTEN SACKEN, C. R.
  1877. Western Diptera: Descriptions of genera and species of Diptera from the region west of the Mississippi, and especially from California. Bull. U. S. Geol. Geogr. Surv., vol. 3, pp. 189-354.
PACKARD, A. S.
  1865-67. Revision of the fossorial Hymenoptera of North America. Proc. Entomol. Soc. Philadelphia, vol. 6, pp. 39-115, 353-444.
  1874. Guide to the study of insects, 4th ed., 715 pp., 15 pls., 668 text figs.
PARKER, F. D.
  1962. A host of *Chrysis (Trichrysis) mucronata* Brullé and an additional host for *Chrysis (Chrysis) coerulans* Fabricius. Pan-Pac. Entomol., vol. 38, p. 140.
PATE, V. S. L.
  1937. The third Nearctic species of *Nitela,* with remarks on the genera *Tenila* Brethes and *Rhinonitela* Williams. Bull. Brooklyn Entomol. Soc., vol. 32, pp. 5-7.
  1942. A review of the myrmecotherous genus *Tracheliodes.* Lloydia, vol. 5, pp. 222-244, 7 figs.
PECK, O.
  1963. A catalogue of the nearctic Chalcidoidea. Canadian Entomol., Sup. 30, pp. 1-1092.
PECKHAM, G. W., and PECKHAM, E. G.
  1895. Notes on the habits of *Trypoxyllon rubrocinctum* and *Trypoxyllon albopilosum.* Psyche, vol. 7, pp. 303-306.
  1898. On the instincts and habits of the solitary wasps. Wisconsin Geol. Nat. Hist. Surv. Bull. 2, pp. 1-245, 14 pls.
  1900. Additional observations on the instincts and habits of the solitary wasps. Bull. Wisconsin Nat. Hist. Soc., vol. 1, pp. 85-93.
  1905. Wasps social and solitary. 311 pp. Cambridge.
RAU, P.
  1922. Ecological and behavior notes on Missouri insects. Trans. Acad. Sci. St. Louis., vol. 24, no. 7, pp. 1-71, 4 pls.
  1926. The ecology of a sheltered clay bank; a study in insect sociology. Trans. St. Louis Acad. Sci., vol. 25, pp. 157-277, 8 pls.
  1928. Field studies in the behavior of the non-social wasps. Trans. St. Louis Acad. Sci., vol. 25, pp. 325-489, 11 pls.
  1930. The nesting habits of the twig-dwelling bee, *Prosopis modestus* Say. Psyche, vol. 37, pp. 173-175.
  1931a. Notes on the homing of several species of wasps. Entomol. News, vol. 42, pp. 199-200.
  1931b. The cocooning habit of the wasp, *Monobia quadridens.* Bull. Brooklyn Entomol. Soc., vol. 26, pp. 4-6.
  1932. The relation of the size of the cell to the sex of the wasp in *Odynerus foraminatus* Sauss. Entomol. News, vol. 43, pp. 119-121.
  1934. Behavior notes on certain solitary wasps. Canadian Entomol., vol. 66, pp. 259-261.
  1935a. The grass-carrying wasp, *Chlorion (Isodontia) harrisi,* Fernald. Bull. Brooklyn Entomol. Soc., vol. 30, pp. 65-68, 1 pl.
  1935b. Additional *Trypoxylon* names in "Jungle Bees and Wasps of Barro Colorado Island". Entomol. News, vol. 46, p. 188.

1935c. Notes on the biology of certain eumenid wasps. Bull. Brooklyn Entomol. Soc., vol. 30, pp. 110-112.

1935d. The courtship and mating of the wasp, *Monobia quadridens*. Entomol. News, vol. 16, pp. 57-58.

1937a. The life history of *Osmia lignaria* and *Osmia cordata*, with notes on *Osmia conjuncta*. Ann. Entomol. Soc. Amer., vol. 30, pp. 324-342, 1 pl.

1937b. A note on the nesting habits of the roach-hunting wasp, *Podium (Parapodium) carolina* Rohwer. Entomol. News, vol. 48, pp. 91-94.

1940. Some mud-daubing wasps of Mexico and their parasites. Ann. Entomol. Soc. Amer., vol. 33, pp. 590-595.

1943a. The nesting habits of certain sphecid wasps of Mexico, with notes on their parasites. Ann. Entomol. Soc. Amer., vol. 36, pp. 647-652, 1 pl.

1943b. The nesting habits of Mexican social and solitary wasps of the family Vespidae. Ann. Entomol. Soc. Amer., vol. 36, pp. 515-536.

1944. The use of old *Polistes* nests by *Odynerus foraminatus* and *Ancistrocerus fulvipes* for nesting purposes. Canadian Entomol., vol. 76, p. 129.

1945. The size of the cell and the sex of the wasp in *Ancistrocerus catskillensis* de Sauss. Ann. Entomol. Soc. Amer., vol. 38, p. 88.

1946. Notes on the behavior of a few solitary wasps. Bull. Brooklyn Entomol. Soc., vol. 41, pp. 10-11.

RAU, P., and RAU, N.

1916. The biology of the mud-daubing wasps as revealed by the contents of their nests. Journ. Anim. Behavior, vol. 6, pp. 27-63, 26 figs.

1918. Wasp studies afield. 372 pp., 68 figs. Princeton.

REINHARD, E. G.

1929. The witchery of wasps. 291 pp., 14 pls., 10 text figs. New York.

RICHARDS, O. W.

1934. The American species of the genus *Trypoxylon*. Trans. Royal Entomol. Soc. London, vol. 82, pp. 173-362, 5 pls.

RILEY, C. V.

1885. Fourth report of the United States Entomological Commission. Misc. Doc. No. 39, House of Representatives, pp. 1-399, 64 pls.

SABROSKY, C. W.

1955. A third species of *Eusiphona*, with remarks on the systematic position of the genus. Entomol. News, vol. 66, pp. 169-173.

SANDHOUSE, G. A.

1940. A review of the nearctic wasps of the genus *Trypoxylon*. Amer. Midl. Nat., vol. 24, pp. 133-176, 4 pls.

SAY, T.

1836. Descriptions of new species of North American Hymenoptera, and observations on some already described. Boston Journ. Nat. Hist., vol. 1, pp. 209-416.

SNELLING, R. R.

1963. A host of *Macrosaigon cruentum* (Genmar) in Georgia. Pan-Pac. Entomol., vol. 39, pp. 87-88.

STAGE, G. I.

1960. First North American host record of the adventive wasp, *Chrysis fuscipennis* Brullé. Pan-Pac. Entomol., vol. 36, pp. 191-195, 1 fig.

STEPHEN, W. P.

1962. Propagation of the leaf-cutter bee for alfalfa seed production. Oreg. State Univ. Agr. Expt. Sta. Bull. 586, 16 pp., 9 figs.

1965. Circadian rhythms in the leafcutter bee, *Megachile rotundata* (Fabr.). Proc. XII Int. Congr. Entomol. London, p. 350.

STEPHEN, W. P., and Osgood, C. E.
1965a. The induction of emergence in the leaf-cutter bee, *Megachile rotundata*, an important pollinator of alfalfa. Jour. Economic Entomol., vol. 58, pp. 284-286.
1965b. Influence of tunnel size and nesting medium on sex ratios in a leaf-cutter bee, *Megachile rotundata*. Jour. Economic Entomol., vol. 58, pp. 965-968.

STEPHEN, W. P., and TORCHIO, P. F.
1961. Biological notes on the leaf-cutter bee, *Megachile (Eutricharaea) rotundata* (Fabricius). Pan-Pac. Entomol., vol. 37, pp. 85-93, 2 figs.

STRAND, E.
1914. Ein nordamerikanisches Eumenidennest nebst descriptiven Bemerkungen über die zugehörigen Wespen. Entomol. Mitt., vol. 3, pp. 116-118, 1 fig.

SUEHIRO, A.
1937. Untitled note on *Isodontia harrisi* Fernald. Proc. Hawaii. Entomol. Soc., vol. 9, p. 358.

SWEZEY, O. H.
1947. Untitled note on *Isodontia harrisi* Fernald. Proc. Hawaii. Entomol. Soc., vol. 13, p. 8.

TANDY, M.
1908. The carpenter wasp (*Monobia quadridens*). Entomol. News, vol. 19, pp. 231-232.

TAYLOR, L. H.
1922. Notes on the biology of certain wasps of the genus *Ancistrocerus*. Psyche, vol. 29, pp. 48-65, 1 pl.

TAYLOR, R. L.
1928. The arthropod fauna of coniferous leaders weeviled by *Pissodes strobi* (Peck.). Psyche, vol. 35, pp. 217-225.

THOMAS, S. J.
1962. Notes on the biology of the cuckoo wasp *Chrysis verticalis* Patton. Amer. Midl. Nat., vol. 67, pp. 364-367.
1963. Comparative post-diapause developmental periods of the cuckoo wasp, *Chrysis verticalis* Patton and its host, *Trypoxylon frigidum* Smith. Papers Michigan Acad. Sci., Arts, Letters, vol. 48, pp. 127-130.

TOWNES, H. K.
1957. Nearctic wasps of the subfamilies Pepsinae and Ceropalinae. Bull. U. S. Nat. Mus. 209, 286 pp., 4 pls., 161 text figs.

TOWNSEND, C. H. T.
1893. Description of the pupa of *Toxophora virgata* O.S. Psyche, vol. 6, pp. 455-457.

TSUNEKI, K.
1964. Supplementary notes on the nesting biology of three species of *Sphex* (*Isodontia*) occurring in Japan. Etizenia, No. 7, 14 pp., 8 pls.

VAN DUZEE, M. C.
1934. Conopidae from North Dakota and the Rocky Mountain region. Ann. Entomol. Soc. Amer., vol. 27, pp. 315-323.

WALSH, B. D.
1869. Wasps and their habits. Amer. Entomol., vol. 1, pp. 122-143, figs. 97-112.

WILLIAMS, F. X.
1929. Notes on the habits of the cockroach-hunting wasps of the genus *Ampulex*, with particular reference to *Ampulex (Rhinopsis) canaliculata* Say. Proc. Hawaii. Entomol. Soc., vol. 7, pp. 315-329, 10 figs.

PLATES

PLATES

Photographs are by the author except as follows: Figures 87, 88, 123, 124, 125, and 131 by Photographic Services, U. S. Department of Agriculture; figure 119 by Photographic Services, University of California at Berkeley; figures 120 and 121 by Photographic Services, Smithsonian Institution. Figures 102, 103, and 122 are by A. D. Cushman, who also made up the plates.

The photographs of nests and individual cells are oriented, insofar as possible, so that the nest entrance or anterior end of the cell is at the right. In the few instances where the nest entrance is at the left this has been noted in the appropriate individual plate explanation; the reversed nests appear as figures 64, 65, and 92-98.

PLATE 1

Fig. 1, traps on branch of scrubby live oak (*Quercus virginiana*) on sandy barrens, Kill Devil Hills, N. C., 1955. Fig. 2, same locality and date but on branch of scrubby Spanish oak (*Q. falcata*). Fig. 3, same locality and date but on limb of loblolly pine (*Pinus taeda*) in open woods. Fig. 4, traps beneath rafter on cabin porch, Plummers Island, Md., 1961.

PLATE 2

Fig. 5, traps tied to dead flowering stalk of agave (*Agave* sp.), Portal, Ariz., 1959. Fig. 6, same locality and date but tied to trunk of dead shrub. Fig. 7, traps tied to dead standing oak trunk, Plummers Island, Md., 1961. Fig. 8, same locality and date but on dead standing barked trunk.

PLATE 2

PLATE 3

Fig. 9, traps beneath branch of scrub hickory (*Hicoria floridana*), Lake Placid, Fla., 1962. Fig. 10, same locality and date but tied to trunk of living carribbean pine (*Pinus caribaea*). Fig. 11, nest D 11 d in 4.8-mm. boring, Derby, N. Y., 1955, supersedure and competition; note spider prey of a trypoxylonine sp. at inner end, a cocoon of *Ancistrocerus c. catskill* (Saussure) in cell 1, cocoons of *Trypargilum clavatum* (Say) in cells 2-5, cocoons of *Trypoxylon frigidum* Smith in cells 6-7 and empty vestibular cell at outer end. Fig. 12, nest C 14 in 4.8-mm. boring, Kill Devil Hills, N. C., 1955, colony of *Crematogaster* ants. Fig. 13, nest D 13 d in 6.4-mm. boring, Derby, N. Y., 1955, lepidopterous larva with cocoon cap across boring entrance.

PLATE 4

Symmorphus canadensis (Saussure) females, about X 12. Fig. 14, Lost River State Park, W. Va., July 8, 1955, at nest entrance in log carrying paralyzed leafminer beetle larva (*Chalepus* sp.). Fig. 15, Arlington, Va., 1955, at nest entrance in cowshed wall with lump of mud to construct cell partition.

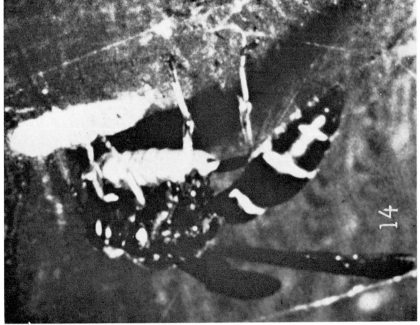

PLATE 5

Symmorphus canadensis (Saussure), nest A 5 in 4.8-mm. boring, Arlington, Va., 1955. Fig. 16, July 12, cell with paralyzed *Chalepus dorsalis* Thunberg larvae. Fig. 17, July 15, cell with half-grown wasp larva. Fig. 18, July 17, cell with full-grown wasp larva eating the last beetle larva.

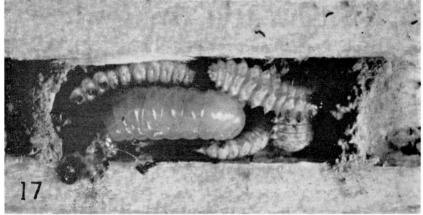

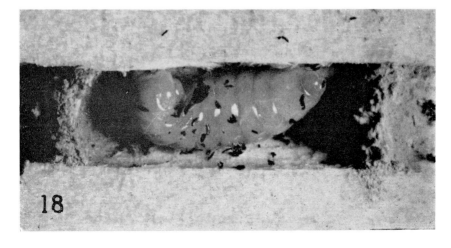

PLATE 6

Fig. 19, two cells of nest A 5 in 4.8-mm. boring, Arlington, Va., August 1955, diapausing larvae of *Symmorphus canadensis* (Saussure) in delicate silken cocoons. Fig. 20, two cells of nest D 5 c in 4.8-mm. boring, Derby, N.Y., August 1955, diapausing larvae of *Symmorphus c. cristatus* (Saussure) in tougher, opaque, silken cocoons; note lack of empty intercalary cells. Fig. 21, three cells of nest D 13 b in 4.8-mm. boring, Derby, N. Y., October 1955, cocoons of *Symmorphus c. cristatus;* note presence of small empty intercalary cells between stored cells. Fig. 22, nest D 5 c in 4.8-mm. boring, Derby, N. Y., July 1, 1955, *Symmorphus c. cristatus;* note nearly full-grown wasp larvae in some cells, paralyzed prey (*Chrysomela* larvae) in other cells in which wasps died, vestibular cell and the thick closing plug. Fig. 23, nest D 7 b in 6.4-mm. boring, Derby, N. Y., July 1955, *Ancistrocerus a. antilope* (Panzer); note wasp prepupae in cells with delicate silken cocoons lining the walls, and vestibular cell divided by a cross partition.

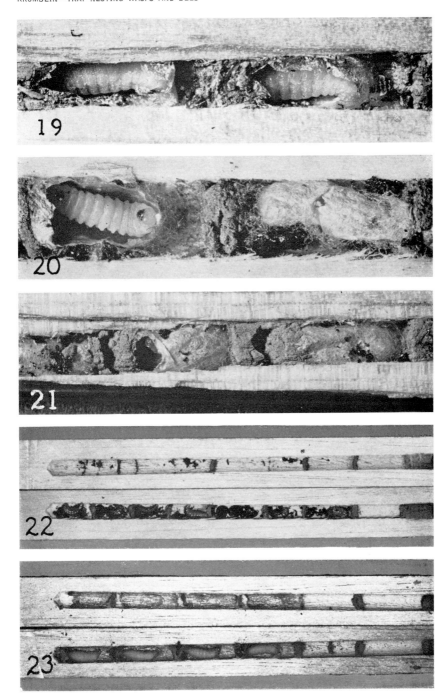

PLATE 7

Monobia quadridens (Linnaeus) in 12.7-mm. borings. Fig. 24, nest P 65, Lake Placid, Fla., July 5, 1962, partially stored cell 4 near outer end of boring; note egg suspended from ceiling and several paralyzed caterpillars on floor. Fig. 25, nest P 65, cells 2-4, July 5; note egg shell on ceiling of cell 2 (lower half of trap) and eggs on ceilings of cells 3 and 4; caterpillars removed from incompletely stored cell 4; note also absence of intercalary cells between stored cells. Fig. 26, nest P 65, cell 3, July 8, partially grown larva. Fig. 27, nest P 65, cell 2, July 8, full-grown larva; note adult female and male mites, *Monobiacarus quadridens* Baker and Cunliffe, on larva. Fig. 28, nest P 65, cell 1, July 8, prepupa (pupation occurred July 14-16). Fig. 29, nest C 294, cells 1-2, Kill Devil Hills, N. C., July 24, 1955, diapausing larvae; note long preliminary sand plug at inner end of boring, empty intercalary cell between stored cells 1 and 2, and thinner partitions capping stored cells than that capping the intercalary cell.

PLATE 8

Monobia quadridens (Linnaeus) females in cells 1 and 2, nest
C 294 in 12.7-mm. boring, Kill Devil Hills, N. C., 1956, development of coloration in pupa and adult; figures 30-36 are of occupant
of cell 1 which pupated May 5-7 and died before adult eclosion;
figures 37-38 are of occupant of cell 2 which pupated May 4 and
eclosed as an adult June 1. Fig. 30, May 11, pale pupa with light
tan eyes. Fig. 31, May 14, pale pupa with black eyes (actually the eyes
reached this stage on May 13). Fig. 32, May 21 (integument began
to darken on mesopleuron and second tergum May 20). Fig. 33,
May 22. Fig. 34, May 23. Fig. 35; May 27; pupal exuvia has now
become loosened and wrinkled. Fig. 36, June 1; eclosion would have
been expected during the next day or two if death had not inter-
vened. Fig. 37, June 1, newly eclosed adult; note that wings are fully
expanded but not hardened or colored. Fig. 38, June 3, fully colored
and hardened adult; emergence from the nest took place on June
5. (Note that figures 32, 34, and 38 are printed in reverse to permit
uniform postioning of cell occupant.)

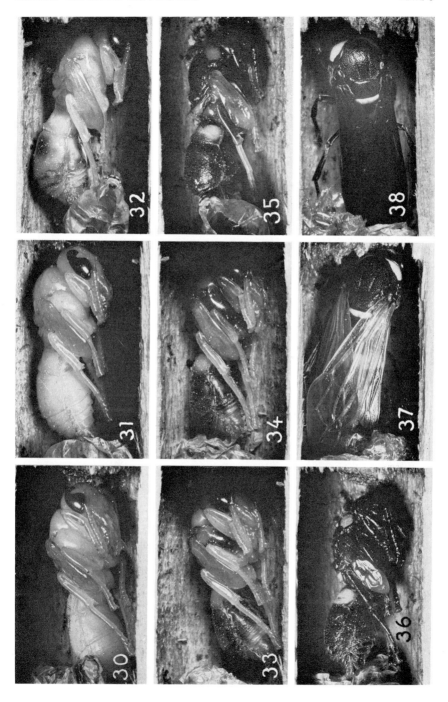

PLATE 9

Fig. 39, nest M 82 in 12.7-mm. boring, Plummers Island, Md., July 24, 1962, *Euodynerus schwarzi* (Krombein); note absence of intercalary cells and full grown wasp larvae at inner end; cell 10 contained a recently hatched wasp larva on this date. Fig. 40, cells 2-3, nest C 276 in 6.4-mm. boring, Kill Devil Hills, N.C., September 23, 1955, diapausing larvae of *Euodynerus megaera* (Lepeletier); note presence of empty intercalary cells between stored cells, and that partitions capping stored cells are narrower than those capping intercalary cells. Fig. 41, nest G 257 in 6.4 mm. boring, Portal, Ariz., March 1962, diapausing larva of *Euodynerus guerrero* (Saussure) in cell 4; note thin partition capping cell 4, the short vestibular cell, and abnormally shaped closing plug inside the boring instead of at the entrance. Fig. 42, nest M 60 in 4.8-mm. boring, September 16, 1962, Plummers Island, Md., mud cells of *Auplopus caerulescens subcorticalis* (Walsh). Fig. 43, nest M 60, September 16, paralyzed immature male clubionid spider *Clubiona obesa* Hentz from cell 4 bearing egg of *Auplopus caerulescens subcorticalis;* note amputation of spider's legs by the wasp. Fig. 44, nest M 60, cells 3-4, September 16. Fig. 45, nest M 48 in 6.4-mm boring, Plummers Island, Md., July 12, 1962, mud cell of *Auplopus m. mellipes* (Say).

PLATE 10

Fig. 46, unnumbered nest in 6.4-mm. boring, Arlington, Va., 1953, *Dipogon* sp., probably *s. sayi* Banks; note wasp cocoons in cells 1-4 and paralyzed spiders in cells 5-6 in which the wasp eggs failed to hatch; note also the partitions of loose debris capping the cells and the long closing plug of loose debris. Fig. 47, paralyzed crab spider, *Xysticus* sp. in cell 5 of above nest. Fig. 48, cells 2-3, nest B 49 in 6.4-mm. boring, Cropley, Md., 1955, cocoons of *Dipogon s. sayi* (♂ in cell 2, ♀ in cell 3); note loose debris from closing partitions adhering to cocoons, and firmer outer mud surface of partition.

Plate 11

Fig. 49, cell 3, nest C 494 in 4.8-mm. boring, Kill Devil Hills, N. C., October 1955, *Ampulex canaliculata* Say; note loose plug of bits of dried leaf and twigs and cocoon of wasp in center. Fig. 50, the same cocoon but at a greater magnification; note detached sclerites of cockroach prey adhering to outer wall of cocoon (arrow indicates venter of abdomen). Fig. 51, the same nest; varnished, brittle inner cocoon 11 mm. long removed from delicate, silken outer sheath.

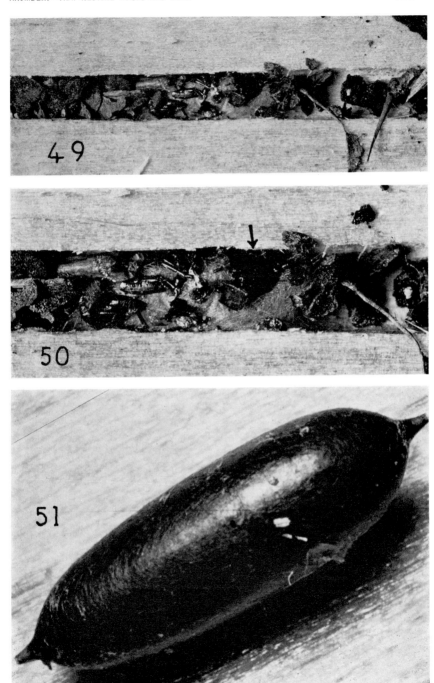

PLATE 12

Fig. 52, cells 4-5, nest P 79 in 4-8-mm. boring, Lake Placid, Fla., June 25, 1962, *Trypargilum johannis* (Richards); note wasp egg attached to spider at outer end of each cell and diversity of prey; contents of cell 4 were preserved and consisted of eight immature and adult salticid (jumping) spiders, three of *Phidippus* sp., four of *Maevia hobbsi* Barnes and one of *Icius* sp., (compare with snare-builder prey of *T. striatum* (Provancher) in fig. 132). Fig. 53, nest M 70 in 6.4-mm. boring, Plummers Island, Md., July 12, 1962, *Trypargilum striatum* (Provancher); note shape of cocoons, long empty cell at inner end and absence of vestibular cell. Fig. 54, nest M 84 in 12.7 mm. boring, Plummers Island, Md., August 8, 1962, *T. striatum;* note normal cocoons in cells 1-2, abnormally shaped cocoons in cells 3-5 and spider prey in cell 6 in which wasp egg failed to hatch. Fig. 55, cell 1, nest M 86 in 6.4-mm. boring, Plummers Island, Md., August 11, 1962, *T. striatum,* normal cocoon; note small amount of mud at inner end of boring, almost always present in nests of all species of *Trypargilum.* Fig. 56, cell 5, nest M 84 in 12.7-mm boring, Plummers Island, Md., August 8, 1962, *T. striatum;* note abnormally flared anterior end of cocoon and suspensory net of fine, unvarnished, silken threads.

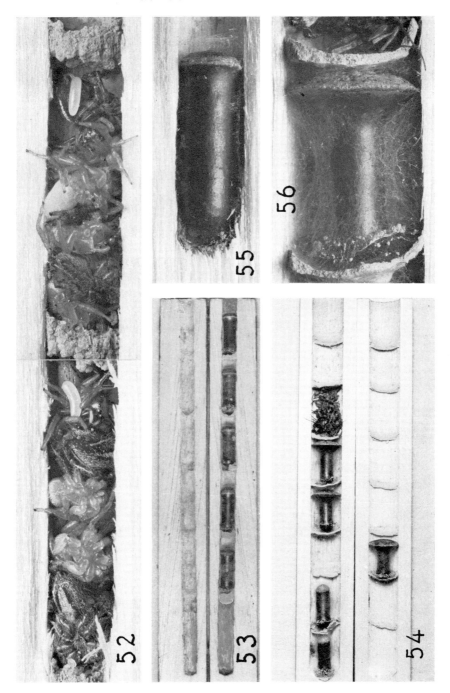

PLATE 13

Fig. 57, nest X 275 in 12.7-mm. boring, Portal, Ariz., July 20, 1959, *Isodontia* (*I.*) *elegans* (Smith), cocoon in cell 1, full-grown larva in cell 2, wasp egg and snowy tree crickets, *Oecanthus quadripunctatus* Beutenmüller, in cell 3; note substantial partitions of fine vegetable fibers and grass blades capping each cell. Fig. 58, nest V 50 in 12.7 mm. boring, Lake Placid, Fla., May 19, 1959, *Isodontia* (*I.*) *mexicana* (Saussure); note five cocoons separated by very flimsy partitions of dried grass, and long compound closing plug with grass stems and leaves protruding from entrance. Fig. 59, nest P 69 in 12.7-mm. boring, Lake Placid, Fla., August 8, 1962, *I. mexicana;* note five cocoons separated by somewhat thicker partitions. Fig. 60, nest H 88 in 12.7-mm. boring, Plummers Island, Md., 11 p.m., July 19, 1956, *Isodontia* sp., probably *auripes* (Fernald); paralyzed snowy tree cricket prey in large brood cell, one nymph of *Neoxabea bipunctata* (DeGeer) and about 15 adults of both sexes of *Oecanthus* sp., probably *angustipennis* Fitch. Fig. 61, same nest as fig. 60 but 10 a.m., July 21; four nearly mature wasp larvae feeding in brood cell. Fig. 62, nest C 390 in 4.8-mm. boring, Kill Devil Hills, N. C., August 7, 1956, *Podium rufipes* (Fabricius); paralyzed nymphal and adult cockroach prey, *Chorisoneura texensis* Saussure and Zehntner; note wasp egg (arrow) attached to innermost cockroach.

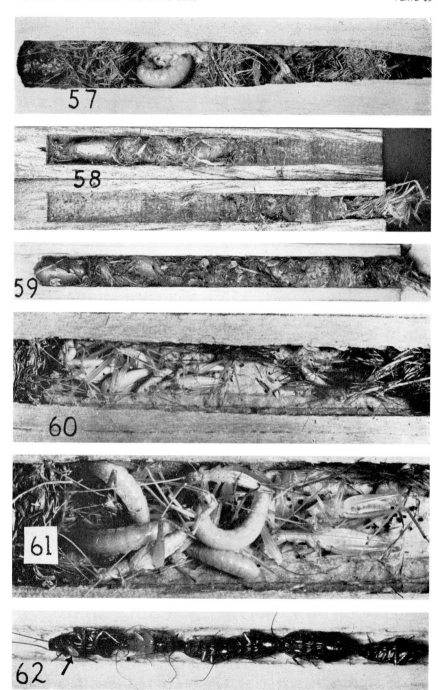

PLATE 14

Fig. 63, nest C 246 in 4.8-mm. boring, Kill Devil Hills, N. C., July 24, 1955, *Podium rufipes* (Fabricius) cocoon; note wings of cockroach prey, *Chorisoneura texensis* Saussure and Zehntner. Fig. 64, nest K 136 in 12.7-mm. boring, Plummers Island, Md., July 23, 1961, *Podium luctuosum* Smith; note debris from inner section of cell partition adhering to each cocoon. Fig. 65, same data as fig. 64, but debris removed from cocoons; note firm mud (outer) section of each cell partition. (Note that nest entrances are at left in figs. 64-65).

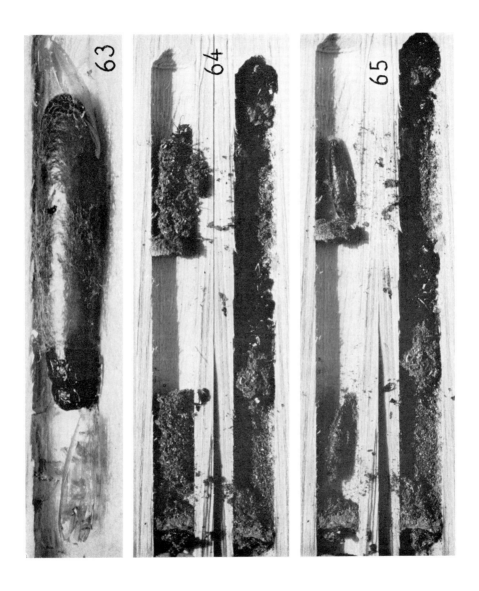

PLATE 15

Fig. 66, nest N 6 in 3.2-mm. boring, Arlington, Va., May 24, 1962, *Passaloecus cuspidatus* Smith; resin partitions capping cells and closing plug indicated by arrows. Fig. 67, same data as fig. 66, but outer half of cell 2 and cell 3; note aphid prey and wasp eggs (indicated by arrows). Fig. 68, nest H 200 in 6.4-mm. boring, Soldier Camp, Santa Catalina Mts., Ariz., March 1962, cocoons 4 and 5 of *Tracheliodes amu* Pate (?); note remains of numerous ant prey, *Liometopum occidentale luctuosum* Wheeler, adhering to cocoons. Fig. 69, same data as fig. 68, but most of ant remains removed from cocoon wall; note wide transverse septum at anterior end spun by the wasp larva.

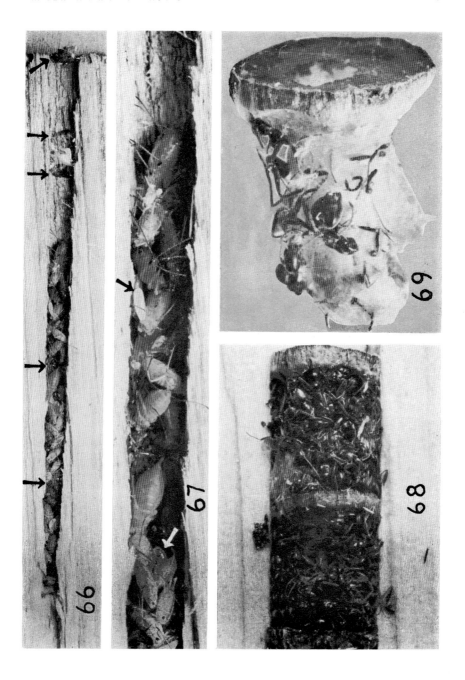

Plate 16

Nesting activities of *Osmia* (*O.*) *l. lignaria* Say females, Plummers Island, Md., 1962. Fig. 70, May 5, in flight near nest entrance; note pollen load on abdominal scopa. Fig. 71, April 28, M 30 alighting at nest entrance. Fig. 72, April 28, M 30 preparing to enter boring head first to regurgitate nectar from crop. Fig. 73, April 28, M 30 entering boring. Fig. 74, April 28, M 30 preparing to back into boring to scrape off pollen. Fig. 75, April 28, M 30 backing into boring. Fig. 76, April 28, M 31 at nest entrance with load of damp mud to make cell partition; note that abdominal scopa now bears no pollen load. Fig. 77, May 5, another female at nest entrance with load of damp mud. (Fig. 70 and 77 are about X2, figs. 71-76 about X 2.7.)

PLATE 17

Fig. 78, nest X 59 in 4.8-mm. boring, Portal, Ariz., July 20, 1959, *Ashmeadiella* (*A.*) *occipitalis* Michener; note female prepupae in cells 1-4 (that in cell 5 preserved before photograph taken), pale female pupae in cells 6-10, a dark female pupa in cell 11, and adult males in cells 12-13; there was no vestibular cell and the outer third of the abnormally long plug of leaf pulp has been cropped in this photograph. Fig. 79, nest X 186 in 6.4-mm. boring, Portal, Ariz., July 21, 1959, *Anthidium maculosum* Cresson; note cottony lining and partitions between cells (cotton stained opposite pollen-nectar masses) and closing plug of tiny pebbles. Fig. 80, nest X 253 in 12.7-mm. boring, Portal, Ariz., July 21, 1959, *Anthidium maculosum* Cresson (?) from which adult bees have emerged; note closing plug of small twigs and bits of earth. Fig. 81, nest G 347 in 6.4-mm. boring, Portal, Ariz., March 1962, *Dianthidium ulkei perterritum* Cockerell, parts of cocoons in cells 4-5; note nipple at anterior end of cocoon in cell 4, and the compound partition capping that cell consisting of a narrow layer of resin at inner end, a thick section of small pebbles and twigs, and another narrow layer of resin which formed base and sides of cell 5. Fig. 82, nest Y 93 in 6.4-mm. boring, Plummers Island, Md., May 15, 1959, *Osmia* (*O.*) *l. lignaria* Say, progressively smaller larvae in cells 1-11; nest completed about May 8. Fig. 83, nest Y 44 in 6.4-mm. boring, Plummers Island, Md., June 2, 1959, cocoons of *O. lignaria;* nest completed April 17. Fig. 84, nest Y 64 in 12.7-mm. boring, Plummers Island, Md., May 15, 1959, *O. lignaria;* note larger female cells 1-12, many of them arranged transversely, and smaller male cells 13-23; nest completed about May 8. Fig. 85, same data as fig. 84, but June 2, 1959, cocoons. Fig. 86, nest A 18 in 3.2-mm. boring, Arlington, Va., June 2, 1959, *Prochelostoma philadelphi* (Robertson), newly hatched larvae; note narrow mud partitions capping cells.

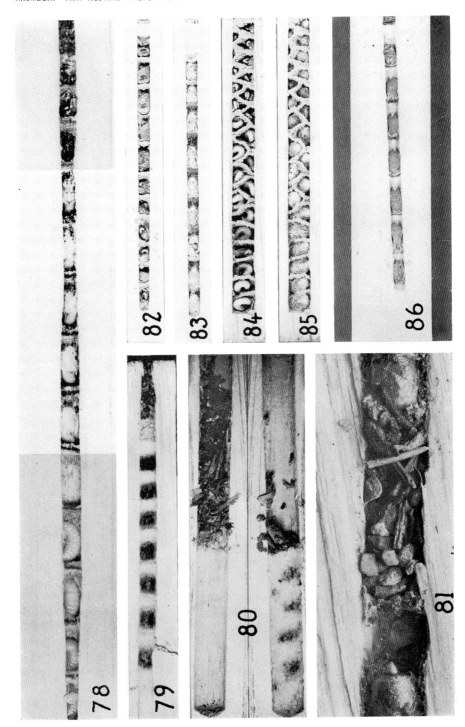

PLATE 18

Fig. 87, cells 5-11 and vestibular cell, nest Y 85 in 6.4-mm. boring, Plummers Island, Md., May 19, 1959, *Osmia* (*O.*) *l. lignaria* Say, progressively smaller larvae in cells 5-10, egg ready to hatch in cell 11; note newly hatched cuckoo wasp larva, *Chrysura kyrae* Krombein, on pollen-nectar mass in cell 7; nest completed about May 15. Fig. 88, cells 4-10, nest Y 91 in 6.4-mm. boring, Plummers Island, Md., June 2, 1959. *O. lignaria,* part of cocoon in cell 3 visible at left, egg died in cell 4, mature bee larva in cell 5, and nearly full-grown larvae in cells 6-10; note first instar larva of *Chrysura kyrae* attached transversely on body of bee larva in cell 6, Fig. 89, cells 3-5, nest Y 47 in 6.4-mm. boring, Plummers Island, Md., March 1960, *Osmia* (*Centrosmia*) *b. bucephala* Cresson, cocoons; note barrel-shaped cells and compound cell partitions. Fig. 90, nest U 19 in 6.4-mm. boring, Plummers Island, Md., May 21, 1963, *Osmia b. bucephala,* partition capping cell 4; note thin layer of leaf pulp on each side of a thick section of rasped wood fibers. Fig. 91, same data as fig. 90, but egg in cell 9 partially submerged in moist pollen-nectar mass.

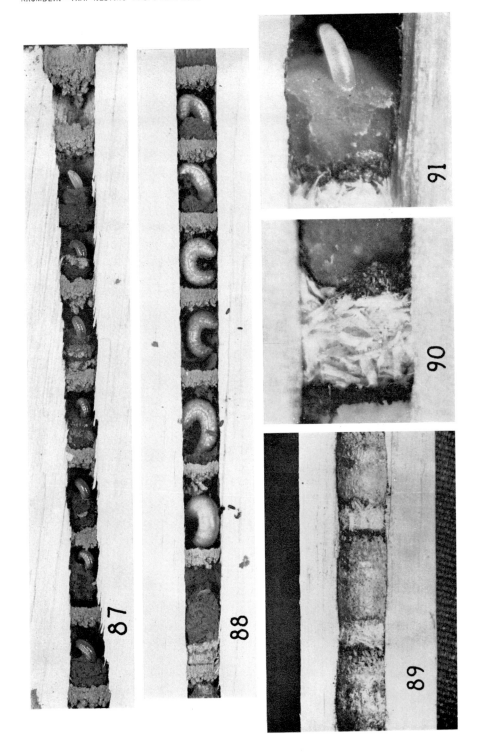

PLATE 19

Nests of *Megachile* (*Sayapis*) *policaris* Say. Fig. 92, nest G 136 in 12.7-mm. boring, Portal, Ariz., May 12, 1961; note large brood cell, enormous pollen-nectar mass with small bee larvae in pockets at intervals, and compound closing plug consisting of small entire leaflets and interspersed septa of leaf pulp. Fig. 93, same data as fig. 92, but somewhat in profile at a greater magnification. Fig. 94, same data as fig. 93 but June 5; larvae on outer part of food mass dead but not from cannibalism. Fig. 95, nest X 255 in 12.7-mm. boring, Portal, Ariz., July 21, 1959; note three brood cells each containing several cocoons, and the compound partitions and plug. Fig. 96, nest X 256 in 12.7-mm. boring, Portal, Ariz., July 21, 1959; note a number of cocoons in brood cells 1-2, some of them opened to show pale, black-eyed bee pupae; brood cell 3 contained a large food mass but none of eggs hatched. Fig. 97, nest X 164 in 6.4-mm. boring, Portal, Ariz., July 21, 1959; note that there are four brood cells, with two cocoons in linear series in cells 1 and 4 (a dead egg also in 4), a dead egg and a small dead larva in cell 2, and a dead egg in cell 3; arrows indicate cell partitions. (Note that nest entrances are at left.)

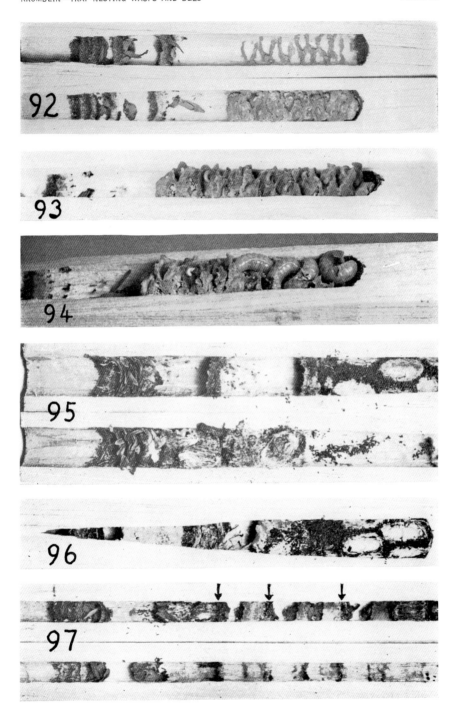

PLATE 20

Fig. 98, nest T 209 in 12.7-mm. boring, Kill Devil Hills, N. C., July 28, 1958, *Megachile (Melanosarus) xylocopoides* Smith containing five stored cells; leaf cuttings unwrapped from cocoon in cell 5 (center of nest); note long closing plug of regularly arranged rectangular and circular leaf cuttings. Fig. 99, nest H 123 in 6.4-mm. boring, Granite Reef Dam, Ariz., May 9, 1961, *Megachile (Litomegachile) gentilis* Cresson, containing 12 stored cells; note short closing plug of circular leaf cuttings. Fig. 100, nest H 132 in 12.7-mm. boring, Scottsdale, Ariz., *M. gentilis,* containing 14 stored cells; note irregularity of cell series in this outsize boring, and the double row of cells in middle of boring. Fig. 101, nest B 66 in 12.7-mm. boring, Lake Placid, Fla., May 22, 1961, *Xylocopa virginica krombeini* Hurd, showing inner surface of two cell partitions; note spiral pattern of closure made from ribbon of tiny wood fibers. (Note that nest entrance of fig. 98 is at left.)

PLATE 21

Fig. 102, *Stenodynerus (Parancistrocerus) f. fulvipes* (Saussure) female, some of *Vespacarus fulvipes* Baker and Cunliffe mite hypopi removed from acarinarium at base of second tergum to show layering of mites in the chamber; about X 10. Fig. 103, ventral aspect of hypopus of *Vespacarus fulvipes,* about X 100. Fig. 104, cell 2, nest C 105 in 4.8-mm. boring, Kill Devil Hills, N. C., May 11, 1956, adult females of *Vespacarus fulvipes* on male pupa of *Stenodynerus f. fulvipes,* about X 6.5. Fig. 105, same data as fig. 104 but about X 16. Fig. 106, same data as fig. 105; note mite eggs on antennae and mouthparts of wasp pupa. Fig. 107, cell 1, nest C 477 in 6.4-mm. boring, Kill Devil Hills, N. C., May 20, 1956; protonymphs of *Vespacarus fulvipes* on clypeus of female pupa of *Stenodynerus f. fulvipes,* about X 22.5. (This plate published originally in Krombein, 1961.)

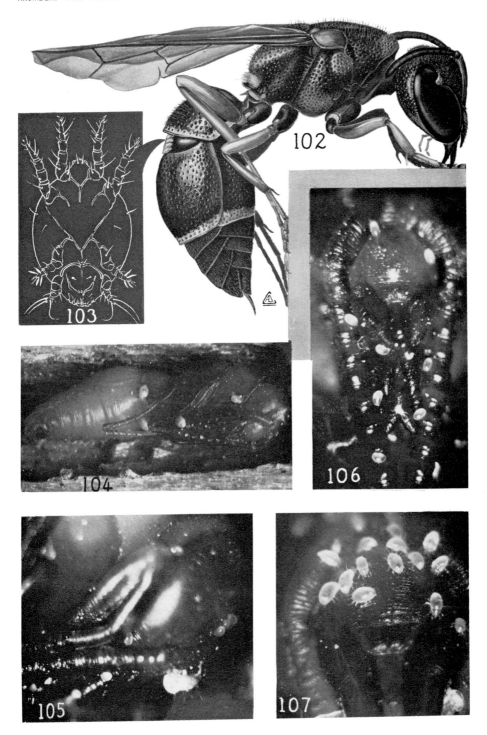

PLATE 22

Fig. 108, nest C 466 in 4.8-mm. boring, Kill Devil Hills, N.C., November 8, 1955, engorged female mites, *Pyemotes ventricosus* (Newport), on diapausing larva of *Stenodynerus* (?). Fig. 109, cell 1, nest C 255 in 6.4-mm. boring, Kill Devil Hills, N. C., August 6, 1955, nymphs of *Vespacarus fulvipes* Baker and Cunliffe clustered mainly on thoracic venter of female pupa of *Stenodynerus (Parancistrocerus) f. fulvipes* (Saussure) 2 days before eclosion of the adult wasp. Fig. 110, same data as fig. 109 but August 10, 2 days after eclosion of adult wasp; note mite hypopi congregated in acarinarium (arrow).

Plate 23

Fig. 111, cell 2, nest K 41 in 6.4-mm. boring, Plummers Island, Md., *Osmia* (*O.*) *l. lignaria* Say; dried pollen grains in cell after infestation and continued breeding for several weeks by *Chaetodactylus krombeini* Baker mites. Fig. 112, same data as fig. 111 but reverse half of cell showing many dead mite protonymphs on cell wall. Fig. 113, same data as fig. 111 but cell 5 at left showing many encysted mite hypopi on bee cocoon. Fig. 114, same data as fig. 111 but cells 10 and 11; note a few encysted mite hypopi on cocoons and more of them on the split surface of the wood between the two halves. (This plate published originally in Krombein, 1962b.)

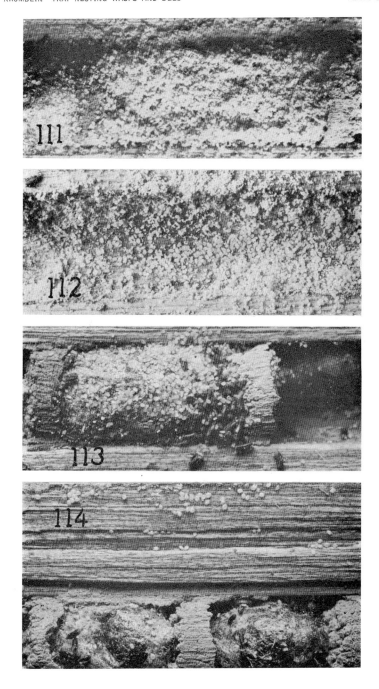

PLATE 24

Fig. 115, nest H 279 in 6.4-mm. boring, Granite Reef Dam, Ariz., March 17, 1962, mature *Macrosiagon c. cruentum* (Germar) larva in cell 2 of an overwintering nest of *Pachodynerus astraeus* (Cameron) *(Trypargilum t. tridentatum* (Packard) cocoon in cell 1); note delicate silken anterior cocoon wall of vespid prepupa (arrow). Fig. 116, same data as fig. 115 but pale pupa of *Macrosiagon* on March 27, a day after pupation occurred. Fig. 117, same data as fig. 116 but April 14, lateral view. Fig. 118, same data as fig. 117, ventral view.

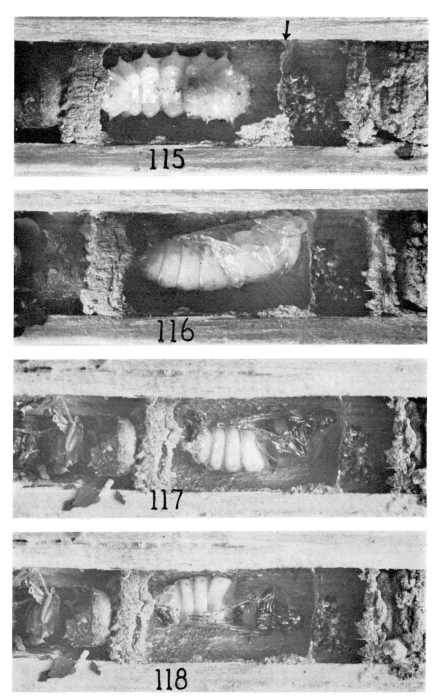

PLATE 25

Fig. 119, cell 4, nest V 24 in 4.8-mm. boring, Lake Placid, Fla., April 1959, five first instar stylopid larvae, *Pseudoxenos hookeri* (Pierce) inside dead embryo of *Euodynerus foraminatus apopkensis* (Robertson) X 82. Fig. 120, same data as fig. 119 but stylopid larva from right end of egg, ventral view, X 273. Fig. 121, same data as fig. 120 but stylopid larva from top of egg, oblique lateral view; note legs and setae. Fig. 122, cell 5, nest M 64 in 6.4-mm. boring, Lake Placid, Fla., March 1957, putative second instar larva of *P. hookeri* recovered from inside mature larva of *E. foraminatus apopkensis*, X 273. Fig. 122a, same data as fig. 122, but head enlarged.

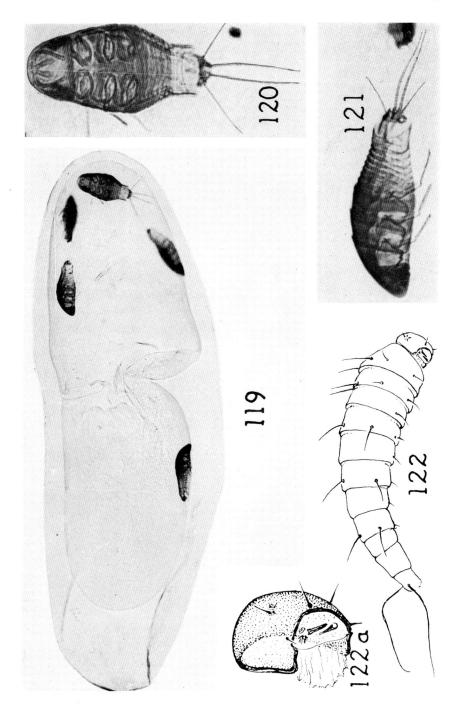

PLATE 26

Fig. 123, cells 2-4, nest V 104 in 4.8-mm. boring, Lake Placid, Fla., May 15, 1959; small *Toxophora amphitea* Walker larva (arrow) on prepupa of *Euodynerus megaera* (Lepeletier) in cell 2. Fig. 124, same data as fig. 123, but May 19; note half-grown *Toxophora* larva in cell 2 and wasp pupae in cells 3-4; adult wasps emerged May 29. Fig. 125, same data as fig. 123, but cells 1-2, June 2, with well-colored *Toxophora* pupae; adult *Toxophora* emerged June 5. Fig. 126, cell 1, nest C 175 in 4.8-mm. boring, Kill Devil Hills, N. C., August 10, 1955, *Anthrax aterrimus* (Bigot) pupa in cocoon of host wasp *Trypargilum collinum rubrocinctum* (Packard). Fig. 127, cell 1, nest C 249, Kill Devil Hills, N. C., August 1955, male *Anthrax aterrimus* with pupal exuvia.

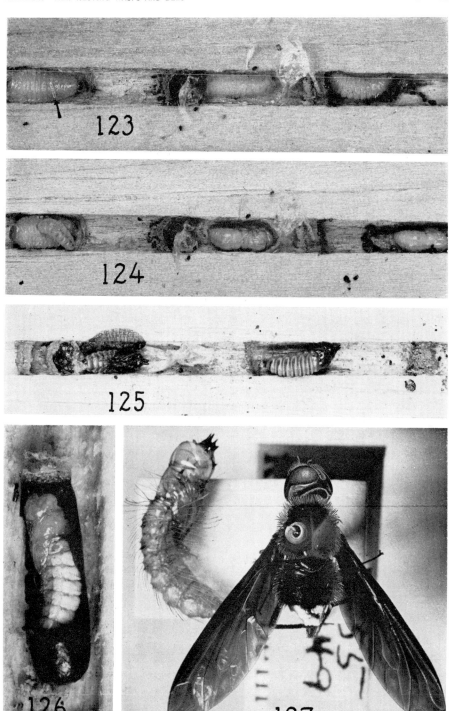

Plate 27

Fig. 128, cells 6-7, nest K 42 in 6.4-mm. boring, Plummers Island, Md., May 3, 1961, eggs of *Osmia* (*O.*) *l. lignaria* Say ready to hatch; note egg of *Chrysura kyrae* Krombein at inner end of pollen-nectar mass in cell 7; bee eggs hatched May 4, chrysidid egg May 6. Fig. 129, same data as fig. 128 but May 6, a few hours after chrysidid egg hatched. Fig. 130, same data as fig. 128, but cells 4-6, May 22; note first instar larva of *C. kyrae* attached to nearly mature *Osmia* larva in cell 5. Fig. 131, cell 6, nest S 48 in 4.8-mm. boring, Plummers Island, Md., May 7, 1958, first instar larva of *Chrysura pacifica* (Say) from nest of *Osmia* (*Nothosmia*) *pumila* Cresson; note sharp mandible, long antennal papilla and numerous setae; photograph made from slide mount.

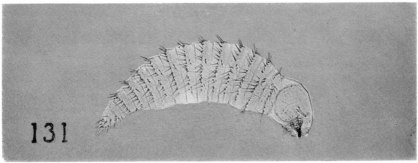

PLATE 28

Fig. 132, cells 4-5, nest P 248 in 6.4-mm. boring, Plummers Island, Md., September 7, 1957, *Trypargilum striatum* (Provancher); note small *striatum* larva in cell 4 on outermost spider and recently hatched *Chrysis* (*Trichrysis*) *carinata* Say larva attacking *striatum* egg on outermost spider in cell 5; also note snarebuilder spider prey and compare with errant spider prey in fig. 52 of *T. johannis* (Richards) and in fig. 133 of *T. clavatum* (Say). Fig. 133, cell 1, nest B 22 in 4.8-mm. boring, Cropley, Md., August 5, 1955, *Trypargilum clavatum* (Say); note host egg on jumping spider near outer end, and newly hatched *C. carinata* (?) larva at extreme outer end of cell. Fig. 134, cells 1-4, nest D 14 c in 6.4-mm. boring, Derby, N. Y., August 10, 1955, *Trypargilum striatum* (Provancher); note cocoon of host wasp in cell 1 and cocoons of *C. carinata* in cells 2-4; also note that cuckoo wasp larvae did not consume all of the spiders stored for the host wasp larvae.

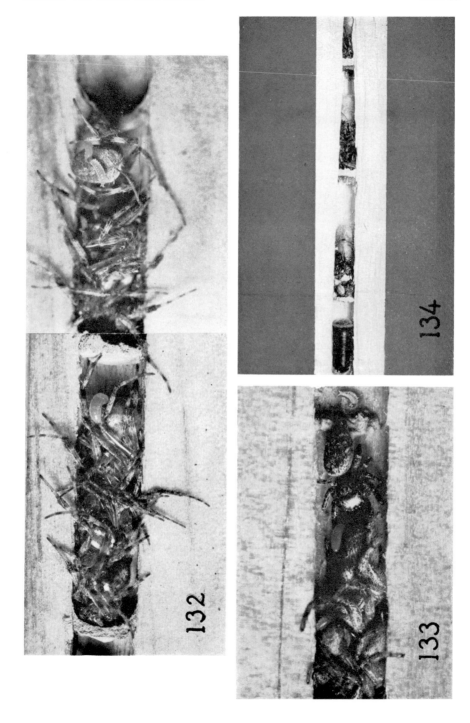

PLATE 29

Fig. 135, nests M 56 (left) and M 42 in 4.8- and 6.4-mm. borings respectively, Plummers Island, Md., July 11, 1962, showing penetration of closing plugs of nests of *Trypargilum collinum rubrocinctum* (Packard) (left) and *Trypargilum striatum* (Provancher) (right) by females of *Sphaeropthalma (S.) pennsylvanica scaeva* (Blake). Fig. 136, cell 12, nest M 56, July 11, cocoon of *T. rubrocinctum* in outer cell of nest showing the mud patch near anterior end applied by mutillid female after she oviposited on resting larva of host wasp. Fig. 137, same data as fig. 136, but cocoon opened to show small mutillid larva feeding on host larva. Fig. 138, same data as fig. 136 but July 20, showing mutillid cocoon inside that of host. Fig. 139, same data as fig. 138; note height of mud patch applied by mother mutillid.

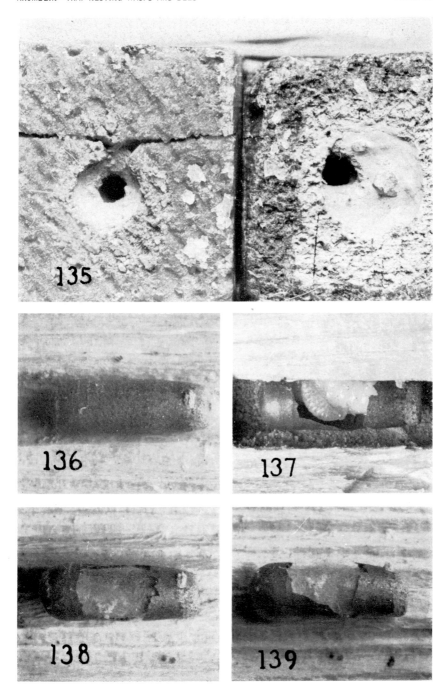

INDEX

Numbers in boldface type indicate plate figures.

557

subexilis, Chalicodoma
  (Chelostomoides), 343
subfasciata subfasciata, Osmia (Dicera-
  tosmia), 311
Suehiro, A., on
  Isodontia mexicana, 244
Supersedure, 16, 11
surrufus, Stenodynerus. See pulvinatus
  surrufus.
Swezey, O. H., on
  Isodontia mexicana, 244
Symmorphus
  albomarginatus, 120
  canadensis, 115, 14-19
  cristatus cristatus, 122, 20-22
Synaldis sp., 220

Tachinidae, as parasites of prey, 69,
  90, 150
Tandy, M., on
  Monobia quadridens, 54
Taylor, L. H., on
  Ancistrocerus a. antilope, 94-97
Taylor, R. L., on
  Trypoxylon frigidum, 226
taylori, Holopyga (?), 443
Temelucha
  grapholithae, 69
Tetrastichus
  johnsoni, 424
  megachilidis, 427
  sp., 426
texana, Coelioxys, 483
texensis, Stenodynerus (Parancistrocerus), 144
Tetragnathidae as prey, 189, 205, 212,
  224, 231
Tettigoniidae as prey, 241, 243, 248
Theridiidae as prey, 186, 189, 196, 201,
  224, 228
Thomas, S. J., on
  Chrysogona verticalis, 450
  Trypoxylon backi, 228
  Trypoxylon frigidum, 226
Thomisidae as prey, 163, 204-205, 212,
  215-216
Thylodrias
  contractus, 376
Thysanoptera, as predators, 371
tigris, Vespacarus, 358
tigris tigris, Ancistrocerus, 110
toltecus, Stenodynerus (Parancistrocerus), 157
toltecus, Vespacarus, 358

Tortonia
  quadridens, 367
Tortricidae as prey, 50, 58, 65, 72, 75,
  88, 92, 111, 135, 138, 148, 151,
  155
Torymidae, 434
Townes, H. K., on
  Auplopus caerulescens subcorti-
    calis, 171
  Auplopus m. mellipes, 172-173
  Dipogon papago anomalus, 168
  Dipogon s. sayi, 165
Townsend, C. H. T., on
  Toxophora virgata, 408
Toxophora
  amphitea, 405, 123-125
  virgata, 407
Tracheliodes
  amu, 257, 68, 69
Trap-nests. See Nests.
Traps
  Field settings, 10-11
  Preparation for field, 10
  Study sites, 14-15
  Types, 8-9
Trichodes
  horni, 376
Trichoptera as prey, 261
Trichrysis. See Chrysis (Trichrysis).
tridentatum archboldi, Trypargilum,
  200
tridentatum tridentatum,
    Trypargilum, 193, 115-118
trilineata, Senotainia, 421
trisetosa, Kennethiella, 360
Trogoderma
  ornatum, 372
Trypargilum, general account, 178
  clavatum, 203, 11, 133
  collinum collinum, 185
  collinum rubrocinctum, 187, 126,
    135-139
  johannis, 210, 52
  striatum, 214, 53-56, 132, 134, 135
  tridentatum archboldi, 200
  tridentatum tridentatum, 193,
    115-118
Trypoxylon, general account, 222
  backi, 227
  carinatum, 228
  clarkei, 229
  frigidum, 223, 11
  johnsoni, 230
Tsuneki, K., on
  Isodontia harmandi, 240